# THE
# BRITISH CATALOGUE
# OF MUSIC
# 1972

The Council of the British National Bibliography, Ltd., by whom this work is published, is a non-profit making organisation set up at the wish of those bodies whose representatives form the Council for the purpose of "compiling, editing and publishing in appropriate bibliographical form lists of books, pamphlets and other recorded material of whatever nature published in Great Britain, the Dominions and Colonies and/or foreign countries, together with such annotations or further information as may be desirable for the use of librarians, bibliographers and others."

During 1972 the Council consisted of the following representatives:

Miss M. F. Webb, B.SC., A.L.A. and
R. J. Fulford, M.A.
>    representing The British Museum.

T. E. Callander, F.L.A. (*Chairman of the Council*), and
Miss J. M. Plaister, B.SC. (ECON.), F.L.A.
>    representing The Library Association.

Haddon Whitaker, O.B.E., M.A. (*Vice-Chairman of the Council*) and
M. Turner
>    representing The Publishers Association.

P. A. Stockham, B.A. and
R. G. Heffer
>    representing The Booksellers Association of Great Britain and Ireland.

Clifford Simmons and
Miss R. Myers, M.A.
>    representing The National Book League.

R. A. Flood, M.B.E., F.L.A.
>    representing The British Council.

Professor O. V. S. Heath, F.R.S.
>    representing The Royal Society.

L. W. Wilson, M.A.
>    representing ASLIB.

M. B. Line, M.A., F.L.A.
>    representing The National Central Library.

E. B. Ceadel, M.A.
>    representing The Joint Committee of the Four Copyright Libraries.

# THE
# BRITISH CATALOGUE
# OF MUSIC

# 1972

*A record of music and books about music recently published in Great Britain, based upon the material deposited at the Copyright Receipt Office of the British Museum, arranged according to a system of classification with a Composer and Title Index, a Subject Index, and a list of music publishers*

Managing Editor: A. J. WELLS, O.B.E., F.L.A.

THE COUNCIL OF THE BRITISH NATIONAL BIBLIOGRAPHY, LTD.

7 RATHBONE STREET, LONDON, W1P 2AL

in association with The Music Department of the British Museum, The U.K. Branch of the International Association of Music Libraries, The Music Publishers Association and The Central Music Library

ISBN 0 900220 40 6

# CONTENTS

Preface

Outline of Classification

Classified Section

Composer and Title Index

Subject Index

List of Music Publishers

1973

Printed in Great Britain by William Clowes & Sons, Limited, London, Beccles and Colchester
and published by the Council of the British National Bibliography, Ltd., 7 Rathbone Street, London, W1P 2AL
(Registered Office: British Museum, London, W.C.1)

## Musical literature

Books about music which normally appear in the *British National Bibliography* are also included in this catalogue. They occur in the sequences lettered A and B. They are indexed in exactly the same way as musical works in the Composer and Title Index and are designated by the qualification "Books" in the Subject Index. Thus, in the second group above, the entry Violin: Books, directing you to AS, indicates that books about the violin will be found at that place.

## Prices

Prices given are those current at the time of the first recording of an entry in this catalogue. In a few cases prices of parts are not given but can be obtained on application to the publisher.

## Abbreviations

Most of the abbreviations used in describing musical works are self-explanatory. The size of a musical work is indicated by one of the following conventional symbols: 8*vo* for works up to 10½ in. in height, 4*to* for works between 10½ and 12 in. in height, and *fol.* for works over 12 in. in height. The abbreviation *obl.* (oblong) is added to show when a work is of unusual proportions, and a single sheet is designated by the abbreviations *s.sh.* The abbreviations used for the description of books in the sections A and B are those in use in the *British National Bibliography*.

# OUTLINE OF THE CLASSIFICATION

The following outline is given for general information only. Users are advised to consult the Subject Index to discover the exact location of required material in the Classified Section.

## MUSICAL LITERATURE

| | |
|---|---|
| A | General works |
| | Common sub-divisions |
| A(B) | Periodicals |
| A(C) | Encyclopaedias |
| A(D) | Composite works, symposia, essays by several writers |
| A(E) | Anecdotes, personal reminiscences |
| A(K) | Economics |
| A(M) | Persons in music |
| A(MM) | Musical profession |
| A(MN) | Music as a career |
| A(P) | Individuals |
| A(Q) | Organisations |
| A(QT) | Terminology |
| A(QU) | Notation |
| A(R) | Printing |
| A(S) | Publishing |
| A(T) | Bibliographies |
| A(U) | Libraries |
| A(V) | Musical education |
| A(X) | History of music |
| A(Y) | Music of particular localities |
| A/AM | Theory of music |
| A/CC | Aesthetics |
| A/CY | Technique of music |
| A/D | Composition |
| A/E | Performance |
| A/F | Recording |
| A/FY | Musical character |
| A/G | Folk music |
| A/GM | Music associated with particular occupations |
| A/H | Dance music |
| A/HM | Ballet music |
| A/J | Music accompanying drama |
| A/JR | Film music |
| A/KD | Music to accompany social customs |
| A/L | Religious music |
| A/LZ | Elements of music |
| A/R | Harmony |
| A/S | Forms of music |
| A/Y | Fugue |
| AB | Works on vocal music |
| AC | Works on opera |
| ACM | Works on musical plays |
| AD-AX | Works on music for particular vocal or instrumental performers, enumerated like D–X below |
| B | Works on individual composers (including libretti and other verbal texts of particular musical works) |
| BZ | Works on non-European music |

## MUSIC (SCORES AND PARTS)

| | |
|---|---|
| C/AY | Collections not limited to work of particular composer, executant, form or character |
| C/AZ | Collections of a particular composer not otherwise limited |
| C/G-C/Y | Collections illustrating music of particular form, character, etc., enumerated like A/G-A/Y above |
| CB | Vocal music |
| CC | Opera. Vocal scores with keyboard |
| CM | Musical plays. Vocal scores with keyboard |
| D | Choral music |
| DC | Religious choral music |
| DF | Liturgical music |
| DH | Motets, Anthems, Hymns |
| DTZ | Secular choral music |
| DX | Cantatas |
| DW | Songs, etc. |
| E | Choral music with instruments other than keyboard |
| EZ | Choral music unaccompanied |
| F | Choral music. Female voices |
| G | Choral music. Male voices |
| J | Unison vocal works |
| K | Vocal solos |
| L | Instrumental music |
| M | Orchestral music |
| N | Chamber music |
| PVV | Music for individual instruments and instrumental groups |
| PW | Keyboard instruments |
| Q | Piano |
| R | Organ |
| RW | String instruments |
| S | Violin |
| SQ | Viola |
| SR | Cello |
| SS | Double bass |
| TQ | Harp |
| TS | Guitar |
| U | Wind instruments |
| V | Woodwind |
| VR | Flute |
| VS | Recorder |
| VT | Oboe |
| VU | Saxophone |
| VV | Clarinet |
| VW | Bassoon |
| W | Brass |
| WS | Trumpet |
| WT | Horn |
| WU | Trombone |
| WX | Bass tuba |
| X | Percussion instruments |
| Z | Non-European music |

1

# CLASSIFIED SECTION

This section contains entries under subjects, executants and instruments according to a system of classification, a synopsis of which appears in the preliminary pages. The key to the classification and to this section is found in the Subject Index at the end of this volume, which is followed by a list of music publishers and their addresses.

The following are used in giving the sizes of musical works:—

*8vo* for works up to 10½″ in height.
*4to* for works between 10½″ and 12″ in height.
*fol.* for works over 12″ in height.
*obl.* indicates a work of unusual proportions.
*s.sh.* means a single sheet.

## A — MUSICAL LITERATURE

**Gammond, Peter**
One man's music/ by Peter Gammond. — London: Wolfe, 1971. — 221p; 24cm.
ISBN 0 7234 0424 0 : £3.00

(B72-02714)

**Hanslick, Eduard**
Am Ende des Jahrhunderts, 1895-1899: musikalische Kritiken und Schilderungen/ von Eduard Hanslick. — 2. Aufl. [reprinted]. — Farnborough: Gregg, 1971. — [1],vi,452p; 20cm. — (The collected musical criticism of Eduard Hanslick; 8) (Hanslick, Eduard. Moderne Oper; 8)
Facsimile reprint of 2nd ed., Berlin: Allgemeiner Verein für Deutsche Litteratur, 1899.
ISBN 0 576 28188 3 : £7.20
ISBN 0 576 28228 6 Set of 9 vols: £51.00

(B72-07355)

**Hanslick, Eduard**
Aus dem Tagebuche eines Musikers: Kritiken und Schilderungen/ von Eduard Hanslick. — Farnborough: Gregg, 1971. — [1],v, 360p; 20cm. — (The collected musical criticism of Eduard Hanslick; 6) (Hanslick, Eduard. Moderne Oper; 6)
Facsimile reprint of 1st ed. Berlin: Allgemeiner Verein für Deutsche Litteratur, 1892.
ISBN 0 576 28186 7 : £6.00
ISBN 0 576 28228 6 Set of 9 vols: £51.00

(B72-07353)

**Hanslick, Eduard**
Aus neuer und neuester Zeit: musikalische Kritiken und Schilderungen/ von Eduard Hanslick. — 3. Aufl. [reprinted]. — Farnborough: Gregg, 1971. — [6],377p; 20cm. — (The collected musical criticism of Eduard Hanslick; 9) (Hanslick, Eduard. Moderne Oper; 9)
Facsimile reprint of 3rd ed., Berlin: Allgemeiner Verein für Deutsche Litteratur, 1900.
ISBN 0 576 28189 1 : £7.20
ISBN 0 576 28228 6 Set of 9 vols: £51.00

(B72-07356)

**Hanslick, Eduard**
Fünf Jahre Musik, 1891-1895: Kritiken/ von Eduard Hanslick. — 3. Aufl. [reprinted]. — Farnborough: Gregg, 1971. — [1],ix,402p; 20cm. — (The collected musical criticism of Eduard Hanslick; 7) (Hanslick, Eduard. Moderne Oper; 7)
Facsimile reprint of 3rd ed., Berlin: Allgemeiner Verein für Deutsche Litteratur, 1896.
ISBN 0 576 28187 5 : £7.20
ISBN 0 576 28228 6 Set of 9 vols: £51.00

(B72-07354)

**Hanslick, Eduard**
Musikalische Stationem/ von Eduard Hanslick. — Farnborough: Gregg, 1971. — [1],vi,361p; 20cm. — (The collected musical criticism of Eduard Hanslick; 2) (Hanslick, Eduard. Moderne Oper; 2)
Facsimile reprint of 1885 reissue, Berlin: Allgemeiner Verein für Deutsche Literatur, 1885.
ISBN 0 576 28182 4 : £6.00
ISBN 0 576 28228 6 Set of 9 vols: £51.00

(B72-07350)

**Hanslick, Eduard**
Musikalisches Skizzenbuch: neue Kritiken und Schildenrungen/ von Eduard Hanslick. — Farnborough: Gregg, 1971. — viii,335p; 20cm. — (The collected musical criticism of Eduard Hanslick; 4) (Hanslick, Eduard. Moderne Oper; 4)
Facsimile reprint of 1st ed., Berlin: Allgemeiner Verein f'ur Deutsche Literatur, 1888.
ISBN 0 576 28184 0 : £6.00
ISBN 0 576 28228 6 Set of 9 vols: £51.00

(B72-07351)

**Hanslick, Eduard**
Musikalisches und Litterarisches: Kritiken und Schilderungen/ von Eduard Hanslick. — 2. Aufl. [reprinted]. — Farnborough: Gregg, 1971. — [1],iv,359p; 20cm. — (The collected musical criticism of Eduard Hanslick; 5) (Hanslick, Eduard. Moderne Oper; 5)
Facsimile reprint of 2nd ed., Berlin: Allgemeiner Verein für Deutsche Litteratur, 1889.
ISBN 0 576 28185 9 : £6.00
ISBN 0 576 28228 6 Set of 9 vols: £51.00

(B72-07352)

**A(BC) — Directories**
The **music** yearbook: a survey and directory with statistics and reference articles. — London: Macmillan. —
1972/3/ edited by Arthur Jacobs. — 1972. — 750,[5]p: ill, facsims, ports; 21cm.
ISBN 0 333 13355 2 : £4.95
ISBN 0 333 13783 3 Pbk: Unpriced

(B72-21772)

**A(C) — Encyclopaedias**
**Ammer, Christine**
Harper's dictionary of music/ by Christine Ammer; drawings by Carmela M. Ciampa and Kenneth L. Donlon. — London: Hale, 1972. — xiii,414p: ill, music; 24cm.
Also published, New York: Harper and Row, 1972.
ISBN 0 7091 3064 3 : £4.00

(B72-10997)

**A(D) — Essays**
**Berlioz, Hector**
A travers chants: études musicales, adorations, boutades et critiques/ par Hector Berlioz. — Farnborough: Gregg, 1970. — [5],336p; 19cm. — (Collected literary works; 5)
Facsimile reprint of 1st ed., Paris: M. Lévy, 1862.
ISBN 0 576 28422 x : £9.60
ISBN 0 576 28417 3 Set of 7 works: £78.00

(B72-06100)

**Berlioz, Hector**
Les Grotesques de la musique/ [par] Hector Berlioz. — Farnborough: Gregg, 1969. — [4],308p: music; 18cm. — (Collected literary works: 4)
Facsimile reprint of 1st ed., Paris: A. Bourdilliat, 1859.
ISBN 0 576 28421 1 : £8.40
ISBN 0 576 28417 3 Set of 7 works: £78.00

(B72-06099)

**Berlioz, Hector**
Voyage musical en Allemagne et en Italie: études sur Beethoven, Gluck et Weber, mélanges et nouvelles/ par Hector Berlioz. — Farnborough: Gregg, 1970. — 2v.([5],422p;[4],370p); 20cm. — (Collected literary works; 2)
Facsimile reprint of 1st ed., Paris: J. Labitte, 1844.
ISBN 0 576 28419 x : £18.60
ISBN 0 576 28417 3 Set of 7 works: £78.00

(B72-06763)

**Stravinsky, Igor**
Themes and conclusions/ [by] Igor Stravinsky. — London: Faber, 1972. — 3-328,[16]p: ill, facsims, music, ports; 23cm.
Index.
ISBN 0 571 08308 0 : £6.00

(B72-28007)

**Vaughan Williams, Ralph**
National music, and other essays/ [by] Ralph Vaughan Williams. — London: Oxford University Press, 1972. — x,246p: music; 21cm.
This collection originally published 1963. — Index.
ISBN 0 19 311207 8 : £2.50

(B72-15421)

**A(D/XFZ84) — Essays. History, 1780-1863**
**Berlioz, Hector**
Les Musiciens et la musique/ [par] Hector Berlioz; introduction par André Hallays. — Farnborough: Gregg, 1969. — [4],l,348p; 17cm. — (Collected literary works; 7)
Facsimile reprint of 1st ed., Paris: Calmann-Lévy, 1903.
ISBN 0 576 28424 6 : £9.60
ISBN 0 576 28417 3 Set of 7 works: £78.00

(B72-06101)

**A(E) — Anecdotes**
**Berlioz, Hector**
Les Soir'ees de l'orchestre/ par Hector Berlioz. — Farnborough: Gregg, 1969. — [5],429p; 19cm. — (Collected literary works; 3)
Facsimile reprint of 1st ed., Paris: M. L'evy, 1853.
ISBN 0 576 28420 3 : £9.60
ISBN 0 576 28417 3 Set of 7 works: £78.00

(B72-06098)

**A(MN) — Careers**
**Incorporated Society of Musicians**
Careers with music/ Incorporated Society of Musicians. — 2nd ed. — London (48 Gloucester Place, W1H 3HJ): Incorporated Society of Musicians, 1972. — 83p; 20cm.
Previous ed. 1970. — Index.
ISBN 0 902900 03 x Pbk: £0.70

(B72-19609)

**A(N/BC) — Biographies. Yearbooks. Directories**
**Who's** who in music, and musicians' international directory. — 6th ed. — London: Burke's Peerage, 1972. — lxix,495p; 26cm.
Previous ed. 1969.
ISBN 0 85011 013 0 : £8.00

(B72-12013)

**A(P) — Hallé, Sir Charles. Biographies**
**Hallé, *Sir Charles***
The autobiography of Charles Hallé, with correspondence and diaries/ edited with an introduction by Michael Kennedy. — London: Elek, 1972. — 215,[8]p: ill, facsim, music, ports; 23cm.
Originally published as 'The life and letters of Sir Charles Hallé'/edited by C.E. Hallé and Marie Hallé. London: Smith, Elder, 1896. — Index.
ISBN 0 236 15448 6 : £3.25

(B72-31293)

**A(RC/XHS64) — Printing. Music covers, 1837-1901**
**Pearsall, Ronald**
Victorian sheet music covers/ [by] Ronald Pearsall. — Newton Abbot: David and Charles, 1972. — 112p: ill, facsims, music; 26cm.
Index.
ISBN 0 7153 5561 9 : £3.25

(B72-28659)

**A(T) — Bibliographies**
**Charles, Sydney Robinson**
A handbook of music and music literature in sets and series/ [by] Sydney Robinson Charles. — New York: Free Press; London: Collier-Macmillan, 1972. — [10],497p; 24cm.
Index.
ISBN 0 02 905400 1 : £5.40

(B72-12964)

**A(U/YC) — Libraries. Great Britain**
**Long, Maureen W**
Musicians and libraries in the United Kingdom/ by Maureen W. Long. — London: Library Association, 1972. — viii,152p: forms; 30cm. — (Library Association. Research publications; no.8)
Bibl.p.151-152.
ISBN 0 85365 355 0 Pbk: £2.25(£1.80 to members of the Library Association)

(B72-08765)

**A(U/YC/BC) — International Association of Music Libraries. United Kingdom Branch. Directories**
**International Association of Music Libraries.** *United Kingdom Branch*
Directory of United Kingdom Branch members/ International Association of Music Libraries, United Kingdom Branch. — [London] (c/o Michael Short, Haldane Library, Imperial College of Science and Technology, SW7 2AZ): International Association of Music Libraries, United Kingdom Branch. — [1972]. — 1972. — 12 leaves; 30cm.
ISBN 0 9502339 0 0 Sd: Free to members only

(B72-12968)

**A(V/YDK) — Education. Wales**
**Great Britain.** *Welsh Office*
Music/ Welsh Office [and the] Welsh Education Office. — [Cardiff] (31 Cathedral Rd, Cardiff CF1 9UJ): [Welsh Education Office], [1971]. — 56,[4]p; 21cm. — (Wales education surveys; no.1)
ISBN 0 903702 00 2 Sd: £0.20

(B72-31877)

**A(VC) — Teaching**
**Rainbow, Bernarr**
Music in the classroom/ by Bernarr Rainbow. — 2nd ed. — London: Heinemann Educational, 1971. — viii,116p: ill, music; 23cm.
Previous ed. 1956. — Bibl.p.107-109. — Index.
ISBN 0 435 81746 9 : £1.25

(B72-26088)

**A(VF) — Schools**
**Marsh, Mary Val**
Explore and discover music: creative approaches to music education in elementary, middle, and junior high schools/ [by] Mary Val Marsh. — New York: Macmillan (N.Y.); London: Collier-Macmillan, 1970. — xv,202p: ill, music; 24cm.
Bibl.p.195-196.
ISBN 0 02 376270 5 Pbk: £2.25

(B72-00905)

**A(VF/YT/X) — Schools. United States. History**
**Tellstrom, A Theodore**
Music in American education: past and present/ [by] A. Theodore Tellstrom. — New York; London: Holt, Rinehart and Winston, 1971. — xv,358p: ill, facsim, form, music, ports; 24cm.
Bibl.p.309-336. — Index.
ISBN 0 03 083579 8 : £4.40

(B72-07977)

**A(VG) — Primary schools**
**Horton, John**
Music/ [by] John Horton. — London: Macmillan [for the Anglo-American Primary Education Project], 1972. — 27p: ill, music; 19x27cm. — (British primary schools today)
'...prepared under the aegis of the Schools Council in England with the support of the Ford Foundation in the United States.' - Preface. — Record (2s. 7in. 33 1/3rpm) as insert. — Simultaneously published, New York: Citation Press, 1972. — Bibl.p.26-27.
ISBN 0 333 13332 3 Pbk: £0.60

(B72-13853)

**A(VK) — Education. Secondary schools**
**Glenn, Neal Edwin**
Secondary school music: philosophy, theory and practice/ [by] Neal E. Glen, William B. McBride, George H. Wilson. — Englewood Cliffs; [Hemel Hempstead: Prentice-Hall, 1970. — xii, 2-275p: music; 24cm.
Bibl. — Index.
ISBN 0 13 797522 8 : £4.00

(B72-50333)

**A(VMWR) — Backward children**
**Ward, David**
Sound approaches for slow learners: a report on experimental work in schools being part of the Music for Slow Learners Project at Dartington College of Arts/ by David Ward. — London: Bedford Square Press for the Standing Conference for Amateur Music, 1972. — 26p: ill, music; 21cm.
Bibl.p.23-24.
ISBN 0 7199 0829 9 Sd: £0.35

(B72-16605)

**A(VP/YDB/X) — Trinity College of Music. History**
**Rutland, Harold**
Trinity College of Music, the first hundred years/ [by] Harold Rutland. — London (Mandeville Place, W.1): Trinity College of Music, 1972. — 72,[8]p: map, ports; 22cm.
Index.
ISBN 0 9502340 0 1 Pbk: £0.70

(B72-13439)

**A(VP/YDJE(X) — Northern School of Music. History**
**Robert-Blunn, John**
Northern accent: the life story of the Northern School of Music/ [by] John Robert-Blunn. — Altrincham: Sherratt, 1972. — 151, [9]p: ill, ports(incl 1 col); 23cm.
Ill. on lining papers. — Index.
ISBN 0 85427 029 9 : £2.00

(B72-18915)

**A(VX) — Musicology**
**Adler, Guido**
Methode der Musikgeschichte/ von Guido Adler. — Farnborough: Gregg, 1971. — [2],iv,222p; 19cm.
Facsimile reprint of 1st ed., Leipzig: Breitkopf und Härtel, 1919. — Bibl.p. 200-222.
ISBN 0 576 28180 8 : £6.60

(B72-03925)

**A(W/YEMB/XFK119) — Concerts. Vienna, 1750-1868**
**Hanslick, Eduard**
Geschichte des Concertwesens in Wien/ von Eduard Hanslick. — Farnborough: Gregg, 1971. — 2v.(xv,438p; xii,534p); 20cm.
Facsimile reprint of 1st ed., Wien [Vienna]: Braumüller, 1869-1870.
ISBN 0 576 28227 4 : £14.40

(B72-07361)

**A(X) — History**
**Jacobs, Arthur**
A short history of Western music/ [by] Arthur Jacobs. — Harmondsworth: Penguin, 1972. — 363p; 18cm. — (Pelican books)
Index.
ISBN 0 14 021421 6 Pbk: £0.60

(B72-21774)

**Jacobs, Arthur**
A short history of Western music: a listener's guide/ [by] Arthur Jacobs. — Newton Abbot: David and Charles, 1972. — 363p; 23cm.
Originally published, Harmondsworth: Penguin, 1972. — Index.
ISBN 0 7153 5743 3 : £3.75

(B72-30740)

**Stevenson, Ronald**
Western music: an introduction/ [by] Ronald Stevenson. — London (25 Thurloe St., S.W.7): Kahn and Averil, 1971. — 216p: music; 23cm.
Bibl. p.209. — Index.
ISBN 0 900707 10 0 : £2.50

(B72-00906)

**A(XA1827) — History. To 1827**
**Raynor, Henry**
A social history of music: from the middle ages to Beethoven/ [by] Henry Raynor. — London: Barrie and Jenkins, 1972. — viii, 373p; 24cm.
Bibl.p.358-361. — Index.
ISBN 0 214 65783 3 : £5.00

(B72-12717)

**A(XM71) — History, 1900-1970**
**Twentieth** century composers. — London: Weidenfeld and Nicolson.

In 5 vols.
Vol.3: Britain, Scandinavia and the Netherlands/ [by] Humphrey Searle and Robert Layton. — 1972. — xvi,200,[16]p: ports; 23cm.
Bibl.p.190-191. — Index.
ISBN 0 297 99377 1 : £3.50

(B72-28679)

**A(XM73) — History, 1900-1972**
**Slonimsky, Nicolas**
Music since 1900/ [by] Nicolas Slonimsky. — 4th ed. — London: Cassell, 1972. — xix,1595p; 24cm.
Fourth ed. originally published, New York: Scribner, 1971. — Previous ed., New York: Coleman-Ross, 1949. — Index.
ISBN 0 304 29069 6 : £21.00

(B72-17502)

**A(XRE201) — History, 1425-1625**
**Hendrie, Gerald**
Renaissance music/ prepared by Gerald Hendrie and Dinah Barsham for the [Renaissance and Reformation] Course Team. — Bletchley (Walton Hall, Bletchley, Bucks.): Open University Press, 1972. — 111p: ill, music, ports; 30cm. — (Arts, a second level course: Renaissance and Reformation; units 17-19) (A201; 17-19)
Bibl.p.101-104. — List of music p.105-106. — List of recordings p.107-110.
ISBN 0 335 00657 4 Pbk: £1.10

(B72-50334)

**A(Y) — MUSIC OF PARTICULAR LOCALITIES**
**A(YB/XFY190) — European music, 1760-1949**
**Blume, Friedrich**
Classic and Romantic music: a comprehensive survey/ [by] Friedrich Blume; translated [from the German] by M.D. Herter Norton. — London (3 Queen Sq., WC1N 3AU): Faber, 1972. — ix,213p; 23cm.
This translation originally published, New York: Norton, 1970. — Translation of two essays in 'Die Musik in Geschichte und Gegenwart'. Kassel: Bärenreiter, 1949. — Bibl.p.195-198. — Index.
ISBN 0 571 08215 7 : £3.00

(B72-24250)

**A(YBU) — Jews**
Yuval: studies of the Jewish Music Research Centre. — Jerusalem: Magnes Press; [London]: Distributed by Oxford University Press.

—
Second title page in Hebrew. — Essays in English, French and Hebrew. — Record (2s. 7 in. 33-1/3rpm.) in pocket in slip case.
Vol.2/ edited by Amnon Shiloah in collaboration with Bathja Bayer. — 1971. — [10],183,[47]p: music; 25cm.
ISBN 0 19 647627 5 : £6.15

(B72-12719)

**A(YC/WE/Q) — Great Britain. Festivals. Organisations**
**British Federation of Music Festivals**
Year book/ British Federation of Music Festivals. — London (106 Gloucester Place, W1H 3DB): British Federation of Music Festivals.
1972. — 1972. — [6],92,[4]p: ports; 24cm.
ISBN 0 901532 03 7 Sd: £0.60

(B72-13440)

**A(YC/XPE26) — Great Britain. History, 1945-1970**
**Routh, Francis**
Contemporary British music: the twenty-five years from 1945 to 1970/ [by] Francis Routh. — London: Macdonald and Co., 1972. — xii,463,[16]p: ill, facsims, music; 23cm.
Bibl.p.407-438. — Index.
ISBN 0 356 03773 8 : £6.95

(B72-26091)

**A(YDK/TC) — Wales. Bibliographies of scores**
**Guild for the Promotion of Welsh Music**
A complete catalogue of contemporary Welsh music/ Guild for
the Promotion of Welsh Music. — [Cwmbran] (c/o G. Williams,
10 Llanerch Path, Fairwater, Cwmbran, Mon. NP4 4QN): Guild
for the Promotion of Welsh Music. —
No.5/ compiled by Robert Smith. — 1972. — 52p; 30cm.
Index.
ISBN 0 901248 01 0 Sd: Unpriced

(B72-19872)

**A(YDLG/XF101) — Scotland. Lowlands. History, 1700-1800**
**Johnson, David,** b.1942
Music and society in lowland Scotland in the eighteenth century/
[by] David Johnson. — London: Oxford University Press, 1972.
— viii,223p,leaf: music, port; 23cm.
Bibl.p.201-208. — List of music, p.209-218. — Index.
ISBN 0 19 316401 9 : £3.30

(B72-26090)

**A(YEMB/XKK16) — Vienna, 1870-1885**
**Hanslick, Eduard**
Concerte, Componisten und Virtuosen der letzten fünfzehn Jahre,
1870-1885: Kritiken/ von Eduard Hanslick. — 2.Aufl., [reprinted].
— Farnborough: Gregg, 1971. — [6],viii,447p; 20cm.
Facsimile reprint of 2nd ed., Berlin: Allgemeiner Verein für Deutsche
Litteratur, 1886.
ISBN 0 576 28226 x : £7.80

(B72-09122)

**A(YK/X) — Spain. History**
**Livermore, Ann**
A short history of Spanish music/ [by] Ann Livermore. —
London (43 Gloucester Cres., N.W.1): Duckworth, 1972. — x,262,
[8]p: ill, 2facsims, music, ports; 23cm.
Bibl.p.254-255. — Index.
ISBN 0 7156 0634 4 : £4.45

(B72-24251)

**A(YM/XMS58) — Russia, 1917-1970**
**Schwarz, Boris**
Music and musical life in Soviet Russia, 1917-1970/ [by] Boris
Schwarz. — London: Barrie and Jenkins, 1972. — [11],550p:
music; 23cm.
Bibl.p.518-525. — Index.
ISBN 0 214 65264 5 : £6.00

(B72-04570)

**A(Z) — MUSIC IN RELATION TO OTHER SUBJECTS**
**A(ZE) — Music-expounded by postage stamps**
**Peat, Sylvester**
Music on stamps/ by Sylvester Peat. — Chippenham (63 St Mary
St., Chippenham, Wilts): Picton Publishing. —
Part 1: A-B. — 1971. — [7],57p: chiefly ill, facsims, ports; 21cm.
ISBN 0 902633 08 2 Sd: £0.44

(B72-03311)

**A/B — PHYSICS OF MUSIC**
**Madsen, Clifford K**
Experimental research in music/ [by] Clifford K. Madsen, Charles
H. Madsen, Jr. — Englewood Cliffs; [Hemel Hempstead]:
Prentice-Hall, 1970. — xii,116p: ill; 24cm. — (Prentice-Hall
contemporary perspectives in music education series)
Bibl.p.94-100. — Index.
ISBN 0 13 295097 9 : Unpriced
ISBN 0 13 295089 8 Pbk: £2.00

(B72-21770)

**A/CB — Analytical guides**
**Tovey,** Sir **Donald Francis**
Essays in musical analysis/ by Donald Francis Tovey. — London:
Oxford University Press. —
[Supplementary volume]: Chamber music; with an editor's note by Hubert J.
Foss. — 1972. — viii,217p: music; 22cm.
Originally published 1944. — Index.
ISBN 0 19 315136 7 Pbk: £0.80

(B72-26081)

Vol.1: Symphonies. — 1972. — viii,223p: music; 22cm.
Originally published 1935.
ISBN 0 19 315137 5 Pbk: £0.80

(B72-26082)

Vol.2: Symphonies (2), variations and orchestral polyphony. — 1972. — xiv,
212p: music; 22cm.
Originally published 1935.
ISBN 0 19 315138 3 Pbk: £0.80

(B72-26083)

Vol.3: Concertos. — 1972. — ix,226p: music; 22cm.
Originally published 1936.
ISBN 0 19 315139 1 Pbk: £0.80

(B72-26084)

Vol.4: Illustrative music. — 1972. — viii,176p: music; 22cm.
Originally published 1937.
ISBN 0 19 315140 5 Pbk: £0.80

(B72-26085)

Vol.5: Vocal music. — 1972. — vi,256p: music; 22cm.
Originally published 1937.
ISBN 0 19 315141 3 Pbk: £0.80

(B72-26086)

Vol.6: Supplementary essays, glossary and index. — 1972. — vii,188p:
music; 22cm.
Originally published 1939. — Index to vols 1-6.
ISBN 0 19 315142 1 Pbk: £0.80

(B72-26087)

**A/CC — AESTHETICS**
**A/CC(P) — Aesthetics & criticism. Music critics. Hanslick, Eduard.**
  **Biographies**
**Hanslick, Eduard**
Aus meinem Leben/ by Eduard Hanslick. — Farnborough: Gregg,
1971. — [7],339,[3],369p,2 leaves: 2ports; 20cm.
Facsimile reprint of 1st ed., Berlin: Allgemeiner Verein für Deutsche
Litteratur, 1894.
ISBN 0 576 28225 1 : £10.20

(B72-07348)

**A/CS — PSYCHOLOGY**
**A/CS(VC) — Psychology. Teaching**
**Franklin, Erik**
Music education: psychology and method/ [by] Erik Franklin;
[translated from the Swedish]. — London: Harrap, 1972. — 142p:
ill, music; 22cm.
Originally published in Swedish, [Stockholm?]: Läromedelsförlagen, 1969. —
Bibl.p.135-137. — Index.
ISBN 0 245 50659 4 Pbk: £1.40

(B72-13438)

**A/D — COMPOSITION**
**A/D(YH/XMS13/P) — Composers. France, 1917-1929. Les Six**
**Harding, James**
The ox on the roof: scenes from musical life in Paris in the
twenties/ [by] James Harding. — London: Macdonald and Co.,
1972. — 261,[8]p: ill, facsim, ports; 23cm.
Bibl.p.245-250. — Index.
ISBN 0 356 03967 6 : £3.00

(B72-14735)

**A/E — PERFORMANCE**
**A/EC(P) — Conductors. Davis, Colin. Biographies**
**Blyth, Alan**
Colin Davis/ [by] Alan Blyth. — Shepperton: Allan, 1972. — 64p:
ill, ports; 25cm. — [Recordmasters; 2]
Title page imprint: London. — List of records p.60-64.
ISBN 0 7110 0319 x : £1.50

(B72-50792)

**A/FD — RECORDED MUSIC**
**A/FD(B) — Periodicals**
**Record** Collector: monthly guide to your kind of music. — London:
Hanover Publications; London (34 Foubert's Place, W.1):
Haymarket Publishing Ltd. —
[No.1]- ; Feb. 1972-. — 1972-. — ill, ports; 42cm.
Twenty-eight p. in 1st issue. — 'Including "Record Bargains" '.
Sd: £0.10

(B72-07362)

**A/FD(WM) — Trade catalogues**
**Electric and Musical Industries.** Record Division
Alphabetical catalogue of EMI records/ EMI Records. — London
(20 Manchester Sq., W1A 1ES): EMI Records. —
1970-71: available and issued up to and including 30 May 1970. — [1970].
— [724]p in various pagings; 26cm.
ISBN 0 901401 03 x : Unpriced

(D72-30323)

**Electric and Musical Industries.** Record Division
Alphabetical catalogue of EMI records/ EMI Records. — London
(20 Manchester Sq., W1A 1ES): EMI Records. —
1971-72: available and issued up to and including 30 June 1971. — [1971].
— [685]p in various pagings; 25cm.
ISBN 0 901401 04 8 : Unpriced

(B72-30324)

**Electric and Musical Industries.** Record Division
Alphabetical catalogue of EMI records/ EMI Records. — London
(20 Manchester Sq., W1A 1ES): EMI Records. —
1972-73: available and issued up to and including 30 June 1972. — [1972].
— [682]p in various pagings; 25cm.
ISBN 0 901401 05 6 : Unpriced

(B72-30325)

**Gramophone and Typewriter Limited**
Catalogue of 'Red Label' gramophone records [1904]/
Gramophone and Typewriter Ltd. — [1st ed. reprinted with
September to November supplements]/ [compiled by E. Bayly]. —
[Bournemouth] (19 Glendale Rd, Bournemouth BH6 4JA): [E.
Bayly], [1972]. — 20p: ill, ports; 31cm.
Fold. ill. as insert. — Facsimile reprint of 1st ed., London: Gramophone and
Typewriter Ltd, 1904 with 1904 supplements.
ISBN 0 902338 14 5 Sd: £0.85

(B72-30321)

**Gramophone and Typewriter Limited**
Catalogue of twelve-inch Monarch records ... March 1904/ Gramophone & Typewriter Ltd. — [1st ed. reprinted with supplements]/ [compiled by E. Bayly]. — [Bournemouth] (19 Glendale Rd, Bournemouth BH6 4JA): [E. Bayly], [1972]. — [35]p: ill, ports; 30cm.
'To the main catalogue we have added supplements together with other interesting leaflets...' - Present editor's note. — Facsimile reprint of 1st ed., London: Gramophone and Typewriter Ltd, 1904.
ISBN 0 902338 15 3 Sd: £0.85

(B72-30322)

**Radio Corporation of America.** *Record Division*
Complete catalogue of RCA Red Seal, RCA Victor, RCA Victrola, RCA International, RCA Neon, Vanguard, Barclay records and tapes/ R.C.A. Ltd, Record Division. — London (50 Curzon St., W1Y 8EU): RCA Ltd, Record Division. —
1971: ... all records listed up to October 31st, 1971. — [1971]. — [4],156p; 26cm.
ISBN 0 9500382 1 0 : £3.50

(B72-30326)

**A/FD(WM) — Trade lists. Decca**
**Decca Record Company**
Decca Group records, musicassettes and stereo 8 cartridges, main catalogue: (alphabetical & numerical). — London: Decca Record Co. —
1972. — [1972]. — [689]p; 26cm.
ISBN 0 901364 03 7 : £5.00

(B72-04763)

**A/FD(WT) — Lists**
The **art** of record buying: a list of recommended microgroove recordings. — London: E.M.G. —
1972. — [1971]. — [2],285p: map; 23cm.
ISBN 0 900982 03 9 : £1.75

(B72-01805)

**Greenfield, Edward**
X The third Penguin guide to bargain records/ [by] Edward Greenfield, Ivan March; edited by Ivan March. — Harmondsworth: Penguin, 1972. — xxii,328p; 18cm.
ISBN 0 14 003454 4 Pbk: £0.60

(B72-21267)

**A/FE(WM) — Cylinder records. Trade lists. Edison-Bell**
**Edison-Bell Consolidated Phonograph Company**
[Catalogue]. Bell 'popular' phonograph records, new catalogue no.9/ Edison-Bell Consolidated Phonograph Co. Ltd. — Bournemouth (19 Glendale Rd, Bournemouth, Hants. BH6 4JA): 'Talking Machine Review', 1971. — 16,[2]p; 25cm.
Notebook format. — Facsimile reprint of 1st ed., London: Edison-Bell Consolidated Phonograph Co., 1903.
ISBN 0 902338 13 7 Sd: Unpriced

(B72-05227)

**Edison-Bell Consolidated Phonograph Company**
[Catalogue]. List of records (no.3) possessing great volume, perfect reproduction and superb quality of tone/ Edison-Bell Consolidated Phonograph Co. Ltd. — Bournemouth (19 Glendale Rd, Bournemouth, Hants. BH6 4JA): 'Talking Machine Review', 1971. — 28,[4]p: ill, ports; 23cm.
Facsimile reprint. — 'It is difficult to give a definite date to the original publication of this catalogue but we feel it to be circa 1900.' - cover.
ISBN 0 902338 12 9 Sd: £0.45

(B72-04764)

**A/FF(WT) — Stereophonic recordings. Lists**
The **stereo** record guide. — [Blackpool] (Squires Gate, Station Approach, Blackpool, Lancs. FY82 SP): Long Playing Record Library Ltd. —
Vol.7: Composer index A-Ma/ by Edward Greenfield, Robert Layton, Ivan March; edited by Ivan March. — 1972. — viii p,p 1027-1330; 23cm.
ISBN 0 901143 02 2 : £1.95

(B72-08760)

**A/FY — MUSICAL CHARACTER**
**A/G(BC) — Folk music. Yearbooks, Directories**
**Folk** directory. — London: English Folk Dance and Song Society. —
1972/ edited by Tony Wales. — 1972. — 168p: ill, ports; 22cm.
ISBN 0 85418 034 6 : £1.00 (£0.75 to members of the EFDSS)
ISBN 0 85418 033 8 Pbk: £0.50 (£0.25 to members of the EFDSS)

(B72-06764)

**A/G(T) — Folk music. Bibliographies**
**Clark, Keith**
Folk song and dance: a list of books/ selected by Keith Clark. — London: National Book League: English Folk Dance and Song Society, 1972. — 48p: ill; 21cm.
ISBN 0 85353 138 2 Sd: £0.30
*Also classified at A/G(YT/T)*

(B72-16428)

**A/G(YDM) — Folk music. Ireland**
**Breathnach, Breand'an**
Folk music & dances of Ireland/ [by] Breand'an Breathnach. — Dublin: Talbot Press, 1971. — [7],152p: ill, music; 20cm.
Bibl.p.151-152.
ISBN 0 85452 014 7 : £1.50

(B72-07358)

**A/G(YG/XA1914 — Folk music. Hungary, to 1914**
**Kodály, Zoltán**
AC Folk music of Hungary/ [by] Zoltán Kodály; [translated from the Hungarian and revised in accordance with the German edition (1956) by Ronald Tempest and Cynthia Jolly]. — 2nd ed./ revised and enlarged by Lajos Vargyas; [translation revised by Laurence Picken]. — London: Barrie and Jenkins, 1971. — 195,[12]p: ill, music, ports; 24cm.
Previous ed. of this translation, London: Barrie and Rockliff, 1960. — Translation of 'A magyar népzene'. 3.kiad. Budapest: Zenemükiadó, 1952.
ISBN 0 214 65327 7 : £2.25

(B72-13442)

**A/G(YT/T) — Folk music.** *United States. Bibliographies*
**Clark, Keith**
Folk song and dance: a list of books/ selected by Keith Clark. — London: National Book League: English Folk Dance and Song Society, 1972. — 48p: ill; 21cm.
ISBN 0 85353 138 2 Sd: £0.30
*Primary classification A/G(T)*

(B72-16428)

**A/GB — Popular music**
**Morse, David**
Motown & the arrival of black music/ [by] David Morse. — London: Studio Vista, 1971. — 111p: ill, facsims, ports; 21cm. — [Rockbooks]
ISBN 0 289 70131 7 : £1.40
ISBN 0 289 70130 9 Pbk: £0.60

(B72-30069)

**Wale, Michael**
Voxpop: profiles of the pop process/ by Michael Wale. — London: Harrap, 1972. — 320p; 22cm.
ISBN 0 245 50904 6 : £2.10
ISBN 0 245 51083 4 Pbk: £1.50

(B72-28678)

**A/GB(M) — Popular music. Musicians**
**Top** pop scene. — London: Purnell, 1972. — [62]p: ports(some col), ill(some col); 28cm.
ISBN 0 361 02016 3 : £0.60

(B72-21771)

**A/GB(WE) — Popular music. Festivals**
**National Association of Youth Clubs.** *Politics Working Party*
Night assembly?/ National Association of Youth Clubs, [Politics Working Party]. — London: N.A.Y.C., [1972]. — [1],11p: ill; 22cm.
ISBN 0 901528 56 0 Sd: £0.03

(B72-16874)

**A/GB(X) — Popular music. History**
**Whitcomb, Ian**
After the ball/ [by] Ian Whitcomb. — London: Allen Lane, 1972. — [8],312p: music(on lining papers); 23cm.
Index.
ISBN 0 7139 0308 2 : £3.00

(B72-28006)

**A/GB(XPQ17) — Popular music, 1955-1971**
**Dallas, Karl**
Singers of an empty day: last sacraments for the superstars/ [by] Karl Dallas; illustrated by Gloria Dallas. — London (25 Thurloe St., S.W.7): Kahn and Averill, 1971. — 208p: ill, ports; 21cm.
Index.
ISBN 0 900707 12 7 : £2.00

(B72-02167)

**Jasper, Tony**
Understanding pop/ [by] Tony Jasper. — London: S.C.M. Press, 1972. — 192p: ill, facsims, ports; 22cm.
Bibl.p.184-187.
ISBN 0 334 01728 9 : £1.95

(B72-10327)

**A/GB(YT/XPE25) — Popular music. United States, 1945-1969**
**Gillett, Charlie**
The sound of the city/ [by] Charlie Gillett. — London: Sphere, 1971. — [8],x,387p; 18cm.
Originally published, New York: Outerbridge and Dienstfrey, 1970. — Bibl. p.371-376. — Index.
ISBN 0 7221 3860 1 Pbk: £0.60

(B72-07349)

**A/GB(ZC) — Folk music - expounding the American Left**
**Denisoff, R. Serge**
Great day coming: folk music and the American left/ [by] R.
Serge Denisoff. — Urbana; London: University of Illinois Press,
1971. — [11],220p: ports; 26cm. — (Music in American life series)
Bibl.p.201-211. — List of records p.198-200. — Index.
ISBN 0 252 00179 6 : £3.60

(B72-30745)

**A/GB(ZF) — Popular music - influenced by blues**
**Middleton, Richard**
Pop music and the blues: a study of the relationship and its
significance/ by Richard Middleton. — London: Gollancz, 1972.
— 271p: music; 23cm.
Bibl.p.255-259. — Index.
ISBN 0 575 01442 3 : £4.00

(B72-29416)

**A/LD(YC/D) — Church music. Great Britain. Essays**
**English** church music: a collection of essays. — Croydon
(Addington Palace, Croydon, CR9 5AD): Royal School of Church
Music. —
1972. — [1972]. — 3-70p; 22cm.
ISBN 0 85402 048 9 Pbk: £0.76

(B72-18918)

**A/LZ — ELEMENTS OF MUSIC**
**A/R — Harmony**
**Rameau, Jean Philippe**
Treatise on harmony/ [by] Jean-Philippe Rameau; translated [from
the French] with an introduction and notes by Philip Gossett. —
New York: Dover Publications; London: Constable, 1971. — [4],
1v,444p: ill, facsims, music; 25cm.
Translation of 'Traité de l'harmonie'. Paris: Jean-Baptiste-Christophe
Ballard, 1722.
ISBN 0 486 22461 9 : £8.75

(B72-01562)

**Thomas de Sancta Maria**
Libro llamado arte de tañer fantasia/ [por] Thomas de Sancta
Maria; introduction by Denis Stevens. — [Farnborough]: Gregg,
1972. — [442]p: music; 28cm.
Spanish text, English introduction. — Facsimile reprint of 1st ed.,
Valladolid: Francisco Fernandez de Cordoua, 1565.
ISBN 0 576 28229 4 : £14.40
*Primary classification AQT/E*

(B72-30746)

**AB — MUSICAL LITERATURE. VOCAL MUSIC**
**AB/E(YDC/BC) — Singers. Home Counties. Directories**
**Singers**: a directory of freelance amateur singers in London and the
Home Counties. — London (14 Barlby Rd, W10 6AR): Autolycus
Publications. —
'72/ [compiled by G.P. Humphreys]. — 1972. — 20p; 21cm.
ISBN 0 903413 00 0 Sd: £0.30

(B72-14106)

**AB/GB/E(P) — The Osmonds. Biographies**
The **fantastic** Osmonds!. — London: 'Daily Mirror' Books, 1972. —
48p: chiefly ports(some col), facsim; 30cm. — (A 'Daily Mirror'
special)
Fold sheet (col. port) as insert.
ISBN 0 600 32890 2 Sd: £0.25

(B72-32462)

**AB/GB/E(P) — The Rolling Stones. Biographies**
**Dalton, David**
Rolling Stones/ edited by David Dalton; designed by Jon
Goodchild. — New York: Amsco Music Publishing; London (78
Newman St., W1E 4JZ): Music Sales Ltd, 1972. — 352p: ill(some
col), facsims(some col), music, ports(some col); 29cm.
List of records p.348-351.
ISBN 0 8256 2653 6 : Unpriced
ISBN 0 8256 2669 2 Pbk: £2.95

(B72-24870)

**AC — MUSICAL LITERATURE. OPERA**
**Hanslick, Eduard**
Aus dem Opernleben der Gegenwart: neue Kritiken und Studien/
von Eduard Hanslick. — Farnborough: Gregg, 1971. — [1],iv,
379p; 20cm. — (The collected musical criticism of Eduard
Hanslick; 3) (Hanslick, Eduard. Moderne Oper; 3)
Facsimile reprint of 1st ed., Berlin: A. Hofmann, 1884.
ISBN 0 576 28183 2 : £6.00
ISBN 0 576 28228 6 Set of 9 vols: £51.00

(B72-07360)

**Hanslick, Eduard**
Die moderne Oper: Kritiken und Studien/ von Eduard Hanslick.
— Farnborough: Gregg, 1971. — ix,341p: music; 20cm. —
(Hanslick, Eduard. Moderne Oper; 1) (The collected musical
criticism of Eduard Hanslick; 1)
Facsimile reprint of 1st ed., Berlin: A. Hofmann, 1875.
ISBN 0 576 28181 6 : £6.00
ISBN 0 576 28228 6 Set of 9 vols: £51.00

(B72-07359)

**Wechsberg, Joseph**
The opera/ [by] Joseph Wechsberg. — London: Weidenfeld and
Nicolson, 1972. — viii,312p; 24cm.
Index.
ISBN 0 297 99508 1 : £4.95

(B72-24252)

**AC(WB/P) — Impresarios. Bing, Sir Rudolph. Biographies**
**Bing,** *Sir* **Rudolf**
5,000 nights at the opera/ [by] Sir Rudolf Bing. — London:
Hamilton, 1972. — [7],285,[33]p: ill, ports; 23cm.
Index.
ISBN 0 241 02201 0 : £4.00

(B72-26658)

**AC(X) — Opera. History**
**Orrey, Leslie**
A concise history of opera/ [by] Leslie Orrey. — London: Thames
and Hudson, 1972. — 252p: ill(some col), facsims(incl 1 col),
music, plans, ports(some col); 22cm. — [The world of art library:
music]
Bibl.p.244. — Index.
ISBN 0 500 18130 6 : £2.50
ISBN 0 500 20124 2 Pbk: £1.50

(B72-28009)

**AC(XA1900) — To 1900**
**Berges, Ruth**
The backgrounds and traditions of opera/ by Ruth Berges. —
[2nd., enlarged, ed.]. — Cranbury: Barnes; London: Yoseloff,
1970. — 269,[48]p: ill, facsim, ports; 24cm.
Previous ed. published as 'Opera: origins and sidelights'. 1961. — Bibl.p.247-
257. — Index.
ISBN 0 498 07672 5 : £3.25

(B72-04571)

**AC(YDL/XQB11) — Opera. Scotland, 1962-1972**
**Wilson, Conrad**
Scottish Opera - the first ten years/ [by] Conrad Wilson; foreword
by Lord Harewood. — London: Collins, 1972. — [8],168,[16]p:
ill(some col), ports; 27cm.
Index.
ISBN 0 00 410584 2 : £5.00

(B72-21778)

**AC(YF/XF/ZB) — Opera. France, 1700. Compared with Italian opera**
**Raguenet, François**
[Paralèle des Italiens et des François, en ce qui regard la musique
et les opéras]. A comparison between the French and Italian
musick and operas/ [by] François Raguenet; translated from the
French with some remarks, to which is added a critical discourse
upon opera's in England, and a means proposed for their
improvement [by Johann Ernst Galliard?]. — [1st English ed.,
reprinted]; introduction by Charles Cudworth. — Farnborough:
Gregg, 1968. — [14],86p; 24cm.
'The Cambridge University library copy ... its margins have been copiously
annotated by some unknown early eighteenth century hand'. —
Introduction. — Facsimile reprint of 1st English ed., London: Printed for
W. Lewis, 1709. — Translation of 'Paralèle des Italiens et des François, en
ce qui regard la musique et les opéras'. Paris: J. Moreau, 1702.
ISBN 0 576 28446 7 : £11.40
*Primary classification AC(YJ/XF/ZB)*

(B72-09123)

**AC(YJ/XF/ZB) — Opera. Italy, 1700. Compared with French opera**
**Raguenet, François**
[Paralèle des Italiens et des François, en ce qui regard la musique
et les opéras]. A comparison between the French and Italian
musick and operas/ [by] François Raguenet; translated from the
French with some remarks, to which is added a critical discourse
upon opera's in England, and a means proposed for their
improvement [by Johann Ernst Galliard?]. — [1st English ed.,
reprinted]; introduction by Charles Cudworth. — Farnborough:
Gregg, 1968. — [14],86p; 24cm.
'The Cambridge University library copy ... its margins have been copiously
annotated by some unknown early eighteenth century hand'. —
Introduction. — Facsimile reprint of 1st English ed., London: Printed for
W. Lewis, 1709. — Translation of 'Paralèle des Italiens et des François, en
ce qui regard la musique et les opéras'. Paris: J. Moreau, 1702.
ISBN 0 576 28446 7 : £11.40
*Also classified at AC(YF/XF/ZB)*

(B72-09123)

**AC(YJN/XF101) — Opera. Naples. History, 1700-1800**
**Robinson, Michael Finlay**
Naples and Neapolitan opera/ [by] Michael F. Robinson. —
Oxford: Clarendon Press, 1972. — ix,281p: music; 28cm. —
(Oxford monographs on music)
Bibl.p.261-268. — Index.
ISBN 0 19 816124 7 : £8.00

(B72-30742)

**AC/E(XA1971) — Opera. Performance, to 1971**
Gishford, Anthony
  Grand opera: the story of the world's leading opera houses and
  personalities/ edited by Anthony Gishford; introduced by
  Benjamin Britten. — London: Weidenfeld and Nicolson, 1972. —
  272p: ill(some col), facsims, ports(some col); 26cm.
  Facsims on lining papers. — Index.
  ISBN 0 297 99472 7 : £4.25

(B72-29419)

**AD — MUSICAL LITERATURE. CHORAL MUSIC**
**AD(TC) — Bibliographies of scores**
Massey Music and Gramophone Record Library
  A list of multiple copies of vocal music available for loan/ Massey
  Music and Gramophone Record Library. — 2nd ed. — Burnley
  (Central Library, Burnley, Lancs.): Burnley Public Libraries, 1969.
  — [2],55p; 33cm.
  ISBN 0 9501268 5 3 Sd: £0.125

(B72-03560)

**AD(YDKRL/WB/XPG26) — Choral music. Llangollen. International
Musical Eisteddfod, 1947-1972**
Humphries, Mary
  A world that sings: an account of the 26 years of the International
  Musical Eisteddfod/ by Mary Humphries. — Cardiff (21 Duffryn
  Close, Cardiff CF2 6HT): John Jones Cardiff Ltd, 1972. — [3],v,
  38,[4]p: ill; 15x21cm.
  ISBN 0 902375 24 5 Pbk: £0.50

(B72-22481)

**AD/EC(P) — Choirmasters. Sargent, A.W.**
Sargent, A W
  Voices, pipes and pedals: the story of a life in music/ by A.W.
  Sargent. — London: Mitre Press, 1971. — 366,[8]p: ill, ports;
  22cm.
  ISBN 0 7051 0108 8 : £1.75

(B72-03928)

**AD/LD(TE/XDXJ112) — Church music. Bibliographies of
manuscripts, 1549-1660**
Daniel, Ralph T
  The sources of English church music, 1549-1660/ compiled by
  Ralph T. Daniel and Peter Le Huray. — London (82 High Rd,
  N2 9BZ): Stainer and Bell for the British Academy, 1972. — 2v.
  (x,159p): music; 25cm. — ('Early English church music'
  supplementary volume; 1)
  Bibl.p.9. — Index.
  ISBN 0 903000 10 5 : £8.00

(B72-22016)

**AD/LD(YD/X) — Church music. England. History**
Long, Kenneth R
  The music of the English church/ by Kenneth R. Long. —
  London: Hodder and Stoughton, 1972. — 480p: music; 26cm.
  Bibl.p.441-451. — Index.
  ISBN 0 340 14962 0 : £7.00

(B72-06767)

**AD/LD/E — Church music. Singing**
Mason, Phil
  In quires and places/ by Phil Mason. — Burton Latimer (1
  Whitney Rd, Burton Latimer, Northants.): Phil Mason, [1971]. —
  [6],20p,2 leaves: ill; 18cm.
  ISBN 0 9500388 1 4 Sd: £0.20

(B72-07980)

**AD/LE(YDBB) — Cathedral music. London. St Paul's Cathedral**
Scott, David, *b.1943*
  The music of St Paul's Cathedral/ [by] David Scott; with
  numerous reproductions, documents and music by Thomas Morley
  and Christopher Dearnley in a pocket inside the back cover. —
  London: Stainer and Bell; [London] (82 High Rd, East Finchley,
  N2 9PW): [Distributed by Publishing Services Partnership], 1972.
  — 32p: ill, facsims(in pocket), music(in pocket); 28cm.
  Four fold. sheets in pocket.
  ISBN 0 903000 08 3 Sd: £0.60

(B72-30071)

**AD/LE(YDJGYB) — Cathedral music. York. York Minster**
Aston, Peter
  The music of York Minster/ [by] Peter Aston; with illustrations,
  portraits and facsimiles and a previously unpublished motet by
  John Thorne (d.1573) in a pocket inside the back cover. —
  London (29 Newman St., W.1): Stainer and Bell, 1972. — [1],16p:
  ill, facsims, music, ports; 28cm.
  Two fold. leaves (ill., facsims, music, ports), and score (4p.) of 'Stella
  coeli'/by John Thorne; transcribed and edited by Peter Aston, in pocket. —
  Bibl.p.15.
  ISBN 0 903000 07 5 Sd: £0.50

(B72-22491)

**ADW(KM/YT) — Songs. National songs. United States**
Sonneck, Oscar George
  Report on 'The star-spangled banner', 'Hail Columbia', 'America',
  'Yankee Doodle'/ by Oscar George Theodore Sonneck. — New
  York: Dover Publications; London: Constable, 1972. — [1],203p:
  facsims, music; 24cm.
  Facsimile reprint of 1st ed., Washington: Government Printing Office, 1909.
  — Bibl.p.157-164. — Index.
  ISBN 0 486 22237 3 Pbk: £1.25

(B72-31292)

**ADW(YD/XDZT12) — Songs. England, 1598-1609**
Cavendish, Michael
  14 ayres in tabletorie, 1598/ [by] Michael Cavendish; [and], Ayres,
  1609/ [by] Alfonso Ferrabosco; [and], Musicke of sundrie kindes,
  1607/ [by] Thomas Ford; [and], Songes of sundrie kindes, 1604/
  [by] Thomas Greaves; [and], Ayres to be sung to the lute,
  ca.1609/ [by] George Handford/ [edited by David Greer]. —
  Menston: Scolar Press, 1971. — [255]p: of music; 37cm. —
  (English lute songs, 1597-1632; vol.5)
  Facsimile reprints.
  ISBN 0 85417 561 x : £12.00

(B72-05572)

**ADW(YD/XE11) — Songs. England, 1600-1610**
Jones, Robert, *fl.1597-1614*
  The first booke of songes and ayres, 1600; [and], The second
  booke of songs and ayres, 1601; [and], Ultimum vale, 1605; [and],
  A musicall dreame, 1609; [and], The muses gardin, 1610/ [by]
  Robert Jones; edited by David Greer. — Menston: Scolar Press,
  1970. — [257]p: of music; 37cm. — (English lute songs,
  1597-1632; vol.7)
  Facsimile reprints.
  ISBN 0 85417 559 8 : £12.00

(B72-05573)

**ADW/G(YDJHT) — Folk songs. Tyneside**
Allan, Thomas
  Allan's illustrated edition of Tyneside songs. — 6th ed.
  [reprinted]; with a new introduction by David Harker. —
  Newcastle upon Tyne: Graham, 1972. — xxx,xvi,578p: ill, facsims,
  ports; 22cm.
  Facsimile reprint of 6th ed., Newcastle upon Tyne: T. & G. Allan, 1891.
  ISBN 0 902833 75 8 : £3.50

(B72-28011)

**ADW/G(YX) — Folk songs. Australia**
Edwards, Ron
  The Overlander song book/ by Ron Edwards; with illustrations by
  the author. — London: Hale, 1972. — [11],303p: ill, music; 25cm.
  Ill. on lining papers. — Originally published, Adelaide: Rigby, 1971. —
  Index.
  ISBN 0 7091 3070 8 : £3.00

(B72-12721)

**ADW/GCW(B) — Songs. Country & western. Periodicals**
Country. — London (61 Berners St., W1P 3AE): Hanover Books
  Ltd. —
  Vol.1, no.1- ; March 1972-. — 1972-. — ill, ports; 30cm.
  Monthly. — 30p. in 1st issue.
  Sd: £0.20

(B72-09749)

**ADW/GM(YD) — Songs. Music hall. England**
Gammond, Peter
  Best music hall and variety songs/ compiled and edited by Peter
  Gammond. — London: Wolfe, 1972. — 512p: music; 26cm. — (A
  Wolfe old time stars' book)
  Index.
  ISBN 0 7234 0451 8 : £5.00

(B72-30743)

**AEZDU — Unaccompanied works. Madrigals**
Yonge, Nicolas
  Musica Transalpina/ [by] Nicolas Yonge. — [1st ed. reprinted];
  with a new introduction by Denis Stevens. — Farnborough:
  Gregg. —
  [Vol.1]. — 1972. — [350]p: chiefly music; 25cm.
  Facsimile reprint of 1st ed. of vol.1, London: Thomas East, 1588.
  ISBN 0 576 28178 6 : £12.00

(B72-26095)

**AK — MUSICAL LITERATURE. VOCAL SOLOS**
**AKDW/HHW/E(P) — Blues singers. Joplin, Janis. Biographies**
Dalton, David
  Janis/ written and edited by David Dalton. — London: Calder
  and Boyars: New English Library, 1972. — vi,154p: ill, facsims,
  ports; 28cm.
  Also published, New York: Simon and Schuster, 1972.
  ISBN 0 7145 0943 4 Pbk: £1.25

(B72-26094)

**AKF/E(P) — Garland, Judy. Biographies**
Deans, Mickey
Weep no more, my lady: an intimate biography of Judy Garland/
by Mickey Deans her last husband and Ann Pinchot. — London:
W.H. Allen, 1972. — 238,[16]p: ill, facsim, ports; 23cm.
ISBN 0 491 00941 0 : £2.50

(B72-08534)

**AKF/E(P) — Smith, Jane Stuart. Biographies**
Carlson, Betty
A singing heart: from Venice to the alps of L'Abri/ by Betty
Carlson. — London: Hodder and Stoughton, 1972. — 158p; 18cm.
— (Hodder Christian paperbacks)
ISBN 0 340 15866 2 Pbk: £0.45

(B72-23640)

**AKFL/E(P) — Sutherland, Joan. Biographies**
Greenfield, Edward
Joan Sutherland/ [by] Edward Greenfield. — Shepperton: Allan,
1972. — 64p: ill, ports; 24cm. — [Recordmasters; 1]
Title page imprint: London. — List of records p.59-64.
ISBN 0 7110 0318 1 : £1.50

(B72-15424)

**AKG/E(P) — Cole, Nat King. Biographies**
Cole, Maria
Nat King Cole: an intimate biography, by Maria Cole with Louie
Robinson. — London: W.H. Allen, 1972. — 184,[8]p: ports;
23cm.
Originally published, New York: Morrow, 1971. — List of records
p.163-184.
ISBN 0 491 00782 5 : £2.10

(B72-23643)

**AKG/E(P) — Dylan, Bob**
Gray, Michael
Song & dance man: the art of Bob Dylan/ [by] Michael Gray. —
London (3 Upper James St., W1R 4BP): Hart-Davis, MacGibbon,
1972. — xiv,337,[4]p: ill, ports; 23cm.
List of recordings p.305-316. — Index.
ISBN 0 261 10000 9 : £2.50

(B72-30744)

**AKG/E(P) — Dylan, Bob. Biographies**
Scaduto, Anthony
Bob Dylan/ [by] Anthony Scaduto. — London (30 Gray's Inn
Rd, WC1X 8JL): Abacus, 1972. — [7],280,[8]p: ports; 20cm.
Originally published, New York: Grosset and Dunlap, 1971; London: W.H.
Allen, 1972. — List of records p.275-276. — Index.
ISBN 0 349 13127 9 Pbk: £0.60

(B72-23642)

Scaduto, Anthony
Bob Dylan/ by Anthony Scaduto. — London: W.H. Allen, 1972.
— [7],280,[8]p: ports; 23cm.
Originally published, New York: Grosset and Dunlap, 1971. — List of
records p.275-276. — Index.
ISBN 0 491 00662 4 : £2.50

(B72-12015)

**AKG/E(P) — Jolson, Al. Biographies**
Freedland, Michael
Al Jolson/ [by] Michael Freedland. — London: W.H. Allen, 1972.
— 318,[16]p: ill, ports; 23cm.
Index.
ISBN 0 491 00633 0 : £3.00

(B72-28010)

**AKGDW/GB/E(D) — Popular songs. Singers. Holly, Buddy**
Laing, Dave
Buddy Holly/ [by] Dave Laing. — London: Studio Vista, 1971. —
111p: ill, facsims, map, ports; 21cm. — [Rockbooks]
List of records p.109-111.
ISBN 0 289 70129 5 : £1.40
ISBN 0 289 70128 7 Pbk: £0.60

(B72-07981)

**AKGDW/HK/E(P) — Presley, Elvis. Biographies**
Hopkins, Jerry
Elvis: a biography/ by Jerry Hopkins. — London (4 Little Essex
St., W.C.2): Open Gate Books, 1972. — 448p: ill, ports; 22cm.
Originally published, New York: Simon and Schuster, 1971. — List of
gramophone records p.429-444. — List of films p.445-446.
ISBN 0 333 13617 9 : £1.95

(B72-21779)

**AKGH/E(P) — Caruso, Enrico. Biographies**
Jackson, Stanley, b.1910
Caruso/ [by] Stanley Jackson. — London: W.H. Allen, 1972. —
x,302,[17]p: ill, ports; 23cm.
Bibl.p.294-296. — Index.
ISBN 0 491 00664 0 : £3.50

(B72-27439)

**AKGH/FD(P/WT) — McCormack, John. Recorded music. Lists**
Roe, Leonard McDermott
The John McCormack discography/ [by] L. McDermott Roe. —
Lingfield: Oakwood Press, 1972. — [1],93p; 14x22cm.
ISBN 0 85361 106 8 Pbk: £1.20

(B72-27620)

**AL — MUSICAL LITERATURE. INSTRUMENTAL MUSIC**
**AL/B — Instruments**
Hindley, Geoffrey
Musical instruments/ [by] Geoffrey Hindley; illustrated by Ron
Geary ... [and others]. — Feltham: Hamlyn, 1971. — 159p:
ill(chiefly col), col ports; 19cm. — (Hamlyn all-colour paperbacks:
arts)
Title page imprint: London. — Bibl.p.156. — Index.
ISBN 0 600 00294 2 Pbk: £0.40

(B72-06765)

Kendall, Alan
The world of musical instruments/ [by] Alan Kendall. —
[Feltham]: Hamlyn, 1972. — 128p: chiefly ill(some col), facsims,
music, ports(some col); 30cm.
Index.
ISBN 0 600 35957 3 : £1.75

(B72-08532)

**AL/E(VC) — Instruments. Performance. Teaching**
Inner London Education Authority. *Music Centre*
Instrumental teaching/ published and prepared by the ILEA
Music Centre to accompany the ETV series. — [London] (Ebury
Bridge, S.W.1.): I.L.E.A. Music Centre, [1972]. — 84p: ill, music;
23cm. — (Publication; no.7168)
Bibl.
ISBN 0 7168 0428 x Sd: Free

(B72-26657)

**ALH(QB/XMP35) — Dance bands. History, 1914-1948**
Rust, Brian Arthur Lovell
The dance bands/ [by] Brian Rust. — Shepperton: Allan, 1972. —
160p: ill, ports; 28cm.
Title page imprint: London. — Index.
ISBN 0 7110 0341 6 : £3.75

(B72-27440)

**AM — MUSICAL LITERATURE. ORCHESTRAL MUSIC**
**AM(TC) — Bibliographies of scores**
Massey Music and Gramophone Record Library
List of orchestral works available for loan/ Massey Music and
Gramophone Record Library. — 2nd ed. — Burnley (Central
Library, Burnley, Lancs.): Burnley Public Libraries, 1970. — [2],
33p; 33cm.
ISBN 0 9501268 6 1 Sd: £0.125

(B72-03561)

**AM/B — Orchestra. Instruments**
Fox, Lilla Margaret
Instruments of the orchestra/ [by] Lilla M. Fox; with drawings by
the author. — [Woking]: Lutterworth Press, 1971. — 144p: ill,
plan; 21cm. — (Fox, Lilla Margaret. A history of musical
instruments)
Title page imprint: London. — Bibl.p.132. — Index.
ISBN 0 7188 1710 9 : £1.25

(B72-03315)

**AM/DF — Orchestration**
Berlioz, Hector
[Grand traité d'instrumentation et d'orchestration. opus 10]. Traité
d'instrumentation et d'orchestration: suivie de 'L'Art du chef
d'orchestre'/ par Hector Berlioz. — Nouvelle éd., [reprinted]. —
Farnborough: Gregg, 1970. — [2],312p: music; 34cm. —
(Collected literary works; 1)
Facsimile reprint of the 1870 ed., Paris: H. Lemoine, 1870. — Originally
published as 'Grand traité d'instrumentation et d'orchestration'. Paris:
Schonenberger, 1844.
ISBN 0 576 28418 1 : £21.00
ISBN 0 576 28417 3 Set of 7 works: £78.00

(B72-06769)

**AMM/E(QB/X) — London Philharmonic Orchestra. History**
Kallaway, Bill
London Philharmonic: music makers since 1932/ by William
Kallaway; with an introduction by Richard Baker. — Havant: K.
Mason, 1972. — 104p: ill, facsims, ports; 26cm.
ISBN 0 900534 75 3 : £2.50

(B72-30072)

**AMM/E(QB/X) — Scottish National Orchestra. History**
Scottish National Orchestra Society
SNO 1971: an anniversary study of the Scottish National
Orchestra (1950-1971), the Scottish Orchestra (1891-1950) and
their antecedents/ Scottish National Orchestra Society. —
Glasgow (150 Hope St., Glasgow, C2): Scottish National
Orchestra Society Ltd, [1971]. — 63p: ill, facsims, ports; 25cm.
'...based upon research made available by Graham Wark...' - note.
ISBN 0 9502512 0 8 Pbk: £0.45

(B72-26096)

**AMME — Symphony orchestra. Symphonies**
Simpson, Robert
The symphony/ edited by Robert Simpson. — Newton Abbot:
David and Charles. —
In 2 vols. — Originally published, Harmondsworth: Penguin, 1967.
Vol.1: Haydn to Dvořak. — 1972. — 382p: music; 23cm.
Index.
ISBN 0 7153 5523 6 : £3.25
(B72-12018)
Vol.2: Mahler to the present day. — 1972. — 282p: music; 23cm.
Index.
ISBN 0 7153 5524 4 : £2.75
(B72-12019)

**AMT — MUSICAL LITERATURE. JAZZ**
**AMT(X) — History**
Fox, Charles
The jazz scene/ [by] Charles Fox; special photography by Valerie
Wilmer. — Feltham: Hamlyn, 1972. — 127p: chiefly ill(some col),
ports(some col); 30cm.
Title page imprint: London. — Ports on lining papers. — Bibl.p.122. —
Index.
ISBN 0 600 02119 x : £1.75
(B72-24869)

Lee, Edward
Jazz: an introduction/ [by] Edward Lee. — London (25 Thurloe
St., S.W.7): Kahn and Averill, 1972. — 188p: music; 23cm.
List of records p.155-159. — Index.
ISBN 0 900707 11 9 : £2.50
(B72-23639)

**AMT/E(M/YTSWK/XNF15) — Performers. Kansas. Kansas City,**
**1926-1940**
Russell, Ross
Jazz style in Kansas City and the Southwest/ by Ross Russell. —
Berkeley; London (2 Brook St., W1Y 1AA): University of
California Press, 1971. — xviii,292,[32]p: ill, ports; 25cm.
Bibl.p.271-278. — List of records.p.263-270. — Index.
ISBN 0 520 01853 2 : £5.95
(B72-02169)

**AMT/E(P) — Foster, Pops. Biographies**
Foster, Pops
The autobiography of a New Orleans Jazzman/ [by] Pops Foster;
as told to Tom Stoddard; introduction by Bertram Turetzky,
interchapters by Ross Russell, discography by Brian Rust. —
Berkeley; London (2 Brook St., W1Y 1AA): University of
California Press, 1971. — xxii,208,[40]p: ill, facsims, ports; 24cm.
Bibl.p.199. — List of records.p.180-197. — Index.
ISBN 0 520 01826 5 : £4.25
(B72-02170)

**AMT/E(QB/XNQ12) — Jazz bands, 1935-1946**
Simon, George Thomas
The big bands/ [by] George T. Simon; with a foreword by Frank
Sinatra. — Revised enlarged ed. — New York: Macmillan (N.Y.);
London: Collier-Macmillan, 1971. — xvi,584p: ill, facsims, ports;
25cm.
Previous ed. 1967. — List of records p.553-560. — Index.
ISBN 0 02 610970 0 : £2.75
(B72-12017)

**AMT/JR — Films**
Meeker, David
Jazz in the movies: a tentative index to the work of jazz musicians
for the cinema/ by David Meeker. — London: British Film
Institute, 1972. — [2],89p: ill, ports; 21cm.
Index.
ISBN 0 85170 030 6 Pbk: £0.50
(B72-15718)

**AP — MUSICAL LITERATURE. INDIVIDUAL INSTRUMENTS**
**& INSTRUMENTAL GROUPS**
**APV/D — Electronic music. Composition**
Oram, Daphne
An individual note: of music, sound and electronics/ [by] Daphne
Oram. — Great Yarmouth (Queen Anne's Rd, Great Yarmouth,
Norfolk): Galliard, 1972. — v,145p,fold leaf: ill; 22cm.
Title page imprint: London. — List of records p.129-136. — Index.
ISBN 0 85249 109 3 Pbk: £0.99
(B72-50001)

**APW — MUSICAL LITERATURE. KEYBOARD**
**INSTRUMENTS**
**APW/B — Instruments**
Ripin, Edwin M
Keyboard instruments: studies in keyboard organology/ edited by
Edwin M. Ripin. — Edinburgh: Edinburgh University Press, 1971.
— vii,84,[64]p: ill, facsim; 23cm.
ISBN 0 85224 202 6 : £3.00
(B72-15427)

**APW/ED(X) — Composition. History**
Matthews, Denis
Keyboard music/ edited by Denis Matthews. — Harmondsworth:
Penguin, 1972. — 386p: music; 19cm. — (A Pelican original)
Index.
ISBN 0 14 021250 7 Pbk: £0.75
(B72-10332)

Matthews, Denis
Keyboard music/ edited by Denis Matthews. — Newton Abbot:
David and Charles, 1972. — 386p: music; 23cm.
Also published, Harmondsworth: Penguin, 1972. — Bibl.p.60-67. — Index.
ISBN 0 7153 5612 7 : £3.50
(B72-15428)

**AQ/E — Piano. Performance**
Barnett, David, b.1907
The performance of music: a study in terms of the pianoforte/
[by] David Barnett. — London: Barrie and Jenkins, 1972. — [7],
232p: music; 23cm.
Also published, New York: Universe Books, 1972.
ISBN 0 214 65403 6 : £4.00
(B72-12722)

Bruxner, Mervyn
Mastering the piano: a guide for the amateur/ [by] Mervyn
Bruxner. — London: Faber, 1972. — 3-139p: music; 23cm.
Index.
ISBN 0 571 09629 8 : £2.25
(B72-28012)

**AQ/E(M/XHH45) — Pianists, 1828-1872**
Lenz, Wilhelm von
The great piano virtuosos of our time/ by W. von Lenz; this
revised translation [from the German] edited by Philip Reder. —
London: Regency Press, 1971. — [7],91p: ports; 20cm.
Revised translation of 'Die grossen Pianoforte - Virtuosen unserer Zeit aus
persönlicher Bekanntschaft'. Berlin: B. Behr's Buchhandlung, 1872.
ISBN 0 7212 0138 5 : £1.20
(B72-13443)

**AQ/E(P) — Frazier, Kathleen. Biographies**
Frazier, Kathleen
My story/ by Kathleen Frazier; amusing sketches by Lyn Lyons.
— Newton Abbot (12 Forde Park, Newton Abbot, Devon): K.
Frazier, [1972]. — 44p: ill, facsim; 21cm.
ISBN 0 9502464 0 9 Sd: £0.50
(B72-26661)

**AQ/E(VC) — Piano. Performance. Teaching**
Last, Joan
The young pianist: a new approach for teachers and students/ [by]
Joan Last. — 2nd ed. — London: Oxford University Press, 1972.
— xii,155,[11]p: ill, music; 21cm.
Previous ed. 1954.
ISBN 0 19 318420 6 : £1.40
(B72-10331)

**AQT/E — Clavichord. Performance**
Thomas de Sancta Maria
Libro llamado arte de tañer fantasia/ [por] Thomas de Sancta
Maria; introduction by Denis Stevens. — [Farnborough]: Gregg,
1972. — [442]p: music; 28cm.
Spanish text, English introduction. — Facsimile reprint of 1st ed.,
Valladolid: Francisco Fernandez de Cordoua, 1565.
ISBN 0 576 28229 4 : £14.40
*Also classified at A/R*
(B72-30746)

**AR/B(YDFKWB) — Organs. Wimborne. Wimborne Minster**
Matthews, Betty
The organs and organists of Wimborne Minster, 1408-1972/ [by]
Betty Matthews. — Bournemouth (9 St Winifred's Rd,
Bournemouth BH2 6NY): Kenneth Mummery Ltd, [1972]. — [2],
22p: 2ill, facsim; 22cm.
ISBN 0 9502449 0 2 Sd: £0.30
(B72-20310)

**AR/E — Organ. Performance**
Reynolds, Gordon
Full swell/ [by] Gordon Reynolds; with drawings by Bernard
Hollowood. — Sevenoaks (Borough Green, Sevenoaks, Kent):
Novello, 1972. — 50p: ill; 19cm.
ISBN 0 85360 039 2 Pbk: £0.40
(B72-22496)

**ARPV/B(YC) — Electric organ. Instruments. Great Britain**
Theatre organ world, 'the organist entertained'. [Specifications - four
major examples of the art of unification in organ building by four
famous firms]/ [with a new introduction by Kenneth Lee]. —
Leeds (23 Portland Cres., Leeds LS1 3DR): Turntable Enterprises,
1972. — [4]p,p159-216; 22cm.
'... the original edition has been reprinted selectively ... The original page
numbers are retained.' - Bibliographic note. — Originally published, [s.l.]:
[s.n.], 1946.
ISBN 0 902844 06 7 Pbk: £0.80
(B72-30747)

**ARW — MUSICAL LITERATURE. STRING INSTRUMENTS**
**AS/B(X) — Violin. Instruments. History**
**Nelson, Sheila M**
The violin and viola/ [by] Sheila M. Nelson. — London: Benn,
1972. — xv,24,277p: ill, facsim, music; 23cm. — (Instruments of
the orchestra)
Bibl.p.257-264. — Index.
ISBN 0 510 36651 1 : £3.00
*Also classified at ASQ/B(X)*

(B72-15430)

**AS/CY — Violin playing. Technique**
**Menuhin, Yehudi**
Violin: six lessons with Yehudi Menuhin. — London (38 Russell
Sq., W.C.1): Faber Music Ltd, 1971. — 3-144p: ill, music; 25cm.
ISBN 0 571 10000 7 : £2.50

(B72-11002)

**AS/E — Violin. Performance**
**Whone, Herbert**
The simplicity of playing the violin/ by Herbert Whone; with
illustrations by the author and a preface by Colin Davis. —
London: Gollancz, 1972. — 126p: ill, music; 24cm.
Index.
ISBN 0 575 01343 5 : £2.20

(B72-11001)

**ASQ/B(X) — Violas. Instruments. History**
**Nelson, Sheila M**
The violin and viola/ [by] Sheila M. Nelson. — London: Benn,
1972. — xv,24,277p: ill, facsim, music; 23cm. — (Instruments of
the orchestra)
Bibl.p.257-264. — Index.
ISBN 0 510 36651 1 : £3.00
*Primary classification AS/B(X)*

(B72-15430)

**ASS/B — Double bass. Instruments**
**Elgar, Raymond**
Introduction to the double bass/ by Raymond Elgar. — 3rd ed.,
revised and reprinted. — St Leonards-on-Sea (31 Charles Rd
West, St Leonards-on-Sea, Sussex): R. Elgar, 1971. — 120p,10
leaves: ill, music; 19cm.
Previous ed. 1965.
ISBN 0 9502431 1 6 : £1.26

(B72-32463)

**AT — MUSICAL LITERATURE. PLUCKED STRING**
**INSTRUMENTS**
**ATJR/B — Lyre guitar. Instruments**
**Bonner, Stephen**
The classic image: European history and manufacture of lyre
guitar, 850-1840/ by Stephen Bonner. — Harlow (128
Bishopsfield, Harlow, Essex): Bois de Boulogne, 1972. — 5-68p:
ill(some col), facsims, music; 29cm.
Limited ed. of 180 numbered and signed copies. — Col. ill. tipped in. —
Bibl.p.66-67. — Index.
ISBN 0 900998 09 1 : £10.00

(B72-50002)

**ATS/BT — Guitar. Maintenance**
**Bowden, George**
Guitar care: a manual to enable the guitar owner to service his
instrument/ by George Bowden. — [Nottingham] (193 Wollaton
St., Nottingham): [G. Bowden], [1971]. — 11p: ill; 19cm.
ISBN 0 9502139 0 x Sd: Unpriced

(B72-03317)

**ATS/HHW/E(M) — Guitarists. Blues**
**Grossman, Stefan**
Ragtime blues guitarists/ by Stefan Grossman. — New York: Oak
Publications; London (78 Newman St., W.1): Music Sales Ltd,
1970. — 132p: ill, facsims, music, ports; 28cm.
ISBN 0 8256 0118 5 Pbk: £1.60

(B72-50003)

**AU — MUSICAL LITERATURE. WIND INSTRUMENTS**
**AV/BC(M) — Woodwind instruments. Instrument makers**
**Langwill, Lyndesay Graham**
An index of musical wind-instrument makers/ by Lyndesay G.
Langwill. — 3rd ed. revised, enlarged and illustrated. —
Edinburgh (7 Dick Place, Edinburgh EH9 2JS): L.G. Langwill,
1972. — xii,232p: ill, facsims; 26cm.
Previous ed. 1962. — Bibl.p.176-181.
ISBN 0 902153 01 3 : £5.00

(B72-12676)

**AVS/E — Recorder. Performance**
**Martin, Nancy**
Learning the recorder/ [by] Nancy Martin. — London: F. Warne,
1970. — 80p: ill, music; 25cm.
Originally published, Wellington: A.H. and A.W. Reed, 1956. — Index.
ISBN 0 7232 1280 5 : £1.00
ISBN 0 7232 1126 4 Pbk: £0.60

(B72-14738)

**AVU(B) — Saxophone. Instruments**
**Richmond, Stanley**
Clarinet and saxophone experience/ [by] Stanley Richmond. —
London: Darton, Longman and Todd, 1972. — xii,137p: ill,
music; 23cm.
ISBN 0 232 51148 9 : £3.25
*Primary classification A VV(B)*

(B72-50004)

**AVV(B) — Clarinet. Instruments**
**Richmond, Stanley**
Clarinet and saxophone experience/ [by] Stanley Richmond. —
London: Darton, Longman and Todd, 1972. — xii,137p: ill,
music; 23cm.
ISBN 0 232 51148 9 : £3.25
*Also classified at AVU(B)*

(B72-50004)

**AWM(TC) — Brass band. Bibliographies of scores**
**Massey Music and Gramophone Record Library**
List of brass and military band works available for loan/ Massey
Music and Gramophone Record Library. — Burnley (Central
Library, Burnley, Lancs.): Burnley Public Libraries, 1971. — 2
leaves,121p; 33cm.
ISBN 0 9501268 4 5 Sd: £0.15

(B72-03562)

**AX — MUSICAL LITERATURE. PERCUSSION**
**INSTRUMENTS**
**AXSR/E(YDED) — Change ringing. Church bells. Hertfordshire**
**Goodman, Lilian Gordon**
A history of ringing in Hertfordshire/ L.G. Goodman, editor. —
[Harpenden] (3 Lea Rd, Harpenden, Herts.): Hertford County
Association of Change Ringers, 1971. — [2],33p: ill; 21cm.
Includes handbell ringing. — 'The first "History of Ringing in
Hertfordshire" was a collection of articles published in the "Ringing World"
in 1953. They were written by H.V. Frost...The present booklet is a
reconstruction of the earlier one with added material...'.
ISBN 0 9502366 0 8 Sd: £0.15

(B72-16879)

**AY — Other instruments**
**Cardew, Cornelius**
Scratch music/ edited by Cornelius Cardew. — London (4
Alwyne Villas, N1 2HQ): Latimer New Dimensions Ltd, 1972. —
5-128p: ill, music; 23cm.
ISBN 0 901539 18 x : £3.00
ISBN 0 901539 17 1 Pbk: £1.60

(B72-24248)

**B — INDIVIDUAL COMPOSERS**
**BBC(N) — Bach, Johann Sebastian. Biographies**
**Reingold, Carmel Berman**
Johann Sebastian Bach/ by Carmel Berman Reingold. — London
(32 Palmer St., S.W.1): F. Watts, 1972. — [7],118p: ill, facsims,
map, music, ports; 22cm. — [Immortals of mankind series]
Originally published, New York: F. Watts, 1970. — Bibl.p.113. — Index.
ISBN 0 85166 320 6 : £1.50

(B72-22482)

**BBCADE — Bach, Johann Sebastian. Religious cantatas**
**Robertson, Alec**
The church cantatas of J.S. Bach/ [by] Alec Robertson. —
London: Cassell, 1972. — xvi,356p; 23cm.
Bibl.p.347. — Index.
ISBN 0 304 93822 x : £5.00

(B72-26660)

**BBCAR — Bach, Johann Sebastian. Organ music**
**Williams, Peter, b.1937**
Bach organ music/ [by] Peter Williams. — London: British
Broadcasting Corporation, 1972. — 71p: music; 20cm. — (British
Broadcasting Corporation. Music guides)
ISBN 0 563 10348 5 Pbk: £0.45

(B72-15429)

**BBDNACM/LK — Banyard, Edmund. One Friday in eternity.**
**Librettos**
**Banyard, Edmund**
One Friday in eternity/ [by] Edmund Banyard; with songs by
Edmund and Stephen Banyard and Peter Casey. — London (82
High Rd, N.2): Galliard Ltd, 1972. — 12p: music; 28cm.
ISBN 0 85249 121 2 Sd: £0.17
*Also classified at BBDNBACM/LK; BCBWACM/LK*

(B72-10328)

**BBDNBACM/LK — Banyard, Stephen. One Friday in eternity.**
**Librettos**
**Banyard, Edmund**
One Friday in eternity/ [by] Edmund Banyard; with songs by
Edmund and Stephen Banyard and Peter Casey. — London (82
High Rd, N.2): Galliard Ltd, 1972. — 12p: music; 28cm.
ISBN 0 85249 121 2 Sd: £0.17
*Primary classification BBDNACM/LK*

(B72-10328)

**BBE(N) — Bantock, Sir Granville. Biographies**
Bantock, Myrrha
  Granville Bantock: a personal portrait/ by Myrrha Bantock. —
  London: Dent, 1972. — xi,203,[16]p: ill, facsims, music, ports;
  24cm.
  List of music p.189-194. — Index.
  ISBN 0 460 03971 7 : £3.50

(B72-11534)

**BBH(WJ) — Bax, Sir Arnold. Catalogues**
Parlett, Graham
  Arnold Bax, a catalogue of his music/ compiled by Graham
  Parlett. — London (10e Prior Bolton St., N.1): Triad Press, 1972.
  — 52p; port; 23cm.
  'Limited ed. of 150 copies of which 125 numbered copies are for sale.' -
  note.
  ISBN 0 902070 04 5 Sd: £1.50

(B72-24473)

**BBJ — Beethoven, Ludwig van**
Edwards, Owain Tudor
  Beethoven/ prepared by Owain Edwards for the [Age of
  Revolutions] Course Team. — Bletchley (Walton Hall, Bletchley,
  Bucks.): Open University Press, 1972. — 107p: ill, facsims, music,
  ports; 30cm. — (Arts, a second level course: the age of
  revolutions; units 25-27) (A202; 25-27)
  Bibl.p.106-107. — Record supplement p.103-105.
  ISBN 0 335 00572 1 Pbk: Unpriced

(B72-22483)

**BBJAQPE/E — Beethoven, Ludwig van. Piano music. Sonatas.**
                    **Performance**
Newman, William Stein
  Performance practices in Beethoven's piano sonatas: an
  introduction/ [by] William S. Newman. — London: Dent, 1972.
  — 100p: ill, music; 23cm.
  Originally published, New York: Norton, 1971. — Bibl.p.96-98. — Index.
  ISBN 0 460 07868 2 : £2.50

(B72-17506)

**BBJH(N) — Bellini, Vincenzo. Biographies**
Weinstock, Herbert
  Vincenzo Bellini: his life and operas/ [by] Herbert Weinstock. —
  London: Weidenfeld and Nicolson, 1972. — xviii,589,[16]p: ill,
  facsim, music, ports; 24cm.
  Originally published, New York: Knopf, 1971. — Bibl.p.549-554. — Index.
  ISBN 0 297 00457 3 : £6.00

(B72-12014)

**BBM(D) — Berlioz, Hector. Essays**
Newman, Ernest
  Berlioz, romantic and classic: writings by Ernest Newman/
  selected and edited by Peter Heyworth. — London: Gollancz,
  1972. — 288p: port; 23cm.
  ISBN 0 575 01365 6 : £3.00

(B72-03314)

**BBM(N) — Berlioz, Hector. Biographies**
Berlioz, Hector
  Mémoires de Hector Berlioz: comprenant ses voyages en Italie, en
  Allemagne, en Russie et en Angleterre, 1803-1865. —
  Farnborough: Gregg, 1969. — [7],512p: music, port; 23cm. —
  (Collected literary works; 6)
  Facsimile reprint of 1st ed., Paris: M. Lévy, 1870.
  ISBN 0 576 28423 8 : £12.60
  ISBN 0 576 28417 3 Set of 7 works: £78.00

(B72-06102)

**BBMMACM — Bernstein, Leonard. West Side story. Librettos**
Laurents, Arthur
  West Side story: a musical/ based on a conception of Jerome
  Robbins; book by Arthur Laurents; music by Leonard Bernstein;
  lyrics by Stephen Sondheim; entire production directed and
  choreographed by Jerome Robbins. — London: Heinemann
  Educational, 1972. — 128p; 20cm.
  Originally published, New York: Random House, 1958; London:
  Heinemann, 1959.
  ISBN 0 435 23529 x : £0.50

(B72-08533)

**BBT — Brahms, Johannes**
James, Burnett
  Brahms - a critical study/ by Burnett James. — London: Dent,
  1972. — xiii,202,[8]p: 1 ill, music, ports; 23cm.
  Bibl.p.189-192. — Index.
  ISBN 0 460 03953 9 : £3.00

(B72-16139)

**BBTAKDW — Brahms, Johannes. Vocal solos. Songs, etc**
Harrison, Max
  The lieder of Brahms/ [by] Max Harrison. — London: Cassell,
  1972. — [6],152p: music; 21cm.
  Bibl.p.142-144. — List of Brahms' songs for one and two voices p.134-141.
  — Index.
  ISBN 0 304 93876 9 : £1.75

(B72-16878)

Sams, Eric
  Brahms songs/ [by] Eric Sams. — London: British Broadcasting
  Corporation, 1972. — 68p: music; 20cm. — (British Broadcasting
  Corporation. Music guides)
  ISBN 0 563 10431 7 Pbk: £0.45

(B72-15425)

**BBTN — Brian, Havergal**
MacDonald, Malcolm
  Havergal Brian: [perspective on the music]/ [by] Malcolm
  MacDonald. — London (5 Mayfield Rd, W.3): Triad Press, 1972.
  — 68p: music, ports; 21cm.
  Limited ed. of 400 numbered copies.
  ISBN 0 902070 03 7 Pkk: £1.25

(B72-04569)

**BBX(N) — Byrd, William. Biographies**
Holst, Imogen
  Byrd/ by Imogen Holst. — London (3 Queen Sq., WC1N 3AU):
  Faber, 1972. — 3-79,[8]p: ill, facsims, music, ports; 26cm. — (The
  great composers)
  Bibl.p.73. — List of works p.74-75. — Index.
  ISBN 0 571 09813 4 : £2.00

(B72-16876)

**BCBWACM/LK — Casey, Peter. One Friday in eternity. Librettos**
Banyard, Edmund
  One Friday in eternity/ [by] Edmund Banyard; with songs by
  Edmund and Stephen Banyard and Peter Casey. — London (82
  High Rd, N.2): Galliard Ltd, 1972. — 12p: music; 28cm.
  ISBN 0 85249 121 2 Sd: £0.17
  *Primary classification BBDNACM/LK*

(B72-10328)

**BCE(ZF) — Chopin, Frédéric. Influenced by Field, John**
Branson, David
  John Field and Chopin/ [by] David Branson. — London: Barrie
  and Jenkins, 1972. — viii,216p: music; 23cm.
  Bibl.p.203. — List of music.p.199-202. — Index.
  ISBN 0 214 65343 9 : £3.00

(B72-08531)

**BDEAC — Davies, Peter Maxwell. Taverner. Librettos**
Davies, Peter Maxwell
  Taverner: an opera in two acts/ by Peter Maxwell Davies; libretto
  by the composer. — London: Boosey and Hawkes, 1972. — 40p;
  19cm.
  ISBN 0 85162 005 1 Sd: £0.50

(B72-18917)

**BDJ(N) — Debussy, Claude. Biographies**
Myers, Rollo Hugh
  Claude Debussy: the story of his life and work/ by Rollo Myers.
  — London: Boosey and hawkes, 1972. — 52,[3]p: facsim, music,
  ports; 19cm.
  List of music p.47-52.
  ISBN 0 85162 003 5 Pbk: Unpriced

(B72-50005)

**BDJAQ — Debussy, Claude. Piano music**
Long, Marguerite
  At the piano with Debussy/ by Marguerite Long; translated [from
  the French] by Olive Senior-Ellis. — London: Dent, 1972. — viii,
  112,[8]p: music, ports; 23cm.
  Translation of 'Au piano avec Claude Debussy'. Paris: Julliard, 1960. —
  Index.
  ISBN 0 460 03821 4 : £2.75

(B72-03316)

**BDKACN — Delibes, Leo. Children's musical plays**
Griffiths, Philip
  My daughter Coppelia: a musical play (adapted from Delibes'
  ballet 'Coppelia')/ by Philip Griffiths and Eric Shaw. — London:
  Oxford University Press, 1971. — [4],24p: music; 22cm.
  ISBN 0 19 338228 8 Sd: £0.40

(B72-03927)

**BDL(N) — Delius, Frederick. Biographies**
Jefferson, Alan
  Delius/ by Alan Jefferson. — London: Dent, 1972. — xi,179p,
  [8]leaves: ill, facsim, music, ports; 20cm. — (The master musicians
  series)
  Bibl.p.151-157. — Index.
  ISBN 0 460 03131 7 : £2.25

(B72-05571)

**BDRAC — Donizetti, Gaetano. Lucia di Lammermoor. Librettos**
Cammarano, Salvatore
Lucia di Lammermoor/ by Gaetano Donizetti; [libretto by Salvatore Cammarano]; translated [from the Italian] and introduced by Ellen H. Bleiler. — New York: Dover Publications; London: Constable, 1972. — [3],186,[32]p: ill, facsims, music, ports; 22cm. — (Dover opera guide and libretto series)
Parallel Italian libretto and English translation. — Bibl.p.185-186. — Contains an English translation of the French text of 'Lucie de Lammermoor', originally translated from the Italian by Alphonse Royer and Gustave Vaez.
ISBN 0 486 22110 5 Pbk: £1.00

(B72-22490)

**BDT — Dowland, John**
Poulton, Diana
John Dowland/ [by] Diana Poulton. — London (3 Queen Sq., WC1N 3AU): Faber and Faber Ltd, 1972. — 3-520,[16]p: ill, facsims, music, ports; 26cm.
Ill. on lining papers. — Bibl.p.460-496. — Index.
ISBN 0 571 08711 6 : £12.00

(B72-10999)

**BELAC — Einem, Gottfried von. The visit of the old lady. Librettos**
Dürrenmatt, Friedrich
The visit of the old lady/ opera in three acts by Gottfried von Einem; opera version of the text by Friedrich Dürrenmatt; English version by Norman Tucker. — London: Boosey and Hawkes, 1972. — 86p; 17cm.
Translation of 'Der Besuch der alten Dame'. Based on the play of the same name, originally published Zürich: Verlag der Arche, 1956.
ISBN 0 85162 006 x Pbk: £0.55

(B72-19611)

**BEP(N) — Elgar, Sir Edward. Biographies**
Burley, Rosa
Edward Elgar: the record of a friendship/ by Rosa Burley and Frank C. Carruthers. — London: Barrie and Jenkins, 1972. — [5], 211p: 2ports; 23cm.
Index.
ISBN 0 214 65410 9 : £2.80

(B72-13441)

**BEP/N(EM) — Elgar, Sir Edward, bart. Biographies. Illustrations**
Moore, Jerrold Northrop
Elgar - a life in photographs/ [compiled by] Jerrold Northrop Moore. — London: Oxford University Press, [1972]. — 112p: chiefly ill, facsims, music, ports; 31cm.
ISBN 0 19 315425 0 : £3.00

(B72-28697)

**BHC — Handel, George Frideric**
Cudworth, Charles
Handel: a biography, with a survey of books, editions and recording/ by Charles Cudworth. — London: Bingley, 1972. — 112p; 23cm. — (The concertgoer's companions)
List of records p.90-101. — Index.
ISBN 0 85157 137 9 : £1.75

(B72-07357)

**BHC(N) — Handel, George Frideric. Biographies**
Flower, *Sir* Newman
George Frideric Handel: his personality and his times/ [by] Newman Flower. — Revised ed. — London: Panther, 1972. — 383p: facsims, music; 18cm.
Revised ed. originally published, London: Cassell, 1959. — Bibl.p.344-367. — Index.
ISBN 0 586 03778 0 Pbk: £0.75

(B72-21775)

**BHC(TD) — Handel, George Frideric. Thematic catalogues**
Bell, Arnold Craig
Handel - chronological thematic catalogue/ by A. Craig Bell. — [2nd ed.]. — Darley [Yorkshire] (Darley, Harrogate, Yorkshire): Grian-aig Press, 1972. — [1],xii,452p: chiefly music; 22cm.
Previous ed. published as 'Chronological catalogue of Handel's works'. Greenock: Grian-aig Press, 1969. — Index.
ISBN 0 9500714 4 7 : £12.00

(B72-32113)

**BHCAMF — Handel, George Frideric. Concertos**
Sadie, Stanley
Handel concertos/ [by] Stanley Sadie. — London: British Broadcasting Corporation, 1972. — 72p: music; 20cm. — (British Broadcasting Corporation. Music guides)
Index.
ISBN 0 563 10349 3 Pbk: £0.45

(B72-28683)

**BHE(N) — Haydn, Joseph. Biographies**
Landon, Howard Chandler Robbins
Haydn/ by H.C. Robbins Landon in association with Henry Raynor. — London (3 Queen Sq., WC1N 3AU): Faber and Faber Ltd, 1972. — 3-107,[8]p: ill, coat of arms, facsims, music, ports; 26cm. — (The great composers)
Bibl.p.101. — Index.
ISBN 0 571 08361 7 : £1.75

(B72-09750)

Stendhal
Lives of Haydn, Mozart and Metastasio/ by Stendhal; translated [from the French], introduced & edited by Richard N. Coe. — London: Calder and Boyars, 1972. — xxxii,370,[11]p: ill, map, music, ports; 23cm. — [Opera library]
Translation of 'Vies de Haydn, de Mozart et de Métastase'. Paris, 1814. — 'Vie de Haydn' adapted from the Italian of Giuseppe Carpani's 'Le Haydine', Milano: Buccinelli, 1812; 'Vie de Mozart' taken from a 'Notice biographique'/ by C. Winckler; 'Vie de Métastase based on an Italian article by Giuseppe Baretti. — Lists of music. — Index.
ISBN 0 7145 0349 5 : £5.50
ISBN 0 7145 0350 9 Pbk: Unpriced

(B72-14734)

**BHJJACM — Heneker, David. Charlie girl. Librettos**
Williams, Hugh
Charlie girl: a comedy musical in two acts/ music and lyrics by David Heneker and John Taylor; book by Hugh and Margaret Williams with Ray Cooney; story conceived by Ross Taylor. — London: Chappell, 1972. — 88p; 26cm.
ISBN 0 85360 040 6 Pbk: £0.75

(B72-23641)

**BHP(N) — Holst, Gustav. Biographies**
Holst, Imogen
Holst/ [by] Imogen Holst. — London: Novello, 1972. — 22p; 19cm. — (Novello short biographies)
List of works p.21-22.
ISBN 0 85360 010 4 Sd: £0.15

(B72-15422)

**BHS(N) — Howells, Herbert. Biographies**
Spearing, Robert
H.H.: a tribute to Herbert Howells on his eightieth birthday/ by Robert Spearing; illustrated by Richard Walker. — London (10e Prior Bolton St., Canonbury, N.1): Triad Press, 1972. — 24p: ill, music, port; 24cm.
Limited ed. of 150 copies, 125 for sale. — List of musical works p.22-23.
ISBN 0 902070 05 3 Sd: £0.90

(B72-30070)

**BLC(N) — Lasso, Orlando di. Biographies**
Sharp, Geoffrey B
Lassus & Palestrina/ [by] Geoffrey B. Sharp. — Sevenoaks; London: Novello, 1972. — 20p; 19cm. — (Novello short biographies)
ISBN 0 85360 038 4 Sd: £0.15
*Also classified at BPC(N)*

(B72-18916)

**BLJ(N) — Liszt, Franz. Biographies**
Rostand, Claude
Liszt/ [by] Claude Rostand; translated [from the French] by John Victor. — London: Calder and Boyars, 1972. — 192p: ill, facsims, geneal table, music, ports; 21cm. — (Illustrated Calderbook; CB78)
Translation of 'Liszt'. Paris: Editions du Seuil, 1960. — Bibl.p.191-192. — Catalogue of Liszt's works p.168-184. — Index.
ISBN 0 7145 0342 8 : £2.50
ISBN 0 7145 0343 6 Pbk: £1.00

(B72-27438)

**BLOC(TD) — Locke, Matthew. Bibliographies of scores**
Harding, Rosamond Evelyn Mary
A thematic catalogue of the works of Matthew Locke: with a calendar of the main events of his life/ compiled by Rosamond E.M. Harding. — Oxford: R.E.M. Harding: Distributed by Blackwell, 1971. — xxxix,177,[15]p,(5fold): ill, facsims, geneal table, ports, music; 26cm.
Bibl.p.150-154. — Index.
ISBN 0 9502117 0 2 : £7.00

(B72-02957)

**BMDACM/LGZ — Maddox, Hugh. Alive. Librettos**
Maddox, Hugh
Alive!/ edited by Hugh Maddox. — [Great Yarmouth] (Queen Anne's Rd, Southtown, Great Yarmouth, Norfolk): [Distributed by Publishing Services Partnership for] Galliard Ltd, 1972. — 24p; 25cm.
'... a folk passion play ... created in the crypt of St Martin-in-the-Fields, London ...'.
ISBN 0 85249 122 0 Sd: £0.17

(B72-10329)

**BMJ(EM) — Mendelssohn, Felix. Illustrations**
Bodleian Library
Felix Mendelssohn Bartholdy/ Bodleian Library. — Oxford: Bodleian Library, 1972. — 22,[38]p: ill, facsims, music, ports; 24cm. — (Bodleian picture books: special series; no.3)
ISBN 0 900177 15 2 Sd: £1.00

(B72-19610)

**BMJAN — Mendelssohn, Felix. Chamber music**
**Horton, John**
Mendelssohn chamber music/ [by] John Horton. — London:
British Broadcasting Corporation, 1972. — 64p: music; 20cm. —
(British Broadcasting Corporation. Music guides)
ISBN 0 563 12205 6 Pbk: £0.45

(B72-15426)

**BMJB(N) — Mendelssohn family. Biographies**
**Kupferberg, Herbert**
The Mendelssohns: three generations of genius/ [by] Herbert
Kupferberg. — London: W.H. Allen, 1972. — xiii,272,[16]p: ill,
facsims, geneal table, ports; 25cm.
Also published, New York: Scribner, 1972. — Bibl.p.253-259. — Index.
ISBN 0 491 00732 9 : £3.50

(B72-17503)

**BMN(N) — Monteverdi, Claudio. Biographies**
**Schrade, Leo**
Monteverdi: creator of modern music/ by Leo Schrade. —
London: Gollancz, 1972. — 384p: music; 22cm.
Originally published, New York: Norton, 1950; London: Gollancz, 1951. —
Bibl.p.371-377. — Index.
ISBN 0 575 01472 5 : £2.50

(B72-17504)

**BMSAC — Mozart, Wolfgang Amadeus**
**Liebner, János**
Mozart on the stage/ by János Liebner; [translated from the
Hungarian]. — London: Calder and Boyars, 1972. — 254p: music;
23cm. — [Opera library]
Translation of 'Mozart a szinpadon'. Budapest: Zenemukiado Vallalat, 1961.
— Bibl.p.254.
ISBN 0 7145 0758 x : £3.25

(B72-14736)

**BPC(N) — Palestrina, Giovanni Pierluigi da. Biographies**
**Sharp, Geoffrey B**
Lassus & Palestrina/ [by] Geoffrey B. Sharp. — Sevenoaks;
London: Novello, 1972. — 20p; 19cm. — (Novello short
biographies)
ISBN 0 85360 038 4 Sd: £0.15
*Primary classification BLC(N)*

(B72-18916)

**BPNN — Porter, Cole**
**Gill, Brendan**
Cole: a biographical essay/ by Brendan Gill; edited by Robert
Kimball. — London: Joseph, [1972]. — xix,283p: ill, facsims,
map, music, ports; 31cm.
Originally published, New York: Holt, Rinehart and Winston, 1971. — List
of Cole Porter songs and productions p.255-283.
ISBN 0 7181 1021 8 : £7.50

(B72-24253)

**BSET — Schoenberg, Arnold**
**Wellesz, Egon**
Arnold Schoenberg/ [by] Egon Wellesz; [translated from the
German by W.H. Kerridge]. — [1st ed. reprinted]; [with a new
preface by the author]. — Great Yarmouth (Queen Anne's Rd,
Great Yarmouth, Norfolk): Galliard Ltd, 1971. — xv,156p: music;
20cm.
Title page imprint: London. — This translation originally published,
London: Dent, 1925. — Translation of 'Arnold Schoenberg'. Leipzig: Tal,
1925.
ISBN 0 85249 104 2 : Unpriced

(B72-01561)

**BSETAN — Schoenberg, Arnold. Chamber music**
**Whittall, Arnold**
Schoenberg chamber music/ [by] Arnold Whittall. — London:
British Broadcasting Corporation, 1972. — 64p: music; 20cm. —
(British Broadcasting Corporation. Music guides)
ISBN 0 563 10489 9 Pbk: £0.45

(B72-22494)

**BSF(N/XHF4) — Schubert, Franz. Biographies, 1825-8**
**Reed, John**
Schubert - the final years/ by John Reed. — London (3 Queen
Sq., WC1N 3AU): Faber, 1972. — 280,[11]p: ill, facsims, music,
port; 23cm.
Index.
ISBN 0 571 09842 8 : £5.00

(B72-26089)

**BSGAKDW — Schumann, Robert. Songs, etc**
**Walsh, Stephen**
The lieder of Schumann/ [by] Stephen Walsh. — London: Cassell,
1971. — viii,128p: music; 21cm.
Index.
ISBN 0 304 93736 3 : £1.75

(B72-01563)

**BSGAKDW — Schumann, Robert. Vocal solos. Songs, etc**
**Desmond, Astra**
Schumann songs/ [by] Astra Desmond. — London: British
Broadcasting Corporation, 1972. — 64p: music; 20cm. — (British
Broadcasting Corporation. Music guides)
Index.
ISBN 0 563 12140 8 Pbk: £0.45

(B72-14737)

**BSGAQ — Schumann, Robert. Piano music**
**Chissell, Joan**
Schumann piano music/ [by] Joan Chissell. — London: British
Broadcasting Corporation, 1972. — 72p: music; 20cm. — (British
Broadcasting Corporation. Music guides)
ISBN 0 563 12241 2 Pbk: £0.45

(B72-22495)

**BSH(N) — Sibelius, Jean. Biographies**
**Levas, Santeri**
Sibelius, a personal portrait/ [by] Santeri Levas; translated [from
the Finnish] by Percy M. Young. — London: Dent, 1972. — xxiii,
165,[8]p: ill, ports; 23cm.
Abridged translation of 'Jean Sibelius: muistelmia suuresta ihmisestä'.
Helsinki: W. Söderström, 1957-. — List of music p.136-151. — List of
records p.154-157. — Index.
ISBN 0 460 03978 4 : £2.95

(B72-11000)

**BSIM — Smetana, Bedrich**
**Clapham, John,** *b.1908*
Smetana/ by John Clapham. — London: Dent, 1972. — 161p,[8]
leaves: facsims, music, ports; 20cm. — (The master musician
series)
Bibl.p.147-149. — List of works p.136-141. — Index.
ISBN 0 460 03133 3 : £2.10

(B72-15423)

**BSQB(N) — Strauss Family. Biographies**
**Bailey, George**
The Strauss family: the era of the Great Waltz/ by George Bailey.
— London: Pan Books, 1972. — 64p: ill(some col), facsims, geneal
table, ports(some col); 18x22cm.
ISBN 0 330 23437 4 Pbk: £0.50

(B72-29417)

**BSU(N) — Strauss, Richard. Biographies**
**Del Mar, Norman**
Richard Strauss: a critical commentary on his life and works/ by
Norman Del Mar. — London: Barrie and Jenkins. —
In 3 vols.
Vol.3. — 1972. — xxi,552,[11]p: facsims, music, plans, ports; 23cm.
Bibl.p.510-511. — Contains an index to vols 1-3.
ISBN 0 214 65158 4 : £7.00

(B72-20309)

**BSUAKDW — Strauss, Richard. Songs, etc**
**Jefferson, Alan**
The lieder of Richard Strauss/ [by] Alan Jefferson. — London:
Cassell, 1971. — x,134p: music; 21cm.
Bibl.p.116. — Index.
ISBN 0 304 93735 5 : £1.75

(B72-01564)

**BSV(N) — Stravinsky, Igor. Biographies**
**McCaldin, Denis**
Stravinsky/ [by] Denis McCaldin. — London: Novello, 1972. —
22p; 19cm. — (Novello short biographies)
Bibl.p.21.
ISBN 0 85360 009 0 Sd: £0.15

(B72-12718)

**BSV(N/XPH24) — Stravinsky, Igor. Biographies, 1948-1971**
**Craft, Robert**
Stravinsky - chronicle of a friendship, 1948-1971/ [by] Robert
Craft. — London: Gollancz, 1972. — xvii,424,xvi,[24]p: ill,
facsims, ports; 26cm.
Ports on lining papers. — Originally published, New York: Knopf, 1972. —
Index.
ISBN 0 575 01503 9 : £4.00

(B72-28680)

**BSV(N/XPS15) — Stravinsky, Igor. Biographies, 1957-1971**
**Horgan, Paul**
Encounters with Stravinsky: a personal record/ [by] Paul Horgan.
— [Abridged ed.]. — London: Bodley Head, 1972. — 224,[10]p:
ill, ports; 23cm.
Full ed., New York: Farrar, Strauss and Giroux, 1972. — Index.
ISBN 0 370 10299 1 : £3.00

(B72-27437)

**BSV(N/XPU13) — Stravinsky, Igor. Biographies, 1959-1971**
**Libman, Lillian**
And music at the close: Stravinsky's last years: a personal
memoir/ by Lillian Libman. — London: Macmillan, 1972. — 400,
[8]p: ill, music(on lining papers), ports; 23cm.
Also published, New York: Norton, 1972. — Index.
ISBN 0 333 14304 3 : £3.50

(B72-30741)

**BSWACF — Sullivan, Sir Arthur Seymour. Savoy operas**
Hardwick, Michael
The Osprey guide to Gilbert and Sullivan/ [by] Michael
Hardwick. — Reading: Osprey, 1972. — 284p; 21cm.
Bibl.p.281-284. — List of records p.271-279.
ISBN 0 85045 100 0 : £2.50
*Also classified at 782.8'1'0924*

(B72-26659)

**BSWACF(C) — Sullivan, Sir Arthur Seymour. Savoy operas.**
**Encyclopaedias**
Ayre, Leslie
The Gilbert and Sullivan companion/ [by] Leslie Ayre; foreword
by Martyn Green; illustrated from the Raymond Mander and Joe
Mitchenson Theatre Collection. — London: W.H. Allen, 1972. —
485p: ill; 24cm.
ISBN 0 491 00832 5 : £4.50

(B72-26093)

**BSWACF/E — Sullivan, Sir Arthur Seymour. Savoy operas. Production**
Taylor, Ian
How to produce concert versions of Gilbert & Sullivan/ by Ian
Taylor. — London: Hale, 1972. — 249p: plans; 23cm.
ISBN 0 7091 2973 4 : £3.50

(B72-31878)

**BSWN(N) — Swann, Donald. Biographies**
Swann, Donald
The space between the bars: a book of reflections/ by Donald
Swann. — London: Hodder and Stoughton, 1972. — 160p; 18cm.
— (Hodder Christian paperbacks)
Originally published 1968.
ISBN 0 340 16001 2 Pbk: £0.45

(B72-16877)

**BVD(N/XPDI5) — Vaughan Williams, Ralph. Biographies, 1944-1958**
Douglas, Roy
Working with R.V.W./ [by] Roy Douglas. — London: Oxford
University Press, 1972. — [6],68p: facsim; 21cm.
ISBN 0 19 315427 7 Pbk: £0.80

(B72-21776)

**BVD(WJ) — Vaughan Williams, Ralph. Exhibitions**
Willetts, Pamela Joan
Ralph Vaughan Williams, 1872-1958: a guide to the centenary
exhibition at the British Museum, 29 September to 15 December
1972/ by Pamela J. Willetts. — London: British Museum, 1972.
— [22]p; 21cm.
ISBN 0 7141 0337 3 Sd: £0.10

(B72-28008)

**BVDAMME — Vaughan Williams, Ralph. Symphonies**
Ottaway, Hugh
Vaughan Williams symphonies/ [by] Hugh Ottaway. — London:
British Broadcasting Corporation, 1972. — 64p; 20cm. — (British
Broadcasting Corporation. Music guides)
ISBN 0 563 12242 0 Pbk: £0.45

(B72-28682)

**BWNRBADU — Wilbye, John. The second set of madrigals**
Wilbye, John
The second set of madrigals, 1609/ [by] John Wilbye. — Menston:
Scolar Press, 1972. — 6v.: of music; 27cm. — (English madrigals,
1558-1630; no.46)
Facsimile reprint of 1st eds, London: John Browne, 1609.
ISBN 0 85417 572 5 : £7.75

(B72-10330)

**BWNTMACM — Wilson, Sandy. The boy friend. Librettos**
Wilson, Sandy
The boy friend: a play in three acts/ [by] Sandy Wilson; with a
preface by Vida Hope and illustrations by the author. —
Harmondsworth: Penguin, 1972. — 123p: ill; 18cm.
Originally published, New York: Dutton; London: Deutsch, 1955.
ISBN 0 14 001350 4 Pbk: £0.25

(B72-06766)

**BZ — LITERATURE ON NON-EUROPEAN MUSIC**
**BZF — India**
Holroyde, Peggy
Indian music: a vast ocean of promise/ by Peggy Holroyde;
foreword by Ravi Shankar. — London: Allen and Unwin, 1972.
— 3-291,[16]p: ill, music, ports; 23cm.
Bibl.p.286-287. — Index.
ISBN 0 04 780020 8 : £5.25

(B72-17505)

**BZHKAC(XFYK101) — China. Peking. Opera, 1770-1870**
Mackerras, Colin P
The rise of the Peking Opera, 1770-1870: social aspects of the
theatre in Manchu China/ [by] Colin P. Mackerras. — Oxford:
Clarendon Press, 1972. — xiii,316p,[3] leaves: ill, maps, plans;
23cm.
Bibl.p.269-285. — Index.
ISBN 0 19 815137 3 : £6.00

(B72-31290)

**C/AY — GENERAL COLLECTIONS**
Epps, David
Spare time for music/ [compiled] by Alan Harverson ... [and
others]; edited by David Epps, Gordon Reynolds. — London:
British Broadcasting Corporation, 1972. — 96p; 4to.
With bibliography.
ISBN 0 563 10689 1 : £1.20

(B72-50793)

Scratch anthology of compositions. — London: The Scratch
Orchestra, 1971. — 48p; 4to.
Unpriced

(B72-50006)

**C/AYD — England**
Jacobean consort music: for recorders or viols/ [edited by Thurston
Dart and William Coates]. — London: Stainer and Bell. —
Selected from volume 9 of Musica Britannica.
Book 1: Five fantasias and two dances of three parts. — 1972. — 3pt.; 4to.
£0.44
*Also classified at STN/AYD - Collections. England; VSN/AYD -*
*Collections. England*

(B72-50009)

Book 2: Seven fantasias of four parts. — 1972. — 3pt.; 4to.
£0.49
*Also classified at STN/AYD - Collections. England; VSN/AYD -*
*Collections. England*

(B72-50010)

Musica Britannica: a national collection of music. — London:
Published for the Royal Music Association by Stainer and Bell. —
Vol.31: Matthew Locke: Chamber music 1/ transcribed and edited by
Michael Tilmouth. — 1971. — xxiii,146p; fol.
£10.00
*Also classified at STN/AZ*

(B72-50007)

Vol.32: Matthew Locke: Chamber music 2/ transcribed and edited by
Michael Tilmouth. — 1971. — xxiii,109p; fol.
£10.00
*Also classified at STN/AZ*

(B72-50008)

Vol.35: Pelham Humfrey: Complete church music, II/ transcribed and
edited by Peter Dennison. — 1972. — xx,125p; fol.
Unpriced
*Also classified at CB/LD/AZ*

(B72-50794)

**C/AZ — Collected works of individual composers**
Ferdinand, *III, Emperor*
Musikalische Werke der Kaiser Ferdinand III, Leopold I und
Joseph I im Aufrage des K.K. Ministeriums für Cultur und
Unterricht/ herausgegeben von Guido Adler. — London: Gregg,
1972. — [660]p; 4to.
Facsimile reprint of the 1st ed., Vienna: Artaria; 1892-3. This reprint
comprises Band 1: Kirchenwerke and Band 2: Gesange aus Oratorien und
Opern; [and], Instrumental Compositionen.
£18.00

(B72-50335)

**CB — VOCAL MUSIC**
Globokar, Vinko
La Ronde: experiment in collective work by an indefinite number
of performers/ by Vinko Globokar. — Frankfurt: Litolff; London:
Peters, 1972. — 7p; 8vo.
Unpriced

(B72-50795)

**CB/LD/AZ — Vocal music. Church music. Collected works of**
**individual composers**
Musica Britannica: a national collection of music. — London:
Stainer and Bell. —
Vol.35: Pelham Humfrey: Complete church music, II/ transcribed and
edited by Peter Dennison. — 1972. — xx,125p; fol.
Unpriced
*Primary classification C/AYD*

**CC — OPERA. VOCAL SCORES**
Argento, Dominick
Postcard from Morocco: an opera/ by Dominick Argento; text by
John Donahue. — New York ([London]): Boosey and Hawkes,
1972. — 292p; 4to.
Vocal score.
£10.00

(B72-50336)

Britten, Benjamin
The prodigal son = Der verlorene Sohn. Op.81: third parable for
church performance/ by Benjamin Britten; libretto by William
Plomer; German translation by Hans Keller, rehearsal score by
David Matthews. — London: Faber music, 1971. — 155p; fol.
Duration 72 min.
Unpriced

(B72-50011)

**Cherepnin, Alexander**
[The nymph and the farmer]. La Fée et le cultivateur = The nymph and the farmer, Op.72: a lyric legend/ by Alexander Cherepnin; texte original français par Siao Yu, English text by Joseph Machlis, deutsch von Ernst Roth. — London: Boosey and Hawkes, 1972. — 55p; 4to.
Vocal score.
£4.50

(B72-50337)

**Davies, Peter Maxwell**
Taverner: an opera in two acts/ by Peter Maxwell DAvies, libretto by the composer. — London: Boosey and Hawkes, 1972. — 260p; 4to.
Vocal score.
Unpriced

(B72-50338)

**Einem, Gottfried von**
Der Besuch der alten Dame = The visit of the old lady. Op.35: Oper in drei Akten/ by Gottfried von Einem; Operafassung von Friedrich Dürrenmatt; English version by Norman Tucker. — London: Boosey and Hawkes, 1972. — 463p; fol.
Vocal score.
£8.00

(B72-50339)

**Humperdinck, Engelbert**
Hansel and Gretel: a fairy opera in three acts/ by Engelbert Humperdinck; [libretto] by Adelheid Wette, translated and adapted into English by Tom Hammond. — London: Schott, 1972. — 118p; 8vo.
Vocal score.
£1.05

(B72-50340)

**Mozart, Wolfgang Amadeus**
La Clemenza di Tito. K.621: opera seria in due atti/ [by] Wolfgang Amadeus Mozart; Text nach Pietro Metastasio von Caterino Massola, deutsche Ubersetzung von Kurt Honolka. — Cassel; London: Bärenreiter, 1971. — 319p; 8vo.
Vocal score by Heinz Moehn.
£3.75

(B72-50341)

**Purcell, Henry**
[King Arthur]. The music in King Arthur: a dramatic opera (1691),/ by Henry Purcell; edited by Margaret Laurie; the words by John Dryden. — Sevenoaks: Novello, 1972. — 165p; 8vo.
Vocal score.
£1.50

(B72-50342)

**Themerson, Stefan**
St Francis and the wolf of Gubbio; or, Brother Francis' lamb chops: an opera in 2 acts/ by Stefan Themerson. — Amsterdam: De Harmonie; London: Gaberbocchus, 1972. — 111p; 4to.
Unpriced

(B72-50796)

## CF — OPERETTAS, VOCAL SCORES
**Posford, George**
Good-night Vienna: an operetta in three acts/ by George Posford; book and lyrics by Eric Maschwitz, additional material by Harold Purcell and Sidney Box. — London: Keith Prowse, [1972]. — 188p; 4to.
Revised version. Vocal score.
£1.25

(B72-50797)

**Schubert, Franz**
[Das Dreimäderlhaus]. Lilac time: operetta in three acts/ [with music adapted from works of Franz Schubert]; new version arranged by Ronald Hanmer, new English book and lyrics by Phil Park. — London: Chappell: Weinberger, 1971. — 174p; 4to.
Vocal score.
Unpriced

(B72-50012)

**Sullivan, Sir Arthur**
The zoo: a musical folly/ by Arthur Sullivan; [words by] B.C. Stephenson ('Bolton Rowe'). — London: [William Reeves], 1969. — 108p; 4to.
Vocal score by Garth Morton.
Unpriced

(B72-50798)

## CLM — BALLAD OPERA. VOCAL SCORES
**Argento, Dominick**
The shoemakers' holiday: a ballad-opera based on the play by Thomas Dekker/ by Dominick Argento; adaptation and additional lyrics by John Olon. — New York; [London]: Boosey and Hawkes, 1971. — 146p; 4to.
Vocal score.
£6.00

(B72-50343)

## CM — MUSICAL PLAYS. VOCAL SCORES
**Bernstein, Leonard**
Mass: a theatre piece for singers, players and dancers/ by Leonard Bernstein; text from the liturgy of the Roman Mass; additional texts by Stephen Schwartz and Leonard Bernstein. — New York: Amberson; [London]: [Chappell], 1971. — 267p; fol.
Vocal score.
Unpriced

(B72-50013)

**Heneker, David**
Charlie girl/ music and lyrics by David Heneker and John Taylor, book by Hugh and Margaret Williams with Ray Cooney. — London: Chappell, 1972. — 188p; 4to.
Vocal score.
£1.75

(B72-50799)

## CM/L — Religious musical plays. Vocal scores
**Garrick, Michael**
Judas kiss: for SATB choir, instrumentalists and soloists/ by Michael Garrick. — London: Robbins Music. —
Vocal score.
Part 1. — 1972. — 84p; 4to.
Unpriced

(B72-50344)

Part 2. — 1972. — 79p; 4to.
Unpriced

(B72-50345)

Part 3. — 1972. — 55p; 4to.
Unpriced

(B72-50346)

## CN — Children's musical plays with keyboard accompaniment
**Delibes, Léo**
[Coppélia]. My daughter Coppelia: a musical play adapted from the ballet/ by Léo Delibes; adapted by Philip Griffiths and Eric Shaw. — London: Oxford University Press, 1971. — 60p; 8vo.
Vocal score.
ISBN 0 19 338227 x : £1.20

(B72-50014)

**Rowley, Alec**
Monsieur de la plume: fragments from the life of Robert Louis Stevenson: music for children's voices and piano/ by Alec Rowley; scored for school orchestra by Christopher Hazell, play by Therese Kitchen, [words of songs by Robert Louis Stevenson]. — London: Ashdown, 1972. — 48p; 8vo.
Vocal score. — The songs were published seperately in 1963.
Unpriced

(B72-50800)

## CN/L — Children's religious musical plays with keyboard accompaniment
**Verrall, Pamela**
Son of Assisi: a musical based on incidents from the life of St Francis of Assisi/ by Pamela Verrall. — London: British and Continental, 1972. — 24p; 4to.
Unpriced

(B72-50801)

## CQC — OPERA. FULL SCORES
**Bach, Johann Christian**
La Clemenza di Scipione. Op. 14/ by Johann Christian Bach. — [Farnborough]: Gregg, 1972. — [6],210p; 8vo.
Facsimile reprint of the edition published, London: Welcker, circa 1778.
£9.60

(B72-50802)

**Brindle, Reginald Smith**
The death of Antigone: opera/ by Reginald Smith Brindle; words by Sophocles, Euripides and the composer. — London: Peters, 1972. — 46p; 4to.
£2.20

(B72-50347)

**Einem, Gottfried von**
Der Besuch der alten Dame= The visit of the old lady. Op.35: opera in three acts after Friedrich Dürrenmatt's tragi-comedy/ by Gottfried von Einem; opera version by Friedrich Dürrenmatt, English version by Norman Tucker. — London: Boosey and Hawkes, 1972. — 522p; 8vo.
Miniature score.
£10.00

(B72-50803)

**Mozart, Wolfgang Amadeus**
Così fan tutte: komische Oper in zwei Akten/ von W.A. Mozart; nach dem Urtext herausgegeben von Georg Schünemann unter Mitarbeit von Kurt Soldan, deutsche Bearbeitung nach der Überlieferung und dem Urtext von Georg Schünemann. — Leipzig: Peters; [London]: [Hinrichsen], [1972]. — 436p; 8vo.
Miniature score.
Unpriced

(B72-50804)

**Vaughan Williams, Ralph**
Riders to the sea: an opera in one act/ by R. Vaughan Williams; based on the play by J.M. Synge. — London: Oxford University Press, 1972. — 100p; 8vo.
Miniature score.
ISBN 0 19 339335 2 : £5.00

(B72-50805)


**CQM — MUSICAL PLAYS. FULL SCORES**
**CQN — Children's musical plays. Full scores**
**Marshall, Nicholas**
Arion and the dolphins: for unison choir and instruments/ by Nicholas Marshall; words by Duke Rapaport. — London: Chester, 1972. — 8p; 4to.
Duration 20 min.
Unpriced

(B72-50348)


**Odam, George**
Tutankhamun/ by George Odam; words by Stuart Allin. — London: Chester, 1972. — 42p; 4to.
With a leaflet (4p.) containing the words inserted.
Unpriced

(B72-50806)


**Paynter, John**
The space-dragon of Galatar/ by John Paynter; words by Paul Townsend. — London: Universal, 1972. — 7p; 8vo.
Unpriced

(B72-50807)


**CQN/L — Children's religious musical plays. Full scores**
**Arch, Gwyn**
A golden legend/ by Gwyn Arch; words by Pat Rooke. — London: British and Continental, 1972. — 27p; 8vo.
Unpriced

(B72-50808)


**D — CHORAL MUSIC WITH KEYBOARD ACCOMPANIMENT**
**Alkan, Charles Henri Valentin**
[Marcia funèbre d'un Pappagallo]. Funeral march on the death of a parrot: for four-part chorus of mixed voices with organ, or piano, or woodwind accompaniment/ by Charles-Valentin Alkan; edited by Raymond Lewenthal. — New York: Schirmer; [London]: [Chappell], 1972. — 37p; 8vo.
Vocal score, with parts for three oboes and bassoon printed severally on pages 30-37.
Unpriced

(B72-50015)


**D/AC — Tutors**
**Schneider, Walther**
Einsingen in Chor: methodische Anleitung und Ubungen zur chorischen Stimmbildung/ von Walther Schneider. — Frankfurt: Litolff; London: Peters, 1972. — 35p; 4to.
Unpriced

(B72-50809)


**DD — ORATORIOS. VOCAL SCORES**
**Handel, George Frideric**
[Joshua]. Josua: oratorio for four solo-voices, choir and orchestra. — Frankfurt; London: Peters. —
Vocal score.
by Georg Friedrich Händel/ words by Thomas Morell, translated into German by Georg Gottfried Gervinus. — 1972. — 163p; 8vo.
Unpriced

(B72-50810)


**DE — RELIGIOUS CANTATAS WITH KEYBOARD ACCOMPANIMENT**
**Bach, Johann Sebastian**
Jesu, der du meine Seele = Jesus, by thy Cross and Passion, S.78: cantata for 14. Sunday after Trinity/ by Johann Sebastian Bach; [edited by] Walter Heinz Bernstein. — Cassel; London: Bärenreiter, 1970. — 43p; 8vo.
Vocal score.
£0.90

(B72-50349)


**Bach, Johann Sebastian**
Wachet auf ruft uns die Stimme = Wake ye maids! hark, strikes the hour. S.140: cantata for 27. Sunday after Trinity/ by Johann Sebastian Bach; [edited by] Alfred Durr. — Cassel; London: Bärenreiter, 1970. — 62p; 8vo.
Vocal score. — Duration 31 min.
£1.00

(B72-50350)


**DE/LF — Christmas**
**Burgon, Geoffrey**
This endris night: a Christmas cantata for tenor solo, women's or boy's voices and brass/ by Geoffrey Burgon; text taken from the Chester mystery plays and mediaeval poems. — London: Stainer and Bell, 1972. — 24p; 4to.
Vocal score.
£0.75

(B72-50811)


**Kellam, Ian**
The joly shepard: cantata no.5, for SATB and small orchestra or two pianos/ by Ian Kellam; words from medieval carols. — Sevenoaks: Novello, 1972. — 69p; 8vo.
Vocal score.
£0.60

(B72-50351)


**Peterson, John W**
The story of Christmas: a cantata/ words and music by John W. Peterson. — London: Marshall, Morgan and Scott, 1972. — 64p; 8vo.
ISBN 0 551 05128 0 : Unpriced

(B72-50016)


**Rorem, Ned**
Praises for the nativity: for four solo voices (SATB) mixed chorus and organ/ by Ned Rorem; texts: 2 collects for Christmastide from the Book of Common Prayer. — New York; [London]: Boosey and Hawkes, 1971. — 43p; 8vo.
£0.75

(B72-50017)


**DE/LG — Lent**
**Bach, Johann Sebastian**
Gleich wie der Regen und Schnee von Himmel fällt = Like as the raindrops and snow from heaven fall, S.18: cantata for Sunday, sexagesimae/ by Johann Sebastian Bach; [edited by] Wolfgang Stockmeier. — Cassel; London: Bärenreiter, 1969. — 23p; 8vo.
Vocal score.
£0.65

(B72-50352)


**DE/LL — Easter**
**Rubbra, Edmund**
Sinfonia sacra: 'The resurrection'. Op.140: for soprano, contralto, baritone, chorus and orchestra/ by Edmund Rubbra; selection of words from the New Testament and verses for chorales by Bernard de Nevers, other words selected by the composer from traditional sources. — South Croydon: Lengnick, 1972. — 53p; 8vo.
Vocal score.
£1.00

(B72-50812)


**DE/LN — Whitsuntide**
**Bach, Johann Sebastian**
Er rufet seinen Schafen mit Namen = He calleth his own sheep each by name: cantata for Whit Tuesday/ by Johann Sebastian Bach; [edited by] Alfred Durr. — Cassel; London: Bärenreiter, 1970. — 27p; 8vo.
£0.65

(B72-50353)


**DFF — ROMAN LITURGY**
**DG — Ordinary of the Mass**
**Dalby, Martin**
Missa fi-fi/ by Martin Dalby. — London: Chester, 1972. — 57p; 8vo.
Vocal score.
Unpriced

(B72-50018)


**Haydn, Joseph**
[Mass no.16, 'Theresa mass']. Missa, Theresa mass/ by Joseph Haydn; [edited by] Heinz Moehn. — Cassel; London: Bärenreiter, 1969. — 168p; 8vo.
Vocal score.
£3.15

(B72-50354)


**Mozart, Wolfgang Amadeus**
[Mass in C major. K.317, 'Coronation']. Missa, C-dur, 'Krönungs-Messe': für vier Solostimme, Chor und Orchester/ [by] Wolfgang Amadeus Mozart; Klavierauszug von Theo Mölich. — Frankfurt: Litolff; London: Peters, 1971. — 53p; 8vo.
Vocal score.
£1.25

(B72-50019)

**DGB — Ordinary of the Mass. Kyrie**
**Haydn, Joseph**
[Mass no.16 in B flat major, 'Theresienmesse'. - Kyrie]. Kyrie: for
four-part chorus of mixed voices with organ or piano
accompaniment/ by Joseph Haydn; arranged and edited by
William Herrmann. — New York: Schirmer; [London]:
[Chappell], 1971. — 15p; 8vo.
Unpriced

(B72-50020)

**Patterson, Paul**
Kyrie: for choir and piano/ by Paul Patterson. — London:
Weinberger, 1972. — 12p; 4to.
Unpriced

(B72-50813)

**DGKAF — Proper of the Mass. Offertory**
**Schubert, Franz**
Intende voci orationis mea: offertory for tenor solo and four-part
chorus of mixed voices with organ or piano accompaniment/ by
Franz Schubert; edited and with keyboard reduction by William
Herrmann. — New York: Schirmer; [London]: [Chappell], 1971.
— 32p; 8vo.
Unpriced

(B72-50021)

**DGKHB — Divine Office. Matins. Te Deum**
**Bizet, Georges**
Te Deum: for mixed voices (with soprano and tenor solo) and
orchestra/ by Georges Bizet; edited by Johannes Wojciechowski.
— First edition. — Hamburg; London: Simrock, 1972. — 62p;
4to.
Vocal score. — Changes and omissions made by the composer in the text
make this work inacceptable in the strictly liturgical sense.
Unpriced
*Primary classification DH*

(B72-50356)

**DGM — ANGLICAN LITURGY**
**Royal School of Church Music**
Festival service books/ Royal School of Church Music. —
Croydon: Royal School of Church Music. —
6/ The Christian year celebrated in music, reading and prayer — 1971. —
64p; 8vo.
ISBN 0 85402 047 0 : Unpriced

(B72-50022)

**DGPP — Evening Prayer. Canticles**
**Blow, John**
[Service in F major. - Excerpts]. Magnificat and Nunc dimittis: for
SATB/ by John Blow; edited and transposed to G major by
Watkins Shaw. — London: Novello, 1971. — 14p; 8vo.
£0.17

(B72-50023)

**Howells, Herbert**
Magnificat and Nunc dimittis 'Collegium magdalenae oxoniense':
for SATB and organ/ by Herbert Howells. — Sevenoaks: Novello,
1972. — 26p; 8vo.
£0.28

(B72-50814)

**Howells, Herbert**
Magnificat and Nunc dimittis in B flat (for the Cathedral Church
of Hereford): for SATB and organ,/ by Herbert Howells. —
Sevenoaks: Novello, 1972. — 20p; 8vo.
£0.21

(B72-50355)

**DGS — Anglican liturgy. Communion**
**Hurford, Peter**
Communion service, series 3/ by Peter Hurford. — Sevenoaks:
Novello, 1972. — 12p; 8vo.
£0.14

(B72-50815)

**DGSKAD — Anglican liturgy. Communion. Sentences**
**Hurford, Peter**
Two sentences: for SATB with divisions and organ/ by Peter
Hurford; [words] from An Order for Holy Communion. —
Sevenoaks: Novello, 1972. — 8p; 8vo.
£0.10

(B72-50816)

**DH — MOTETS, ANTHEMS, HYMNS, ETC.**
**Bizet, Georges**
Te Deum: for mixed voices (with soprano and tenor solo) and
orchestra/ by Georges Bizet; edited by Johannes Wojciechowski.
— First edition. — Hamburg; London: Simrock, 1972. — 62p;
4to.
Vocal score. — Changes and omissions made by the composer in the text
make this work inacceptable in the strictly liturgical sense.
Unpriced
*Also classified at DGKHB*

(B72-50356)

**Drayton, Paul**
How like an Angel came I down: anthem for SATB and organ/
by Paul Drayton; words by Thomas Traherne. — Sevenoaks:
Novello, 1972. — 8p; 8vo.
£0.14

(B72-50357)

**Drayton, Paul**
The spacious firmament: SSATTBB/ by Paul Drayton; [words by]
J. Addison. — London: Oxford University Press, 1971. — 12p;
8vo.
Duration 3 1/2 min.
Unpriced

(B72-50024)

**Gilbert, Norman**
Praise to the Lord, the Almighty: SATB/ by Norman Gilbert;
[words by] J. Neander, tr. C. Winkworth and others. — London:
Oxford University Press, 1972. — 7p; 8vo.
ISBN 0 19 351112 6 : Unpriced

(B72-50817)

**Graves, Richard**
Come, my way, my truth, my life: anthem for SATB and organ/
by Richard Graves; words by George Herbert. — London:
Novello, 1972. — 4p; 8vo.
Unpriced

(B72-50025)

**Krol, Bernhard**
Vier Gesänge auf den Heiligen Geist. Op.45: für gemischten Chor
und Orgel/ [by] Bernhard Krol. — Hamburg; London: Simrock,
1972. — 15p; 4to.
Unpriced

(B72-50818)

**Naylor, Peter**
Come, dearest Lord: anthem for SATB and organ/ by Peter
Naylor; words by Isaac Watts. — Sevenoaks: Novello, 1972. —
8p; 8vo.
£0.10

(B72-50358)

**Thiman, Eric Harding**
Christ is the world's light: anthem for SATB and organ/ by Eric
H. Thiman; words by F. Pratt Green. — Sevenoaks: Novello,
1972. — 8p; 8vo.
£0.10

(B72-50026)

**Traver, James Ferris**
Praise the Lord our King: for mixed chorus and organ with
optional brass accompaniment/ [words and music by] James Ferris
Traver. — New York: Galaxy; London: Galliard, 1972. — 8p;
8vo.
Unpriced

(B72-50359)

**DH/LF — Christmas**
**Bayco, Fredric**
A Christmas alleluya: S.A.T.B./ words and music by Fredric
Bayco. — London: Oxford University Press, 1971. — 8p; 8vo.
ISBN 0 19 351111 8 : Unpriced

(B72-50027)

**DH/LP — Harvest**
**Nicholson, *Sir* Sydney Hugo**
Let us with a gladsome mind: anthem for harvest or other
festivals/ by Sydney H. Nicholson; words by John Milton. —
Croydon: Royal School of Church Music, 1972. — 4p; 8vo.
Unpriced

(B72-50028)

**DJ — MOTETS**
**Porpora, Nicolò Antonio**
Credidi: motet for SSAA, strings & organ continuo/ by N.A.
Porpora; edited by D.E. Hyde. — Sevenoaks: Novello, 1972. —
8vo.
Vocal score.
£0.35

(B72-50029)

**DK — ANTHEMS**
**Billings, William**
[The singing master's assistant. - *Excerpts]*. Peace be on earth =
Retrospect: an anthem from sundry Scriptures, [for] SATB (or
male chorus or mixed chorus)/ by William Billings; edited by
Oliver Daniel. — New York: Peters; [London]: [Hinrichsen], 1970.
— 19p; 8vo.
Unpriced
*Also classified at GDK*

(B72-50360)

**Drayton, Paul**
Ecce ancilla Domini: anthem for the Annunciation/ by Paul
Drayton. — London: Oxford University Press, 1972. — 8p; 8vo.
ISBN 0 19 350330 1 : Unpriced

(B72-50030)

**Edwards, D W**
The day of Pentecost: for choir, or solo voice, or as an organ
solo/ by D.W. Edwards; [text from] Acts 2. — West Kirby (67
Lang Lane, West Kirby, Wirral, Cheshire): D.W. Edwards, 1972.
— 4p; 8vo.
Unpriced
*Also classified at KDK; RJ*

(B72-50819)

**Greene, Maurice**
Acquaint thyself with God: anthem for alto (or tenor) solo,
chorus, and organ/ by Maurice Greene; edited by H. Diack
Johnstone; from Job 22. — Sevenoaks: Novello, 1971. — 14p; 8vo.
£0.17

(B72-50031)

**Hurd, Michael**
O come, let us sing unto the Lord: anthem for SATB and organ/
by Michael Hurd; [text from] Psalm 95. — Sevenoaks: Novello,
1972. — 7p; 8vo.
£0.10

(B72-50032)

**Tye, Christopher**
Give almes of thy goods/ by Christopher Tye; edited by A.
Ramsbotham, revised edition by Anthony Greening, [text]:
Offertory sentence, from Tobit 4. — London: Oxford University
Press, 1972. — 6p; 8vo.
ISBN 0 19 352113 x : Unpriced

(B72-50361)

**DM — HYMNS**
Amazing grace: early American melody, SATB and piano; words by
John Newton. — London: Keith Prowse, 1972. — 2p; 8vo.
Unpriced

(B72-50362)

**Billings, William**
[The psalm singer's amusement. - *Excerpts*]. The bird: SATBB/ by
William Billings; edited by Oliver Daniel, words by Tate and
Brady. — New York: Peters; [London]: [Hinrichsen], 1971. — 4p;
8vo.
£0.40

(B72-50363)

**Edwards, D W**
Hymns and choruses/ words & music by D.W. Edwards. —
Bristol (159 Station Rd. Kingswood, Bristol): D.W. Edwards. —
Book 1. — 1969. — 7p; 8vo. —
Unpriced

(B72-50364)

Book 2. — 1969. — 8p; 8vo. —
Unpriced

(B72-50365)

**Prichard, Rowland H**
[Hyfrydol]. Hymn for our time: for three-part chorus of mixed
voices with piano (or organ) accompaniment/ by Rowland H.
Prichard; music [arranged] and based on the hymn-tune 'Hyfrydol'
by John Ness Beck; words by William P. Merrill. — New York:
Schirmer; [London]: [Chappell], 1971. — 11p; 8vo.
Unpriced

(B72-50033)

**Spencer, Sheila R**
Margetts; (hymn)/ by Sheila R Spencer; (words by) Michael J.
Stayt. — Harrow: Flying Dragon Publications, 1971. — s.sh.; 8vo.
£0.04

(B72-50366)

**Talmadge, Charles L**
Lord Jesus, think on me: for mixed chorus and organ/ by Charles
L. Talmadge; [words by] Synesius, tr. Allen W. Chatfield. — New
York: Galaxy; London: Galliard, 1972. — 4p; 8vo.
Unpriced

(B72-50820)

**DM/AY — Collections**
**Clifton, Geoffrey**
In every corner sing/ selected by Geoffrey Clifton. — London:
Nelson, 1972. — 168p; 8vo.
For '...the daily school assembly'.
ISBN 0 17 437012 1 : Unpriced

(B72-50367)

**Green, F Pratt**
26 hymns/ [selected by] F. Pratt Green. — London: Epworth
Press, 1971. — 61p; 8vo.
ISBN 0 7162 0181 x : £0.40

(B72-50036)

**Hathaway, W G**
Selected Christian songs/ compiled by W.G. Hathaway and F.W.
Birkenshaw. — Ewell: Gospel Music. —
Album 12. — 1972. — 35p; 8vo.
Unpriced

(B72-50368)

**Hymns** of eternal truth: with music. — Bradford: Sherborne Road
Church Trust, 1972. — 8vo.
Unpriced

(B72-50369)

**Kaan, Fred**
Pilgrim praise: hymns/ [compiled] by Fred Kaan. — London:
Galliard, 1972. — 116p; 4to.
ISBN 0 85249 108 5 : £1.54

(B72-50034)

**Lewis, Peter**
Sing life, sing love/ [compiled] by Peter Lewis, Roy Lawrence and
Gordon Simpson; arranged for schools by William M. McIntyre.
— Edinburgh: Holmes McDougall, 1972. — 8vo.
Melody ed. (55p.) Pianoforte ed. (55p.).
ISBN 0 7157 1005 2 : Unpriced

(B72-50370)

**Songs** for the seventies: a collection of contemporary hymns. —
Great Yarmouth: Galliard, 1972. — 57p; 8vo.
£0.83

(B72-50035)

**DM/KDD — Weddings**
Two wedding hymns: set to chorale melodies. — Croydon: Royal
School of Church Music, 1972. — 4p; 8vo.
Contents: Schmücke dich/ by J. Crüger; set to 'Bless O God, this glad
endeavour' - Liebster Jesu/ by J.R. Ahle; harmony by J.S. Bach; set to
'Father, Thou that hearest prayer'.
Unpriced

(B72-50821)

**DM/LRT/AY — Temperance. Collections**
**Coleman, Emmet G**
The temperance songbook: a peerless collection of temperance
songs and hymns for the Women's Christian Temperance Union,
Loyal Temperance Union, Prohibitionists, Temperance Praise
Meetings, Medal contests, etc./ edited by Emmet G. Coleman. —
London: Wolfe, 1971. — 80p; 8vo.
Edition of 1907 reprinted.
ISBN 0 7234 0486 0 : £1.25

(B72-50037)

**DM/LSB/AY — Roman Catholic Church. Collections**
**Ainslie, John**
Praise the Lord/ edited by John Ainslie, Stephen Dean, Paul
Inwood. — Revised ed. — London: Chapman, 1972. — 8vo.
Melody ed. (318p.) & Full music ed. (388p.).
ISBN 0 225 65838 0 : Unpriced

(B72-50822)

**DM/LSET/AY — Lutheran churches. Collections**
**Rödding, Gerhard**
Choralbuch zum Evangelischen Kirchengesangbuch: mit den
Begleitsätzen des Württembergischen Choralbuches bearbeitet von
Karl Gerok und Hans-Arnold Metzger und mit Begleitsätzen zu
den Liedern des Anhangs zum Rheinisch-Westfälisch-Lippischen
Gesangbuch/ herausgegeben von Gerhard Rödding. — Cassel;
[London]: Bärenreiter, 1970. — 396p; obl.fol.
Unpriced

(B72-50371)

**DP — CAROLS**
**DP/LF — Carols. Christmas**
**Burnett, Michael**
Three medieval carols: for SATB and organ (no.2 unaccompanied/
by Michael Burnett. — Sevenoaks: Elkin, 1972. — 18p; 8vo.
Contents: Nowell sing we, both old and new. — I sign of a maiden. —
Tyrley, tyrlow.
£0.21

(B72-50372)

**Carter, Sydney**
[Nine carols or ballads. - *Excerpts*]. Every star shall sing a carol/
words and melody by Sydney Carter, arranged for mixed chorus
by Katherine K. Davis. — New York; London: Chappell, 1972.
— 7p; 8vo.
Unpriced

(B72-50823)

**Coleman, Henry**
Come shepherds/ by Henry Coleman; arranged by Frank E.
Brown, [words by] Sister Florence. — London: Leonard, Gould
and Bolttler, 1972. — 4p; 8vo.
£0.06

(B72-50824)

**Cornelius, Peter**
[Weihnachtslieder Op.8. - Die Könige]. The kings: SSATB (acc. or
unacc.)/ by Peter Cornelius; arranged by Laurence H. Davies,
[words by] Peter Cornelius, tr. H.N. Bate. — London: Oxford
University Press, 1972. — 3p; 8vo.
ISBN 0 19 343029 0 : Unpriced
*Also classified at EZDP/LF*

(B72-50373)

**Hoddinott, Alun**
Puer natus: SSAATTBB (or SSAA or TTBB)/ by Alun
Hoddinott/ German words translated by W. Moelwyn Merchant.
— London: Oxford University Press, 1972. — 6p; 8vo.
ISBN 0 19 343030 4 : Unpriced
*Also classified at GDP/LF*

(B72-50374)

**Marriott, Michael J**
Little shepherd: SATB/ by Michael Marriott. — London: Cramer,
1971. — 6p; 8vo.
£0.09

(B72-50038)

**Mathias, William**
A Babe is born. Op.55: S.A.T.B./ by William Mathias; words
anon. — London: Oxford University Press, 1971. — 11p; 8vo.
ISBN 0 19 343023 1 : Unpriced

(B72-50039)

**Méhul, Etienne**
[Joseph. - Ah, lorsque la mort trop cruelle]. A crib-side carol/ by
Etienne Méhul; arranged for SATB (or unison voices) and piano
or organ, with English words by Richard Graves. — London:
Novello, 1972. — 8vo.
£0.07

(B72-50375)

**Nops, Marjory**
Oh hurry, hurry to Bethlehem: a carol for SATB, organ or guitar/
by Marjory Nops. — London: British and Continental, 1972. —
4p; 8vo.
Unpriced

(B72-50825)

**Rutter, John**
Love came down at Christmas: SATB/ by John Rutter; [words
by] Christina Rossetti. — London: Oxford University Press, 1971.
— 3p; 8vo.
ISBN 0 19 343025 8 : Unpriced

(B72-50040)

**Stent, Keith**
Two carols in modern vein/ arranged for SATB & orchestra by
Keith Stent. — Sevenoaks: Novello, 1972. — 12p; 8vo.
Vocal score. — Contents: We three kings of Orient are/ words and melody
by J.H. Hopkins. — Ding dong! merrily on high/ melody from Thoinot
Arbeau's Orchésographie; words by G.R. Woodward.
£0.20

(B72-50376)

**Tate, Phyllis**
Sailing in: a Christmas carol, SATB/ by Phyllis Tate; traditional
words. — London: Oxford University Press, 1971. — 10p; 8vo.
ISBN 0 19 343021 5 : Unpriced

(B72-50041)

**DP/LF/AY — Christmas. Collections**
Four Christmas carols. — South Croydon: Lengnick, 1972. — 12p;
8vo.
Contents: When Christ was born/ by Peter Smith - All so still/ by Richard
Lloyd; words by W. Graham Robertson - Love came down at Christmas/
R.O. Morris; harmonised by David Squibb, words by Christina Rossetti -
Christ is born of maiden fair/ by Anthony Britten and Colin Yorke.
£0.15

(B72-50826)

The **Oxford** book of carols/ [edited by] Percy Dearmer, Ralph
Vaughan Williams, Martin Shaw. — [Revised ed.]. — London:
Oxford University Press, 1972. — 454p; 8vo.
Revised ed. originally published 1964.
ISBN 0 19 313120 x : £0.90

(B72-50827)

**DP/LF/AYTLD — Christmas. Collections. Afro-American**
**Clark, Rogie**
Six Afro-American carols for Christmas/ [composed and with]
arrangements for mixed chorus (SATB) by Rogie Clark. —
London: Piedmont: [Distributed by] Weinberger, 1971. — 7p; 8vo.
£0.15

(B72-50828)

**DP/LFP — Carols. Epiphany**
**Johns, Sybil Marian**
A carol for to-day/ by Sybil Marian Johns. — Llandaff (41 Padua
Rd, Llandaff, Cardiff): S.M. Johns, 1971. — 2sh; 8vo.
Unpriced
*Primary classification JDP/LFP*

(B72-50089)

**DPDE — CAROL CANTATAS**
**DPDE/LF — Carol cantatas. Christmas**
**Parry, William Howard**
Rise up shepherd: a hymn-sequence with readings for voices with
optional baritone solo with accompaniments for piano and
optional instruments/ by William Howard Parry. — London:
Keith Prowse, 1971. — 4to.
Score (11p.) & 10 parts.
£0.50

(B72-50042)

**DU — MADRIGALS, ETC.**
**Schein, Johann Hermann**
[Diletti pastorali, nos.1, 5, 6, 13, 15]. Hirten last: fünf weltliche
Madrigale, für fünf stimmen und Basso Continuo/ [by] Johann
Hermann Schein; herausgegeben von Adam Adrio. — Cassel;
[London]: Bärenreiter, 1971. — 36p; 8vo.
£0.95

(B72-50377)

**DW — SONGS, ETC.**
**Dickinson, Peter**
Outcry: a cycle of nature poems for contralto solo, SATB and
orchestra/ by Peter Dickinson. — Sevenoaks: Novello, 1971. —
59p; 8vo.
Vocal score.
£1.10

(B72-50043)

**Haydn, Joseph**
[Selections]. Die drei- und vierstimmigen Gesänge/ [by] Joseph
Haydn; herausgegeben von Bernard Paumgartner. — Cassel;
London: Bärenreiter, 1971. — 77p; 4to.
£2.00

(B72-50378)

**DW/LC — Spirituals**
**Hudson, Hazel**
Deep river; [and], Wade in the water; [and], Gonna lay down my
burden: a quodlibet arranged from three negro spirituals for either
trebles 1 and 2, or basses 1 and 2, or treble 1 and bass 2/ arr. by
Hazel Hudson. — London: Ashdown, 1972. — 8p; 8vo.
£0.09
*Primary classification FLDW/LC*

(B72-50431)

**Hudson, Hazel**
Nobody knows; [and], Balm in Gilead: a quodlibet based on two
negro spirituals, for either trebles 1 and 2, or basses 1 and 2, or
treble 1 and bass 2/ arr. by Hazel Hudson. — London: Ashdown,
1972. — 8p; 8vo.
£0.09
*Primary classification FLDW/LC*

(B72-50432)

**Hudson, Hazel**
Steal away - Were you there?: a quodlibet based on two negro
spirituals, (for either trebles 1 and 2, or basses 1 and 2, or treble 1
and bass 2)/ arr. by Hazel Hudson. — London: Ashdown, 1972.
— 10p; 8vo.
£0.10
*Primary classification FLDW/LC*

(B72-50430)

**Nelson, Havelock**
Plenty good room: negro spiritual/ arranged for SATB and piano
by Havelock Nelson. — London: Boosey and Hawkes, 1972. —
8p; 8vo.
Unpriced

(B72-50044)

**Nelson, Havelock**
Weary travellers: negro spiritual, SATB and piano/ Trinidadian
melody arranged by Havelock Nelson. — [London]: Boosey and
Hawkes, 1972. — 6p; 8vo.
Unpriced

(B72-50829)

**DW/LF — Christmas**
**Head, Michael**
Five Finnish Christmas songs: for mixed chorus and orchestra (or
piano)/ by Michael Head; words from the Finnish by Robert
Armstrong. — London: Boosey and Hawkes. —
1: Christmas = No, onkos tullut kesä. — 1972. — 10p; 8vo.
Vocal score. .
£0.14

(B72-50830)

2: When it is Christmas = Kun joulu on. — 1972. — 11p; 8vo.
Vocal score.
£0.14

(B72-50831)

3: A sparrow on Christmas morning = Varpunen jouluaamuna. — 1972. —
8p; 8vo.
Vocal score.
£0.09

(B72-50832)

4: Christmas bells = Joulun kellot. — 1972. — 10p; 8vo.
Vocal score.
£0.14

(B72-50833)

5: Uncle Frost = Halla. — 1972. — 10p; 8vo.
Vocal score.
£0.14

(B72-50834)

## DX — SECULAR CANTATAS

**Baird, Tadensz**
Goethe-Briefe: Kantate für Bariton, gemischten Chor und
Orchester nach Texten von Johann Wolfgang von Goethe und
Charlotte von Stein in einer Auswahl des Komponisten/ [by]
Tadensz Baird; Klavierauszug vom Komponisten. — Frankfurt;
London: Peters, 1971. — 29p; 4to.
£2.20

(B72-50379)

**Barber, Samuel**
The lovers. Op.43: for baritone, mixed chorus and orchestra/ by
Samuel Barber; based on 'Twenty poems of love and a song of
despair' by Pablo Neruda. — New York; London: Schirmer, 1972.
— 76p; 4to.
Vocal score.
Unpriced

(B72-50045)

**Bedford, David**
Star clusters, Nebulae and Places in Devon/ by David Bedford. —
London: Universal, 1971. — 52p; 4to.
Unpriced

(B72-50046)

**Blow, John**
Awake, awake my lyre: for soprano (or tenor), solo optional
baritone, chorus, strings and continuo/ by John Blow; edited by
Watkins Shaw, words by Abraham Cowley. — London:
Hinrichsen, 1968. — 8p; 8vo.
Vocal score.
Unpriced

(B72-50047)

**McCabe, John**
Aspects of whiteness: cantata for SSAATTBB and piano, by John
McCabe/ words by Herman Melville. — Sevenoaks: Novello,
1972. — 85p; 4to.
Duration 19 min.
£1.75

(B72-50380)

**Purcell, Henry**
[Ode for Queen Mary's birthday, 1694]. Come ye sons of art/ by
Henry Purcell; edited by Michael Tippett and Walter Bergmann.
— London: Schott, 1971. — 42p; 8vo.
£0.75

(B72-50048)

**Rose, John Luke**
The pleasures of youth. Op.11: cantata for mixed chorus and
orchestra/ by John Luke Rose. — London: Boosey and Hawkes,
1972. — 84p; 8vo.
Vocal score.
Unpriced

(B72-50835)

**Vogt, Paul G**
Fiesta: ein Anti-Lehrstück mit Musik/ von Paul G. Vogt; Text
von Anton Zink. — Mainz; London: Schott, 1972. — 64p; 4to.
Vocal score.
£3.20

(B72-50381)

## E — CHORAL WORKS WITH ACCOMPANIMENT OTHER THAN KEYBOARD

### EMDE/KDN — With orchestra. Religious cantatas. Funerals
**Josephs, Wilfred**
Requiem. Op.39: for solo bass-baritone, chorus, string quintet and
orchestra/ by Wilfred Josephs. — London: Weinberger, 1972. —
88p; 8vo.
Hebrew text. — Incorporates the quintet for strings, op.32.
Unpriced

(B72-50049)

### EMDE/LF — With orchestra. Religious cantatas. Christmas
**Telemann, Georg Philipp**
Ruft es aus in alle Welt. (In Festo Nativatatis): Weihnachts
Kantate, für Sopran, Alt, Tenor, Bass, Vierstimmigen gemischten
Chor, drei Trompeten, Pauken, Streicher und Basso continuo/
[by] Georg Philipp Telemann; herausgegeben von Gustav Fock. —
Cassel; London: Bärenreiter, 1970. — 32p; 8vo.
£1.25

(B72-50382)

### EMDG — With orchestra. Ordinary of the Mass
**Liszt, Franz**
Missa solennis: [S.A.T.B. solos, chorus and orchestra]/ composuit
Franciscus Liszt. — Farnborough: Gregg, 1971. — [4],130p; fol.
A reprint of the edition published in Philadelphia [Penn.]: Schuberth, 1871.
Unpriced

(B72-50050)

### EMDGKAV — With orchestra. Requiem masses
**Tavener, John**
Celtic requiem: for soprano, children's choir, chorus and
orchestra/ by John Tavener. — London: Chester, 1972. — 49p;
4to.
'I have compiled the libretto from words taken from the Missa pro
Defunctis, poems of Blathmac (translated by James Carney, Henry Vaughan,
Cardinal Newman and children's singing games and nonsense rhymes.' -
Composer's note.
Unpriced

(B72-50383)

### EMDM — With orchestra. Hymns
**Vaughan Williams, Ralph**
The Old Hundredth psalm tune: All people that on earth do
dwell, for mixed or unison voices and orchestra/ by R. Vaughan
Williams; rescored by David Stone. — London: Oxford University
Press, 1972. — 4to.
Score (16p.) & 19 parts.
ISBN 0 19 369530 8 : Unpriced

(B72-50836)

### EMDX — With orchestra. Secular cantatas
**Delius, Frederick**
[A mass of life]. Eine Messe des Lebens = A mass of life: für
Sopran, Alt, Tenor, Bariton, gemischten Chor und grosses
Orchester/ [by] Frederick Delius; Worte von Friedrich Nietzsche,
zusammengestellt von Fritz Cassirer, English translation by John
Bernhoff. — London: Boosey and Hawkes, 1972. — 203p; 8vo.
A list of errata prepared by R. Threlfall is inserted. — This edition is a
reprint in reduced format of the full score originally published in 1907 in
two volumes by Harmonie Verlag, Berlin.
£6.00

(B72-50384)

**Durkó, Zsolt**
Altamira: for chamber choir and orchestra/ by Zsolt Durkó. —
London: Boosey and Hawkes, 1971. — 35p; 8vo.
Miniature score.
£1.50

(B72-50051)

**Penderecki, Krysztof**
Kosmogonia: für Soli, Chor und Orchester/ [by] Krysztof
Penderecki. — Mainz; London: Schott, 1972. — 51p; fol.
Unpriced

(B72-50837)

### ENYEXSDW/G/AYB — With trumpet, strings & percussion. Folk songs. Collections. Europe
**Bresgen, Cesar**
Europäische Volks-und Kinderlieder: in leichten Chorsätzen (3
Oberstimmen und 1 Unterstimme) mit Instrumenten (Blockflöten,
Gitarre, Violine, Klarinette, Trompete, Violoncello ad lib.,
Stabspiele, Schlagwerk/ [compiled by] Cesar Bresgen. — Mainz;
London: Schott. —
Band 1. — 1972. — 59p; 8vo. —
£1.40

(B72-50385)

**Bresgen, Cesar**
Europäische Volks-und Kinderlieder: in leichten Chorsätzen (3
Oberstimmen und 1 Unterstimme) mit Instrumenten (Blockflöten,
Gitarre, Violine, Klarinette, Trompete, Violoncello ad lib.,
Stabspiele, Schlagwerk/ [compiled by] Cesar Bresgen. — Mainz;
London: Schott. —
Band 2. — 1972. — 48p; 8vo. —
£1.20

(B72-50386)

### ENYFPDX — With woodwind, keyboard & percussion. Secular cantatas
**Pitfield, Thomas**
Planibestiary: a zoological sequence in space for speakers, soloists,
SAB choir, flute, oboe, bassoon, piano & percussion/ words and
music by Thomas Pitfield. — South Croydon: Lengnick, 1972. —
30p; 4to.
£0.75

(B72-50838)

### ENYFVDW — With clarinet, keyboard & percussion. Songs, etc
**Boyd, Jack**
Prologue for an unwritten play: for SATB chorus with B flat
clarinet, orchestra chimes (or hand bells) and piano/ by Jack
Boyd; words by Stephen Crane. — New York: Warner; [London]:
[Blossom], 1972. — 11p; 8vo.
Unpriced

(B72-50839)

**ENYGNTDH — With strings, keyboard & percussion trio. Motets, Anthems, Hymns, etc**
MacLellan, Gene
  Put your hand in the hand: for mixed chorus SATB/ words [and music] by Gene MacLellan, choral arrangement by Alan Foust. — London: Ardmore and Beechwood, 1970. — 8p; 8vo.
Unpriced

(B72-50387)

**ENYLDE — With keyboard & percussion. Religious cantatas**
Lord, David
  The history of the Flood: for narrator, chorus, percussion, and piano duet/ by David Lord; words by John Heath-Stubbs. — London: Oxford University Press, 1971. — 4to.
Score (39p.) & chorus/narrator part (19p.).
ISBN 0 19 337380 7 : £1.50

(B72-50052)

**ERXMDX — With string orchestra. Secular cantatas**
Blow, John
  Awake awake my lyre: for soprano (or tenor) solo, optional baritone, chorus, strings and continuo/ by John Blow; edited by Watkins Shaw, words by Abraham Cowley. — London: Hinrichsen, 1968. — 31p; 4to.
Unpriced

(B72-50053)

**ESDW — With violin. Songs, etc**
Burkhard, Willy
  Chor-Duette. Opus 22, 2: für gemischten Stimmen teilweise mit Violine oder Flöte/ [von] Willy Burkhard; nach Gedichten von C.F. Meyer. — Cassel; [London]: Bärenreiter, 1971. — 10p; 8vo.
£0.40

(B72-50388)

**ESRDX — With cello. Secular cantatas**
Bassett, Leslie
  Moon canticle: large mixed chorus a cappella and violoncello obbligato/ by Leslie Bassett. — New York; London: Peters, 1971. — 38p; 8vo.
Duration 17 min.
£1.20

(B72-50389)

**EWNDM/AY — With brass ensemble. Hymns. Collections**
Ehmann, Wilhelm
  Junktim-Sätze: Doppelchörige Choralsätze, für bläser oder Sänger und Bläser/ herausgegeben von Wilhelm Ehmann. — Cassel; [London]: Bärenveiter, 1970. — vii,66p; 8vo.
£1.50

(B72-50390)

**EWNPRDE — With brass septet & organ. Religious cantatas**
Zipp, Friedrich
  Lobe den Herren, den mächtigen König der Ehren: Choralkantate für vierstimmigen gemischten Chor, Gemeindegesang (ad lib.), sechsstimmigen Bläserchor und Orgel/ [von] Friedrich Zipp; herausgegeben von Wilhelm Ehmann. — Cassel; London: Bärenreiter, 1971. — 31p; 8vo.
y1.75

(B72-50391)

**EZ — UNACCOMPANIED CHORAL WORKS**
**EZDG — Roman liturgy. Ordinary of the Mass**
Obrecht, Jacob
  Missa L'homme armé: for mixed choir (SATB) à cappella/ by Jacob Obrecht; edited by Gábor Darvas. — London: Boosey and Hawkes, 1972. — 43p; 8vo.
£1.00

(B72-50840)

**EZDGPP — Anglican liturgy. Evening Prayer. Canticles**
McCabe, John
  Norwich canticles: Magnificat; and, Nunc dimittis: for SATB unaccompanied/ by John McCabe. — Sevenoaks: Novello, 1972. — 14p; 8vo.
£0.17

(B72-50841)

**EZDH — Motets, Anthems, Hymns, etc**
Bach, Johann Sebastian
  Fürchte dich nicht, ich bin bei dir. S.228: motet for two four-part mixed choirs/ by Johann Sebastian Bach; edited by Konrad Ameln. — Cassel; London: Bärenreiter, 1967. — 35p; 8vo.
£0.35

(B72-50392)

Bach, Johann Sebastian
  Komm, Jesu, komm. S.229: motet for two four-part mixed choirs/ by Johann Sebastian Bach; edited by Konrad Ameln. — Cassel; London: Bärenreiter, 1967. — 20p; 8vo.
£0.40

(B72-50393)

Bach, Johann Sebastian
  Singet dem herrn ein neues Lied. S.225: motet for two four-part mixed choirs/ by Johann Sebastian Bach; edited by Konrad Ameln. — Cassel; London: B¨arenreiter, 1967. — 36p; 8vo.
£0.50

(B72-50394)

Hopson, Hal H
  O brother man, fold to thy heart thy brother: SATB/ by Hal H. Hopson; text: John Greenleaf Whittier. — New York: Warner; [London]: [Blossom Music], 1971. — 6p; 8vo.
Unpriced

(B72-50054)

Horovitz, Joseph
  Sing unto the Lord a new song: motet for SATB with divisions, unaccompanied/ by Joseph Horovitz; [words] adapted from Psalm 96. — Sevenoaks: Novello, 1972. — 22p; 8vo.
£0.35

(B72-50842)

Micheelsen, Hans Friedrich
  Gelobet seist du, Jesu Christ: Choralmotette für vier-bis sechsstimmigen Chor a cappella/ [by] Hans Friedrich Michaelsen. — Cassel; [London]: Bärenreiter, 1970. — 15p; 8vo.
£0.60

(B72-50395)

Rhodes, Joseph W
  Responses: for SATB chorus, a cappella/ by Joseph W. Rhodes. — New York: Warner; [London]: [Blossom Music], 1972. — 8p; 8vo.
£0.35

(B72-50843)

Rohwer, Jens
  Die Seligpreisungen: ein Lobgesang für Chor und Gemeinde/ [by] Jens Rohner; Worte [from] Jesus Sirach 1/ Matthäus 5. — Cassel; [London]: Bärenreiter, 1971. — 4p; 8vo.
£0.10

(B72-50396)

Ruppel, Paul Ernst
  Ernte des Lebens/ [by] Paul Ernst Ruppel; Worte [from] 2. Korinther [and] Gerhard Valentin, [with] Osterlied/ [by] Paul Ernst Ruppel; Worte: Alter Osterruf [and] Gerhard Valentin. — Cassel; [London]: Bärenreiter, 1970. — 2p; 8vo.
Unpriced

(B72-50397)

Wood, James
  Thy Kingdom come= Adveniat regnum tuum: for mixed chorus a capella/ by James Wood; words by Katherine Tynan. — New York: Galaxy; London: Galliard, 1972. — 3p; 8vo.
Unpriced

(B72-50844)

**EZDH/AYE — Motets, Anthems, Hymns, etc. Collections. Germany**
Ameln, Konrad
  Biblische Motetten: für das Kirchen jahr/ herausgegeben von Konrad Ameln und Harald Kümmerling. — Cassel; London: Bärenreiter. —
Band 1: Erster Advent bis letzter Sonntag nach Epiphanias. — 1970. — 102p; 8vo.
£2.00

(B72-50398)

**EZDH/LF — Motets, Anthems, Hymns, etc. Christmas**
Rocherolle, Eugénie R
  And so it was (Christmas): for SATB chorus and piano/ words and music by Eugénie R. Rocherolle. — New York: Warner; [London]: [Blossom Music], 1972. — 11p; 8vo.
Unpriced

(B72-50055)

**EZDH/LL — Motets, Anthems, Hymns, etc. Easter**
Billings, William
  [Selections]. Two Easter anthems: SATB a cappella/ by William Billings; edited by Oliver Daniel. — New York: Peters; [London]: [Hinrichsen], 1971. — 8p; 8vo.
Contents: Crucifixion. — Resurrection.
£0.50

(B72-50399)

Mellers, Wilfrid
  Resurrection canticle: for sixteen solo voices/ by Wilfrid Mellers; the poem by Gerard Manley Hopkins. — Great Yarmouth: Galliard, 1972. — 32p; 4to.
£0.83

(B72-50056)

**EZDJ — Motets**
**Tallis, Thomas**
[O sacrum convivium]. I call and cry to thee: anthem for
SAATB/ by Thomas Tallis; edited by Paul Doe. — Sevenoaks:
Novello, 1972. — 11p; 8vo.
£0.17

(B72-50845)

**Wilson, Thomas**
Ave Maria and Pater noster/ by Thomas Wilson. — Great
Yarmouth: Galliard, 1971. — [4]p; 8vo.
£0.10
*Also classified at EZDTF*

(B72-50057)

**EZDJ/AY — Motets. Collections**
**Slim, H Colin**
A gift of madrigals and motets/ [compiled by] H. Colin Slim. —
Chicago; London: Chicago University Press. —
Vol. 1: Description and analysis. — 1972. — xiii,306,[23]p; 4to. —
ISBN 0 226 76271 8 : Unpriced
*Primary classification EZDU/AY*
Vol.2: Transcriptions. Description and analysis. — 1972. — 451p; 4to. —
ISBN 0 226 76272 6 : Unpriced
*Primary classification EZDU/AY*

**EZDK — Anthems**
**Bliss, *Sir* Arthur**
Put thou thy trust in the Lord: introit for double choir
(unaccompanied)/ by Arthur Bliss; [text from] Psalm 37. —
Sevenoaks: Novello, 1972. — 4p; 8vo.
£0.07

(B72-50846)

**Gibbons, Orlando**
I am the resurrection and the life: SAATB (unacc.)/ by Orlando
Gibbons; edited and completed by D.L. Humphreys. — London:
Oxford University Press, 1971. — 7p; 8vo.
Duration 3 1/2 min.
ISBN 0 19 350323 9 : Unpriced

(B72-50058)

**Hayes, William**
[Cathedral music. - *Excerpts*]. Lord, how long wilt thou be
angry?: anthem for SAATB (unaccompanied)/ by William Hayes;
edited by Bernard Rose, [text from] Psalm 79. — 8p; 8vo.
£0.10

(B72-50847)

**Lekberg, Sven**
The truth of the Lord endureth forever: for four-part chorus of
mixed voices a cappella/ by Sven Lekberg; [from] Psalm 117. —
New York: Schirmer; [London]: [Chappell], 1971. — 8vo.
Unpriced

(B72-50059)

**Marlow, Richard**
O Lord God: anthem for SATB unaccompanied)/ by Richard
Marlow; [text] from the collect for Sexagesima. — [Sevenoaks]:
Novello, 1972. — 4p; 8vo.
Page 4 contains the music in tonic sol-fa notation.
£0.07

(B72-50848)

**Tallis, Thomas**
Hear the voice and prayer: anthem for S (or A) ATB/ by Thomas
Tallis; edited by Paul Doe, [text from] 1 Kings 8. — [Sevenoaks]:
Novello, 1972. — 6p; 8vo.
£0.10

(B72-50849)

**Tallis, Thomas**
If ye love me: SATB/ by Thomas Tallis; transcribed and edited by
Peter le Huray. — London: Oxford University Press, 1971. — 3p;
8vo.
ISBN 0 19 352138 5 : Unpriced

(B72-50060)

**EZDM — Hymns**
**Billings, William**
[The New England Psalm singer. - *Excerpts*]. Chester: SATB a
cappella/ by William Billings; edited by Oliver Daniel. — New
York: Peters; [London]: [Hinrichsen], 1971. — 3p; 8vo.
£0.40

(B72-50400)

**Billings, William**
[The singing master's assistant. - *Excerpts*]. David's lamentation:
SATB a cappella/ by William Billings; edited by Oliver Daniel.
— New York: Peters; [London]: [Hinrichsen], 1971. — 3p; 8vo.
£0.40

(B72-50401)

**Praetorius, Michael**
[Musae Sioniae. - *Excerpts*]. 'Allein Gott in der Hör sei Ehr'.
[T].3, no.11, T1.9, no.54, T1.5, no.21]: chorale arrangements for
three, four and eight voices/ by Michael Praetorius; edited by
Ulrich W. Zimmer. — Cassel; London: Bärenreiter, 1971. — 16p;
8vo.
£0.60

(B72-50402)

**Rutter, John**
From east to west: SATB unacc/ by John Rutter; [words by]
Coelius Sedulius, [translated from the Latin] by J. Ellerton. —
London: Oxford University Press, 1971. — 3p; 8vo.
ISBN 0 19 343026 6 : Unpriced

(B72-50061)

**Schütz, Heinrich**
Ausgewählte geistliche Chorsätze, zum Schutz-Jahr 1972/ [by]
Heinrich Schütz. — Cassel; [London]: Bärenreiter, 1972. — 32p;
8vo.
£0.50

(B72-50403)

**EZDP/LF — Carols. Christmas**
**Billings, William**
[The psalm singer's amusement. - *Excerpts*]. The angel's carol:
SATBB a capella/ by William Billings; edited by Oliver Daniel. —
New York: Peters; [London]: [Hinrichsen], 1972. — 7p; 8vo.
£0.50

(B72-50404)

**Billings, William**
[The singing master's assistant. - *Excerpts*]. Bethlehem: SAATB a
cappella/ by William Billings; edited by Oliver Daniel, works by
Dr Watts. — New York: Peters; [London]: [Hinrichsen], 1971. —
3p; 8vo.
£0.40

(B72-50405)

**Cornelius, Peter**
[Weihnachtslieder Op.8. - Die Könige]. The kings: SSATB (acc. or
unacc.)/ by Peter Cornelius; arranged by Laurence H. Davies,
[words by] Peter Cornelius, tr. H.N. Bate. — London: Oxford
University Press, 1972. — 3p; 8vo.
ISBN 0 19 343029 0 : Unpriced
*Primary classification DP/LF*

(B72-50373)

**Ferguson, Barry**
Two carols: for SATB unaccompanied/ by Barry Ferguson. —
Sevenoaks: Novello, 1972. — 4p; 8vo.
Contents: Behold a simple tender babe/ words by Robert Southwell. —
Christ's love-song/ words anon.
£0.07

(B72-50406)

**Jackson, Francis**
Can I not syng but hoy? Op. 40, no.2: a Christmas carol, SATB
unacc./ by Francis Jackson; words anon. — York: Banks, 1972.
— 8p; 8vo.
£0.08

(B72-50850)

**Nops, Marjory**
Shepherds in fields: SATB/ words and music by Marjory Nops,
with optional guitar accompaniment by Blanche Munro. —
London: British and Continental, 1972. — 4p; 8vo.
Unpriced

(B72-50851)

**Nops, Marjory**
There was a Maid: a carol for SATB, organ, piano or
unaccompanied/ by Marjory Nops; words and music by Marjory
Nops. — London: British and Continental, 1972. — 11p; 8vo.
Unpriced

(B72-50852)

**Pope, Alan**
Alleluia, now may we mirthës make: SATB(unacc.)/ by Alan
Pope; words, anon. — London: Oxford University Press, 1972. —
3p; 8vo.
ISBN 0 19 343035 5 : Unpriced

(B72-50853)

**Rose, Gregory**
Everlasting Mary: carol/ words and music by Gregory Rose. —
London: Boosey and Hawkes, 1972. — 4p; 8vo.
£0.05

(B72-50854)

**Surplice, Alwyn**
The stork carol/ by Alwyn Surplice; [words] anonymous. —
Croydon: Royal School of Church Music, 1972. — 8vo.
Unpriced

(B72-50855)

**EZDP/LF/AY — Carols. Christmas. Collections**
**Dinham, Kenneth J**
Four carols of other nations: SATB (unacc.)/ arranged by K.J.
Dinham. — York: Banks, 1972. — 8p; 8vo.
1. Zvim na semljimir: ancient Croatian carol, Yugoslavian melody - 2. Shiao
bao-bao; words and music by Francis Roots Hadden, based on a Chinese
melody - 3. Vamos, pastorcitos! Puerto Rican. — 4. Dzisiaj w Betlejem;
translated from the Polish by Alice Zientio.
£0.08

(B72-50856)

**EZDP/LGM — Carols. New Year**
**Reda, Siegfried**
Neujahrslied 'Der du die Zeit in Handen hast'/ Weise: Siegfried
Reda, Sätze: Karl Marx, Worte: Jochen Klepper. — Cassel;
London: Bärenreiter, 1970. — 2p; 8vo.
£0.05

(B72-50407)

**EZDTF — Lord's Prayer**
**Wilson, Thomas**
Ave Maria and Pater noster/ by Thomas Wilson. — Great
Yarmouth: Galliard, 1971. — [4]p; 8vo.
£0.10
*Primary classification EZDJ*

(B72-50057)

**EZDU — Madrigals**
**Lechner, Leonard**
Deutsche Sprüche von Leben und Tod: four-part mixed chorus/
by Leonard Lechner; edited by Walther Lipphardt. — Cassel;
[London]: Bärenreiter, 1971. — 18p; 8vo.
£0.70

(B72-50408)

**Lechner, Leonhard**
Das Hohelied Salomonis: for four part mixed chorus/ by
Leonhard Lechnere edited by Walther Lipphardt. — Cassel;
London: Bärenreiter, 1971. — 19p; 8vo.
£0.70

(B72-50409)

**EZDU/AY — Chansons. Collections**
**Attaingnant, Pierre**
[Vingt et sept chansons musicales à quatre parties. - *Excerpts*].
Fourteen chansons: for four recorders or voices, ATTB,/
[compiled by] Pierre Attaingnant; edited by Bernard Thomas,
texts edited and translated by Alan Robson. — London: Pro
musica, 1972. — 4to.
Unpriced
*Also classified at VSNSK/AAY*

(B72-50857)

**EZDU/AY — Madrigals. Collections**
**Slim, H Colin**
A gift of madrigals and motets/ [compiled by] H. Colin Slim. —
Chicago; London: Chicago University Press. —
Vol. 1: Description and analysis. — 1972. — xiii,306,[23]p; 4to. —
ISBN 0 226 76271 8 : Unpriced
*Also classified at EZDJ/AY*

(B72-50858)

Vol.2: Transcriptions. Description and analysis. — 1972. — 451p; 4to. —
ISBN 0 226 76272 6 : Unpriced
*Also classified at EZDJ/AY*

(B72-50859)

**EZDU/AYHP — Chansons. Collections. Paris**
**Thomas, Bernard**
Three Parisian chansons: for 4 voices (SATB)/ edited by Bernard
Thomas, texts edited and translated by Alan Robson. — Lustleigh
(North Horton, Lustleigh, Newton Abbot, Devon): Antico, 1972.
— 9p; 4to.
Vous estes trop jeune pour estre m'amye/ by Nicolas Gombert - Ce n'est pas
jeu/ by Passereau - Gentil mareschal/ anon.
Unpriced

(B72-50860)

**EZDU/X/AY — Madrigals. Canons. Collections**
**Thomas, Bernard**
Seven double canons: for four instruments or voices/ edited by
Bernard Thomas, texts edited and translated by Alan Robson. —
London: Pro musica, 1972. — 16p; 4to.
Unpriced
*Also classified at LNS/X/AY*

(B72-50861)

**EZDU/X/AYH — Chansons. Canons. Collections. France**
**Thomas, Bernard**
Four double canons: for 4 voices or instruments; (ATTB)/ edited
by Bernard Thomas. — Lustleigh: Antico, 1972. — 9p; 4to.
Unpriced
*Also classified at LNS/X/AYH*

(B72-50862)

**EZDW — Songs, etc**
**Billings, William**
[The psalm-singer's amusement. - *Excerpts*]. Modern music: SATB
a cappella/ by William Billings; edited by Oliver Daniel. — New
York: Peters; [London]: [Hinrichsen], 1971. — 11p; 8vo.
£0.75

(B72-50410)

**Billings, William**
[The singing master's assistant. - *Excerpts*]. Lamentation over
Boston; [and], Jargon: SATB (or male chorus or mixed quartet)/
by William Billings; edited by Oliver Daniel. — New York:
Peters; [London]: [Hinrichsen], 1971. — 15p; 8vo.
£0.75
*Also classified at GEZDW*

(B72-50411)

**Bush, Geoffrey**
A menagerie: three part-songs for SATB (unaccompanied)/ by
Geoffrey Bush. — London: Elkin, 1971. — 24p; 8vo.
Contents: 1.Tiger; words by William Blake - 2.Cuckoo; words by
Shakespeare - 3.Monkey-house; words by Thomas Weelkes.
£0.40

(B72-50062)

**Gow, David**
Music: for chorus (SATB)/ by David Gow; words by Carl
Nielsen, English translation by Reginald Spink. — London:
Chester, 1972. — 16p; 8vo.
Unpriced

(B72-50863)

**Hoyland, Victor**
EM: for 24 voices/ by Victor Hoyland. — London: Universal,
1972. — 2 s. sh.; 8vo.
Unpriced

(B72-50864)

**Kodály, Zoltán**
The arms of Hungary: SATB unaccompanied/ by Zoltán Kodály;
[words by] Mihály Vörösmarty, English translation by Geoffry
Russell-Smith. — London: Boosey and Hawkes, 1972. — 3p; 8vo.
£0.05

(B72-50412)

**Kodály, Zoltán**
Greeting on St John's day: SAB unaccompanied/ by Zoltán
Kodály; English translation by Geoffry Russell-Smith. — London:
Boosey and Hawkes, 1972. — 4p; 8vo.
£0.05

(B72-50413)

**Mellers, Wilfrid**
Cloud canticles: for double chorus/ by Wilfrid Mellers; words
from Ronald Johnson's 'The book of the green man'. — Great
Yarmouth: Galliard, 1972. — 28p; 4to.
£0.83

(B72-50063)

**Paynter, John**
Landscapes: a choral suite for mixed voices (with optional oboe)/
by John Paynter; poems by T.S. Eliot. — London: Oxford
University Press, 1972. — 21p; 8vo.
Unpriced

(B72-50064)

**Paynter, John**
The windhover: SATB unacc./ by John Paynter; words by Gerard
Manley Hopkins. — London: Oxford University Press, 1972. —
8p; 8vo.
Duration 5-1/2 min.
ISBN 0 19 343006 1 : Unpriced

(B72-50414)

**Stoker, Richard**
The noble nature: two part songs for SATB a cappella,/ by
Richard Stoker; poems [by] Ben Jonson. — London: Leeds Music,
1971. — 8p; 8vo.
Contents: The noble nature. — Truth.
Unpriced

(B72-50065)

**Swayne, Giles**
Three Shakespeare songs: for unaccompanied mixed voices/ by
Giles Swayne. — London: Oxford University Press, 1972. — 20p;
8vo.
Contents: Hark! hark! the lark - Where the bee sucks, there suck I - Full
fathom five thy father lies.
ISBN 0 19 343729 5 : £0.50

(B72-50865)

**Thomas, Mansel**
Two Welsh love songs: SATB unacc./ arranged by Mansel
Thomas.; words by Iolo Davies. — London: Oxford University
Press, 1972. — 6p; 8vo.
Someone - Shore to shore.
ISBN 0 19 343032 0 : Unpriced

(B72-50866)

**Willan, Healey**
I beheld her, beautiful as a dove: SATB unacc./ by Healey Willan;
[words] from responsaries from an Office of Our Lady (8th
century). — London: Oxford University Press, 1971. — 4p; 8vo.
ISBN 0 19 343027 4 : Unpriced

(B72-50415)

**Williamson, Malcolm**
Love, the sentinel: for chorus a capella [sic]/ by Malcolm
Williamson; [words by] Alfred, Lord Tennyson. — London:
Weinberger, 1972. — 16p; 8vo.
£0.15

(B72-50066)

**Wilson, Richard**
Home from the range: for full chorus of mixed voices a cappella/
by Richard Wilson; text by Stephen Sandy. — New York:
Schirmer; [London]: [Chappell], 1971. — 30p; 8vo.
Unpriced

(B72-50067)

**EZDX — Secular cantatas**
**Bush, Geoffrey**
A nice derangement of epitaphs: for unaccompanied voices, by
Geoffrey Bush. — London: Elkin, 1972. — 44p; 8vo.
£1.25

(B72-50068)

# F — FEMALE VOICES, CHILDREN'S VOICES
## FDE — Religious cantatas
**Arch, Gwyn**
The promised land/ by Gwyn Arch; words by Pat Rooke. —
London: Feldman, 1971. — 41p; 8vo.
Vocal score.
£0.40

(B72-50069)

## FDGK — Roman liturgy. Proper of the Mass
**Eben, Peter**
Liturgische Gesänge/ [by] Peter Eben. — Cassel; London:
Bärenreiter, 1970. — 10 vol; 8vo.
£1.25

(B72-50416)

## FDGKJ — Roman liturgy. Divine Office. Vespers
**Mozart, Wolfgang Amadeus**
[Vesperae solemnes de confessore. K.339. - Excerpts]. Laudate
Dominum. K.339, no.5/ by W.A. Mozart; arranged for soprano
solo, SSA and piano or organ with an English translation adapted
from Psalm 117 by John C. Phillips. — Sevenoaks: Novello, 1972.
— 7p; 8vo.
£0.10

(B72-50867)

## FDH — Motets, Anthems, Hymns, etc
**Burns, Wilfred**
A common prayer/ by Wilfred Owen; words 16th century. —
London: Bosworth, 1971. — 4p; 8vo.
Staff & tonic sol-fa notation.
£0.07

(B72-50070)

**Dexter, Harry**
Give us, O Lord/ by Harry Dexter; words by E. Vickers Kirk —
London: Ashdown, 1972. — 7p; 8vo.
£0.09

(B72-50868)

**Gilbert, Norman**
Praise to the Lord, the Almighty: two-part/ by Norman Gilbert;
[words by] J. Neander, tr. C. Winkworth and others. — London:
Oxford University Press, 1972. — 6p; 8vo.
ISBN 0 19 341506 2 : Unpriced

(B72-50869)

**Middleton, James Roland**
Sanctify, O Lord: a chorister's prayer/ by James Roland
Middleton; words: origin unknown. — Croydon: Royal School of
Church Music, 1972. — 3p; 8vo.
Unpriced

(B72-50417)

## FDK — Anthems
**Palmer, Florence Margaret Spencer**
Oh how great is thy goodness: two-part (S.A.) anthem with piano
accompaniment/ by Peggy Spencer Palmer; [text from] Psalm 31.
— London: Cramer, 1971. — 8p; 8vo.
Staff & tonic sol-fa notation.
£0.09

(B72-50071)

## FDP/LEZ — Carols. Advent
**Harley, E Daker**
Blessed art thou Mary: Advent carol for soprano solo SA and
piano or organ/ words and music by E. Daker Harley. —
Sevenoaks: Novello, 1972. — 4p; 8vo.
£0.07

(B72-50418)

## FDP/LF — Carols. Christmas
**Dowland, John**
[First booke of songes. - If my complaints]. The Galliard carol:
SSA and piano/ by John Dowland; arranged by Raymond
Monelle, words [by] Robert Herrick. — [London]: Boosey and
Hawkes, 1972. — 14p; 8vo.
Unpriced

(B72-50870)

**Monelle, Raymond**
Nowell sing we, both all and some: Christmas carol, SSA and
piano/ by Raymond Monelle; words from the Selden MS. —
London: Boosey and Hawkes, 1972. — 11p; 8vo.
Unpriced

(B72-50871)

**Pasfield, William Reginald**
Thou whose birth on earth: carol for Christmas/ by W.R.
Pasfield; words by A.C. Swinburne. — London: Ashdown, 1972.
— 3p; 8vo.
£0.05

(B72-50419)

**Verrall, Pamela**
The rose of Bethlehem: S.S.A./ words and music by Pamela
Verrall. — London: British and Continental, 1972. — 4p; 8vo.
Unpriced

(B72-50872)

**Verrall, Pamela Motley**
A star for Maria: a carol in two parts with optional descant for
voices or instruments/ by Pamela M. Verrall. — London: British
and Continental, 1972. — [2]p; 8vo.
Unpriced

(B72-50873)

## FDP/LF/AY — Carols. Christmas. Collections
**Lane, Philip**
Three carols/ arranged and orchestrated by Philip Lane. — Great
Yarmouth: Galliard, 1972. — [15]p; 4to.
Vocal score. — Contents: My dancing day - De Virgin Mary- Deck the hall.
£0.50

(B72-50874)

## FDP/LFM — Carols. New Year
**Britten, Benjamin**
[Friday afternoons. Op.7 - Excerpts]. A new year carol. [Op.7,
no.5]/ by Benjamin Britten; arranged for S.S.A. and piano; words
anon. — London: Boosey and Hawkes, 1971. — 4p; 8vo.
£0.05

(B72-50072)

## FDW — Songs, etc
**Bennett, F Roy**
Evening/ words and music by F. Roy Bennett. — London:
Ashdown, 1972. — 4p; 8vo.
£0.05

(B72-50420)

**Blower, Maurice**
In midst of woods: part-song for SSA and piano/ by Maurice
Blower; words anonymous. — Sevenoaks: Elkin, 1971. — 7p; 8vo.
£0.10

(B72-50073)

**Brahms, Johannes**
[Intermezzo for piano in E flat major. Op.117, no.1]. Sleep soft,
my babe/ [set to melody of] Brahms; arranged for two-part
singing with piano by Harry Dexter, words by H.D. — London:
Ashdown, 1972. — 7p; 8vo.
£0.09

(B72-50421)

**Dexter, Harry**
What is the meaning of it all?: two-part song with piano
accompaniment/ words and music by Harry Dexter. —
Sevenoaks: Novello, 1972. — 12p; 8vo.
£0.10

(B72-50875)

**Dexter, Harry**
The wild horseman: arranged for two-part singing, with piano
accompaniment/ by Harry Dexter. — London: Ashdown, 1972.
— 7p; 8vo.
Based on Schumann's Op.68 (with an altered time signature).
£0.09

(B72-50074)

**Pitfield, Thomas Baron**
Cheshire soul-caking song: two-part/ music arranged and words adapted by Thomas Pitfield. — London: Oxford University Press, 1971. — 4p; 8vo.
Duration 1 1/2 min.
Unpriced

(B72-50075)

**Schubert, Franz**
Ave Maria. Op.52, no.6/ by Franz Schubert; arranged for SATB by Frank E. Brown, words by Sir Walter Scott. — London: Gould & Bolttler, 1972. — 12p; 8vo.
Staff & tonic sol-fa notation.
£0.89

(B72-50422)

**Stapleton, Eric**
In praise of Essex/ by Eric Stapleton. — London: Feldman, 1971. — 4p; 8vo.
Unpriced

(B72-50076)

**Thiman, Eric Harding**
Love will find out the way: for S.A. and piano/ by Eric H. Thiman; words anonymous. — Sevenoaks: Novello, 1972. — 7p; 8vo.
£0.10

(B72-50077)

**Tomlins, Greta**
Salute to spring: SSA/ by Greta Tomlins. — [South Croydon]: Lengnick, 1971. — 12p; 8vo.
Contents:- 1.The snowdrop; words by Tennyson - 2.To violets; words by Herrick - 3.Canterbury bells; words by Greta Tomlins.
£0.13

(B72-50078)

**Verrall, Pamela Motley**
The dove/ by Pamela Verrall. — London: Bosworth, 1970. — 3p; 8vo.
Staff and tonic sol-fa notation.
Unpriced

(B72-50876)

**Verrall, Pamela Motley**
The lollipop tree: two-part song (with optional recorders, glockenspiel, xylophone and timps)/ by Pamela M. Verrall. — London: Bosworth, 1970. — 8vo.
Piano score (4p.) & 4 parts.
£0.175

(B72-50877)

**FDW/AY — Songs, etc. Collections**
**Sturman, Paul**
A collection of seven two-part songs/ collected by Paul Sturman. — London: Feldman, 1972. — 21p; 8vo.
£0.35

(B72-50079)

**FDW/G/AYC — Folk songs. Collections. Great Britain**
**Hunt, Reginald**
More fun with tunes: couplings of national songs/ arranged by Reginald Hunt. — London: Boosey and Hawkes, 1972. — 28p; 8vo.
£0.60

(B72-50080)

**FDW/LC — Spirituals**
**Nelson, Havelock**
Sister Mary had - a but one child: negro spiritual, SSA and piano/ melody arranged by Havelock Nelson. — [London]: Boosey and Hawkes, 1972. — 8p; 8vo.
Unpriced

(B72-50878)

**FDW/LF — Songs, etc. Christmas**
**Rocherolle, Eugénie R**
Christmas day is comin': for unison, two-part or three part chorus/ words and music by Eugénie R. Rocherolle. — New York: Warner; [London]: [Blossom Music], 1972. — 8vo.
Unpriced

(B72-50423)

**FDX — Secular cantatas**
**Arnold, Malcolm**
Song of freedom. Op.109: for chorus of sopranos and altos, and piano/ by Malcolm Arnold. — London: Henrees Music, 1972. — 32p; 8vo.
Vocal score.
Unpriced

(B72-50879)

**FE/LDW — With instruments. Songs, etc**
**Pehkonen, Elis**
Genesis: for voices, instruments and tapes/ by Elis Pehkonen. — London: Universal, 1972. — 25sh; obl.fol.
Printed on one side of the leaf only.
Unpriced

(B72-50880)

**FE/NYDSRDP/LF — With descant recorders, strings, keyboard & percussion. Carols. Christmas**
**Hunt, Reginald**
Welcome Yule: carol for voices, violins or flutes, descant recorders, guitars, percussion and piano/ by Reginald Hunt; words 15th century. — London: Ashdown, 1972. — 8p; 8vo.
Duration 2 mins.
£0.09

(B72-50424)

**FE/NYFSDP/LF — With recorders, keyboard & percussion. Carols. Christmas**
**Verrall, Pamela Motley**
The Christmas journey: S.A./ by Pamela M. Verrall. — London: British and Continental, 1972. — [2]p; 8vo.
Unpriced

(B72-50881)

**FE/NYFSDP/LF/AYK — With recorders, keyboard & percussion. Carols. Christmas. Collections. Spain**
**Pfaff, Philip**
Christmas in Spain: six traditional Spanish carols, for unison and two-part voices, recorders, tuned and untuned percussion, and piano/ arranged and with English verses by Philip Pfaff. — London: Chappell, 1972. — 20p; 4to.
£0.50

(B72-50882)

**FE/NYFSRDX — With descant recorders, keyboard & percussion. Secular cantatas**
**Byrt, John**
Dives and Lazarus: a folk ballad, for soloists, choir [two-part], descant recorders, percussion, piano, guitar (optional) and double bass (optional)/ by John Byrt. — London: Oxford University Press, 1972. — fol
Score (24p.), Chorus score (7p.) & 4 parts.
ISBN 0 19 335490 x : £1.10

(B72-50425)

**FE/NYLDX — Female voices, Children's voices with keyboard and percussion. Secular cantatas**
**Britten, Benjamin**
Children's crusade = Kinderkreuzzug. Op.82: a ballad for children's voices and orchestra/ by Benjamin Britten; words by Bertold Brecht, English translation by Hans Keller. — London: Faber Music, 1970. — ix,105p; fol.
Unpriced

(B72-50426)

**FE/XDP/LF — With percussion. Carols. Christmas**
**Verrall, Pamela**
The little king's carol: calypso/ words and music by Pamela Verrall. — London: British and Continental, 1972. — 3p; 8vo.
Unpriced

(B72-50883)

**FEZDP/LF — Unaccompanied female voices, children's voices. Carols. Christmas**
**Verrall, Pamela Motley**
The star carol: SSA/ words and music by Pamela M. Verrall. — London: British and Continental, 1972. — [2]p; 8vo.
Unpriced

(B72-50884)

**FEZDW — Unaccompanied female voices, children's voices. Songs, etc**
**Bartók, Béla**
[Chorus music]. 18 part songs: for unaccompanied choir/ by Béla Bartók; English translation by Geoffry Russell-Smith. — London: Boosey and Hawkes. —
Vol.1. — 1972. — 15p; 8vo.
£0.40

(B72-50885)

Vol.2. — 1972. — 23p; 8vo.
£0.40

(B72-50886)

Vol.3. — 1972. — 15p; 8vo.
£0.40

(B72-50887)

**Kodály, Zoltán**
Eve, my sweet: S.fl unaccompanied/ by Zoltán Kodály; English translation by Geoffry Russell-Smith. — London: Boosey and Hawkes, 1972. — 3p; 8vo.
£0.05

(B72-50428)

**Kodály, Zoltán**
False spring: SSA unaccompanied/ by Zoltán Kodály; English translation by Geoffry Russell-Smith. — London: Boosey and Hawkes, 1972. — 3p; 8vo.
£0.05

(B72-50429)

**Kodály, Zoltán**
Grow, tresses = Hajinšvesztö: SSA unaccompanied/ by Zoltán Kodály; English translation by Geoffry Russell-Smith. — London: Boosey and Hawkes, 1972. — 4p; 8vo.
£0.05

(B72-50888)

**Kodály, Zoltán**
Mid the oak trees: folk song SSA unaccompanied/ arranged by Zoltán Kodály; English translation by Geoffry Russell-Smith. — London: Boosey and Hawkes, 1972. — 3p; 8vo.
£0.05

(B72-50427)

**Kodály, Zoltán**
Wine, sweet wine = Méz, méz: SSSAAA unaccompanied/ by Zoltán Kodály; English translation by Geoffry Russell-Smith. — London: Boosey and Hawkes, 1972. — 8p; 8vo.
Unpriced

(B72-50889)

**FLDH — Treble voices. Motets, Anthems, Hymns, etc**
**Holman, Derek**
Thee we adore/ by Derek Holman; words by St Thomas Aquinas; translated by Bishop J.R. Woodford. — Croydon: Royal School of Church Music, 1971. — 4p; 8vo.
Unpriced

(B72-50081)

**FLDK — Treble voices. Anthems**
**Purcell, Henry**
Thou knowest, Lord, the secrets of our hearts. Z.580/ by Henry Purcell; arranged, two-part, by Laurence H. Davies, words from the Book of Common Prayer. — London: Oxford University Press, 1971. — 3p; 8vo.
ISBN 0 19 351113 4 : Unpriced

(B72-50890)

**FLDP/LF — Treble voices. Carols. Christmas**
**Pehkonen, Elis**
Lute-book lullaby: for treble voices and organ/ by Elis Pehkonen; words by W. Ballet. — London: Chappell, 1972. — 6p; 8vo.
Unpriced

(B72-50891)

**Pehkonen, Elis**
Torches: for treble voices and organ/ by Elis Pehkonen; words translated by J.B. Trend. — London: Chappell, 1972. — 8p; 8vo.
Unpriced

(B72-50892)

**FLDW/LC — Soprano voices. Spirituals**
**Hudson, Hazel**
Steal away - Were you there?: a quodlibet based on two negro spirituals, (for either trebles 1 and 2, or basses 1 and 2, or treble 1 and bass 2)/ arr. by Hazel Hudson. — London: Ashdown, 1972. — 10p; 8vo.
£0.10
*Also classified at GXDW/LC; DW/LC*

(B72-50430)

**FLDW/LC — Treble voices. Spirituals**
**Hudson, Hazel**
Deep river; [and], Wade in the water; [and], Gonna lay down my burden: a quodlibet arranged from three negro spirituals for either trebles 1 and 2, or basses 1 and 2, or treble 1 and bass 2/ arr. by Hazel Hudson. — London: Ashdown, 1972. — 8p; 8vo.
£0.09
*Also classified at GXDW/LC; DW/LC*

(B72-50431)

**Hudson, Hazel**
Nobody knows; [and], Balm in Gilead: a quodlibet based on two negro spirituals, for either trebles 1 and 2, or basses 1 and 2, or treble 1 and bass 2/ arr. by Hazel Hudson. — London: Ashdown, 1972. — 8p; 8vo.
£0.09
*Also classified at GXDW/LC; DW/LC*

(B72-50432)

**FLE/NYLNSDX — Treble voices with keyboard & percussion quartet. Secular cantatas**
**Platts, Kenneth**
All seasons shall be sweet. Opus 6: for treble voices, percussion and piano/ by Kenneth Platts. — London: Ashdown, 1972. — 4to.
Score (22p) & part.
Unpriced

(B72-50433)

**FLEZDW — Unaccompanied soprano voices. Songs, etc**
**Kodály, Zoltán**
The good housewife: folk-song, S.S. unaccompanied/ arranged by Zoltán Kodály; English translation by Geoffry Russell-Smith. — London: Boosey and Hawkes, 1972. — 3p; 8vo.
£0.05

(B72-50434)

**G — MALE VOICES**
**GDK — Anthems**
**Billings, William**
[The singing master's assistant. - *Excerpts*]. Peace be on earth = Retrospect: an anthem from sundry Scriptures, [for] SATB (or male chorus or mixed chorus)/ by William Billings; edited by Oliver Daniel. — New York: Peters; [London]: [Hinrichsen], 1970. — 19p; 8vo.
Unpriced
*Primary classification DK*

(B72-50360)

**GDP/LF — Carols. Christmas**
**Hoddinott, Alun**
Puer natus: SSAATTBB (or SSAA or TTBB)/ by Alun Hoddinott/ German words translated by W. Moelwyn Merchant. — London: Oxford University Press, 1972. — 6p; 8vo.
ISBN 0 19 343030 4 : Unpriced
*Primary classification DP/LF*

(B72-50374)

**GEZDH — Unaccompanied male voices. Motets, Anthems, Hymns, etc**
**Kodály, Zoltán**
God's mercy: T. Bar. B. unaccompanied/ by Zoltán Kodály; [words by] Sándor Petöfi, English translation by Geoffry Russell-Smith. — London: Boosey and Hawkes, 1972. — 8p; 8vo.
£0.09

(B72-50435)

**GEZDW — Unaccompanied male voices, Songs, etc**
**Billings, William**
[The singing master's assistant. - *Excerpts*]. Lamentation over Boston; [and], Jargon: SATB (or male chorus or mixed quartet)/ by William Billings; edited by Oliver Daniel. — New York: Peters; [London]: [Hinrichsen], 1971. — 15p; 8vo.
£0.75
*Primary classification EZDW*

(B72-50411)

**GEZDW — Unaccompanied male voices. Songs, etc.**
**Tindle, Anna**
My land/ by Anna Tindle; arranged for unaccompanied TTBB by Harry Dexter, words by Peter Tindle. — London: Ashdown, 1972. — 80p; 8vo.
Duration 3 mins.
£0.09

(B72-50436)

**GEZDW/LC — Unaccompanied male voices. Songs. Spirituals**
**Heath, Fenno**
Guide my head: spiritual arranged for four-part chorus of men's voices a cappella/ by Fenno Heath. — New York: Schirmer; [London]: [Chappell], 1971. — 8p; 8vo.
Unpriced

(B72-50082)

**GEZDW/XD/AZ — Unaccompanied male voices. Songs, etc. Catches. Collected works of individual composers**
**Purcell, Henry**
Come, let us drink: compleat, pleasant and divertive/ contriv'd by the late famous Mr. Henry Purcell; newly edited by Michael Nyman. — Great Yarmouth: Galliard, 1972. — 56p; obl.8vo.
£0.93

(B72-50893)

**GXDW/LC — Bass voices. Spirituals**
**Hudson, Hazel**
Deep river; [and], Wade in the water; [and], Gonna lay down my burden: a quodlibet arranged from three negro spirituals for either trebles 1 and 2, or basses 1 and 2, or treble 1 and bass 2/ arr. by Hazel Hudson. — London: Ashdown, 1972. — 8p; 8vo.
£0.09
*Primary classification FLDW/LC*

(B72-50431)

**Hudson, Hazel**
Nobody knows; [and], Balm in Gilead: a quodlibet based on two
negro spirituals, for either trebles 1 and 2, or basses 1 and 2, or
treble 1 and bass 2/ arr. by Hazel Hudson. — London: Ashdown,
1972. — 8p; 8vo.
£0.09
*Primary classification FLDW/LC*

(B72-50432)

**Hudson, Hazel**
Steal away - Were you there?: a quodlibet based on two negro
spirituals, (for either trebles 1 and 2, or basses 1 and 2, or treble 1
and bass 2)/ arr. by Hazel Hudson. — London: Ashdown, 1972.
— 10p; 8vo.
£0.10
*Primary classification FLDW/LC*

(B72-50430)

## HY — SPEAKING CHORUS
**Jergenson, Dale**
The vision: full chorus and seven soloists/ by Dale Jergenson;
[words by] Lawrence Ferlinghetti. — New York: Schirmer;
[London]: [Chappell], 1971. — 13p; 8vo.
Unpriced

(B72-50083)

## HYE/LDW — Speakers with instruments. Songs, etc
**Pehkonen, Elis**
Three limericks: for voices, instruments and piano/ by Elis
Pehkonen; words by Edward Lear. — London: Lengnick, 1972. —
7p; 4to.
£0.25

(B72-50437)

## HYE/NYENQ — Speaker. With wind, strings & percussion. Sextets
**Walton, *Sir* William**
Façade: an entertainment/ by William Walton; the poems by
Edith Sitwell. — London: Oxford University Press, 1972. —
xxxix,111p; 4to.
Limited ed. of 1000 copies, of which 250 are signed by the composer. — In
slip case, with 7in. 33-1/3r.p.m. disc of the original recording of 1929.
ISBN 0 19 359402 1 : £12.00
ISBN 0 19 359403 x Signed ed: £30.00

(B72-50084)

## J — VOICES IN UNISON
### JDE — Religious cantatas
**Hazell, Chris**
Holy Moses: pop cantata for unison voices and piano/ words and
music by Chris Hazell. — Sevenoaks: Novello, 1972. — 8vo.
Score (50p.) & 2 parts. — Duration 22 min.
£0.50

(B72-50894)

### JDGS — Anglican liturgy. Communion
**Barrett-Ayres, Reginald**
Communion service, series 3: for congregational use/ by Reginald
Barrett-Ayres. — Borough Green: Novello, 1972. — 12p; 8vo.
£0.14

(B72-50438)

**Gelineau, Joseph**
An order for Holy Communion, (Series 3)/ by Joseph Gelineau.
— London: Ascherberg, Hopwood & Crew, 1972. — 8p; 8vo.
Unpriced

(B72-50895)

**Nourse, John**
A short Communion service: for unison voices and organ/ by
John Nourse. — [Sevenoaks]: Novello, 1972. — 10p; 8vo.
Also suitable for Series 2.
£0.14

(B72-50896)

**Rutter, John**
Communion service: for congregational use with optional SATB
choir/ by John Rutter. — London: Oxford University Press, 1972.
— 8vo.
Vocal score (11p.) & congregational part (7p.).
ISBN 0 19 351638 1 : Unpriced

(B72-50085)

### JDH — Motets, Anthems, Hymns
**Bach, Johann Sebastian**
[Selections]. Come, let us all this day/ melody and bass by J.S.
Bach, [words by J. Troutbeck] interludes and inner parts by
Gerald H. Knight; and, Prepare thyself, Zion, from the Christmas
Oratorio. — Croydon: Royal School of Church Music, 1972. —
7p; 8vo.
Unpriced

(B72-50439)

### JDK — Anthems
**Dearnley, Christopher**
[Two anthems]/ transcribed and edited by Christopher Dearnley.
— Croydon: Royal School of Church Music, 1972. — 8p; 8vo.
Contents: The Gentiles shall come/by Maurice Green. — In the light of the
unwise/by James Nares.
Unpriced

(B72-50086)

**Holman, Derek**
Jesus Christ the apple tree/ by Derek Holman; words anon. —
Croydon: Royal School of Church Music, 1972. — 4p; 8vo.
Unpriced

(B72-50440)

**Wesley, Samuel Sebastian**
[Blessed be the God and Father. - *Excerpts*]. Love one another/
by S.S. Wesley; words from I St Peter; [and], O worship the
Lord/ by John Travers; words from Psalm 96. — Croydon: Royal
School of Church Music, 1972. — 7p; 8vo.
Unpriced

(B72-50441)

### JDM — Hymns
**Long, Kenneth Roy**
Fight the good fight/ by Kenneth R. Long; words by J.S.B.
Monsell. — Croydon: Royal School of Church Music, 1971. —
4p; 8vo.
Unpriced

(B72-50087)

### JDP/LF — Carols. Christmas
**Morris, Peter**
In freezing winter night: carol for unison voices and piano/ by
Peter Morris; words by Robert Southwell. — London: Elkin,
1972. — 4p; 8vo.
Unpriced

(B72-50088)

**Thackray, Roy**
Pleasure it is: unison/ by Roy Thackray; words by William
Cornish. — London: Oxford University Press, 1972. — [2]p; 8vo.
ISBN 0 19 351115 0 : Unpriced

(B72-50897)

**Thomas, Mansel**
The song of little Jesus = Cân y baban Jesu: unison/ by Mansel
Thomas; Welsh words by Thomas Parry, English words by D.H.
Davis. — London: Oxford University Press, 1972. — 3p; 8vo.
ISBN 0 19 342049 x : Unpriced

(B72-50898)

### JDP/LFP — Carols. Epiphany
**Johns, Sybil Marian**
A carol for to-day/ by Sybil Marian Johns. — Llandaff (41 Padua
Rd, Llandaff, Cardiff): S.M. Johns, 1971. — 2sh; 8vo.
Unpriced
*Also classified at DP/LFP*

(B72-50089)

### JDR — Psalms
**Williamson, Malcolm**
Carols of King David: for unison choir, congregation and organ/
by Malcolm Williamson. — London: Weinberger. —
No.2: O Jerusalem: Psalm 122. — 1972. — 4p; 8vo.
£0.05

(B72-50090)

No.4: Who is the king of glory?: Psalm 24. — 1972. — 4p; 8vo.
£0.05

(B72-50091)

No.5: The King of love: Psalm 23/ [metrical text by Sir Henry W. Baker].
— 1972. — 4p; 8vo.
£0.05

(B72-50092)

### JDW — Songs, etc
**Bennett, F Roy**
The wind sings on the mountain/ words and music by F. Roy
Bennett. — London: Ashdown, 1972. — 4p; 8vo.
£0.05

(B72-50442)

**Dvořák, Antonín**
[Slavonic dances. Op.72, no.2]. Moon rainbow/ by Anton Dvořák;
words and arrangement by Laurence H. Davies. — London:
Ashdown, 1972. — 3p; 8vo.
£0.05

(B72-50443)

### JDW/G/AY — Folk songs. Collections
**Stuart, Forbes**
A medley of folk-songs/ compiled, with commentaries, by Forbes
Stuart, musical arrangements by Geoffrey Winters. — London:
Longman, 1971. — 160p; 4to.
ISBN 0 582 15331 x : Unpriced

(B72-50444)

THE BRITISH CATALOGUE OF MUSIC

**JDW/G/AYH — Folk songs. Collections. France**
The Faber book of French folk songs/ arranged and translated by
Elizabeth Poston; collected and selected by Paul Arma, [guitar
accompaniments arranged by Margot Toplis.]. — London: Faber
Music, 1972. — [13],152p; 8vo.
ISBN 0 571 09944 0 : £3.00

(B72-50899)

**JE/NYLDX — With keyboard & percussion. Secular cantatas**
Cardew, Cornelius
The great learning: the first chapter of the Confucian classic with
music in 7 paragraphs/ by Cornelius Cardew. — London (26
Avondale Park Gardens, W.11): Experimental Music Catalogue,
1971. — [23]sh; obl.4to.
Unpriced

(B72-50093)

**JE/TSDG — With guitar. Ordinary of the Mass**
Rock, Gordon F
A Mass for all ages and Offertory hymn/ by Gordon Rock. —
Aylesbury: Gordon F. Rock, 1972. — 12p; 8vo.
Unpriced

(B72-50094)

Rock, Gordon F
Missa de saeculis/ by Gordon Rock. — Aylesbury: Gordon F.
Rock, 1972. — 8p; 8vo.
Unpriced

(B72-50095)

**JE/TSDM/AY — With guitar. Hymns. Collections**
Gilbert, Bryan
Songs for one step forward/ selected and arranged by Bryan
Gilbert. — London: Marshall, Morgan and Sc tt, 1972. — 32p;
8vo.
£0.30

(B72-50096)

**JE/TSDW — With guitar. Songs, etc**
Maddox, Hugh
[Alive!. - Excerpts]. Five new songs/ edited by Hugh Maddox. —
Great Yarmouth: Galliard, 1972. — 7p; 8vo.
ISBN 0 85249 141 7 : £0.27

(B72-50445)

Taylor, Jeremy
Jeremy Taylor: [songs]. — Great Yarmouth: Galliard. —
Vol.1. — 1971. — 24p; obl.8vo. —
ISBN 0 85249 099 2 : Unpriced

(B72-50900)

**JE/TSDW/G/AY — With guitar. Folk songs. Collections**
Sounds like folk. — London: EFDS Publications. —
No.1: Songs for and about drinking. — 1972. — 36p; 8vo.
£0.30

(B72-50446)

**JE/TSDW/G/AYT — With guitar. Folk songs. Collections. United
States**
Glazer, Tom
A new treasury of folk songs/ compiled and arranged by Tom
Glazer; with an introduction to folk guitar accompaniment for the
beginner. — London: Corgi Books, 1971. — 182p; 8vo.
£0.30

(B72-50901)

**JE/XTPDW/LF — With glockenspiel & piano. Songs. Christmas**
Verrall, Pamela
Ring ding bells: a song for Christmas/ by Pamela Verrall. —
London: British and Continental, 1972. — 3p; 8vo.
Unpriced

(B72-50902)

**JEZDW/G/AYC — Unaccompanied voices. Folk songs. Collections.
Great Britain**
The High Level Ranters song and tune book/ [edited by] Johnny
Handle ... [and others]. — Great Yarmouth: Galliard, 1972. —
44p; obl.8vo.
ISBN 0 85249 151 4 : £0.55

(B72-50447)

**JEZDW/G/AYDFK —·Unaccompanied voices. Folk songs.
Collections. Dorset**
Brocklebank, Joan
A Dorset book of folk songs/ edited by Joan Brocklebank and
Biddie Kindersley. — London: English Folk Dance and Song
Society, 1971. — 32p; 8vo.
ISBN 0 85418 042 7 : £0.20

(B72-50448)

**JEZDW/G/AYDJJ — Unaccompanied voices. Folk songs.
Collections. Tyneside**
Polworth, Gwen
Come you not from Newcastle?: a collection of North Country
songs/ [compiled] by Gwen Polworth. — Newcastle upon Tyne (6
Queen's Terrace, Newcastle upon Tyne 2): Frank Graham, 1972.
— 48p; 8vo.
£0.60

(B72-50903)

**JEZDW/G/AYFSM — Unaccompanied voices. Folk songs.
Collections. South Moravia**
Max, Wenzel
Deutsche Volksweisen aus Südmähren: im Auftrag des deutschen
Volksliederarchivs/ herausgegeben von Wenzel Max. — Cassel;
London: Bärenreiter, 1971. — 99p; 8vo.
£1.00

(B72-50449)

**JFDM — Female voices, Children's voices. Hymns**
Larbalestier, Philip George
Life's olympics: a demonstration service of song and praise for
young people/ by Philip George Larbalestier; words by G.
Scott-Archer. — Leeds: John Blackburn, 1972. — 15p; 8vo.
Staff & tonic sol-fa notation.
Unpriced

(B72-50097)

Pasfield, William Reginald
Loving shepherd of thy sheep: unison anthem for children's voices
with organ (or piano)/ by W.R. Pasfield; words by Jane E.
Leeson. — London: Ashdown, 1972. — 3p; 8vo.
£0.05

(B72-50450)

**JFDM/AY — Female voices, Children's voices. Hymns. Collections**
Maynard, John
So much to sing: over 50 songs for young people/ compiled and
selected by John Maynard. — London: Vanguard Music, 1971. —
64p; 4to.
Unpriced

(B72-50098)

**JFDM/GJ/AY — Female voices, Children's voices. Children's hymns.
Collections**
Illsley, Derrick
Hymns for the new generation/ by Derrick Illsley. — Cambridge:
Rainbow Music, 1971. — 52p; 4to.
Gramophone record enclosed.
Unpriced

(B72-50099)

**JFDM/LSL/AY — Female voices, Children's voices. Hymns.
Unitarian Church, Collections**
Knight, Sydney H
Songs for living and words of worship: a hymn and worship book
for the young/ editor Sydney H. Knight, associate editor Gabor
Kereki, musical editor David Dawson; prepared by the Unitarian
Religious Education Department. — London: The Lindsey Press,
1972. — xxix,231p; 8vo.
£1.25

(B72-50100)

**JFDP — Female voices, Children's voices. Carols**
Cope, Cecil
The apple: unison song/ by Cecil Cope; [words by] Helen Wood.
— London: Boosey and Hawkes, 1972. — 5p; 8vo.
£0.09

(B72-50904)

**JFDP/LF — Female voices, Children's voices. Carols. Christmas**
Rubbra, Edmund
To Him we sing, Op. 34: unison carol for children's voices and
piano/ by Edmund Rubbra; words anon. — South Croydon:
Lengnick, 1972. — 4p; 8vo.
£0.05

(B72-50905)

**JFDW — Female voices, Children's voices. Songs, etc**
Jenkyns, Peter
Snakes: song for unison voices and piano/ words and music by
Peter Jenkyns. — London: Elkin, 1972. — 4p; 8vo.
£0.07

(B72-50906)

**JFDW/G/AY — Female voices, Children's voices. Folk songs.
Collections**
Brace, Geoffrey
35 songs from 35 counties/ compiled by Geoffrey Brace. —
Cambridge: Cambridge University Press, 1972. — 8vo.
Piano ed. (71p.) & melody ed. (52p.).
£1.60

(B72-50907)

**JFDW/GJ — Female voices, Children's voices. Children's songs**
Ager, Laurence
London sparrow: unison song for children/ by Laurence Ager;
words by Freda Elton Young. — London: Cramer, 1972. — 4p;
8vo.
Staff & tonic sol-fa notation.
£0.06

(B72-50451)

**JFDW/GJ/AY — Female voices, Children's voices. Childrens songs.
Collections**
Poston, Elizabeth
The baby's song book/ compiled by Elizabeth Poston. — London:
Bodley Head, 1972. — 190p; 4to.
£4.20

(B72-50452)

**JFDW/GJ/AYDJGX — Female voices, children's voices. Children's
songs. Humberside**
Reaks, Brian
Nursery songs from Humberside/ words and music by Brian
Reaks. — London: British and Continental, 1971. — 9p; 4to.
£0.25

(B72-50101)

**JFDW/GJ/AYE — Female voices, Children's voices. Children's
songs. Collections. Germany**
Wenz, Josef
Die goldene Brücke: Volkskinderlieder für Hans und
Kindergarten, Spielplatz und Schule/ herausgegeben von Josef
Wenz. — Cassel; [London]: Bärenreiter, 1970. — 94p; obl.8vo.
£1.00

(B72-50453)

**JFDW/GK/AY — Female voices, Children's voices. Nursery rhymes.
Collections**
Hudson, Hazel
Nursery rhymes with a new look/ arranged and updated by Hazel
Hudson. — London: Edwin Ashdown, 1971. — 59p; 4to.
Unpriced

(B72-50102)

**JFDW/GK/AY — Unison female voices, children's voices. Nursery
rhymes. Collections**
Waters, Frank
Nursery songs and carols/ [arranged] by Frank Waters. —
London: Franklin Watts, 1971. — [49]p; 8vo.
ISBN 0 85166 258 7 : £0.25

(B72-50103)

**JFE/LDW — Female voices, Children's voices. With instruments.
Songs, etc**
Adams-Jeremiah, Dorothy
Sing, say and play: a book of junior music making and poetry for
primary and junior schools/ by Dorothy Adams Jeremiah; with
piano and instrumental accompaniments by Mansel Thomas. —
South Croydon: Lengnick, 1972. — 45p; 8vo.
£0.45

(B72-50104)

**JFE/LPDM/AY — Female voices, Children's voices with instruments
& piano. Hymas. Collections**
Smith, Peter
New orbit: songs and hymns for under elevens/ general editor:
Peter Smith, musical editor: June B. Boyce. — London: Galliard,
1972. — 188p; 4to.
ISBN 0 85249 134 4 : Unpriced

(B72-50908)

**JFE/NYDSRDW/G/AY — Female voices, Children's voices with
descant recorder, strings, keyboard & percussion.
Folk songs. Collections**
Pont, Kenneth
Music workshop books/ arranged for unison voices and
instrumental group by Kenneth Pont. — London: Oxford
University Press. —
Book 1. — 1972. — 4to & obl.8vo.
Score (41p.), choral score (21p.), recorder playing score (17p.) & 3 parts.
ISBN 0 19 344905 6 : £1.45

(B72-50909)

Book 2. — 1972. — 4to & obl.8vo.
Score (40p.), choral score (21p.), recorder playing score (18p.) & 3 parts.
ISBN 0 19 344912 9 : £1.45

(B72-50910)

**JFE/NYFSDP/LF — Female voices, Children's voices with recorders,
keyboard & percussion. Carols. Christmas**
Burtch, Mervyn
Babe of Bethlehem: a nativity, for unison voices, piano, recorders,
tuned and untuned percussion/ by Mervyn Burtch; words by
Wendy U. Rees. — London: Chappell, 1972. — 24p; 4to.
£0.50

(B72-50911)

Miller, Peter
Two carols for children. Op216: for unison voices, piano, recorder
and percussion/ words and music by Peter Miller. — London:
Keith Prowse, 1972. — 5p; 4to.
£0.25

(B72-50912)

**JFE/NYFSRDW — Female voices, Children's voices with recorders,
keyboard & percussion. Songs, etc**
Bizet, Georges
[Carmen. - Avec la garde montante]. Street boys' song = Choeur
des gamins/ by Georges Bizet; arranged for voices, descant
recorders, percussion and piano by John Horton, French words by
H.Meilhac and L. Halévy, translated by John Horton. — London:
Schott, 1972. — 4to.
Score (8p.) & 2 parts.
£0.60

(B72-50913)

**JFE/TSDW/GJ/AYH — Female voices, Children's voices with
guitar. Children's songs. Collections. France**
Rockwell, Anne
Savez-vous planter les choux?, and other French songs/ selected
by Anne Rockwell. — London: Hamilton, 1972. — 64p; obl.8vo.
ISBN 0 241 02256 8 : £1.80

(B72-50914)

**JFE/XPQDW — Female voices, Children's voices with melodic
percussion. Songs, etc**
Paynter, John
Autumn: for voices and instruments/ by John Paynter; text
translated by Harold G. Henderson from a haika by Gyodai. —
London: Universal, 1972. — s.sh; obl.fol.
Unpriced

(B72-50915)

**JFE/XPQDX — Female voices, Children's voices. With melodic
percussion. Secular cantatas**
Arch, Gwyn
Robert Brown - instant hero: for voices, glockenspiels or
chime-bars and piano/ [by] Gwyn Arch; lyrics by Pat Rooke. —
London: Feldman, 1972. — 20p; 8vo.
Unpriced

(B72-50454)

**JFEZDW/AY — Unaccompanied female voices, children's voices.
Songs, etc. Collections**
Smith, Hettie
Diamond jubilee songbook/ compiled by Hettie Smith. — London:
Girl Guides Association, 1971. — 32p; 8vo.
£0.10

(B72-50916)

**JFEZDW/GJ/AYCG — Unaccompanied female voices, children's
voices. Children's songs. Collections. Great Britain.
Gypsies**
Hurley, Bernard
The Romano Drum song book/ music editor Bernard Hurley; text
editor Thomas Acton. — Oxford: Romanestan Publications. —
With a leaflet (6p.), containing explanatory notes.
Vol.1. — 1972. — 20p; 8vo.
£0.25

(B72-50105)

**JFEZDW/PP — Unaccompanied female voices, children's voices.
Songs, etc. Pentatonic music**
Kodály, Zoltán
Pentatonic music/ by Zoltán Kodály; [edited by Geoffry
Russell-Smith]. — London: Boosey and Hawkes. —
Tonic sol-fa notation.
Vol.3: 100 Cheremissian melodies. — 1972. — 32p; obl.8vo.
£0.30

(B72-50917)

**JFTE/XTPRDW — High voices with chime bars. Songs, etc**
Paynter, John
First star: for voices and instruments/ by John Paynter; words
anonymous. — London: Universal, 1972. — s.sh; obl.fol.
Unpriced

(B72-50918)

**JN — SINGLE VOICES IN COMBINATION**
**JNEDE — Vocal duets. Religious cantatas**
Erbse, Heimo
Das Hohelied Salomo's. Opus 26a: Sopran, Bariton und Klavier/
[by] Heimo Erbse. — Frankfurt; London: Peters, 1971. — 85p;
4to.
£4.50

(B72-50455)

**JNEDGC — Vocal duets. Roman liturgy. Ordinary of the Mass.
Gloria**
Rorem, Ned
Gloria: for two solo voices and piano/ by Ned Rorem. — New
York; [London]: Boosey and Hawkes, 1972. — 23p; 4to.
£1.25

(B72-50919)

**JNEDW — Vocal duets. Songs, etc**
**McKellar, Kenneth**
Island love: duet for soprano and tenor/ words and music by Kenneth McKellar. — London: Boosey and Hawkes, 1972. — 4p; 4to.
£0.35

(B72-50920)

**JNEE/NVPNPDW — Vocal duets. With woodwind & string septet. Songs, etc**
**Berio, Luciano**
El mar la mar: per soprano, mezzo-soprano e 7 strumenti/ [by] Lusiano Berio; parole di Rafael Alberti. — London: Universal, 1972. — 15p; 4to.
Unpriced

(B72-50106)

**JNFDE/MDW — Vocal trios with orchestra. Songs, etc**
**Maw, Nicholas**
Scenes and arias: for soprano, mezzo-soprano, contralto and orchestra/ by Nicholas Maw; words anon. — London: Boosey and Hawkes, 1971. — 140p; 4to.
£7.50

(B72-50107)

**JNFEDJ — Vocal duets. Motets**
**Scarlatti, Domenico**
Salve regina, A-moll: für Sopran, Alt und Basso continuo/ [by] Domenico Scarlatti; herausgegeben von Loek Hautus. — Cassel; London: Bärenreiter, 1971. — 4to.
Score (16p.) & 3 parts.
£1.00

(B72-50456)

**JNFEE/WTPDW — Female voices. Duets. With horn & piano. Songs etc**
**Tate, Phyllis**
A Victorian garland: three poems by Matthew Arnold set for soprano and contralto solo voices, horn, and piano by Phyllis Tate. — London: Oxford University Press, 1972. — 39p; 4to.
Duration 15 min.
ISBN 0 19 345824 1 : £1.80

(B72-50921)

**JNFLEE/NYDTNPDW — Soprano duets. With oboe, strings, Keyboard & percussion. Septets. Songs, etc**
**Crumb, George**
Ancient voices of children: a cycle of songs for soprano, boy soprano, oboe, mandolin, harp, electric piano, percussion/ by George Crumb; texts by García Lorca. — New York: Peters; [London]: [Hinrichsen], 1970. — 8p; fol.
£6.00

(B72-50457)

**JNFLEE/SNTRDE — Soprano duets. With two violins & organ. Religious cantatas**
**Bernhard, Christoph**
[Geistlicher Harmonien, erster Teil. *Excerpts*]. Jauchzet dem Herrn, alle Welt: für zwei Soprane, zwei Violinen und Basso continuo/ [by] Christoph Bernhard; herausgegeben von Bruno Grusnick. — Cassel; London: Bärenreiter, 1971. — 4to.
Score (12p.) & 5 parts. — The parts for sopranos and for violins are in duplicate.
£1.00

(B72-50458)

**K — VOCAL SOLOS**
**K/EG/AL — Sight reading. Examinations**
**London College of Music**
Examinations in pianoforte playing and singing sight reading tests, as set throughout 1971: Grades I-VIII and diplomas. — London: Ashdown, 1972. — 15p; 4to.
£0.30
*Primary classification Q/EG/AL*

(B72-50170)

**KDH — MOTETS, ANTHEMS, HYMNS, ETC. SOLOS**
**Lowe, Augustus**
Perpetuity: a church solo/ by Augustus Lowe; words by Edgar Newgass. — London: Edgar Newgass; [Distributed by] Paterson, 1972. — 3p; 4to.
£0.20

(B72-50922)

**Thomas, Mansel**
Four prayers from the Gaelic/ by Mansel Thomas; English translations by Alexander Carmichael, Welsh version by Enid Parry. — Cardiff: University of Wales Press, 1971. — 25p; 4to.
Unpriced

(B72-50108)

**KDJ — MOTETS. SOLOS**
**KDK — Anthems**
**Edwards, D W**
The day of Pentecost: for choir, or solo voice, or as an organ solo/ by D.W. Edwards; [text from] Acts 2. — West Kirby (67 Lang Lane, West Kirby, Wirral, Cheshire): D.W. Edwards, 1972. — 4p; 8vo.
Unpriced
*Primary classification DK*

**KDW — SONGS, ETC. SOLOS**
**Bartlett, Ian J**
Two songs for Feste/ edited by Ian J. Bartlett. — Banbury: Piers Press, 1971. — [6]p; fol.
Contents: 1.Come away death; music by King Henry VIII - 2.I am gone, sir.
£0.25

(B72-50110)

**Bliss, *Sir* Arthur**
Three songs/ by Arthur Bliss; words by William H. Davies. — Sevenoaks: Novello, 1972. — 12p; 4to.
These songs, originally composed in 1923, have been slightly revised for this publication.
Unpriced

(B72-50923)

**Burt, James**
Amazing grace: traditional [melody] arranged [with] piano or organ [accompaniment]/ by James Burt. — London: Chappell, 1972. — 3p; 4to.
£0.20

(B72-50459)

**Dvořák, Antonín**
[Symphony no.9 in E minor. Op.95. - Largo]. A New World prayer/ adapted from the symphony [by] Anton Dvořák; words by A.J. Burton. — South Croydon: Lengnick, 1972. — 4p; 4to.
£0.20

(B72-50924)

**Friml, Rudolf**
[The vagabond king. - Come all you beggars]. Song of the brigands/ by Rudolf Friml; lyric by Brian Hooker. — London: Feldman, 1972. — 5p; 4to.
As sung in 'Maid of the mountains'.
£0.20

(B72-50460)

**Holst, Gustav**
Margrete's cradle-song. Op.4, no.2/ by Gustav Holst; words by Henrik Ibsen, English words by William Archer. — London: Bosworth, 1972. — 6p; 4to.
The opus number is quoted from Imogen Holst's biography of the composer.
£0.20

(B72-50925)

**Humperdinck, Engelbert**
[Hänsel and Gretel. - *Excerpts*]. Hänsel and Gretel song book. — London: Francis, Day and Hunter. —
by Engelbert Humperdinck/ arr. by Dudley E. Bayford, [libretto by Adelheid Wette], words [translated] by Constance Bache. — 1972. — 28p; 4to.
£0.35

(B72-50461)

**Jackson, Roy Garrick**
Glory of Scotland/ words & music by Roy Garrick Jackson. — London: Chappell-Solomon, 1972. — 5p; 4to.
£0.20

(B72-50462)

**Kershaw, Doug**
Lou'siana man: the Doug Kershaw songbook, by Doug Kershaw. — New York: Collier Books; London: Collier-Macmillan, 1971. — 144p; 4to.
ISBN 0 02 061050 5 : £0.90

(B72-50111)

**Khachaturian, Aram**
[Spartak. - Adagio]. For my love/ by Aram Khachaturian; the song version of the theme from the T.V. series, arranged and composed by Edward Charles & Norman Newell. — London: Plantagenet music, 1971. — 4p; 4to.
£0.20

(B72-50112)

**Larbalestier, Philip George**
The heart's awakening: a song cycle/ by P.G. Larbalestier; words, Lee Tranter. — Leeds: Regina Music, 1972. — 7p; 4to.
Contents: Reverie. — Cameo. — Awakening.
£0.35

(B72-50463)

**Lekberg, Sven**
The spring and the fall: for voice and piano/ by Sven Lekberg;
poem by Edna St Vincent Millay. — New York: Schirmer;
[London]: [Chappell], 1971. — 7p; 4to.
Unpriced

(B72-50113)

**Lennon, John**
Imagine/ words and music by John Lennon. — London: Wise
Publications, Music Sales, 1971. — 43p; 4to.
£0.95

(B72-50464)

**Lennon, John**
Imagine/ words and music by John Lennon. — London: Wise
Publications, Music Sales, 1971. — 43p; 4to.
£0.95

(B72-50465)

**Raynor, John**
Eleven Songs/ by John Raynor. — Yarmouth: Galliard, 1971. —
48p; 8vo.
ISBN 0 85249 040 2 : Unpriced

(B72-50466)

**Rodgers, Richard**
Rodgers & Hammerstein revisited/ by Richard Rodgers. —
London: Williamson Music. —
Vol.1. — 1972. — 60p; 4to.
£0.75

(B72-50114)

Vol.2. — 1972. — 51p; 4to.
£0.75

(B72-50115)

**Roe, Betty**
9 songs: for voice and keyboard/ by Betty Roe. — London:
Thames, 1972. — 36p; 4to.
Unpriced

(B72-50116)

**Rome, Harold**
Gone with the wind: souvenir music album/ words and music by
Harold Rome. — London: Chappell, 1972. — 31p; 4to.
£0.75

(B72-50467)

**Rota, Nina**
[The godfather. - Love theme]. Speak softly, love/ by Nina Rota;
words by Larry Kusik. — London: Chappell, 1972. — 4p; 4to.
£0.25

(B72-50468)

**Schumann, Robert**
Dichterliebe/ by Robert Schumann; edited by Arthur Komar. —
London: Chappell, 1972. — 136p; 8vo.
Miniature score. — Also included are four songs not generally known to
have originally belonged to Dichterliebe. — With bibliography.
ISBN 0 900277 04 1 : Unpriced

(B72-50469)

**Sondheim, Stephen**
Company: song book/ music and lyrics by Stephen Sondheim. —
London: Valando Music, 1972. — 47p; 4to.
£0.60

(B72-50117)

**Thomson, Virgil**
Portrait of F.B. (Frances Blood): for voice and piano/ by Virgil
Thomson; poem by Gertrude Stein. — New York: Schirmer;
[London]: [Chappell], 1971. — 15p; 4to.
Unpriced

(B72-50118)

**Webber, Andrew Lloyd**
[Jesus Christ superstar. - *Excerpts*]. Jesus Christ superstar: a rock
opera/ by Andrew Lloyd Webber; lyrics by Tim Rice. — London:
Leeds Music, 1972. — 64p; 4to.
£1.25

(B72-50119)

**Wilson, Sandy**
The boy friend: song album/ words and music by Sandy Wilson.
— London: Chappell, 1972. — 34p; 4to.
£0.60

(B72-50120)

**KDW/AYDL — Songs, etc. Collections. Scotland**
A song of Scotland. — London: Wise, Music Sales, 1972. — 77p;
4to.
£1.25

(B72-50926)

**KDW/AZ — Songs, etc. Complete works of individual composers**
**Strauss, Richard**
[Songs]. Lieder/ by Richard Strauss; complete edition, edited by
Franz Trenner. — London: Boosey and Hawkes. —
A reprint, in octavo, of the original folio ed. of 1964.
Vol. 1. — 1972. — 344p; 8vo.
£7.50

(B72-50927)

Vol. 2. — 1972. — 366p; 8vo.
£7.50

(B72-50928)

Vol. 3. — 1972. — 290p; 8vo.
£7.50

(B72-50929)

Vol. 4. — 1972. — 616p; 8vo.
£10.00

(B72-50930)

**KDW/G/AYDFR — Folk songs. Collections. Cornwall**
**Dunstan, Ralph**
Cornish dialect & folk songs: a sequel to the 'Cornish song book'/
[compiled by] Ralph Dunstan. — Padstow: Loedenek Press;
London: Ascherburg, Hopwood & Crewe, 1972. — 50p; 4to.
A reprint of the original edition of 1933.
£1.20

(B72-50470)

**KDW/GB/AY(XHS64) — Popular songs. Collections, 1837-1901**
**Turner, Michael R**
The parlour song book: a casquet of vocal gems/ the music edited
by Antony Miall, edited and introduced by Michael R. Turner. —
London: Joseph, 1972. — 374p; 8vo.
ISBN 0 7181 0381 5 : £5.00

(B72-50931)

**KDW/HHW/AY — Blues. Collections**
**Handy, William Christopher**
Blues: an anthology, complete words and music of 53 great songs/
edited by W.C. Handy, revised by Jerry Silverman. — New York:
Macmillan; London: Collier-Macmillan, 1972. — 224p; 4to.
Unpriced

(B72-50471)

**KDW/JR — Films**
**Barry, John**
This way Mary: love theme from the film 'Mary, Queen of Scots'/
by John Barry; lyrics by Don Black. — London: Leeds Music,
1972. — 3p; 4to.
£0.20

(B72-50121)

**Barry, John**
Wish now was then: from the film, 'Mary, Queen of Scots'/ by
John Barry; lyrics by Don Black. — London: Leeds Music, 1972.
— 3p; 4to.
£0.20

(B72-50109)

**Bricusse, Leslie**
Willy Wonka and the chocolate factory: vocal selections/ by Leslie
Bricusse and Anthony Newley. — London: Taradam Music, 1971.
— 32p; 4to.
£0.75

(B72-50122)

**Kander, John**
Cabaret: souvenir music album/ by John Kander; lyrics by Fred
Ebb. — London: Valando Music, 1972. — 35p; 4to.
£0.75

(B72-50472)

**KDW/JR — Songs. Films**
**Rota, Nino**
The godfather: souvenir song album/ by Nino Rota; [with
orchestral excerpts arranged for keyboard]. — London: Chappell,
1972. — 70p; 4to.
£1.25
*Also classified at QPK/JR; RK/JR*

(B72-50932)

**KDW/L/AY — Religious songs. Collections**
**Mickelson, Paul**
Pat Boone rapture theme songs/ arranged by Paul Mickelson;
piano scores by James G. Boersma, guitar notation by Peter Bye.
— London: Marshall, Morgan and Scott, 1972. — 37p; 8vo.
ISBN 0 551 05159 0 : £0.40

(B72-50123)

**KE — VOCAL SOLOS WITH ACCOMPANIMENT OTHER THAN KEYBOARD**
**KE/NYERNSDX — With flute, strings & percussion quartet. Secular cantatas**
Henze, Hans Werner
El Cimarr´on-Biography of the runaway slave Esteban Montejo: recital for four musicians/ by Hans Werner Henze; text from the book by Miguel Barnet, translated and adapted for music by Hans Magnus Enzensberger, English version by Christopher Keene. — Mainz; London: Schott, 1972. — 99p; 8vo.
Duration 76 mins. Singer, flautist and guitarist also play percussion instruments.
£2.40
(B72-50933)

**KE/NYERNTDW — With flute, string & percussion trio. Songs, etc**
Jong, Conrad de
Hist whist: for voice, flute, viola and percussion/ by Conrad de Jong; poem by E.E. Cummings. — New York: Schirmer; [London]: [Chappell], 1971. — 10p; 4to.
Unpriced
(B72-50124)

**KE/TSDW — With guitar. Songs, etc**
Donald, Mike
North by north-east/ songs of Mike Donald; photographs by John Edenbrow. — Great Yarmouth: Galliard, 1972. — [1],22p: ill, port; obl.8vo.
ISBN 0 85249 154 9 : £0.44
(B72-50934)

**KE/TSDW/AY — With guitar. Songs. Collections**
Criswick, Mary
Elizabethan and Jacobean songs: for voice and guitar/ arranged by Mary Criswick. — London: Stainer and Bell, 1972. — 23p; 4to.
£0.75
(B72-50935)

Taylor, Jeremy
Jeremy Taylor - [songs]. — London: Galliard. —
[Vol.] 2. — 1972. — 24p; obl.8vo. —
ISBN 0 85249 102 6 : Unpriced
(B72-50936)

**KE/TSDW/AY — With guitar. Songs. Collections**
Williams, Patrick
Easy album for the organ/ arranged by Patrick Williams. — London: Bosworth. —
3rd. — 1972. — 29p; 4to.
£0.60
(B72-50937)

**KE/TSDW/K/G/KDX/AYC — With guitar. Ballads. Bawdy. Collections. Great Britain**
McCarthy, Tony
Bawdy British folk songs/ compiled and arranged, with guitar chords, by Tony McCarthy. — London: Wolfe, 1972. — 127p; 8vo.
ISBN 0 7234 0492 5 : £0.60
(B72-50938)

**KE/VSSNUDW/G/AYD — With treble recorder duet. Folk songs. Collections. Great Britain**
Dinn, Freda
Eight English songs: for voice and two treble recorders/ arranged by Freda Dinn. — London: Schott, 1972. — 12 ill; 4to.
£0.70
(B72-50473)

**KE/VVPDW — With clarinet & piano. Songs, etc**
Spohr, Louis
Six German songs. Op.103: for voices, clarinet and piano/ by Louis Spohr; edited by Friedrich Leinert. — Cassel; London: Bärenreiter, 1971. — 4to.
Score (24p.) & part.
£0.90
(B72-50474)

**KEZ — UNACCOMPANIED VOCAL SOLOS**
**KEZDW — Songs, etc**
Bowman, J.H.
Grannie's songs/ collected and arranged by J.H. Bowman. — Crewe: Sagittar Books, 1971. — [8],33p; 8vo.
Unpriced
(B72-50125)

Douglas, Katherine
Sar-Orain le Catriona Dhughlas/ airs and words by Katherine Douglas; [edited by] Donald Budge. — Dunvegan: Domhnall Budge, 1971. — 23p; 4to.
Staff and tonic sol-fa notation.
£0.30
(B72-50126)

**KEZDW/G/AYD — Folk song collections. England**
Purslow, Frank
The constant lovers: more English folk songs from the Hammond & Gardiner Mss/ selected and edited by Frank Purslow. — London: English Folk Dance Society Publications, 1972. — iv, 149p; 8vo.
£0.50
(B72-50127)

**KEZDW/K/G/AY — Ballads. Collections**
Bronson, Bertrand Harris
The traditional tunes of the Child ballads: with their texts, according to the extant records of Great Britain and America/ [compiled by] Bertrand Harris Bronson. — Princeton [N.J.]: Princeton University Press; [London]: [Oxford University Press].
—
This is the musical counterpart to the famous Francis James Child collection of English and Scottish ballads for which Professor Child's canon established the text.
Vol. 4 Ballads 245 to 299, with addenda to volumes 1-4. — 1972. — xvi, 576p; 4to.
Unpriced
(B72-50939)

Bronson, Bertrand Harris
The traditional tunes of the Child ballads: with their texts, according to the extant records of Great Britain and America/ [compiled by] Bertrand Harris Bronson. — Princeton [N.J.]: Princeton University Press; [London]: [Oxford University Press].
—
This is the musical counterpart to the famous Francis James Child collection of English and Scottish ballads for which Professor Child's canon established the text.
Vol.2: Ballads 54 to 113. — [1962]. — xx,565p; 4to.
Unpriced
(B72-50940)

Bronson, Bertrand Harris
The traditional tunes of the Child ballads: with their texts, according to the extent records of Great Britain and America/ [compiled by] Bertrand Harris Bronson. — Princeton [N.J.]: Princeton University Press; [London]: [Oxford University Press].
—
This is the musical counterpart to the famous Francis James Child collection of English and Scottish ballads for which Professor Child's canon established the text.
Vol.3: Ballads 114 to 243. — 1966. — xvii,496p; 4to.
£10.00
(B72-50941)

**KF — FEMALE VOICE, CHILD'S VOICE**
**KFE/TSDW/G/AY — With guitar. Folk songs. Collections**
Silverman, Jerry
The liberated woman's songbook: seventy-seven singable folk songs about women and their battles with husbands, lovers, the devil, the system ... and themselves with lyrics, guitar arrangements, and entertaining photographs/ compiled by Jerry Silverman. — New York: Collier Books; London: Collier-Macmillan, 1971. — ix,145p; 4to.
ISBN 0 02 082040 2 : £1.25
(B72-50128)

**KFLDH — Soprano voice. Motets, Anthems, Hymns, etc**
Parry, *Sir* Charles Hubert Hastings
[Hear my words, ye people. *Excerpts*]. He delivered the poor/ by C. Hubert H. Parry; [text from] Psalm 72, Isaiah 61. — Croydon: Royal School of Church Music, 1971. — 4p; 8vo.
Unpriced
(B72-50129)

**KFLE/MDW — Soprano voice with orchestra . Songs, etc**
Bach, Johann Christian
[La Clemenza di Scipione. - Infelice! in van m'affano]. Arsinda: Rezitativ und Arie, für Sopran und Orchester/ [by] Johann Christian Bach; herausgegeben von Ray mond Meylan. — Frankfurt; London: Peters, 1971. — 69p; 4to.
£3.50
(B72-50475)

**KFLE/NUUNTDGKK — Soprano voice with saxophone, strings & keyboard trio. Divine Office. Vespers. Magnificat**
Gaslini, Giorgio
Magnificat: per voce di soprano, saxofone contralto, contrabasso, pianoforte/ [by] Giorgio Gaslini. — London: Universal, 1970. — 4to.
Score (4p.) & 2 parts.
Unpriced
(B72-50476)

**KFLE/SNTPWDX — Soprano voice with two violins & keyboard. Secular cantatas**
Scarlatti, Alessandro
Arianna: Kantate für Sopran, zwei Violinen und Basso continuo/ by Alessandro Scarlatti; herausgegeben von Raymond Meylan. — Frankfurt; London: Peters, 1970. — 22p; 8vo.
£2.00
(B72-50477)

**KFLE/SSDW — Soprano voice with double bass. Songs, etc**
**Roe, Betty**
Jazz songs for soprano & double bass/ by Betty Roe; deutsche
Übersetzung: Stefan de Haan. — London 8 Cecil Rd, W.3: Yorke,
1972. — 3p; 4to.
Contents: Euphonium dance/lyric by Jacqueline Froom. — Madam and the
minister/ lyric by Langston Hughes.
Unpriced

(B72-50478)

**KFNE/VRDX — Mezzo-soprano with flute. Secular cantatas**
**Karkoschka, Erhard**
Psylex (1968): für Mezzosopran, Flöte und Tonband/ [by] Erhard
Karkoschka in zwei Akten zu je drei Szenen; nach Texten und
dem Fischer-Lexikon Psychologie von Peter R. Hofstatter. —
Regensburg: Bosse; [London]: [Bärenreiter], 1969. — 19p; 4to.
£2.25

(B72-50479)

**KFQDX — Contralto voice. Secular cantatas**
**Handel, George Frideric**
La Solitudine: cantata for alto solo and basso continuo/ [by]
Georg Friedrich Händel; first edition edited by Malcolm Boyd,
German words: Walther Durr. — Cassel; London: Bärenreiter,
1970. — 4to.
Score (11p.) & 2 parts.
£1.00

(B72-50480)

**KFQE/MRDX — Contralto voice with chamber orchestra. Secular**
**cantatas**
**Raxach, Enrique**
Paraphrase: pour voix d'alto et 11 instrumentistes/ [by] Enrique
Raxach. — London: Peters, Hinrichsen, 1971. — vii,39p; 8vo.
Duration 14 1/2 min.
£1.80

(B72-50130)

**KFT — HIGH VOICE**
**KFTDW — Songs, etc**
**Berkeley, Lennox**
Counting the beats: song for high voice and piano/ by Lennox
Berkeley; poem by Robert Graves. — London: Thames, 1972. —
5p; 4to.
Unpriced

(B72-50131)

**Brahms, Johannes**
[Selections]. Ausgewählte Lieder: für Gesang und Klavier/ by
Johannes Brahms; Ausgabe für hohe Stimme herausgegeben von
Max Friedlaender. — Frankfurt; London: Peters, 1970. — 97p;
8vo.
£1.40

(B72-50481)

**Schubert, Franz**
[Selections]. Ausgewählte Lieder: für Gesang und Klavier/ [by]
Franz Schubert; Ausgabe für hohe Stimme herausgegeben von
Max Friedlaender. — Frankfurt; London: Peters, 1970. — 87p;
8vo.
£1.40

(B72-50482)

**Schubert, Franz**
Goethe songs: original pitch (high)/ by Franz Schubert; edited by
Walther Dürr. — Cassel; London: Bärenreiter, 1971. — 69p; 8vo.
£1.15

(B72-50483)

**Schubert, Franz**
Two songs: original pitch (high)/ by Franz Schubert; edited by
Christa Landon. — First edition. — Cassel; London: Bärenreiter,
1970. — 7p; 8vo.
£0.50

(B72-50484)

**Schumann, Robert**
[Selections]. Ausgewählte Lieder: für Gesang und Klavier/ [by]
Robert Schumann; Ausgabe für hohe Stimme herausgegeben von
Max Friedlaender. — Frankfurt; London: Peters, 1970. — 73p;
8vo.
£1.40

(B72-50485)

**KFTE/SPLRDE — With violin & organ. Religious cantatas**
**Telemann, Georg Philipp**
[Harmonischer Gottes-Dienst - Excerpts]. Ew'ge Quelle, milder
Strom: Kantate auf den Sonntag Cantate, für mittlere Stimme,
Querflöte (Violine) und Basso continuo/ [by] Georg Philipp
Telemann; herausgegeben von Gustav Fock. — Cassel; London:
Bärenreiter, 1971. — 4to.
Score (11p.) & 3 parts.
£1.00

(B72-50486)

**Telemann, Georg Philipp**
[Harmonischer Gottes-Dienst. - Excerpts]. Gott will Mensch und
sterblich werden: Kantate zum Fest der Verkündigung Maria, für
hohe Stimme, Violine und Basso continuo/ [by] Georg Philipp
Telemann; herausgegeben von Gustav Fock. — Cassel; London:
Bärenreiter, 1971. — 4to.
Score (12p.) & 3 parts.
£1.00

(B72-50487)

**Telemann, Georg Philipp**
[Harmonischer Gottes-Dienst - Excerpts]. Jauchzt, ihr Christen,
seid vergnügt: Kantate am dritten Osterfreitag, für hohe Stimme,
Violine and Basso Continuo/ [by] Georg Philipp Telemann;
herausgegeben von Gustav Fock. — Cassel; London: Bärenreiter,
1971. — 4to.
Score (12p.) & 3 parts.
£1.00

(B72-50488)

**KFV — MIDDLE VOICE**
**KFVE/VRPLRDE/LFP — With flute & organ. Religious cantatas.**
**Epiphany**
**Telemann, Georg Philipp**
[Harmonischer Gottes-Dienst. Excerpts]. Ihr Völker, hört: Kantate
am Fest der Heiligen drei Könige, für mittlere Stimme, Querflöte
und Basso continuo/ [by] Georg Philipp Telemann; herausgegeben
von Gustav Fock. — Cassel; London: Bärenreiter, 1971. — 4to.
Score (14p.) & 3 parts.
£1.00

(B72-50489)

**KFX — LOW VOICE**
**KFXDH/AY — Motets, Anthems, Hymns, etc. Collections**
**Bach, Johann Sebastian**
[Selections]. Die Gesänge zu Georg Christian Schmellis
'Musicalischen Gesang-Buch' [S.439-507] sowie sechs Lieder aus
dem 'Klavierbüchlein für Anne Magdalena Bach'. S.511-14, 516,
517/ harmonised by Johann Sebastian Bach; Ausgabe für tiefe
Stimme bearbeitet von Günther Raphael. — Cassel; London:
Bärenreiter, 1970. — 78p; 8vo.
Unpriced

(B72-50490)

**KFXDW — Songs, etc**
**Burkhard, Willy**
Frage, Op.9: ein Liederzyklus für tiefe Stimme/ [by] Willy
Burkhard; nach Gedichten von Lenau, Eichendorff, Dehmel,
Spitteler, Fankhauser. — Cassel; [London]: Bärenreiter, 1971. —
24p; 8vo.
£1.50

(B72-50491)

**KG — MALE VOICE**
**KGHDW — Tenor voice. Songs, etc**
**Britten, Benjamin**
Who are these children? Op. 84: lyrics, rhymes and riddles, for
tenor and piano/ by Benjamin Britten; [words] by William Soutar.
— London: Faber Music, 1972. — 33p; fol.
Duration 20 min.
Unpriced

(B72-50942)

**KGHE/MDW — Tenor voice with orchestra. Songs, etc**
**Tippett, Sir Michael**
Songs for Dov: for tenor and orchestra/ music and text by
Michael Tippett. — London: Schott, 1972. — vii,93p; 8vo.
Duration 25 min.
£1.50

(B72-50943)

**KGHE/NUPNQDX — Tenor voice with woodwind, string &**
**keyboard sextet. Secular cantatas**
**Tate, Phyllis**
Apparitions: a ballad sequence for tenor, harmonica, string quartet
and piano/ by Phyllis Tate. — London: Oxford University Press,
1972. — 60p; 4to.
ISBN 0 19 345822 5 : £2.50

(B72-50132)

**KGHE/NYHXSDX — Tenor voice. With trumpet & percussion.**
**Secular cantatas**
**Victory, Gerard**
Kriegslieder = Tears of battle: for solo tenor, mixed chorus,
trumpet and percussion/ by Gerard Victory; text by August
Stramm. — Sevenoaks: Fairfield Music, 1972. — 37p; 4to.
Duration 14 min.
£1.00

(B72-50133)

**KGNDW — Baritone voice. Songs, etc**
**Bush, Geoffrey**
5 mediaeval lyrics: for baritone and piano/ by Geoffrey Bush. —
Sevenoaks: Elkin, 1971. — 16p; 4to.
£0.75

(B72-50134)

**KGNE/MDW — Baritone voice with orchestra. Songs, etc**
Erbse, Heimo
F'unf Orchesterges'ange nach Georg Trakl. Op.27: f'ur Bariton und Orchester/ [by] Heimo Erbse. — Frankfurt; London: Peters, 1971. — 114p; 8vo.
Miniature score.
£3.20
(B72-50492)

Reimann, Aribert
Zyklus: cycle for baritone and orchestra/ by Aribert Reimann after poems by Paul Celan. — Mainz; London: Schott, 1972. — 79p; 8vo.
£3.00
(B72-50494)

Wagner-Régeny, Rudolf
Hermann-Hesse-Gesänge, 'Gesänge des Abschieds': für Bariton und Orchester/ [by] Rudolf Wagner-Régeny. — Leipzig: Peters; [London]: [Hinrichsen], 1971. — 21p; 4to.
£2.80
(B72-50493)

**KGNE/NXNSDH — Baritone voice with string & keyboard quartet. Motets, Anthems, Hymns, etc**
Kröll, Georg
Cantio: für Bariton und 2 Violoncello, Kontrabass und Orgel/ [by] Georg Kröll. — Regensburg: Bosse; [London]: [Bärenreiter], 1970. — 10ff.; obl.fol.
£2.25
(B72-50495)

**KGNE/RXMPWTDX — Baritone voice with French horn & string orchestra. Secular cantatas**
Crosse, Gordon
For the unfallen. Op.9: for tenor voice, solo French horn and string orchestra/ by Gordon Crosse; four poems by Geoffrey Hill. — London: Oxford University Press, 1971. — 72p; 8vo.
Vocal score.
ISBN 0 19 345267 7 : £2.50
(B72-50135)

**KGXDW — Bass voice. Songs, etc**
Ridley, George
Blaydon races/ words and music by George Ridley, arranged by Peter Haysom. — London: Boosey and Hawkes, 1972. — 10p; 4to.
£0.30
(B72-50944)

**KGXE/MDE — Bass voice with orchestra. Religious cantatas**
Zimmerman, Bernd Alois
'I turned and saw all the injustices that are committed under the sun': ecclesiastical action for two speakers, bass soloist and orchestra/ by Bernd Alois Zimmerman. — Mainz; London: Schott, 1972. — 59p; 4to.
£3.20
(B72-50945)

**KGXE/SNTPWDE — Bass voice with two violins & keyboard. Religious cantatas**
Schelle, Johann
Sechs Kantaten. — Cassel; London: Bärenreiter. —
Score (60p.) & 4 parts.
für Bass, zwei Violinen und Basso continuo/ [by] Johann Schelle/ herausgegeben von Alfred Dürr. — 1971. — 4to.
£3.65
(B72-50496)

**KHY — Speaker with piano**
Holloway, Stanley
The world of Stanley Holloway: [songs and musical monologues by various composers and writers]/ [compiled by] Stanley Holloway. — London: Francis, Day and Hunter, 1972. — 44p; 4to.
£0.75
(B72-50497)

**KHYE/MPQ — Speaker with piano & orchestra**
Patterson, Paul
Rebecca/ by Paul Patterson; words by Hilaire Belloc. — London: Weinberger, 1972. — 8p; obl.fol.
Unpriced
(B72-50946)

**LH — DANCES**
**LH/G/AYC — Folk dances. Collections. Great Britain**
Darke, Dennis
Band call: 76 tunes for folk dance musicians and bands/ edited by Dennis Darke. — London: English Folk Dance and Song Society, 1972. — [1],21p; 8vo.
£0.40
(B72-50498)

**LJ — Miscellaneous works**
Bussotti, Sylvano
Sette gogli: una collezione occulta/ di Sylvano Bussotti. — London: Universal, 1972. — 7 sh; fol.
'... three pieces for a single performer, three pieces for just two or three performers, and one composition for a chamber orchestra of any size desired...' - Composer's note.
Unpriced
(B72-50947)

Morgan, Robert
L'Après - midi du Dracoula for sound - producing instruments; [and], Elegant journey with stopping points of interest: for chamber orchestra or percussion ensemble/ by Robert Morgan. — Mainz: Ars viva; [London]: [Schott], 1972. — 2p.; 4to.
£2.00
*Also classified at MRJ; XN*
(B72-50499)

**LN — ENSEMBLES**
Kagel, Mauricio
Prima vista: für Diapositivbilder und unbestimmte Schallquellen/ [by] Mauricio Kagel. — London: Universal, 1971. — [74]p; obl.8vo.
Unpriced
(B72-50136)

**LN/ED — Accompaniment**
Noble, Robert
Folk tunes to accompany: a guide to simple accompaniment for beginners of all ages/ by Robert Noble. — Sevenoaks: Novello. —
Book 4: Music for Christmas: 30 folk carols. — 1972. — 29p; obl.8vo. — £0.45
(B72-50500)

**LNPQ — Six instruments & piano**
Hashagen, Klaus
'Septagle': Studie für 7 Spieler - 6 beliebige Instrumente und Klavier/ [by] Klaus Hashagen. — Regensburg: Bosse; [London]: [Bärenreiter], 1969. — 18ff; 4to.
£0.95
(B72-50501)

**LNR — Quintets**
Thomas, Bernard
Andernaken: anon., for five instruments, ATTBB/ [edited by] B.T. — London: Pro musica, 1972. — 4to.
Unpriced
(B72-50948)

Woodcock, Clement
'Browning' fantasy: for five instruments, SATTB/ by Woodcock; [edited by Bernard Thomas]. — London: Pro musica, 1972. — 4to.
Score (4p.) & 5 parts.
Unpriced
(B72-50949)

**LNS — Quartets**
Isaac, Heinrich
A la bataglia: for four instruments, ATTB, by Heinrich Isaac/ [edited by] Bernard Thomas. — London: Pro musica, 1972. — 4to.
Score (8p.) & 4 parts.
Unpriced
(B72-50950)

**LNS/X/AY — Quartets. Canons. Collections**
Thomas, Bernard
Seven double canons: for four instruments or voices/ edited by Bernard Thomas, texts edited and translated by Alan Robson. — London: Pro musica, 1972. — 16p; 4to.
Unpriced
*Primary classification EZDU/X/AY*

**LNS/X/AYH — Quartets. Canons. Collections. France**
Thomas, Bernard
Four double canons: for 4 voices or instruments; (ATTB)/ edited by Bernard Thomas. — Lustleigh: Antico, 1972. — 9p; 4to.
Unpriced
*Primary classification EZDU/X/AYH*

**LNSGN — Quartets. Fanfares**
Chagrin, Francis
Two fanfares: for four equal instruments with optional percussion/ by Francis Chagrin. — Sevenoaks: Novello, 1972. — 4to.
Score (6p.) & 5 parts.
£1.30
(B72-50951)

**LNSH — Quartets. Dances.**
Du Tertre, Etienne
Septème livre de danceries: for four instruments, SATB/ by Etienne Du Tertre; edited by Bernard Thomas. — London: Pro musica, 1972. — 20p; 4to.
Unpriced
(B72-50952)

**LNSH — Quartets. Dances**
Gervaise, Claude
Sixi`eme livre de danceries: for four instruments, SATB/ by Claude Gervaise; [edited by] Bernard Thomas. — London: Pro musica, 1972. — 32p; 4to.
Unpriced

(B72-50953)

Gervaise, Claude
Troisième livre de danceries: for four instruments, SATB/ Claude Gervaise; [edited by] Bernard Thomas. — London: Pro Musica, 1972. — 31p; 4to.
Unpriced

(B72-50954)

**LNSK/DW — Arrangements. Songs, etc**
Rodgers, Richard
[Oklahoma!. - *Excerpts*]. Four songs/ by Richard Rodgers; arranged for instrumental quartet by Felton Rapley. — London: Williamson, 1971. — 4to.
Score (20p.) & 5 parts.
Unpriced

(B72-50137)

**LNT — Trios**
Ruffo, Vincenzo
[Capricci in musica a tre voci. - *Excerpts*]. Four pieces, [nos. 9,15,23,5]: for threee instruments, ATB/ By Vincenzo Ruffo; [edited by] Bernard Thomas. — London: Pro musica, 1972. — 4to.
Score (8p.) & 3 parts. — Contents: La Disperata - Danza - La Piva - La Gamba.
Unpriced

(B72-50955)

Thomas, Bernard
Three late 15th century instrumental pieces: for 3 instruments (ATB)/ edited by Bernard Thomas. — Lustleigh (North Horton, Lustleigh, Newton Abbot, Devon): Antico, 1972. — 9p; 4to.
Unpriced

(B72-50956)

**LNTGN — Trios. Fanfares**
Chagrin, Francis
Two fanfares: for three equal instruments with optional percussion in no.2/ by Francis Chagrin. — Sevenoaks: Novello, 1972. — 4to.
Score (6p.) & 4 parts.
£1.10

(B72-50502)

**ME — SYMPHONIES**
Stamitz, Johann
[Symphony in D major. Op.5, no.5]. Rococo symphony/ by Johann Stamitz; arranged by C.P. Arnell and K.W. Rokos. — London: Bosworth, 1972. — 4to.
Score (40p.), Piano conductor (18p.) & 17 parts.
£2.25

(B72-50957)

**MF — CONCERTOS**
Pehkonen, Elis
Concerti with orchestra for young players/ by Elis Pehkonen. — London: Universal, 1972. — 18p; 4to.
Duration 14 mins.
Unpriced

(B72-50138)

**MG — Suites**
Fegers, Karl
Suite nach französischen Volksliedern: für 3 Blockflöten (2 Sopran - und 1 Altflöte), 1-3 andere Instrumente (Violine, Klarinette, Akkordeon o.a.) Gitarre oder Bass, Stabspiele (Xylophone, Glockenspiel) oder Klavier/ [by] Karl Fegers. — Mainz; London: Schott, 1972. — 19p; 8vo.
£0.90

(B72-50503)

**MH — DANCES**
Dexter, Harry
Scottish street dance for string orchestra with ad lib. melody instruments/ by Harry Dexter. — London: Ashdown, 1972. — 4to.
Score (7p.) & 7 parts.
£1.05

(B72-50504)

Grieg, Edvard
Symphonic dance. [Op.64, no.2]/ by Edward Grieg; arranged by A.W. Benoy. — London: Oxford University Press, 1972. — 24p; 4to.
Score (24) & 25 parts.
ISBN 0 19 363819 3 : Unpriced

(B72-50505)

**MHW — Waltzes**
Waldteufel, ´Emile
Two waltzes/ by Emil Waldteufel; arranged for junior orchestra by A.W. Benoy. — London: Oxford University Press, 1972. — 4to.
Contents: The skater's waltz. — The mermaid waltz.
ISBN 0 19 368017 3 : £0.90

(B72-50139)

**MJ — MISCELLANEOUS WORKS**
Handel, George Frideric
[Ariodante. - Overture, 3rd section]. Rigaudon/ by G.F. Handel; arranged by Llifon Hugh-Jones. — London: Bosworth, 1972. — 4to.
Score (13p.), Piano score (2p.) & parts. — There is no name or tempo indicated in Handel's autograph. The music is entitled Bourrée in Beecham's Amaryllis suite.
£1.80

(B72-50958)

Mozart, Wolfgang Amadeus
[Sympony no.40 in G minor. K.550. - Allegro molto]. Exposition of Mozart's Symphony no.40 (1st movement)/ the original work, with a few adaptations, arranged for school or amateur orchestra by K.W. Rokos. — London: Bosworth, 1971. — 4to.
Score (21p.), piano score (4p.) & 18 parts.
£2.30

(B72-50959)

**MK — ARRANGEMENTS**
Mussorgsky, Modest
[Pictures at an exhibition. - *Excerpts*]. Bydlo and two promenades/ by Modest Mussorgsky; arranged by Denis Bloodworth. — London: Oxford University Press, 1972. — 4to.
Score (12p.) & 23 parts.
ISBN 0 19 366175 6 : Unpriced

(B72-50506)

**MK/AH — Arrangements. Dances**
Granados, Enrique
[Danzas españolas. - *Excerpts*]. Villanesca. [Vol.2, no.4]/ by Enrique Granados; arranged by David Stone. — London: Boosey and Hawkes, 1972. — 4to.
Score (18p.), Piano conductor (5p.) & 26 parts.
£3.65

(B72-50960)

**MM — WORKS FOR SYMPHONY ORCHESTRA**
**MM/HM — Ballet music**
Schedrin, Rodion
Anna Karenina: ballet in three acts/ by Rodion Schedrin. — London: Anglo-Soviet Music: [Distributed by] Boosey and Hawkes, 1972. — 344p; fol.
£10.00

(B72-50961)

**MM/JR — Film music**
Josephs, Wilfred
Rail. Op.57: symphonic picture for orchestra/ by Wilfred Josephs. — New York: Galaxy; London: Galliard, 1972. — 68p; 4to.
Unpriced

(B72-50140)

**MME — Symphonies**
Beethoven, Ludwig van
Symphony no.5 in C minor. Op. 67/ by Ludwig van Beethoven; edited by Elliot Forbes. — London: Chappell, 1972. — 202p; 8vo.
Miniature score.
ISBN 0 900277 08 4 : £1.75

(B72-50962)

Berlioz, Hector
[Episode de la vie d'un artiste]. Fantastic symphony/ by Hector Berlioz; edited by Edward T. Cone. — London: Chappell, 1972. — 305p; 8vo.
Miniature score. — With bibliography.
ISBN 0 900277 02 5 : Unpriced

(B72-50507)

Gerhard, Roberto
Symphony 3 (Collages)/ by Roberto Gerhard. — London: Oxford University Press, 1972. — 85p; 8vo.
ISBN 0 19 363618 2 : £5.00

(B72-50508)

Kelterborn, Rudolf
[Symphony no.2]. Sinfonie 2: in two movements for large orchestra/ [by] Rudolf Kelterborn. — Cassel; London: Bärenreiter, 1970. — 105p; 8vo.
Miniature score. — Duration 20 min.
£3.15

(B72-50509)

**Prokofiev, Sergei**
[Symphony no.7. Opus 131]. Sinfonie Nr.7. Opus 131/ von Sergej Prokofjew; herausgegeben von W. Lewitskaja. — Leipzig: Peters; [London]: [Hinrichsen], 1970. — 166p; 8vo.
Miniature score.
Unpriced

(B72-50963)

**Shostakovich, Dmitri**
Symphony no.7. Opus 60/ by Dmitri Schostakowitsch. — Leipzig: Peters; [London]: [Hinrichsen], 1972. — 182p; 8vo.
Miniature score.
Unpriced

(B72-50964)

**Vaughan Williams, Ralph**
[Symphony no.2]. A London Symphony/ by Ralph Vaughan Williams. — Centenary ed. — London: Stainer & Bell, 1972. — vii,193p; 4to.
£2.50

(B72-50510)

**MMEM — Sinfoniettas**
**Hoddinott, Alun**
Sinfonietta 4. Opus 72, no.3/ by Alun Hoddinott. — London: Oxford University Press, 1972. — 69p; 8vo.
ISBN 0 19 364652 8 : £2.00

(B72-50965)

**MMF — Concertos**
**Menotti, Gian Carlo**
Triplo concerto a tre/ by Gian Carlo Menotti. — New York; London: Schirmer, 1972. — 80p; 8vo.
Duration 20 min.
Unpriced

(B72-50141)

**MMHKEF — Fox-trots**
**Davies, Peter Maxwell**
St Thomas Wake: foxtrot for orchestra on a pavan by John Bull/ by Peter Maxwell Davies. — London: Boosey and Hawkes, 1972. — 109p; fol.
Unpriced

(B72-50511)

**Davies, Peter Maxwell**
St Thomas Wake: foxtrot for orchestra on a pavan by John Bull/ by Peter Maxwell Davies. — London: Boosey and Hawkes, 1972. — 109p; 8vo.
Miniature score.
£2.50

(B72-50512)

**MMJ — Miscellaneous works**
**Brindle, Reginald Smith**
Apocalypse: for orchestra/ by Reginald Smith Brindle. — London: Hinrichsen, 1971. — 53p; fol.
£7.50

(B72-50142)

**Brown, Earle**
From here/ by Earle Brown. — New York; London: Universal, 1972. — 4to & obl.4to.
Unpriced

(B72-50966)

**Bruckner, Anton**
Overture in G minor/ by Anton Bruckner; edited by Arthur D. Walker. — London: Eulenburg, 1972. — vii,74p; 8vo.
Miniature score.
£0.75

(B72-50513)

**Debussy, Claude**
Prélude à l'après-midi d'un faune/ by Claude Debussy; herausgegeben von Max Pommer. — Leipzig: Peters; [London]: [Hinrichsen], 1971. — xiii,33p; 4to.
£3.50

(B72-50143)

**Debussy, Claude**
Prélude à l'après-midi d'un faune/ [by] Claude Debussy; herausgegeben von Max Pommer. — Leipzig: Peters; [London]: [Hinrichsen], 1970. — xxix,33p: facsim; 8vo.
£0.75

(B72-50144)

**Debussy, Claude**
[Prélude à l'après-midi d'un faune]. Prelude to 'The afternoon of a faun'/ by Claude Debussy; an authoritative score with Mallarmé's poem, backgrounds and sources, criticism and analysis, edited by William W. Austin. — London: Chappell, 1972. — vi,167p; 8vo.
Miniature score.
Unpriced

(B72-50967)

**Einem, Gottfried von**
Hexameron. Op.37/ by Gottfried von Einem. — London: Boosey and Hawkes, 1971. — [4],96p; 8vo.
Duration 28 1/2 min.
£1.75

(B72-50145)

**Einem, Gottfried von**
Hexameron. Op.37/ by Gottfried von Einem. — London: Boosey and Hawkes, 1972. — 96p; fol.
£5.25

(B72-50514)

**Farkas, Ferenc**
Festive overture = Commemoratio agriae: for orchestra/ by Ferenc Farkas. — London: Boosey and Hawkes, 1972. — 63p; 8vo.
Miniature score.
£1.25

(B72-50968)

**Gelalian, Boghos**
Sept sequences pour orchestre/ [by] Boghos Gelalian. — Leipzig: Peters; [London]: [Hinrichsen], 1971. — 22p; 4to.
£3.00

(B72-50515)

**Halffter, Cristòbal**
Planto por las victimas de la violencia: para conjunto instrumental y transformacion electronica del sonido/ [by] Cristòbal Halffter. — London: Universal, 1971. — 38p; fol.
Unpriced

(B72-50146)

**Henze, Hans Werner**
Heliogabalus imperator: allegoria per musica/ di Hans Werner Henze. — Mainz; London: Schott, 1972. — 120p; 4to.
£4.80

(B72-50969)

**Kelemen, Milko**
Floreal: für Orchester/ [by] Milko Kelemen. — Frankfurt; London: Peters, 1971. — 76p; 8vo.
Miniature score.
£2.40

(B72-50516)

**Kelly, Brian**
Sancho Panza: orchestral overture/ by Brian Kelly. — London: Chappell, 1971. — 4to.
Score (39p.) & 35 parts.
£4.25

(B72-50147)

**Killmayer, Wilhelm**
Sinfonia 1: Fogli per orchestra; [and], Sinfonia 2: Ricordanze/ [by] Wilhelm Killmayer. — Mainz; London: Schott, 1972. — 31p; 8vo.
£1.90

(B72-50970)

**Panufnik, Andrzej**
Kátyń epitaph/ by Andrzej Panufnik. — London: Boosey and Hawkes, 1972. — 9p; 4to.
£1.00

(B72-50517)

**Panufnik, Andrzej**
[Uwertura bohaterska]. Heroic overture/ by Andrzej Panufnik. — London: Boosey and Hawkes, 1972. — 57p; 8vo.
Miniature score.
UNpriced

(B72-50518)

**Panufnik, Andrzej**
[Uwertura bohaterska]. Heroic overture/ by Andrzej Panufnik. — London: Boosey and Hawkes, 1972. — 57p; 8vo.
Miniature score.
Unpriced

(B72-50519)

**Webern, Anton von**
Orchestra pieces, (1913)/ by Anton von Webern; edited by Friedrich Cerha. — New York; London: Boosey and Hawkes, 1972. — 22p; 4to.
'... here published for the first time ...' - Publisher's note.
£2.40

(B72-50520)

**MP — WORKS FOR SOLO INSTRUMENT (S) & ORCHESTRA**
**MPQ — Piano & orchestra**
**Bennett, Richard Rodney**
Party piece: for piano and small orchestra/ by Richard Rodney Bennett. — London: Universal, 1971. — 43p; 4to.
Duration 8 1/2 mins.
Unpriced

(B72-50148)

**Heider, Werner**
Bezirk: für Klavier und Orchester/ [by] Werner Heider. —
Frankfurt; London: Peters, 1971. — 54p; 4to.
Duration 13 min.
£3.50

(B72-50521)

**MPQF — Piano & orchestra. Concertos**
**Prokofiev, Sergei**
[Concerto for piano, no.5, in G major. Op.55]. Piano concerto 5.
Opus 55/ by Serge Prokofieff. — London: Boosey and Hawkes,
1972. — 124p; 8vo.
Duration 29 min.
£1.75

(B72-50971)

**Prokofiev, Sergei**
London: Boosey and Hawkes, 1972. — London: Boosey and
Hawkes, 1972. — 144p; 8vo.
Miniature score.
Unpriced

(B72-50972)

**MPRF — Organ & orchestra. Concertos**
**Genzmer, Harald**
[Concerto for organ]. Konzert für Orgel und Orchester/ [by]
Harald Genzmer. — Frankfurt; London: Peters, 1971. — 102p;
8vo.
Miniature score.
£3.00

(B72-50522)

**MPSFL — Violin & orchestra. Concertinos**
**Berio, Luciano**
[Concertino for violin]. Concertino per clarinetto, violino
concertante, celesta, opera & archi/ [by] Luciano Berio. —
London: Universal, 1972. — 32p; 8vo.
Duration 11 min.
Unpriced

(B72-50973)

**MPSQ — Viola & orchestra**
**Berio, Luciano**
Chemins 2 su sequenza 6: per viola & 9 strumenti/ [by] Luciano
Berio. — London: Universal, 1972. — 39p; 4to.
Unpriced

(B72-50974)

**MPSQF — Viola & orchestra. Concertos**
**Hoffstetter, Roman**
[Concerto for viola in C major]. Konzert, C-Dur: für Viola,
Streicher, 2 Oboen und 2 Hörner/ [by] Roman Hoffstetter;
erstmals herausgegeben und mit Kadenzen versehen von Walter
Lebermann. — Mainz; London: Schott, 1972. — 34p; 4to.
£1.80

(B72-50975)

**Jentzsch, Wilfried**
Concerto espressivo: für Viola und Orchester/ [by] Wilfried
Jentzsch. — Leipzig: Peters; [London]: [Hinrichsen], 1971. — 4to.
Score (56p.) & part.
£4.00

(B72-50523)

**MPSRF — Cello & orchestra. Concertos**
**Schumann, Robert**
[Concerto for cello in A minor. Op.129]. Cello concerto, A minor.
Op.129/ by Robert Schumann; revised by Max Hochkofler. —
London: Eulenburg, 1972. — viii,92p; 8vo.
Miniature score.
£0.80

(B72-50149)

**Zimmermann, Bernd Alois**
[Concerto for cello in the form of a 'pas de trois']. Concerto pour
violoncelle et orchestra en forme de 'pas de trois' [sic]/ by Bernd
Alois Zimmermann. — Mainz; London: Schott, 1972. — 67p; 4to.
Study score.
Unpriced

(B72-50524)

**MPTSF — Guitar & orchestra. Concertos**
**Bennett, Richard Rodney**
Concerto for guitar and chamber ensemble/ by Richard Rodney
Bennett. — London: Universal, 1971. — 64p; 8vo.
Unpriced

(B72-50150)

**MPWSF — Trumpet & orchestra. Concertos**
**Haydn, Michael**
[Concerto for trumpet, strings & basso continuo no.1 in C major].
Concerto no.1 in C major: for solo trumpet, strings and continuo
(bassoon ad lib.)/ by Michael Haydn; edited by E.H. Tarr. —
London: Musica rara, 1971. — 4to.
Score (28p.) & 8 parts.
Unpriced

(B72-50151)

**MPWSG — Trumpet & orchestra. Suites**
**Clarke, Jeremiah**
[Suite for trumpet & orchestra in D major]. Suite in D major: for
trumpet, 2 oboes, bassoon, strings and continuo/ by Jeremiah
Clarke; continuo realisation by R.P. Block; edited by R.L. Minter.
— London: Musica rara, 1971. — 4to.
Score (17p.) & 9 parts.
Unpriced

(B72-50152)

**MR — WORKS FOR CHAMBER ORCHESTRA**
**MR/T — Variations**
**Berkeley, Lennox**
Windsor variations: for chamber orchestra/ by Lennox Berkeley.
— London: Chester, 1972. — 56p; 8vo.
Miniature score.
Unpriced

(B72-50976)

**Schurmann, Gerard**
Variants for small orchestra/ by Gerard Schurmann. —
Sevenoaks: Novello, 1972. — 51p; 8vo.
Duration 16 min.
£3.50

(B72-50977)

**MRE — Symphonies**
**Bach, Johann Christian**
Symphony in B flat major. (Overture, Lucio Silla). Op.18, no.2/
by Johann Christian Bach; edited by Gwilym Beechey. — London:
Eulenburg, 1972. — vi,27p; 8vo.
Miniature score.
£0.40

(B72-50525)

**Cimarosa, Domenico**
[Symphony in D major]. Sinfonia D-dur: für Kammerorchester/
[by] Domenico Cimarosa; zum ersten Mal herausgegeben von
Bernhard Päuler. — Frankfurt; London: Peters, 1971. — 24p; 4to.
£2.00

(B72-50526)

**Paisiello, Giovanni**
[Symphony in D major]. Sinfonia, D-dur: für Kammerorchester/
von Giovanni Paisiello; zum ersten Mal herausgegeben von
Bernhard Päuler. — Frankfurt: Litolff; London: Peters, 1972. —
31p; 4to.
Unpriced

(B72-50978)

**Telemann, Georg Philipp**
[Serenate auf die erste hundertjährige Jubelfeyer der Hamburgische
Löbliche Handlungs-Deputation - Excerpts]. Symphonie: für
Kammerorchester und Basso continuo/ [by] Georg Philip
Telemann; herausgegeben und bearbeitet von Wilhelm
Brückner-Rüggerberg. — Hamburg; London: Simrock, 9172. —
36p; 4to.
Unpriced

(B72-50153)

**MRG — Suites**
**Copland, Aaron**
Appalachian spring. (Ballet for Martha): suite; version for 13
instruments/ by Aaron Copland. — London: Boosey and Hawkes,
1972. — 66p; 4to.
£6.00

(B72-50527)

**Copland, Aaron**
Appalachian spring. (Ballet for Martha): suite; version for 13
instruments/ by Aaron Copland. — London: Boosey and Hawkes,
1972. — 66p; 8vo.
Miniature score.
£1.25

(B72-50528)

**Leighton, Kenneth**
Veris gratia. Opus 9: suite for oboe, cello & strings/ by Kenneth
Leighton. — Sevenoaks: Novello, 1972. — 67p; 4to.
£1.60

(B72-50529)

**MRH — Dances**
**Cherubini, Luigi**
Contredanses: für Orchester/ [by] Luigi Cherubini; zum ersten
Mal herausgegeben von Claudio Gallico und Sergio Albertini. —
Frankfurt; London: Peters, 1971. — 51p; 4to.
£3.00

(B72-50530)

**MRJ — Miscellaneous works**
**Bedford, David**
Trona/ by David Bedford. — London: Universal, 1971. — 22p;
obl.8vo.
Unpriced

(B72-50154)

**Birtwistle, Harrison**
Verses for ensembles: [for 13 woodwind, brass and percussion instruments]/ by Harrison Birtwistle. — London: Universal, 1972. — 115p; 8vo.
Duration 28 min.
Unpriced

(B72-50979)

**Brown, Earle**
Event - Synergy 2: [for 19 wind and string instruments]/ by Earle Brown. — London: Universal, 1972. — 12sh; 4to.
Unpriced

(B72-50980)

**Morgan, Robert**
L'Après - midi du Dracoula for sound - producing instruments; [and], Elegant journey with stopping points of interest: for chamber orchestra or percussion ensemble/ by Robert Morgan. — Mainz: Ars viva; [London]: [Schott], 1972. — 2p.; 4to.
£2.00
*Primary classification LJ*

(B72-50499)

**Musgrave, Thea**
Night music: for chamber orchestra/ by Thea Musgrave. — London: Chester, 1972. — 74p; 8vo.
Duration 18 min.
Unpriced

(B72-50531)

**Standford, Patric**
Nocturne: for small orchestra/ by Patric Standford. — Sevenoaks: Novello, 1971. — 11p; 4to.
£0.60

(B72-50155)

**Standford, Patric**
Notte: for chamber orchestra/ by Patric Standford. — Sevenoaks: Novello, 1972. — 40p; 4to.
£1.25

(B72-50981)

## MS — WORKS FOR LIGHT ORCHESTRA
### MSHVKK — Light orchestra. Rumbas
**Ford, Les**
Frisky/ by Les Ford. — London: Feldman, 1971. — 4to.
Score (7p.) & 11 parts.
Unpriced

(B72-50156)

### MSHW — Waltzes
**Fucik, Julius**
Frühlingsbotschaft: Konzertwalzer/ von J. Fucik [und] Reisinger. — Cologne; London: Bosworth, 1972. — 8vo.
Piano-conductor (5p.) & 26 parts.
£0.50

(B72-50982)

### MSJ — Miscellaneous works
**Pearson, Johnny**
Sleepy shores/ by Johnny Pearson; arranged by Gordon Rees. — London: Keith Prowse Music, 1971. — 8vo.
Unpriced

(B72-50157)

## NU — WIND, STRINGS & KEYBOARD
### NUPNQ — Woodwind, strings & keyboard. Sextets
**Bland, William**
Like a mad animal ...: for double bass, piano, violin, viola, alto flute and clarinet/ by William Bland. — London: Yorke, 1972. — 6pt; 4to.
Unpriced

(B72-50983)

**Durkó, Zsolt**
Fire music: sextet for flute (doubling piccolo and alto flute in G), clarinet in B flat (doubling bass clarinet-B flat), piano, violin, viola and violoncello/ [by] Zsolt Durkó. — London: Boosey and Hawkes, 1972. — 35p; 4to.
£2.50

(B72-50984)

### NUPNQHJN — Woodwind, string & keyboard sextets. Chaconnes
**Telemann, Georg Philipp**
[Suite for tenor oboe, two violins & basso continuo, with Chaconne for two flutes, tenor oboe, two violins & basso continuo in F minor. *Excerpts]*. Chaconne/ by Georg Philipp Telemann; edited by Frans Brüggen for two recorders, two violins, viola and continuo. — London: Schott, 1971. — 4to.
Score (8p.) & 6 parts.
£1.60

(B72-50158)

### NUPNSE — Woodwind, string & keyboard. Quartets. Sonatas
**Fasch, Johann Friedrich**
[Sonata for flute, violin, bassoon & basso continuo in D major]. Sonata in D major for flute, violin, bassoon and basso continuo/ by Johann Friedrich Fasch; first edition edited by Reinhard Gerlach. — Cassel; London: Bärenreiter, 1970. — 4to.
Score (20p.) & 4 parts.
£1.40

(B72-50532)

### NURNT — Flute, strings & keyboard. Trios
**Okumara, Hajime**
Jahresanfang in Japan: Trio für Flöte, Violoncello und Klavier (1969)/ [by] Hajime Okumara. — Regensburg: Bosse; [London]: [Eulenburg], 1971. — 4to.
Score (20p.) & 2 parts.
£2.25

(B72-50533)

**Pleyel, Ignaz Joseph**
[Trio for piano, flute and cello. Op.29]. Grand trio: for piano, flute and cello/ by Ignace Pleyel; edited by Georg Merwein. — London: Musica rara, 1971. — 4to.
Unpriced

(B72-50159)

### NUSRNS — Descant recorder, strings & keyboard. Quartets
**Chagrin, Francis**
Preludes for four: for treble recorder (or flute), violin, cello and harpsichord (or piano)/ by Francis Chagrin. — Sevenoaks: Novello, 1972. — 4to.
Score (21p.) & 3 parts.
£1.50

(B72-50534)

### NUSSNTE — Treble recorder, string & keyboard trio. Sonatas
**Handel, George Frideric**
[Trio sonata for treble recorder, violin & basso continuo in C minor. Op.2, no.1]. Trio sonata in C minor: for treble recorder, violin (two violins) AND BASSO CONTINUO/ by Georg Friedrich Händel; edited by Siegfried Flesch. — Cassel; London: Nagel, 1971. — 4to.
Score (15p.) & 3 parts.
£1.15

(B72-50535)

**Handel, George Frideric**
[Trio sonata for treble recorder, violin & basso continuo in F major. Op.2, no.4]. Trio sonata in F major: for treble recorder, violin (two violins) and basso continuo/ by Georg Friedrich Händel; edited by Siegfried Flesch. — Cassel; London: Nagel, 1971. — 4to.
Score (12.) & 3 parts.
£1.00

(B72-50536)

### NUVNT — Clarinet, strings & keyboard. Trios
**Khachaturian, Aram**
[Trio for clarinet, violin & piano (1932)]. Trio für Klarinette, Violine und Klavier (1932)/ [by] Aram Chatschaturjan. — Leipzig: Peters; [London]: [Hinrichsen], 1971. — 4to.
Score (27p.) & 2 parts.
£2.00

(B72-50537)

**Muczynski, Robert**
Fantasy trio. Op.26: for clarinet, cello and piano/ by Robert Muczynski. — New York: Schirmer; [London]: [Chappell], 1971. — 4to.
Score (24p.) & 2 parts.
Unpriced

(B72-50160)

### NUVNTE — Clarinet, strings & keyboard. Trios. Sonatas
**McCabe, John**
Sonata for clarinet, cello & piano (1969)/ by John McCabe. — Sevenoaks: Novello, 1972. — 4to.
Score (21p.) & 2 parts.
£1.50

(B72-50161)

### NUXSNTK/LE — Trumpet, strings & keyboard trios. Arrangements. Sonatas
**Gabrielli, Domenico**
[Sonata for trumpet, cello & string orchestra in D major]. Sonata no.4 in D: for trumpet, strings and basso continuo/ by Domenico Gabrielli; edited by Edward H. Tarr. — London: Musica rara, 1972. — 4to.
The numbering of this work is the editor's. — Reduction for trumpet, cello and piano score (7p.) & 2 parts.
£1.00

(B72-50985)

**NUXTNTH — Horn, strings & keyboard. Trios. Dances**
McCabe, John
  Dance-movements: for horn, violin & piano/ by John McCabe. —
  Sevenoaks: Novello, 1972. — 4to.
  Score (56p.) & 2 parts.
  £2.25

(B72-50162)

**NUXUNSE — Trombone, strings & keyboard quartet. Sonatas**
Bertali, Antonio
  [Sonata for two violins, trombone & organ continuo, no.1, in D
  minor]. Sonata á 3, no.1 in D minor: for 2 violins, trombone and
  organ continuo/ by Antonio Bertali; [edited by] John D. Hill,
  Robert Paul Block. — London: Musica rara, 1971. — 4to.
  Score (12p.) & 4 parts.
  £1.50

(B72-50986)

Bertali, Antonio
  [Sonata for two violins, trombone & organ continuo, no.2 in D
  minor]. Sonata á 3, no.2 in D minor: for 2 violins, trombone and
  organ continuo/ by Antonio Bertali; [edited by] John D. Hill,
  Robert Paul Block. — London: Musica rara, 1971. — 4to.
  Score (12p.) & 4 parts.
  £1.50

(B72-50987)

**NV — WIND & STRINGS**
**NVRNS — Flute & strings. Quartets**
Danzi, Franz
  [Quartet for flute & strings in D major. Op.56, no.1]. Quartet in
  D major: for flute, violin, viola and cello/ by Franz Danzi; [edited
  by] David Lasocki. — London: Musica rara, 1972. — 4pt; 4to.
  The opus number refers to the André edition.
  Unpriced

(B72-50988)

Pleyel, Ignaz
  [Quartet for flute & strings in F major. Op.17, no. 2]. Quartet in
  F major. Op.17, no.2: for flute, violin, viola and cello/ by Ignace
  Pleyel; [edited by] David Lasocki. — London: Musica rara, 1972.
  — 4pt; 4to.
  The opus number refers to the Preston edition.
  Unpriced

(B72-50989)

**NVRNTE — Flute & strings. Trios. Sonatas**
Debussy, Claude
  Sonata for flute, viola & harp/ by Claude Debussy; edited by
  Erich List, harp fingering by Margarete Kluvetarsch. — Leipzig:
  Peters; [London]: [Hinrichsen], 1970. — 4to.
  Score (45p) & 2 parts.
  £2.00

(B72-50539)

**NVRNTG — Flute & strings trio. Suites**
Papastavrou, Krinió
  'St Nicholas': suite for flute, viola & harp/ by Krinió
  Papastravrou. — Ipswich (Stackwood Cottage, Monks Eleigh,
  Ipswich): Krinió Papastavrou, 1967. — 21p; 8vo.
  Miniature score.
  Unpriced

(B72-50540)

**NVSNTG — Recorder & strings. Trios. Suites**
Gubby, Roy
  Suite for three recorders: treble (tenor 1), tenor 2 and bass (or
  cello)/ by Roy Gubby. — London: Boosey and Hawkes, 1972. —
  12p; 4to.
  Duration 7 min.
  £0.50
  Primary classification VSNTG

(B72-50746)

**NVVNR — Clarinet & strings. Quintets**
Mozart, Wölfgang Amadeus
  [Allegro for clarinet, two violins, viola & cello in B flat
  major.K.Anh.91]. Allegro in B flat.K.Anh.91: fragment of a
  quintet for clarinet, two violins, viola and violoncello/ by
  Wolfgang Amadeus Mozart; completed by Robert D. Levin. —
  Cassel; London: Nagel, 1970. — 4to.
  Score (18p.) & 5 parts.
  £2.00

(B72-50541)

**NVVNS — Clarinet & strings. Quartets**
Vanhal, Jan
  [Quartet for clarinet, viola & cello in F major]. Quartet in F: for
  clarinet, violin and cello/ by J.B. Wanhall; edited by Georgina
  Dobrée. — London: Musica rara, 1971. — 4pt; 4to.
  Unpriced

(B72-50163)

**NVXPNR — Brass & strings. Quintets**
Brown, Earle
  Times five: [for flute, trombone, harp, violin, cello and 4 channels
  of tape sound]/ by Earle Brown. — New York; London:
  Universal, 1972. — 2p; 4to.
  Unpriced

(B72-50990)

**NWNR — Wind & keyboard. Quintets**
Herzogenberg, Heinrich von
  [Quintet for oboe, clarinet, horn, bassoon & piano in E flat major.
  Op.43]. Quintet. Op.43: for oboe, clarinet, horn, bassoon &
  pianoforte/ by Heinrich von Herzogenberg. — London: Musica
  rara, 1971. — 4to.
  Score (72p.) & 4 parts.
  Unpriced

(B72-50164)

**NWNRG — Quintets, Suites**
Fischer, Johann Caspar Ferdinand
  [Le Journal de printemps. - Suites 5, 6]. Suites for four strings or
  wind instruments and basso continuo, nos.5 in G major, 6 in F
  major/ by Johann Caspar Ferdinand Fischer; edited by Waldemar
  Wohl. — Cassel; London: Bärenreiter, 1971. — 4to.
  Score (24p.) & 5 parts.
  £1.50
  Primary classification NXNRG

(B72-50545)

**NWNSF — Woodwind & keyboard quartets. Concertos**
Vivaldi, Antonio
  [Concerto for treble recorder in G minor. P.402]. Concerto in G
  minor: for flute, (clarinet), oboe and bassoon [or] treble recorder,
  oboe and basso continuo ad lib/ by Antonio Vivaldi; [edited by]
  David Lasocki, realization of the basso continuo part by Robert
  Paul Block. — London: Musica rara, 1971. — 4to.
  Score (16p.) & 4 parts.
  Unpriced

(B72-50165)

**NWPNT — Woodwind & keyboard. Trios**
Beethoven, Ludwig van
  Trio for piano, flute & bassoon in G major. [K-H37]/ by Ludwig
  van Beethoven. — London: Eulenburg, 1972. — v,32p; 8vo.
  Miniature score.
  £0.60

(B72-50166)

Donizetti, Gaetano
  [Trio for flute, bassoon & piano in F major]. Trio: für Flöte,
  Fagott und Klavier/ von Gaetano Donizetti; zum ersten Mal
  herausgegeben von Bernhard Päuler. — Frankfurt; London:
  Peters, 1972. — 4to.
  Score (23p.) & 2 parts.
  Unpriced

(B72-50991)

Kiesewetter, Peter
  Szenen: für Flöte, Oboe und Klavier/ [by] Peter Kiesewetter. —
  Regensburg: Bosse; [London]: [Bärenreiter], 1971. — fol.
  Score (20p.) & part. — The parts for flute and oboe are printed in score.
  £4.75

(B72-50542)

**NWPNTE — Woodwind & keyboard trios. Sonatas**
Jones, Kelsey
  Sonata da camera: for flute, oboe and harpsichord/ by Kelsey
  Jones. — London: Peters, 1972. — 4to.
  Score (28p.) & 2 parts.
  Unpriced

(B72-50992)

**NWSRH — Descant recorders & keyboard. Dances**
Dexter, Harry
  Scottish street dance: descant recorders and/or melody
  instruments and piano/ by Harry Dexter. — London: Ashdown,
  1972. — 3p; 4to.
  This piano part can be used to support the strings in the orchestral version.
  Unpriced

(B72-50543)

**NWXP — BRASS & KEYBOARD**
**NWXPNRE — Brass & keyboard quintet. Sonatas**
Bertali, Antonio
  [Sonatas for brass quintet & basso continuo, nos.1-6]. Six sonatas:
  for 2 trumpets, 3 trombones and continuo (2 trumpets, horn, 2
  trombones and continuo)/ by Antonio Bertali; [edited by] John D.
  Hill, Robert Paul Block. — London: Musica rara, 1972. — 4to.
  Score (25p.) & 5 parts.
  Unpriced

(B72-50993)

**NWXPNSE — Brass & keyboard quartets. Sonatas**
Legrenzi, Giovanni
[Sonata for two trumpets, bassoon & string orchestra, in A minor.
Lib.3. Op.8, 'La Buscha']. Sonata, 'La Buscha': for 2 trumpets
(cornetti), bassoon, and strings/ by Giovanni Legrenzi; [edited by]
Robert Block. — London: Musica rara, 1972. — 4to.
Reduction for two trumpets, bassoon & piano. — Score (8p.) & 5 parts.
£1.00

(B72-50994)

**NWXPNSK/LF — Brass & keyboard quartets. Concertos**
Biscogli, Francesco
[Concerto for trumpet, oboe, bassoon & string orchestra].
Concerto for trumpet, oboe, bassoon, violins and continuo/ by
Francesco Biscogli; [edited by] Michael Talbot. — London:
Musica rara, 1972. — 4to.
Reduction for trumpet, oboe, bassoon & piano. — Score (47p.) & 4 parts.
Unpriced

(B72-50995)

**NX — STRINGS & KEYBOARD**
**NXNQE — Sextets. Sonatas**
Telemann, Georg Philipp
[Sonata for two violins, two violas, cello & harpsichord in F
minor]. Sonata in F minor for two violins, two violas, violoncello
and harpsichord (double bass ad lib)/ by Georg Philipp Telemann;
edited by Klaus Hofmann. — Cassel; London: Bärenreiter, 1971.
— 25p; 4to.
£1.50

(B72-50544)

**NXNRG — Quintets. Suites**
Fischer, Johann Caspar Ferdinand
[Le Journal de printemps. - Suites 5, 6]. Suites for four strings or
wind instruments and basso continuo, nos.5 in G major, 6 in F
major/ by Johann Caspar Ferdinand Fischer; edited by Waldemar
Wohl. — Cassel; London: Bärenreiter, 1971. — 4to.
Score (24p.) & 5 parts.
£1.50
*Also classified at NWNRG*

(B72-50545)

**NXNS — Quartets**
Jacob, Gordon
Quartet for piano and strings/ by Gordon Jacob. — Sevenoaks:
Novello, 1972. — 4to.
Score (64p.) & 3 parts.
£2.75

(B72-50546)

**NXNT — Trios**
Brown, Earle
Music for violin, cello & piano/ by Earle Brown. — New York;
[London]: Universal, 1972. — 4to.
Score (7p.) & 2 parts.
Unpriced

(B72-50996)

Donizetti, Gaetano
[Trio for strings & piano in E flat major]. Trio: für Violine,
Violoncello und Klavier/ von Gaetano Donizetti; zum ersten Mal
herausgegeben von Bernhard Päuler. — Frankfurt; London:
Peters, 1972. — 4to.
Score (20p.) & 2 parts.
Unpriced

(B72-50997)

Handel, Georg Frideric
[Sonatas for two violins & basso continuo. Op.5 nos.7,1]. Two
triosonatas for two violins and basso continuo/ by Georg
Friedrich Händel; edited by Siegfried Flesch, continuo realization
by Max Schneider. — Cassel; London: Nagel, 1970. — 4to.
Score (24p.) & 3 parts.
£1.25

(B72-50547)

Zoephel, Klaus
[Trio for violin, cello & piano]. Trio für Violine, Violoncello und
Klavier/ [by] Klaus Zoephel. — Leipzig: Peters; [London]:
[Hinrichsen], 1971. — 4to.
Score (42p.) & 2 parts.
£2.00

(B72-50548)

**NXNTE — Trios. Sonatas**
Handel, George Frideric
[Triosonata for two violins & basso continuo in G minor. Op.2,
no. 8]. Trio sonata in G minor: for two violins and basso
continuo/ by Georg Friedrich Händel; edited by Siegfried Flesch.
— Cassel; London: Nagel, 1970. — 4to.
Score (16p.) & 3 parts.
£1.00

(B72-50549)

Telemann, Georg Philipp
[Trio sonata for violin, viola da gamba & harpsichord in G
major]. Sonate, G-dur: f'ur Violine, Viola da gamba (Viola) und
Cembalo/ [by] Georg Philipp Telemann; herausgegeben von
Karlheinz Schultz-Hauser. — Leipzig: Peters; [London]:
[Hinrichsen], 1970. — 4to.
Score (12p.) & 3 parts.
£1.60

(B72-50550)

**NYD — WIND, STRINGS, KEYBOARD & PERCUSSION**
**NYDPNP — Woodwind, strings, keyboard & percussion. Septets**
Feldman, Morton
The viola in my life/ by Morton Feldman. — New York;
[London]: Universal. —
2: Flute, clarinet, violin, viola (solo), cello, piano, percussion. — 1972. —
14p; 8vo.
Unpriced

(B72-50998)

Komorous, Rudolf
York: per flauto, oboe (ossia tromba), fagotto, mandolina,
pianoforte, triangolo e contrabasso/ di Rudolf Komorous. —
London: Universal, 1972. — 15p; obl.4to.
Unpriced

(B72-50999)

**NYDRNQ — Flute, strings, keyboard & percussion. Sextets**
Feldman, Morton
The viola in my life/ by Morton Feldman. — New York;
[London]: Universal. —
1: Flute, violin, viola (solo), cello, piano, percussion. — 1972. — 10p; 8vo.
Unpriced

(B72-51000)

**NYDSRNM — Descant recorders, string, keyboard & percussion.**
Nonets
Ford, Les
The clockshop/ by Les Ford. — London: Feldman, 1971. — 4to.
Score (8p.) & 5 parts.
Unpriced

(B72-50167)

**NYE — WIND, STRINGS & PERCUSSION**
**NYENN — Octets**
Durkó Zsolt
Iconography no.2: for horn solo and chamber ensemble/ by Zsolt
Durkó. — London: Boosey and Hawkes, 1972. — 22p; 8vo.
£1.50

(B72-51001)

**NYF — WIND, KEYBOARD & PERCUSSION**
**NYFR — Flute, keyboard & percussion**
Lawson, Peter
Valentia extramaterial: flute, piano, 2 or 4 percussion/ by Peter
Lawson. — London: Peters, 1972. — 21p; 4to.
Duration 8 min.
£1.50

(B72-50551)

**NYFSRNQ — Descant recorder, keyboard & percussion. Sextets**
Braun, Gerhard
5 Miniaturen: für Sopranblockflöte, Klavier und Schlagzeug/ [by]
Gerhard Braun. — Regensburg: Bosse; [London]: [Bärenreiter],
1970. — 11ff.; obl.fol.
With a leaf of instructions.
£1.85

(B72-50538)

**PWP — KEYBOARD SOLOS**
**PWP/AY(XD126) — Collections, 1500-1625**
Speckner, Anna Barbara
Aus alten Spielbüchern: 32 Tänze und Stücke aus dem 16, und 17.
Jahrhundert, für Tasteninstrumente/ gesetzt von Anna Barbara
Speckner. — Mainz; London: Schott, 1972. — 52p; 8vo.
£1.20

(B72-51002)

**PWP/T — Miscellaneous works**
Mozart, Wolfgang Amadeus
[Variations for piano. K. 24 & 25]. Eight variations in G.K. 24;
[with], Seven variations in D. K 25 for piano/ by Wolfgang
Amadeus Mozart; edited by Kurt von Fischer. — Cassel; London:
Nage, 1970. — 14p; 4to.
£0.50

(B72-50552)

**PWP/Y — Fugues**
Bach, Johann Sebastian
Das wohltemperierte Klavier. S.846-893/ von Johann Sebastian
Bach; neue Urtext-Ausgabe nach den Quellen von Alfred Kreutz.
— Leipzig: Peters; [London]: [Hinrichsen]. —
Miniature score.
Band 1. — 1971. — 134p; 8vo.
Unpriced

(B72-51003)

Band 2. — 1971. — 151p; 8vo.
Unpriced

(B72-51004)

**PWP/Y/AYE(XF) — Fugues. Collections. Germany, 1700**
**Doflein, Erich**
Little fugues for piano with a preparatory course in fugal playing:
27 short and easy fugues by German composers around 1700/
edited by Erich Doflein. — Enlarged edition. — Cassel; London:
Bärenreiter, 1971. — 24p; obl.8vo.
£0.65

(B72-50553)

**PWPJ — Miscellaneous works**
**Bach, Johann Sabastian**
Fifteen 2-part inventions. S.772-786/ by J.S. Bach; urtext, [edited
by] Ludwig Landshoff. — New York; London: Peters, 1972. —
31p; 4to.
£0.45

(B72-50554)

**Bach, Johann Sebastian**
Fifteen 3-part inventions (sinfonias). S.787-801/ by J.S. Bach;
urtext, [edited by] Ludwig Landshoff. — New York; London:
Peters, 1972. — 31p; 4to.
£0.45

(B72-50555)

**Bach, Wilhelm Friedemann**
[Fantasias for keyboard]. Klavier fantasien/ by Wilhelm
Friedemann Bach; herausgegeben von Peter Schlenning. — Mainz;
London: Schott, 1972. — 71p; 4to.
£2.00

(B72-50556)

**Boyce, William**
Ten voluntaries: for the organ or harpsichord/ by William Boyce;
a facsimile reproduction of the eighteenth-century edition. —
London: Oxford University Press, 1972. — 25p; obl.fol.
ISBN 0 19 375302 2 : £1.00

(B72-50557)

**Schulz, Johann Abraham Peter**
[Six diverses pièces. Op.1, nos.2-3, 5-6]. Vier Stücke: fur Klavier
oder Cembalo/ by Johann Abraham Schulz; nach den Erstdruck
herausgegeben von Walter Frickert. — Leipzig: Peters; [London]:
[Hinrichsen], 1971. — 23p; 4to.
£1.75

(B72-50558)

**Selected works for keyboard instruments**, *by Johann Joseph Fux,*
*edited by Friedrich W. Riedel*
[Selections]. Cassel; London: Nagel, 1972. — 31p; 4to.
£1.15

(B72-50559)

**PWPPR — Right hand**
**Berberian, Cathy**
Morsicat(h)y: per la mano destra/ [by] Cathy Berberian. —
London: Universal, 1972. — 11p; 4to.
With an illustration of a mosquito, - Pages 10 and 11 contain blank music
staves. — 'The author, on receipt of the coupon to be found in the envelope
in the back cover, will write a personal message to the pianist (or
harpsichordist)'. — Publisher's note.
Unpriced

(B72-50168)

**Q — PIANO**
**Q/AF — Exercises**
**Lerche, Juliane**
New compendium of piano technique/ by Juliane Lerche. —
Leipzig: Peters; [London]: [Hinrichsen]. —
Book 2, which appeared in the 1971 annual volume, (B71-50448) was
incorrectly entered under the name of Lerchner.
Book 3: Alternation of the hands. — 1971. — 4to.
£1.25

(B72-50560)

**Pointon, Malcolm**
8, 4, 5: eight pieces in the five-finger position for beginner pianists
of any age/ by Malcolm Pointon. — London: Boosey and
Hawkes, 1972. — 8p; 4to.
£0.40

(B72-50169)

**Schmitt, Aloys**
[Exercises préparatoires aux 60 études. Op. 16. - *Excerpts].*
Preparatory exercises, Op. 16: for piano/ by Aloys Schmitt. —
London: Chappell, 1972. — 16p; 4to.
£0.45

(B72-51005)

**Wendt, Wolfgang**
Studies for the piano/ edited by Wolfgang Wendt. — Leipzig;
London: Peters. —
Book 1: Basic kinds of touch: portato-legato-staccato. — 1971. — 60p; 4to.
—
Unpriced

(B72-51006)

**Q/AL — Examinations**
**Associated Board of the Royal Schools of Music**
Pianoforte examinations, 1973/ Associated Board of the Royal
Schools of Music. — London: Associated Board of the Royal
Schools of Music. —
Grade 1: Lists A and B (primary). — 1972. — 11p; 4to.
£0.35

(B72-51007)

**Associated Board of the Royal Schools of Music**
Pianoforte examinations 1973/ Associated Board of the rRoyal
Schools of Music. — London: Associated Board of the Royal
Schools of Music. —
Grade 2: lists A and B (elementary). — 1972. — 14p; 4to.
£0.35

(B72-51008)

**Associated Board of the Royal Schools of Music**
Pianoforte examinations, 1973/ Associated Board of the Royal
Schools of Music. — London: Associated Board of the Royal
Schools of Music. —
Grade 3: Lists A and B (transitional). — 1972. — 14p; 4to.
£0.35

(B72-51009)

Grade 4: Lists A and B lower. — 1972. — 12p; 4to.
£0.35

(B72-51010)

Grade 5: List A (higher). — 1972. — 11p; 4to.
£0.35

(B72-51011)

Grade 5: List B (higher). — 1972. — 13p; 4to.
£0.35

(B72-51012)

Grade 6: List A (intermediate). — 1972. — 18p; 4to.
£0.35

(B72-51013)

Grade 6: List B (intermediate). — 1972. — 17p; 4to.
£0.35

(B72-51014)

Grade 7: List A (advanced). — 1972. — 22p; 4to.
£0.35

(B72-51015)

Grade 7: List B (advanced). — 1972. — 19p; 4to.
£0.35

(B72-51016)

**Q/EG — Sight reading**
**Keilmann, Wilhelm**
[Ich spiele vom Blatt]. Introduction to sight reading: at the piano
or other keyboard instrument/ by Wilhelm Keilmann. —
Frankfurt: Litolff; London: Peters, 1972. — 58p; 4to.
Unpriced

(B72-51017)

**Q/EG/AL — Sight reading. Examinations**
**London College of Music**
Examinations in pianoforte playing and singing sight reading tests,
as set throughout 1971: Grades I-VIII and diplomas. — London:
Ashdown, 1972. — 15p; 4to.
£0.30
*Also classified at K/EG/AL*

(B72-50170)

**QNS — FOUR PIANOS**
**Hampton, Calvin**
Catch-up: for four pianos or tape recorder and two pianos/ by
Colvin Hampton. — New York; London: Peters, 1970. — 2pt;
4to.
Comprises two versions published together.
£1.25

(B72-50561)

**QNU — TWO PIANOS, 4 HANDS**
**Konietzny, Heinrich**
Toccatina for two pianos/ by Heinrich Konietzny. — Hamburg
(London): Simrock, 1972. — 10p; 4to.
Unpriced

(B72-50562)

**Boulez, Pierre**
Structures: 2 pianos à 4 mains/ de Pierre Boulez. — London:
Universal. —
Livre 2: Chapitre 1 - Première pièce - Deuxième pièce - Textes 1,2,3 - Textes
4, 5, 6- Encart 1-4. — 1967. — 9 nos; 4to.
The pieces which constitute Livre 2, (nine in all), are published individually
in a folder.
Unpriced

(B72-51018)

**Vorisek, Jan Hugo**
Grand overture in C minor: for two pianos. Op. 16/ by Jan
Vaclav Vorisek; edited by Olga Zuckerova. — Cassel; London:
B¨arenreiter, 1971. — 32p; 4to.
£1.50

(B72-50563)

## QNUF — Concertos
**Sitsky, Larry**
Concerto for two solo pianos/ by Larry Sitsky. — London:
Boosey and Hawkes, 1971. — 45p; 4to.
Two copies.
£2.50

(B72-50171)

## QNUK/LF — Arrangements, Concertos
**Bennett, Richard Rodney**
[Concerto for piano]. Piano concerto/ by Richard Rodney
Bennett; arrangement for 2 pianos, 4 hands by the composer. —
London: Universal, 1971. — 77p; 4to.
Unpriced

(B72-50172)

**Mozart, Wolfgang Amadeus**
[Concerto for piano, no.17, in G major. K.453]. Piano concerto, G
major, no.17. K.453/ by W.A. Mozart; with the composer's
cadenzas; edited with the orchestral accompaniment arranged for a
second piano by Thomas A. Johnson. — London: Peters, 1972. —
70p; 4to.
Unpriced

(B72-51019)

**Williamson, Malcolm**
[Concerto for piano, no.3]. Concerto no.3: for piano and
orchestra/ by Malcolm Williamson. — London: Weinberger, 1972.
— 96p; 4to.
Reduction for two pianos.
Unpriced

(B72-51020)

## QNV — ONE PIANO, 4 HANDS
**Johnson, Thomss Arnold**
The vicar of Bray: piano duet/ arranged by Thomas A. Johnson.
— London: Bosworth, 1972. — 5p; 4to.
Unpriced

(B72-51021)

**Weber, Carl Maria von,** *Freiherr*
[Selections]. Twelve easy pieces for piano duet. Op.3 and Op.10/
by Carl Maria von Weber; edited by Jurgen Kindermann. —
Cassell; London: Barenreiter, 1970. — 61p; obl.fol.
£1.25

(B72-50564)

**Debussy, Claude**
[Children's corner - Excerpts]. Golliwog's cake-walk/ by Claude
Debussy; arranged for piano duet by Thomas A. Johnson. —
London: Peters, 1972. — 9p; 4to.
Unpriced

(B72-51022)

## QNVK — Arrangements
**Britten, Benjamin**
[Simple symphony. Op.4. *Excerpts*]. Playful pizzicato/ by
Benjamin Britten; arranged for piano duet by Howard Ferguson.
— London: Oxford University Press, 1972. — 12p; 4to.
ISBN 0 19 372375 1 : £0.50

(B72-50173)

**Warlock, Peter**
[Cod-pieces. Liber 1. - *Excerpts*]. Two cod-pieces. [Nos.3.4]/ by
Peter Warlock; arranged for piano duet by Fred Tomlinson. —
London: Thames, 1972. — 9p; 4to.
Contents: Beethoven's binge. — The old codger.
Unpriced

(B72-50174)

## QNVK/AHVL — Arrangements. Sarabandes
**Britten, Benjamin**
[Simple symphony. Op.4. *Excerpts*]. Sentimental sarabande/ by
Benjamin Britten; arranged for piano duet by Howard Ferguson.
— London: Oxford University Press, 1971. — 11p; 4to.
ISBN 0 19 372374 3 : £0.50

(B72-50175)

## QP — PIANO SOLOS
## QP/AY — Collections
**[Wickham, E H ]**
Golden classics: a selection of the world's best loved classics for
piano/ [compiled by E.H.W.]. — London: Keith Prowse, 1972. —
192p; 4to.
Unpriced

(B72-50565)

## QP/AZ — Collected works of individual composers
**Liszt, Franz**
[Selections]. Piano works/ by Franz Liszt. — Cassel; London:
B¨arenreiter. —
[Vol.1]: Studies 1/ edited by Zoltan Gardonyi, Istvan Szelenyi. — 1970. —
116p; 4to.
Contents: ´Etudes d'ex´ecution transcendante.
£2.00

(B72-50566)

**Liszt, Franz**
[Selections]. Piano works/ by Franz, Liszt. — Cassel; London:
Bärenreiter. —
[Vol.2]: Studies 2/ edited by Zoltán Gardonyi, Istvan Szelenyi. — 1971. —
117p; 4to.
Contents: Trois 'etudes de concert' - Trois caprices poètiques - Ab irato -
Two concert studies-Grandes études de Paganini.
£2.00

(B72-50567)

## QP/AZ — Complete works of individual composers
**Brahms, Johannes**
Complete shorter works for solo piano/ by Johannes Brahms;
edited by Eusebius Mandyczewski. — New York: Dover
Publications; London: Constable, 1972. — 180p; 4to.
Unabridged republication of volume 14 of the collection Johannes Brahms;
Sämtliche Werke; Ausgabe der Gesellschaft der Musikfreunde in Wien,
published Breitkopf und Härtel, 1928. Translation into English of
Revisionsbericht and table of contents. — Contents: Ops.4,10,39,79,116-119.
£2.00

(B72-51023)

**Brahms, Johannes**
Complete sonatas and variations for solo piano/ by Johannes
Brahms; edited by Eusebius Mandyczewski. — New York: Dover
Publications; London: Constable, 1972. — 178p; 4to.
Unabridged republication of volume 13 of the collection Johannes Brahms;
Sämtliche Werke; Ausgabe der Gesellschaft der Musikfreunde in Wien,
published Leipzig: Breitkopf und Härtel, 1928. Translation into English of
Revisionbericht and table of contents.
£2.00

(B72-51024)

**Brahms, Johannes**
Complete transcriptions, cadenzas and exercises for solo piano/ by
Johannes Brahms; edited by Eusebius Mandyczewski. — New
York: Dover Publications; London: Constable, 1972. — 178p; 4to.
Unabridged republication of volume 15 of the collection Johannes Brahms;
Sämtliche Werke; Ausgabe der Gesellschaft der Musikfreunde in Wien,
published Leipzig: Breitkopf und Härtel, 1928. Translation into English of
Revisionsbericht and table of contents.
£2.00

(B72-51025)

## QP/T — Variations
**Burkhard, Willy**
Variationen über ein Volkslied. Op.8: für Klavier/ [by] Willy
Burkhard. — Cassel; London: Bärenreiter, 1971. — 12p; 4to.
£1.00

(B72-50568)

**Coulthard, Jean**
Variations on Bach: for piano/ by Jean Coulthard. — Sevenoaks:
Novello, 1972. — 4to.
£0.50

(B72-50569)

**Leighton, Kenneth**
Six studies: study-variations. Op.56: for piano/ by Kenneth
Leighton. — Sevenoaks: Novello, 1972. — 37p; 4to.
£0.90

(B72-51026)

**Mozart, Wolfgang Amadeus**
Twelve variations in C major, 'Ah, vous dirai - je maman', K.265:
for piano/ by Wolfgang Amadeus Mozart; edited by Kurt von
Fischer. — Cassel; London: Nagel, 1970. — 11p; 4to.
£0.35

(B72-50570)

**Mozart, Wolfgang Amadeus**
[Variations for piano in G major, Unser dummer Pöbel meint. K.
455]. Ten variations in G major, 'Unser dummer Pöbel meint. K.
455: for piano/ by Wolfgang Amadeus Mozart; edited by Kurt
von Fischer. — Cassel; London: Nagel, 1970. — 15p; 4to.
£0.40

(B72-50571)

**Standford, Patric**
Variations for piano. Opus 23/ by Patric Standford. — Sevenoaks:
Novello, 1972. — 8p; 4to.
£0.50

(B72-51027)

**QP/Y — Fugues**
**Burkhard, Willy**
Drei Prʾaludien und Fugen. Op.16: fʾur Klavier/ [by] Willy
Burkhard. — Cassel; London: Bʾarenreiter, 1971. — 24p; 4to.
£1.50

(B72-50572)

**QPE — Sonatas**
**Bach, Carl Philipp Emanuel**
[Sonatas for piano]. Sechs Klavier-Sonaten/ [by] Carl Philipp
Emanuel Bach; herausgegeben von Hans von Bülow. — Neu
revidierte Ausgabe. — London: Peters, 1971. — 75p; 4to.
£1.25

(B72-50176)

**Burnier, Victor**
Sonata para os três tempos: piano/ de Victor Burnier. — Rio de
Janeiro: Arthur Napoleão; [London]: [Essex Music], 1972. — 10p;
8vo.
Unpriced

(B72-51028)

**Rorem, Ned**
[Sonata for piano, no.1]. Sonata 1: piano/ by Ned Rorem. — New
York; London: Peters, 1971. — 20p; 4to.
£1.80

(B72-50573)

**Rorem, Ned**
[Sonata for piano, no.3]. Sonata 3: piano/ by Ned Rorem. — New
York; London: Peters, 1971. — 26p; 4to.
£2.20

(B72-50574)

**Schubert, Franz**
[Sonata for piano in E flat. D.568]. Sonata, E flat. Opus. 122:
piano solo/ by Schubert. — London: Peters, 1972. — 26p; 4to.
Unpriced

(B72-51029)

**Williamson, Malcolm**
[Sonata for piano, no.2]. Piano sonata no.2/ by Malcolm
Williamson. — London: Weinberger, 1972. — 20p; 4to.
Unpriced

(B72-50575)

**QPEM — Sonatinas**
**Faith, Richard**
[Sonatinas for piano, nos 1-3]. Three sonatinas: for piano/ by
Richard Faith. — New York: Schirmer; [London]: [Chappell],
1971. — 11p; 4to.
Unpriced

(B72-50177)

**Hopkins, Antony**
Sonatine for piano/ by Antony Hopkins. — London: Oxford
University Press, 1971. — 11p; 4to.
ISBN 0 19 372902 4 : £0.45

(B72-50178)

**Lee, Noël**
Sonatine for piano solo/ by Noël Lee. — London: Oxford
University Press, 1971. — 9p; 4to.
ISBN 0 19 373205 x : £0.50

(B72-50179)

**QPG — Suites**
**Kadosa, Pál**
Suite for piano no.1. Op.1/ by Pál Kadosa. — London: Boosey
and Hawkes, 1971. — 11p; 4to.
£0.75

(B72-50180)

**Kadosa, Pál**
Suite for piano, no.3, Op.1, no.3/ by Pál Kadosa. — London:
Boosey and Hawkes, 1972. — 4p; 4to.
£0.50

(B72-51030)

**QPGM — Marches**
**Longmire, John**
[Nautical suite. - *Excerpts]*. Ship ahoy: for piano/ by John
Longmire. — London: Bosworth, 1972. — 3p; 4to.
Unpriced

(B72-51031)

**QPH — Dances**
**Field, John**
[La Danse des ours]. Bears' dances: piano solo/ by John Field and
David Branson. — London: Bosworth, 1972. — 3p; 4to.
In fact, this piece is by John Field and arranged by David Branson. The
coda is added from Field's piano duet version.
£0.15

(B72-51032)

**QPHG — Suites**
**Pike, Eleanor Franklin**
A little dance suite. Op.45: for piano/ by Eleanor Franklin Pike.
— London: Ashdown, 1971. — 9p; 4to.
Unpriced

(B72-50181)

**QPHM — Gavottes**
**Crossman, Gerald**
Gavottina for accordion or piano/ by Gerald Crossman. —
London: Bosworth, 1971. — 2p; 4to.
£0.15
*Primary classification RSPMHM*

**QPHR/T — Minuets. Variations**
**Burkhard, Willy**
Variationen über ein Menuett von Joseph Haydn. Op.29: für
Klavier/ [by] Willy Burkhard. — Cassel; London: Bärenreiter,
1971. — 12p; 4to.
£1.00

(B72-50576)

**QPHVH — Polkas**
**Nazareth, Ernesto**
A meno vesedá: polca/ [by] Ernesto Nazareth. — Rio de Janeiro:
Arthur Napoleão; [London]: [Essex Music], 1972. — [3]p; 4to.
Unpriced

(B72-50577)

**QPHVR — Tangos**
**Espalhafatoso**: chôro (tango brejeiro) [for] piano,/ [by] Ernesto
Nazareth. — Rio de Janeiro: Arthur Napoleão; [London]: [Essex
Music], 1972. — [3]p; 4to.
Unpriced

(B72-50578)

**QPHW — Dances. Waltzes**
**Liszt, Franz**
[Two episodes from Lenau's Faust, no.2. - First Mephisto waltz].
Mephisto waltz no.1/ by Franz Liszt; edited by Emil von Sauer.
— London: Peters, 1971. — 25p; 4to.
£0.50

(B72-50182)

**QPJ — Miscellaneous works**
**Ager, Laurence**
Book of birthdays/ by Laurence Ager. — Manchester; London:
Forsyth, 1972. — 13p; 4to.
Unpriced

(B72-50183)

**Bahk, Junsang**
Mark: für Klavier/ by Junsang Bahk. — Frankfurt; London:
Peters, 1971. — 10p; fol.
£2.80

(B72-50579)

**Bliss, *Sir* Arthur**
Triptych for piano/ by Arthur Bliss. — Sevenoaks: Novello, 1972.
— 20p; 4to.
Duration 14 min.
£0.60

(B72-51033)

**Brydson, John**
Five note excursions/ by John Brydson. — London: Freeman,
1972. — 10p; 4to.
£0.25

(B72-50580)

**Chapple, Brian**
Trees revisited: for piano/ by Brian Chapple. — London: Chester,
1972. — 16p; 4to.
Unpriced

(B72-50581)

**Cumming, Richard**
Twenty-four preludes: for solo piano/ by Richard Cumming. —
New York; [London]: Boosey and Hawkes, 1971. — 43p; 4to.
£1.75

(B72-50184)

**Debussy, Claude**
[Selections]. Selected piano works/ by Claude Debussy; edited by
Eberhardt Klemm. — Leipzig: Peters; [London]: [Hinrichsen]. —
Volume 5: Douze études. — 1970. — 91p; 4to.
£1.85

(B72-50582)

**Debussy, Claude**
L'Isle joyeuse: piano solo/ by Claude Debussy; edited by H.
Swarsenski. — London: Peters, 1972. — 16p; 4to.
Unpriced

(B72-51034)

**Dello Joio, Norman**
Lyric pieces for the young: for piano/ by Norman Dello Joio. —
London: Boosey and Hawkes, 1972. — 16p; fol.
£0.50

(B72-50583)

**Denisov, Edisson**
[Bagatelles for piano]. Bagatellen: für Klavier/ [by] Edisson
Denisov. — Leipzig: Peters; [London]: [Hinrichsen], 1971. — 15p;
4to.
£0.65

(B72-50584)

**Donizetti, Gaetano**
Allegro in F: für Klavier/ [by] Gaetano Donizetti; herausgegeben
von Raymond Meylan. — Frankfurt: Litolff; London: Peters,
1971. — 12p; 4to.
£0.80

(B72-50185)

**Drakeford, Richard**
Hors d'oeuvres: eight pieces for piano/ by Richard Drakeford. —
Sevenoaks: Elkin, 1972. — 8p; 4to.
£0.30

(B72-50186)

**Finney, Ross Lee**
24 piano inventions/ by Ross Lee Finney. — New York; London:
Peters, 1971. — 23p; 4to.
£1.50

(B72-50585)

**Genzmer, Harald**
Dialoge: für Klavier/ [by] Harald Fenzmer. — New York;
London: Peters, 1971. — 26p; 4to.
£1.80

(B72-50586)

**Glasser, Stanley**
Three pieces, Op. 2.: for piano/ by Stanley Glasser. — London:
Essex Music, 1969. — 13p; 4to.
Unpriced

(B72-50587)

**Gompers, Montague**
The disappointed fairy/ by Montague Gompers. — London (48
Addison Gdns, W.14): Montague Gompers, 1972. — 3p; 4to.
Unpriced

(B72-51035)

**Grieg, Edvard**
[Lyric pieces. Op. 12]. Lyrical pieces. Opus 12: for piano/ by
Edvard Grieg. — London: Chappell, 1972. — 16p; 4to.
£0.45

(B72-51036)

**Hummel, Bertold**
Invocation 52: piano solo/ by Bertold Hummel. — Hamburg;
London: Simrock, 1972. — 4to.
Unpriced

(B72-50588)

**Judd, Margaret**
Hop-a-long Jenny/ by Margaret Judd. — London: Bosworth,
1971. — 3p: 4to.
Unpriced

(B72-51037)

**Kagel, Mauricio**
Metapiece (Mimetics): für Klavier/ by Mauricio Kagel. —
London: Universal, 1971. — vi,13p; obl.4to.
Unpriced

(B72-50187)

**Khachaturian, Aram**
Children's album: for piano solo/ by Aram Khachaturian. —
London: Peters, 1971. — 27p; 4to.
£0.60

(B72-50589)

**Last, Joan**
Tom Tiddler's tunes: little piano pieces/ by Joan Last. — London:
Bosworth. —
Book 1. — 1971. — 7p; 8vo.
Unpriced

(B72-50188)

Book 2. — 1971. — 9p; 8vo.
Unpriced

(B72-50189)

**Le Fanu, Nicola**
Chiaroscuro: for piano/ by Nicola Le Fanu. — Borough Green:
Novello, 1971. — 24p; 4to.
£1.00

(B72-50190)

**Lees, Benjamin**
Odyssey: piano solo/ by Benjamin Lees. — London: Boosey and
Hawkes, 1972. — 12p; 4to.
£0.65

(B72-51038)

**Liszt, Franz**
[Selections]. Ab irato; [and], Two concert studies for piano solo/
by Franz Liszt; edited by Zoltán Gárdonyi, Istvan Szelenyi. —
Cassel; London: Bärenreiter, 1971. — 28p; 4to.
£0.90

(B72-50590)

**Liszt, Franz**
[Etudes d'execation transcendante, no.4]. Mazeppa for piano solo/
by Franz List; edited by Zoltan Gardonyi, Istvan Szelenyi. —
Cassel; London: Bärenreiter, 1971. — 16p; 4to.
£0.65

(B72-50591)

**Liszt, Franz**
[Etudes d'exécution transcendante, no.5]. Feux follets: for piano
solo/ by Franz Liszt; edited by Zoltán Gárdonyi, István Szelényi.
— Cassel; London: Bärenreiter, 1971. — 12p; 4to.
£0.65

(B72-50592)

**Liszt, Franz**
[Etudes d'exécution transcendante, no.7]. Eroica: for piano solo/
by Franz Liszt; edited by Zoltán Gárdonyi, István Szelényi. —
Cassel; London: Bärenreiter, 1971. — 11p; 4to.
£0.50

(B72-50593)

**Liszt,, Franz**
[Etudes d'exécution transcendante, no.8]. Wilde Jagd: for piano
solo/ by Franz Liszt; edited by Zoltán Gárdonyi, István Szelényi.
— Cassel; London: Bärenreiter, 1971. — 14p; 4to.
£0.65

(B72-50594)

**Liszt, Franz**
[Etudes d'exécution transcendante, no.9]. Ricordanza: for piano
solo/ by Franz Liszt; edited by Zoltán Gárdonyi, István Szelényi.
— Cassel; London: Bärenreiter, 1971. — 15p; 4to.
£0.65

(B72-50595)

**Liszt, Franz**
[Etudes d'exécution transcendante, no.10]. Study in F minor for
piano solo/ by Franz Liszt; edited by Zoltán Gárdonyi, István
Szelényi. — Cassel; London: Bärenreiter, 1971. — 14p; 4to.
£0.65

(B72-50596)

**Liszt, Franz**
[Etudes d'exécution transcendante, no.11]. Harmonies du Soir: for
piano solo/ by Franz Liszt; edited by Zoltán Gárdonyi, István
Szelényi. — Cassell; London: Bärenreiter, 1971. — 11p; 4to.
£0.50

(B72-50597)

**Liszt, Franz**
Grandes études de Paganini: for piano solo/ by Franz Liszt;
edited by Zoltán Gárdonyi, Istvan Szelenyi. — Cassel; London:
Bärenreiter, 1971. — 55p; 4to.
£1.25

(B72-50598)

**Liszt, Franz**
Trois études de concert: trois caprices poetiques, for piano solo/
by Franz Liszt; edited by Zoltán Gárdonyi, Istvan Szelenyi. —
Cassel; London: Bárenreiter, 1971. — 40p; 4to.
£0.90

(B72-50599)

**Lobb, John**
Three short solos: for piano/ by John Lobb. — London:
Bosworth, 1972. — 4p; 4to.
Contents: Mountain scenery - By a weeping willow - On the river.
£0.15

(B72-51039)

**McCabe, John**
Aubade. (Study no.4): for piano/ by John McCabe. — Sevenoaks:
Novello, 1972. — 8p; 4to.
Duration 7 min.
£0.45

(B72-50600)

**McCabe, John**
Intermezzi for piano/ by John McCabe. — London: Novello,
1971. — 16p; 4to.
Unpriced

(B72-50191)

**McCabe, John**
Sostenuto: study no.2 (1969), for piano/ by John McCabe. —
Sevenoaks: Novello, 1972. — 8p; 4to.
£0.50

(B72-50601)

**Mayerl, William**
The jazz master: a collection of famous piano solos from the
golden age of jazz/ by Billy Mayerl. — London: Keith Prowse,
1972. — 128p; 4to.
£1.00

(B72-51040)

**Nikolovski, Vlastimir**
[Omladinski album]. Jugendalbum: für Klavier/ [by] Vlastimir
Nikolovski. — Leipzig: Peters; [London]: [Hinrichsen], 1971. —
19p; 4to.
Unpriced

(B72-50602)

**Panufnik, Andrzej**
Reflections: piano solo/ by Andrzej Panufnik. — London: Boosey
and Hawkes, 1971. — 12p; 4to.
Duration 12 min.
£0.75

(B72-50192)

**Pitfield, Thomas**
Bits and pieces for piano/ by Thomas Pitfield. — Manchester:
Forsyth, 1972. — 8p; 4to.
Unpriced

(B72-50603)

**Pitfield, Thomas Baron**
Homage to Tchaikovsky: for piano solo/ by Thomas B. Pitfield.
— London: Freeman, 1972. — 4p; 4to.
Based on the Russian folk tune used by Tchaikovsky in 'Serenade for
strings'.
£0.20

(B72-51041)

**Skriabin, Alexander**
[2 poèmes. Op.63. - Excerpts]. Étrangèté. Op.63, no.2: piano solo/
by Skriabin. — London: Peters, 1972. — 5p; 4to.
£0.25

(B72-50604)

**Stevenson, Ronald**
Peter Grimes fantasy on themes from Britten's opera: piano solo/
by Ronald Stevenson. — London: Boosey and Hawkes, 1972. —
12p; 4to.
Unpriced

(B72-51042)

**Villa-Lobos, Heitor**
[Cirandinhas, no.7]. Todo o mundo passo/ by H. Villa-Lobos. —
Rio de Janeiro: Arthur Napoleão; [London]: [Essex Music], 1972.
— 2p; 4to.
Unpriced

(B72-50605)

**Wade, Steuart**
Wayside sketches: six characteristic pieces for piano/ by Steuart
Wade. — London: Keith Prowse Music, 1971. — 17p; 4to.
£0.25

(B72-50193)

**QPK — Arrangements**
**Bach, Johann Sebastian**
Toccata and fugue in D minor. / by J.S. Bach; arranged for piano
solo by Thomas A. Johnson. — New York; London: Peters, 1972.
— 12p; 4to.
£0.40

(B72-50606)

**Khachaturian, Aram**
[Spartak - Excerpts]. The 'Onedin Line'/ by Aram Khachaturian;
theme as adapted for B.B.C. T.V.'s series, piano arrangement by
Anthony Isaac. — London: Palace Music, 1971. — 4p; 4to.
£0.20

(B72-50194)

**Khachaturian, Aram**
[Spartak - Excerpts]. The 'Onedin Line' theme/ by Aram
Khachaturian; from the B.B.C. T.V. series, adapted and arranged
by John Keating. — London: Essex Music International, 1971. —
6p; 4to.
£0.20

(B72-50195)

**Saint-Saens, Camille**
[Selections]. The music of Saint-Saëns/ arranged by Dudley E.
Bayford. — London: Francis, Day and Hunter, 1972. — 23p; 4to.
£0.35

(B72-50607)

**Tchaikovsky, Peter**
[Symphony no.5 in E minor. Op.64. - Andante cantabile]. Andante
da 5a sinfonia/ [by] Tchaikovsky; tema da novela 'O tempo não
apayu', [arranged by] Gaó Gurgel. — São Paulo: MCA; [London]:
[Leeds Music], 1972. — [2]; 4to.
Unpriced

(B72-50608)

**QPK/AAY — Arrangements. Collections**
The New climax albums: for piano. — Sevenoaks: Paxton. —
No.1. — 1972. — 48p; 4to. —
£0.47

(B72-51043)

**Pickles, Sydney**
Duets for piano/ set by Sydney Pickles. — London: Freeman,
1972. — 15p; 4to.
£0.30

(B72-50609)

**QPK/AGM — Arrangements. Marches**
**Banks, Eric**
The Red Arrows march/ by Eric Banks and Cecil Bolton. —
London: Robbins Music, 1972. — 6p; 4to.
£0.20

(B72-50610)

**QPK/AGM/JS — Arrangements, Marches. Television**
**Farnon, Robert J**
Colditz march/ by Robert J. Farnon; arranged for piano by Frank
Harlow. — London: Leeds Music, 1972. — 4p; 4to.
£0.25

(B72-51044)

**QPK/AGM/JS — Arrangements. Marches. Television music**
**Zacharias, Helmut**
Munich melody: original theme of BBC TV Olympic Grandstand/
by Helmut Zacharias. — London: Ardmore and Beechwood, 1972.
— 4p; 4to.
Unpriced

(B72-51045)

**QPK/AHW/JR — Arrangements. Waltzes. Films**
**Rota, Nino**
[The godfather. - Excerpts]. The godfather waltz/ by Nino Rota.
— London: Famous Chappell, 1972. — 4p; 4to.
A simplified arrangement is also included.
£0.20

(B72-50611)

**QPK/DW — Arrangements. Songs, etc**
**Lennon, John**
The Beatles year: piano vocal [or] easy organ/ by John Lennon,
Paul McCartney ... [and others]. — London: Northern Songs,
1972. — 130p; 4to.
Unpriced
Also classified at RK/DW

(B72-50612)

**QPK/DW/JR — Arrangements. Songs, etc. Films**
**Rota, Nino**
[The godfather. - Waltz]. Come live your life with me/ by Nino
Rota; words by Larry Kusik and Billy Mestrel. — London:
Famous Chappell, 1972. — 4p; 4to.
A simplified arrangement for piano or organ is also included.
£0.20

(B72-50613)

**QPK/HM/AYH — Arrangements. Ballet music. Collections. France**
**Moore, Elizabeth**
Ballet music from the French operas/ arranged by Elizabeth
Moore. — London: Cramer, 1972. — 47p; 4to.
Contents: Carmen/ by G. Bizet - Le Prophète/ by G. Meyerbeer - L'Etoile
du nord/ by G. Meyerbeer - Les Contes d'Hoffmann/ by J. Offenbach.
Unpriced

(B72-51046)

**QPK/JM — Arrangements. Incidental music**
**Grieg, Edvard**
[Peer Gynt -. Excerpts]. Morning/ by Edward Grieg; arranged by
Harry Dexter. — London: Keith Prowse Music, 1972. — 5p; 4to.
£0.15

(B72-50614)

**QPK/JR — Arrangements. Films**
**Bennett, Richard Rodney**
Nicholas and Alexandra: theme/ by Richard Rodney Bennett;
arranged by Sid Engel. — London: Columbia Music, Chappell,
1971. — 5p; 4to.
£0.20

(B72-50196)

**Lanchbery, John**
[Tales of Beatrix Potter - Excerpts]. Peter Rabbit and the tales of
Beatrix Potter: music from the film/ by John Lanchbery; arranged
for easy piano by John Brimhall. — London: EMI Film Music,
1971. — 23p; 4to.
Unpriced
(B72-50197)

**Ralston, Alfred**
[Young Winston. - *Excerpts*]. Jennie's theme: from the film/ by
Alfred Ralston. — London: Chappell, 1972. — 3p; 4to.
£0.25
(B72-51047)

**Rota, Nino**
The godfather: souvenir song album/ by Nino Rota; [with
orchestral excerpts arranged for keyboard]. — London: Chappell,
1972. — 70p; 4to.
£1.25
*Primary classification KDW/JR*

**Rota, Nino**
The godfather - love theme/ by Nino Rota. — London: Famous
Chappell, 1972. — 49; 4to.
A simplified arrangement is also included.
£0.20
(B72-50615)

**Williams, Charles**
The dream of Olwen: piano solo/ by Charles Williams. —
London: Lawrence Wright Music, 1972. — 8p; 4to.
£0.25
(B72-51048)

**QPK/JR/AY — Arrangements. Films. Collections**
**Bolton, Cecil**
Themes from T.V. and film classics/ arranged by Cecil Bolton. —
London: Francis, Hunter and Day, 1972. — 65p; 4to.
£0.75
*Also classified at QPK/JS/AY*
(B72-50616)

**QPK/JS — Arrangements. Television**
**Horovitz, Joseph**
The search for the Nile/ theme by Joseph Horovitz. — London:
Francis, Day and Hunter, 1972. — 4p; 4to.
£0.20
(B72-50617)

**Josephs, Wilfred**
The British Empire: echoes of Britannia's rule: title music from
the BBC TV series/ by Wilfred Josephs. — London: Essex Music,
1971. — 3p; 4to.
Echoes include 'Rule Britannia'.
£0.20
(B72-50198)

**Lockyer, Malcolm**
Pathfinders march: theme in the TV series/ by Malcolm Lockyer.
— London: Berry Music, Campbell, Connelly, 1972. — 4p; 4to.
£0.20
(B72-50618)

**Roper, Alan**
Clochemerle/ theme arranged and adapted by Alan Roper. —
London: Francis, Day and Hunter, 1972. — 4p; 4to.
£0.20
(B72-50619)

**QPK/JS/AY — Arrangements. Television. Collections**
**Bolton, Cecil**
Themes from T.V. and film classics/ arranged by Cecil Bolton. —
London: Francis, Hunter and Day, 1972. — 65p; 4to.
£0.75
*Primary classification QPK/JR/AY*
(B72-50616)

**QPPR — Right hand**
**Elias, Brian**
Five piano pieces for right hand/ by Brian Elias. — London:
Chester, 1972. — 4p; 4to.
Unpriced
(B72-50620)

**Schultze-Biesantz, Clemens**
One hand alone: album of 17 well-known pieces arranged for
either left hand or right hand solo/ by Schultze-Biesantz. —
London: Peters, 1972. — 27p; 4to.
Unpriced
(B72-51049)

**QRNU — HARPSICHORD DUETS**
**Browne, Earle**
Nine rarebits: for 1 or 2 harpsichords/ by Earle Browne. —
London: Universal, 1972. — [3]p; 4to.
Unpriced
*Primary classification QRPJ*

**QRNUE — Two harpsichords, 4 hands. Sonatas**
**Pasquini, Bernardo**
[Sonata for two harpsichords in D minor]. Sonata in D minor: for
two pianos (harpsichords)/ by Bernardo Pasquini; in its original
form and arranged for performance [and] edited by Werner
Danckert. — Cassel; London: Nagel, 1971. — 11p; 4to.
£0.75
(B72-50621)

**QRP — HARPSICHORD SOLOS**
**QRP/AZ — Collected works of individual composers**
**Handel, George Frideric**
Keyboard works/ by Georg Friedrich Händel. — Cassel; London:
Bärenreiter. —
Vol.2: Second set of 1733/ edited by Peter Northway. — 1970. — viii,96p;
fol.
£1.85
(B72-50622)

**QRPEM — Sonatinas**
**Maconchy, Elizabeth**
Sonatina for harpsichord/ by Elizabeth Maconchy. — South
Croydon: Lengnick, 1972. — 14p; 4to.
£0.50
(B72-51050)

**QRPJ — Miscellaneous works**
**Browne, Earle**
Nine rarebits: for 1 or 2 harpsichords/ by Earle Browne. —
London: Universal, 1972. — [3]p; 4to.
Unpriced
*Also classified at QRNU*
(B72-51051)

**QSQ — VIRGINALS**
**QSQ/AZ — Complete works of individual composers**
**Rogers, Benjamin**
Complete keyboard works/ by Benjamin Rogers; transcribed and
edited by Richard Rastall. — London: Stainer and Bell, 1972. —
15p; fol.
Unpriced
(B72-51052)

**R — ORGAN**
**R/AY — Collections**
**Funk, Heinrich**
Service music for the organ: preludes, interludes and postludes
grouped according to keys/ edited by Heinrich Funk. — London:
Hinrichsen. —
Vol.3. — 1972. — 152p; obl.4to.
Previous vols entered under title.
£2.70
(B72-50623)

**Graf, Adolf**
Choralvorspiele für den gottesdienstlichen Gebrauch/
herausgegeben von Adolf Graf. — Cassel; London: Bärenreiter. —
Band 3. — 1971. — 163-241p; obl.fol.
£1.75
(B72-50624)

**Phillips, Gordon**
Anthology of organ music: works for two manuals and pedals/
edited by Gordon Phillips. — London: Hinrichsen. —
Vol.7: Works by Boyvin, Couperin, Reichardt, Adams, Merkel, Beechey. —
1971. — 29p; obl.4to
£0.90
(B72-50199)
Vol.8: Works by Le Bègue, J.S. Bach, Albrechtsberger, Rembt, S.S. Wesley,
Guilmant, Spooner. — 1971. — 32p; obl.4to.
£0.90
(B72-50200)
Vol.9: Works by Marchand, Guilain, Vivaldi, A.W. Bach, Karg-Elert,
Eberlin, Stevens, Guilmant. — 1971. — 32p; obl.4to.
£0.90
(B72-50201)
Vol.10: Works by J.S. Bach, Russell, Merkel, Rheinberger, Sowerby. —
1971. — 36p; obl.4to.
£0.90
(B72-50202)
Vol.11: Works by Boyvin, du Mage, Raison, J.S. Bach, Martini, Rinck,
Cooke. — 1971. — 30p; obl.4to.
£0.90
(B72-50203)
Vol.12: Works by de Grigny, J.S. Bach, Krebs, Vierling, Chipp, Phillips. —
1971. — 32p; obl.4to.
£0.90
(B72-50204)

**Timme, Traugott**
Choralvorspiele in tiefer Lage zum Auswahlchoralbuch/
herausgegeben von Traugott Timme. — Cassel; London:
Bärenreiter, 1971. — 91p; obl.fol.
£3.15
(B72-50625)

**Trevor, Caleb Henry**
Organ music for manuals/ edited by C.H. Trevor. — London:
Oxford University Press. —
Book 1. — 1972. — 32p; 4to.
ISBN 0 19 375833 4 : £0.65

(B72-50206)

Book 2. — 1972. — 32p; 4to. —
ISBN 0 19 375834 2 : £0.65

(B72-50207)

The progressive organist: all grades Associated Board standard/
edited by C.H. Trevor. — London: Elkin. —
Book 8. — 1971. — 30p; 4to.
£0.55

(B72-50205)

**R/AYD — Collections. England**
**Trevor, Caleb Henry**
Old English organ music for manuals/ edited by C.H. Trevor. —
London: Oxford University Press. —
Book 5. — 1972. — 24p; 4to.
ISBN 0 19 375828 8 : £0.50

(B72-50208)

Old English organ music for manuals/ edited by C.H. Trevor. —
London: Oxford University Press. —
Book 6. — 1972. — 24p; 4to. —
ISBN 0 19 375829 6 : £0.50

(B72-50626)

**R/AYE — Germany**
**Graf, Adolf**
Freie Orgelstücke alter Meister/ herausgegeben von Adolf Graf.
— Cassel; London: Bärenreiter. —
Band 2. — 1971. — 152p; obl.fol.
£3.00

(B72-50627)

**R/AZ — Collected works of individual composers**
**Liszt, Franz**
Complete organ works/ by Ferenc Liszt; edited by Sándor
Margittay. — London: Boosey and Hawkes, 1971. — 112p; obl.
4to.
£2.50

(B72-50630)

**Pachelbel, Johann**
Orgelwerke/ by Johann Pachelbel; zum ersten Mal herausgegeben
von Traugott Fedtke. — Frankfurt; London: Peters. —
Band 1: Choralfugen und Choräle aus dem Weimarer Tabulaturbuch, 1704.
— 1972. — 66p; obl. 4to.
Unpriced

(B72-51053)

**Scheidemann, Heinrich**
Orgelwerke/ [by] Heinrich Scheidemann. — Cassel; London:
Bärenreiter. —
[Band 1]: Magnificat - Bearbeitungen/ herausgegeben von Gustav Fock. —
1970. — iii,101p; obl.fol.
£2.75

(B72-50628)

**Scheidemann, Heinrich**
Orgelwerke/ [by] Heinrich Scheidemann. — Cassel; London:
Bärenreiter. —
Band 3: Praeambulen, Fugen, Fantasien, Canzonen und Toccaten/
herausgegeben von Werner Breig. — 1971. — vii,80p; 4to.
The previous volume was incorrectly classified at RJ in the 1968 annual
volume, since there was no indication of further volumes to be published.
£2.25

(B72-50629)

**R/LL — Easter**
**Routh, Francis**
Lumen Christi. Op. 15: a meditation on the festival of Easter:
organ solo/ by Francis Routh. — London: Boosey and Hawkes,
1972. — 34p; 4to.
£1.30

(B72-50631)

**R/Y — Fugues**
**Stevenson, Ronald**
Prelude and fugue on a theme by Liszt/ by Ronald Stevenson. —
London: Oxford University Press, 1971. — 12p; 4to.
ISBN 0 19 375780 x : £0.50

(B72-50209)

**RE — Sonatas**
**Jackson, Francis**
[Soneta for organ in G minor. Op.35]. Sonata in G minor. Op.35/
by Francis Jackson. — London: Oxford University Press, 1972. —
38p; 4to.
Duration 22 min.
ISBN 0 19 375484 3 : £1.50

(B72-50632)

**RF — Concertos**
**Reda, Siegfried**
Ich weiss ein lieblich Engelspiel: Choralkonzert für Orgel/ [by]
Siegfried Reda. — Cassel; London: Bärenreiter, 1970. — 22p;
obl.fol.
£1.50

(B72-50633)

**RG — Suites**
**Howells, Herbert**
Partita: for organ/ by Herbert Howells. — Sevenoaks: Novello,
1972. — 41p; obl. 4to.
Duration 25 min.
£1.00

(B72-51054)

**RJ — Miscellaneous works**
**Bach, Johann Sebastian**
[Clavierübung. Tl.3. - *Excerpts]*. Duets. S.802-805/ by Johann
Sebastian Bach; edited by Manfred Tessmer. — Cassel; London:
Bärenreiter, 1971. — 16p; obl.fol.
£0.50

(B72-50634)

**Edwards, D W**
The day of Pentecost: for choir, or solo voice, or as an organ
solo/ by D.W. Edwards; [text from] Acts 2. — West Kirby (67
Lang Lane, West Kirby, Wirral, Cheshire): D.W. Edwards, 1972.
— 4p; 8vo.
Unpriced
*Primary classification DK*

**Englert, Giuseppe**
Palaestra 64: pro organo/ [by] Giuseppe Englert. — London:
Peters, 1972. — 10p; obl.fol.
£1.25

(B72-50635)

**Finney, Ross Lee**
Five fantasies: for organ/ by Ross Lee Finney. — New York;
London: Peters. —
No.1: So long as the mind keeps silent/ edited by Robert Noehren. — 1970.
— 9p; obl. 4to.
£1.00

(B72-50636)

No.2: There are no summits without abysses/ edited by Robert Noehren. —
1970. — 10p; obl. 4to.
£1.00

(B72-50637)

No.3: Advice which the hours of darkness give/ edited by Marilyn Mason.
— 1970. — 9p; obl. 4to.
£1.00

(B72-50638)

No.4: The leaves on the trees spoke/ edited by Robert Noehren. — 1970. —
5p; obl. 4to.
£1.00

(B72-50639)

No.5: Each answer hides future questions/ edited by Marilyn Mason. —
1970. — 11p; obl. 4to.
£1.00

(B72-50640)

**Forbes, Sebastian**
Haec dies/ by Sebastian Forbes. — London: Oxford University
Press, 1971. — 18p; 4to.
ISBN 0 19 375381 2 : £0.75

(B72-50210)

**Gowers, Patrick**
Toccata/ by Patrick Gowers. — London: Oxford University Press,
1972. — 23p; 4to.
£1.00

(B72-50211)

**Klebe, Giselher**
Fantasie und Lobpreisung. Op.58: für Orgel/ [by] Giselher Klebe.
— Cassel; London: Bärenreiter, 1971. — 16p; obl.fol.
£1.25

(B72-50641)

**Leighton, Kenneth**
Improvisation: 'In memoriam Maurice de Sausmarez',/ by
Kenneth Leighton. — Sevenoaks: Novello, 1972. — 7p; obl.4to.
Duration 5 min.
£0.33

(B72-51055)

**Macer, Aubrey William John**
'Lead us, heavenly Father ...': chorale improvisation/ by A.W.J.
Macer. — London: Cramer, 1972. — 4p; 4to.
Based on the hymn-tune 'Mannheim', originally adapted by Lowell Mason
from a chorale by F. Filitz.
£0.24

(B72-51056)

**Marshall, Philip**
Three short improvisations: for organ/ by Philip Marshall. —
London: Ashdown, 1972. — 11p; 4to.
Contents: Processional fanfare. — Quodlibet. — Morning canticle.
Unpriced

(B72-50212)

**Raxach, Enrique**
The looking glass: for organ/ by Enrique Raxach. — London:
Hinrichsen, 1971. — [5]p; obl.fol.
£1.25

(B72-50213)

**Raxach, Enrique**
The looking-glass: for organ/ by Enrique Raxach. — London:
Peters, 1972. — 3ff; obl. fol.
With a seperate copy of 'Performing directions' in English and German
inserted.
Unpriced

(B72-51057)

**Standford, Patric**
Metamorphosis/ by Patric Standford. — Sevenoaks: Novello,
1972. — 9p; 4to.
£0.33

(B72-51058)

**Stover, Harold**
Te decet hymnus Deus in Sion: organ solo/ by Harold Stover. —
London: Boosey and Hawkes, 1972. — 8p; 4to.
£0.40

(B72-50642)

**Williamson, Malcolm**
Peace pieces: for organ, by Malcolm Williamson. — London:
Weinberger. —
Book 1. — 1972. — 28p; obl.4to.
Unpriced

(B72-50214)

Book 2. — 1972. — 28p; obl.4to.
Unpriced

(B72-50215)

**Wood, Hugh**
Capriccio. Op.8/ by Hugh Wood. — Sevenoaks: Novello, 1971. —
12p; obl.4to.
£0.45

(B72-50216)

**RK — Arrangements**
**Mahler, Gustav**
[Symphony no.5 in C minor. - *Excerpts*]. Adagietto/ by Gustav
Mahler; abridged arrangement for organ by W.R. Pasfield. —
London: Ashdown, 1971. — 5p; 4to.
Unpriced

(B72-50217)

**Wills, Arthur**
Concerto for organ, strings and timpani/ by Arthur Wills; organ
solo part with orchestral reduction arranged by Christopher Slater.
— London: Boosey and Hawkes, 1971. — 44p; 4to.
£1.50

(B72-50218)

**RK/AHJ — Arrangements. Allemandes**
**Greene, Maurice**
[Choice lessons for the harpsichord or spinnet. - Allmand in D
major] Prelude in D/ by Maurice Greene; arr. for the organ by
Patrick Williams. — London: Leonard, Gould & Bolttler, 1972.
— 4p; 4to.
£0.18

(B72-51059)

**RK/DM/JS/AY — Arrangements. Hymns. Television music.**
**Collections**
Hymns for today: a selection of hymns from the television series 'A
hymn for today'. — London: High-Fye Music, 1972. — 24p; 4to.
Unpriced

(B72-50219)

**RK/DW — Arrangements. Songs, etc**
**Bock, Jerry**
Fiddler on the roof: selection for all organs/ by Jerry Bock. —
London: Valando, 1972. — 40p; 4to.
£0.60

(B72-50643)

**Coward, *Sir* Noël**
Noel Coward for all organs/ arranged by James Burt. — London:
Chappell, 1972. — 23p; 4to.
£0.60

(B72-51060)

**Lennon, John**
The Beatles year: piano vocal [or] easy organ/ by John Lennon,
Paul McCartney ... [and others]. — London: Northern Songs,
1972. — 130p; 4to.
Unpriced
*Primary classification QPK/DW*

(B72-50612)

**MacLeod, Anne Campbell**
Skye boat song: air (founded on an old 'chanty')/ composed by
A.C. MacLeod; Arranged for the organ by Frank E. Brown. —
London: Cramer, 1971. — 4p; 4to.
£0.18

(B72-50220)

**RK/DW — Arrangements. Songs. etc**
**Sullivan, *Sir* Arthur**
[Selections]. Gilbert and Sullivan song book: for all-organs/
arranged by Dudley E. Bayford. — London: Francis, Day &
Hunter, 1972. — 45p; 4to.
£0.75

(B72-50644)

**RK/DW/AY — Arrangements. Songs, etc. Collections**
**Bayford, Dudley Escott**
Arias from famous operas: for all-organs/ arranged by Dudley E.
Bayford. — London: Francis, Day & Hunter, 1972. — 29p; 4to.
£0.60

(B72-50645)

**RK/JR — Arrangements. Films**
**Rota, Nino**
The godfather: souvenir song album/ by Nino Rota; [with
orchestral excerpts arranged for keyboard]. — London: Chappell,
1972. — 70p; 4to.
£1.25
*Primary classification KDW/JR*

**RK/KDD — Arrangements. Weddings**
**Mendelssohn, Felix**
[A midsummer night's dream. Excerpts]. Wedding march/ by
Felix Mendelssohn; arranged for all organs by Harry Dexter. —
London: Ashdown, 1971. — 7p; 4to.
Unpriced

(B72-50221)

**RPV — ELECTRIC ORGANS**
**RPV/AC — Tutors**
**Rothenberg, Peter**
The electronic organ: a course for beginners/ by Peter
Rothenberg. — Mainz; London: Schott, 1972. — 72p; 4to.
Unpriced

(B72-50646)

**RPVH/AY — Dances. Collections**
**Scheffau, Rolf**
Tanzrhythmen für electronische Orgel/ bearbeitet von Rolf
Scheffau. — Mainz; London: Schott. —
Band 1. — 1972. — 24p; 4to. —
£1.20

(B72-51061)

Band 2. — 1972. — 23p; 4to. —
£1.20

(B72-51062)

**RPVK/DW/G/AY — Arrangements. Folk songs, Collections**
**Rothenberg, Peter**
Folksongs: for 2 manuals and pedal/ [arranged by] Peter
Rothenberg. — Mainz; London: Schott, 1972. — 20p; 4to.
£1.20

(B72-51063)

**RSPM — UNACCOMPANIED ACCORDION SOLOS**
**RSPM/AF — Exercises**
**Delroy, Albert**
Three advanced studies: accordion solo/ by Albert Delroy. —
Leicester: Charnwood Music, 1972. — 4p; 4to.
Unpriced

(B72-51064)

**RSPMEM — Sonatinas**
**Walker, Wilfred**
[Sonatina for accordion, no.1, in C major]. Sonatina no.1 in C:
accordion solo/ by Wilfred Walker. — Leicester: Charnwood
Music, 1971. — 6p; 4to.
£0.25

(B72-51065)

**Walker, Wilfred**
[Sonatina for accordion, no.2 in G major]. Sonatina no.2 in G:
accordion solo/ by Wilfred Walker. — Leicester: Charnwood
Music, 1971. — 5p; 4to.
£0.26

(B72-51066)

**RSPMGM — Marches**
Crossman, Gerald
    Fortitude: march [for] accordion solo/ by Gerald Crossman. —
    Leicester: Charnwood Music, 1972. — 4p; 4to.
Unpriced

(B72-51067)

Spratley, Philip
    Trent march: accordion solo/ by Philip Spratley. — Leicester:
    Charnwood Music, 1971. — 6p; 4to.
£0.22

(B72-51068)

**RSPMH — Dances**
Walker, Wilfred
    Playa las canteras: Spanish dance: accordion solo/ by Wilfred
    Walker. — Leicester: Charnwood Music, 1971. — [2]p; 4to.
£0.19

(B72-51069)

**RSPMHM — Gavottes**
Crossman, Gerald
    Gavottina for accordion or piano/ by Gerald Crossman. —
    London: Bosworth, 1971. — 2p; 4to.
£0.15
*Also classified at QPHM*

(B72-51070)

**RSPMHPD — Jotas**
Jacobi, Wolfgang
    Jota: Spanish dance: accordion solo/ by Wolfgang Jacobi. —
    Leicester: Charnwood Music, 1971. — 4p; 4to.
£0.30

(B72-51071)

**RSPMHVH — Polkas**
Wright, Rosemary
    Music-box polka: accordion solo/ by Rosemary Wright. —
    Leicester: Charnwood Music, 1971. — [2]p; 4to.
Unpriced

(B72-51072)

**RSPMHW — Waltzes**
Bishop, Chiz
    Bunty: musette waltz, [for] accordion solo/ by Chiz Bishop. —
    Leicester: Charnwood Music, 1972. — [3]p; 4to.
Unpriced

(B72-51073)

Bishop, Chiz
    El Salto de agna: accordion solo/ by Chiz Bishop. — Leicester:
    Charnwood Music, 1972. — [3]p; 4to.
Unpriced

(B72-51074)

Staquet, Willy
    Bluette: continental accordion solo/ by Willy Staquet and Albert
    Delroy. — Leicester: Charnwood Music, 1971. — [2]p; 4to.
£0.19

(B72-51075)

**RSPMJ — Miscellaneous works**
Blair, Jimmy
    La Mantilla: Spanish serenade: accordion solo/ by Jimmy Blair.
    — Leicester: Charnwood Music, 1972. — 5p; 4to.
Unpriced

(B72-51076)

Crossman, Gerald
    Michella: accordion solo/ by Gerald Crossman. — Leicester:
    Charnwood Music, 1971. — [3]p; 4to.
Unpriced

(B72-51077)

Pasby, Cyril
    The gay puppet: accordion solo/ by Cyril Pasby. — Leicester:
    Charnwood Music, 1972. — [3]p; 4to.
Unpriced

(B72-51078)

Pitfield, Thomas Baron
    Kalinka: traditional Russian folksong/ arranged for accordion solo
    by Thomas Pitfield. — Leicester: Charnwood Music, 1971. —
    [3]p; 4to.
£0.22

(B72-51079)

Pitfield, Thomas Baron
    Song of rest: accordion solo/ by Thomas Pitfield. — Leicester:
    Charnwood Music, 1972. — [2]p; 4to.
Unpriced

(B72-51080)

Shepherd, Audrey
    Three simple solos: [for] accordion/ by Audrey Shepherd. —
    Leicester: Charnwood Music, 1972. — [2]p; 4to.
Unpriced

(B72-51081)

**RSPMK — Arrangements**
Kozeluch, Leopold
    [La Ritrovata figlia. Op. 39. - *Excerpts*]. Andantino/ by Leopold
    Kozeluh (sic); arranged for accordion solo by Chiz Bishop. —
    Leicester: Charnwood Music, 1972. — 2p; 4to.
Unpriced

(B72-51082)

**RSPMK/DW — Arrangements. Songs, etc**
Rossini, Gioacchino Antonio
    [Il Barbiere di Siviglia. - *Excerpts*]. Largo al factotum/ by Rossini;
    arranged [for] accordion solo by Chiz Bishop. — Leicester:
    Charnwood Music, 1972. — 7p; 4to.
Unpriced

(B72-51083)

**RSPMK/DW/AYC — Arrangements. Songs. Collections. Great**
                     **Britain**
Krupp, Karlheinz
    London - Bridge: Lieder und Tänze aus Grossbritannien, für
    Akkordeon mit 2. Stimme ad lib./ bearbeitet von Karlheinz
    Krupp. — Mainz; London: Schott, 1972. — 4to.
Score (23p.) & part.
£0.80

(B72-51084)

**RXM — STRING ORCHESTRA**
**RXM/AF — Exercises**
Fletcher, Stanley
    New tunes for strings/ by Stanley Fletcher; instructional design by
    Paul Rolland. — New York; [London]: Boosey and Hawkes. —
Book 1. — 1972. — 4to.
Teacher's book (68p.) & 4 parts.
£4.90

(B72-51085)

Book 2. — 1972. — 4to.
Teacher's book (64p.) & 4 parts.
£4.90

(B72-51086)

**RXM/AYLC — Collections. Poland**
Panufnik, Andrzej
    Old Polish music/ compiled by Andrzej Panufnik. — London:
    Boosey and Hawkes, 1971. — 111p; 8vo.
£2.50

(B72-50222)

**RXME — Symphonies**
Angelo, Bacchi
    [Symphony for string orchestra in D major]. Sinfonia, D-Dur: für
    Streichorchester und zwei Hörner ad lib./ by Bacchi Angelo;
    herausgegeben von Adalbert Strehlow, Continuo-Aussetzung von
    Lorenz Stolzenbach. — Leipzig: Peters; [London]: [Hinrichsen],
    1971. — 12p; 4to.
£1.20

(B72-50647)

Bononcini, Giovanni Battista
    [Sinfonie da chiesa. Op. 5. - *Excerpts*]. Sinfonia 1 und 9, [for
    strings and basso continuo]/ [by] Giovanni Battista Bononcini;
    herausgegeben von Nikolaus Harnoncourt;
    Generalbassbearbeitung: Helmut May. — Mainz; London: Schott,
    1972. — 22p; 4to.
£1.40

(B72-51087)

**RXMEM — Sinfoniettas**
Járdányi, Pál
    [Sinfonietta for string orchestra]. Sinfonietta per archi/ di Pál
    Járdányi. — London: Boosey and Hawkes, 1972. — 16p; 4to.
Unpriced

(B72-51088)

**RXMEM — Sonatinas**
Thiele, Siegfried
    [Sonatina for young people's string orchestra]. Sonatine: für
    Jugendstreichorchester/ [by] Siegfried Thiele. — Leipzig: Peters;
    [London]: [Hinrichsen], 1971. — 15p; 4to.
£1.20

(B72-50648)

**RXMG — Suites**
Holst, Gustav
    St Paul's suite: for string orchestra/ by Gustav Holst. — London:
    Curwen Edition, 1972. — 23p; 8vo.
Unpriced

(B72-50649)

**Telemann, Georg Philipp**
[Suite for string orchestra in F major]. Overture F-dur. (Suite): f'ur Streichorchester und Cembalo (zwei Oboen und Fagott ad libitum)/ [by] G. Philipp Telemann; herausgegeben von Willi Maertens. — Leipzig: Peters; [London]: [Hinrichsen], 1970. — 23p.
4to: £2.10

(B72-50650)

**RXMJ — Miscellaneous works**
**Dexter, Harry**
Pizzicato for a poodle: for string orchestra/ by Harry Dexter. — London: Ashdown, 1972. — 8vo.
Score (7p.) & 5 parts.
Unpriced

(B72-50651)

**Hovhaness, Alan**
Armenian rhapsody, no.3. Op.189: for string orchestra,/ by Alan Hovhaness; based on an ancient religious melody and a folk song. — New York; London: Peters, 1971. — 10p; 8vo.
Duration 6 min.
£1.50

(B72-50652)

**Jomelli, Nicolò**
[Il Parataio. - Overture]. Sinfonia D-Dur: für Streichorchester und zwei Horner ad lib/ [by] Nicolò Jomelli; herausgegeben von Adalbert Strehlow, Continuo-Aussetzung von Lorenz Stolzenbach. — Leipzig: Peters; [London]: [Hinrichsen], 1971. — 16p; 4to.
£1.20

(B72-50653)

**Josephs, Wilfred**
Elegy for strings. Op.13/ by Wilfred Josephs. — London: Weinberger, 1971. — 10p; 8vo.
Unpriced

(B72-50223)

**Kasandiev, Vasil**
Complexi sonori: für Streicher/ [by] Wassil Kasandjiev. — Frankfurt; London: Peters, 1971. — 4to.
With a separate leaf headed 'Explanation of symbols' in German and English, inserted.
£2.00

(B72-50654)

**Veerhoff, Carlos**
Textur: fur Streicher/ von Carlos H. Veerhoff. — Frankfurt: Litolff; [London]: [Hinrichsen], 1972. — 67p; 8vo.
Miniature score.
Unpriced

(B72-51089)

**Wangenheim, Volker**
Klangspiel 1: für Streicher/ [by] Volker Wangenheim. — Frankfurt; London: Peters, 1971. — 15p; 4to.
£2.20

(B72-50655)

**RXMK/DW/G/AYC — Arrangements. Folk songs. Collections. Great Britain**
**Hedges, Anthony**
A British folk song suite/ arranged for string orchestra by Anthony Hedges. — London: British and Continental Music, 1972. — 8p; 4to.
Unpriced

(B72-50656)

**RXMP — SOLO INSTRUMENT (S) & STRING ORCHESTRA**
**RXMPPWF — Keyboard & string orchestra. Concertos**
**Corrette, Michel**
[Concerto for keyboard & string orchestra in A major. Op 26, no.2]. Concerto 2, A-Dur: für Cembalo oder Orgel und Streicher/ [by] Michel Corrette; herausgegeben von Hugo Ruf. — Mainz; London: Schott, 1972. — 28p; 4to.
£1.20

(B72-51090)

**RXMPRF — Organ & string orchestra. Concertos**
**Sammartini, Giuseppe**
[Concerto for organ in A Major. Op.9 No.1]. Concerto 1, A major: for harpsichord (organ), two violins and basso continuo/ by Giuseppe Sammartini; edited by Hedda Illy. — Cassel; London: Bärenreiter, 1971. — 4to.
Score (40p.) & 3 parts.
£2.15

(B72-50657)

**RXMPSK/LF — Violin & string orchestra. Arrangements. Concertos**
**Bach, Johann Sebastian**
[Concerto for harpsichord in F minor. S.1056]. Concerto in G minor for violin, strings and basso continuo/ by Bach; reconstructed from BWV 1056; edited by Wilfried Fischer. — Cassel; London: B¨arenreiter, 1970. — 59-72p; fol.
A reissue of pages 59-72 of 'Neue Ausgabe s¨amtlicher Werke', ser.7, Supp. Bd.7.
£1.25

(B72-50658)

**RXMPSNTK/LF — Three violins & string orchestra. Arrangements. Concertos**
**Bach, Johann Sebastian**
[Concerto for three harpsichords in D major. S.1064]. Concerto in D major for three violins, strings and basso continuo/ by Bach; reconstructed from BWV 1064; edited by Wilfried Fischer. — Cassel; London: Bärenreiter, 1970. — 103-138p; fol.
A reissue of pages 103-138 of 'Neue Ausgabe sämtlicher Werke', ser.7. Supp. Bd.7.
£1.85

(B72-50659)

**RXMPVSRF — Descant recorder & string orchestra. Concertos**
**Sammartini, Giuseppe**
[Concerto for descant recorder & string orchestra in F major]. Concerto in F: for descant recorder, strings and harpsichord (piano)/ by Giuseppe Sammartini; edited by Johannes Brinckmann, with realisation for the basso continuo by Wilhelm Mohr. — London: Schott, 1972. — 4to.
Score (32p.) & 6 parts.
Unpriced

(B72-50224)

**RXMPVSSF — Treble recorder & string orchestra. Concertos**
**Boismortier, Joseph Bodin de**
[Concerto for treble recorder & string orchestra in G major. Op.21, no.3]. Konzert für Altblockflöte mit Violinen oder Querflöten und Generalbass, G-Dur/ [by] Joseph Bodin de Boismortier; herausgegeben von Erich Doflein. — Mainz; London: Schott, 1972. — 30p; 4to.
£1.60

(B72-50660)

**RXMPVTF — Oboe & string orchestra. Concertos**
**Albinoni, Tommaso**
[Concerto for oboe & string orchestra in G minor. Op.9, no.8]. Concerto a 5: for oboe and strings/ by Tommaso Albinoni; edited by Franz Giegling. — London: Musica rara, 1972. — 4to.
Score (36p.) & 5 parts.
Unpriced

(B72-51091)

**Besozzi, Alessandro**
[Concerto for oboe & string orchestra in G major]. Concerto in G major: for oboe, strings and basso continuo/ by Alessandro Besozzi; [edited by] David Lasocki, realization of basso continuo by R.P. Block. — London: Musica rara, 1972. — 4to.
Score (34p.) & 5 parts.
Unpriced

(B72-51092)

**RXMPVTPLWSF — Trumpet, oboe & string orchestra. Concertos**
**Hertel, Johann Wilhelm**
[Concerto for trumpet, oboe & string orchestra in E flat major]. Doppel Konzert, Es-dur: für Trompete, Oboe, Streicher und Basso continuo/ [by] Johann Wilhelm Hertel; herausgegeben von Edward H. Tarr. — Mainz; London: Schott, 1972. — 39p; 4to.
£2.00

(B72-51093)

**RXMPVTQK/LF — Oboe d'amore & string orchestra. Arrangements. Concertos**
**Bach, Johann Sebastian**
[Concerto for harpsichord in A major. S.1055]. Concerto in A major for oboe d'amore, strings and basso continuo/ by Bach; reconstructed from BWV 1055; edited by Wilfried Fischer. — Cassel; London: Bärenreiter, 1970. — 33-56p; fol.
A reissue of pages 33-56 of 'Neue Ausgabe sämtlicher Werke', ser.7, Supp. Bd.7.
£1.50

(B72-50661)

**RXMPVVF — Clarinet & string orchestra. Concertos**
**Stamitz, Carl**
[Concerto for clarinet & string orchestra, no.1, in F major]. Konzert No.1, F - Dur: für Klarinette (C oder B)/ [by] Carl Stamitz; herausgegeben und mit Kadenzen versehen von Walter Lebermann. — Mainz; London: Schott, 1972. — 62p; 4to.
£3.00

(B72-51094)

**RXMPWNTE — Brass trio & string orchestra. Sonatas**
Biscogli, Francesco
[Concerto for trumpet, oboe, bassoon & string orchestra in D
Major]. Concerto for trumpet, oboe, bassoon, violins and
continuo/ by Francesco Biscogli; [edited by] Michael Talbot. —
London: Musica rara, 1972. — 4to.
Score (70p.) & 7 parts.
Unpriced

(B72-51095)

Legrenzi, Giovanni
[Sonata for two trumpets, bassoon & string orchestra, in A minor.
Lib.3, Op.8, 'La Buscha']. Sonata, 'La Buscha': for 2 trumpets
(cornetti), bassoon, and strings/ by Giovanni Legrenzi; edited by
Robert Paul Block. — London: Musica rara, 1972. — 4to.
Score (12p.) & 8 parts.
£1.00

(B72-51096)

**RXMPWS — Trumpet & string orchestra**
Stradella, Alessandro
[Il Barcheggio. - Sinfonia to part 2]. Sinfonia: for trumpet, 2
violins and continuo/ by Alessandro Stradella; edited by Robert
Paul Block. — London: Musica rara, 1971. — 4to.
Score (6p.) & 4 parts.
£3.00

(B72-51097)

**RXMPWSE — Trumpet & string orchestra. Sonatas**
Baldassare, Pietro
[Sonata for trumpet & string orchestra, no.1, in F major]. Sonata
in F, no.1: for cornetto (trumpet), strings and continuo/ by Pietro
Baldassare; edited by R.P. Block and John Beer. — London:
Musica rara, 1972. — 4to.
Score (13p.) & 5 parts.
Unpriced

(B72-51098)

Baldassare, Pietro
[Sonata for trumpet & string orchestra, no.2, in F major]. Sonata
in F, no.2: for solo trumpet (cornetto) and strings/ by Pietro
Baldassare; edited by R.P. Block and John Beer. — London:
Musica rara, 1972. — 4to.
Score (12p.) & 5 parts.
Unpriced

(B72-51099)

Cazzati, Mauritio
[Sonata for trumpet & string orchestra. Op.35, no.10, 'La
Cappara']. Sonata à 5, 'La Cappara': for trumpet and strings/ by
Mauritio Cazzati. Op.35, no.10; [edited by] Robert Paul Block and
Edward H. Tarr. — London: Musica rara, 1972. — 4to.
Score (8p.) & 6 parts. — This work issued with Op.35, nos.11-12.
£2.50

(B72-51100)

Cazzati, Mauritio
[Sonata for trumpet & string orchestra. Op.35, no.11, 'La
Bianchina']. Sonata à 5, 'La Bianchina': for trumpet and strings/
by Mauritio Cazzati, Op.35, no.11; [edited by] Robert Paul Block
and Edward H. Tarr. — London: Musica rara, 1972. — 4to.
This work issued with Op.35, nos.10 and 12. — Score (16p.) & 8 parts.

(B72-51101)

Cazzati, Mauritio
[Sonata for trumpet & string orchestra. Op.35, no.12, 'La
Zambecari]. Sonata à 5, 'La Zambecari': for trumpet and strings/
by Mauritio Cazzati, Op.35, no.12; [edited by] Robert Paul Block
and Edward H. Tarr. — London: Musica rara, 1972. — 4to.
£2.50

(B72-51102)

Grossi, Andrea
[Sonata for trumpet & string orchestra in D major. Op.3, no.10].
Sonata decima: for trumpet and strings/ by Andrea Grossi; edited
by Robert Paul Block. — London: Musica rara, 1972. — 4to.
Score (18p.) & 7 parts.
£2.00

(B72-51103)

**RXMPWSF — Trumpet & string orchestra. Concertos**
Hertel, Johann Wilhelm
[Concerto for trumpet & string orchestra in E flat]. Concerto no.2
in E flat: for trumpet, strings and major continuo/ by Johann
Wilhelm Hertel; edited by Edward H. Tarr. — London: Musica
rara, 1972. — 4to.
The numbering of this work is the editor's. — Score (22p.) & 6 parts.
Unpriced

(B72-51104)

Molter, Johann Melchior
[Concerto for trumpet, strings & basso continuo no.1 in D major.
MWV IV/14]. Concerto no.1 in D major: for solo trumpet, strings
and continuo (bassoon ad lib.)/ by J.M. Molter; edited by Michael
Talbot. — London: Musica rara, 1971. — 4to.
Score (24p.) & 9 parts.
Unpriced

(B72-50225)

Molter, Johann Melchior
[Concerto for trumpet, strings & basso continuo, no.2 in D major.
MWV IV/13]. Concerto no.2: for solo trumpet, strings and
continuo (bassoon ad lib)/ by J.M. Molter; [edited by] Michael
Talbot. — London: Musica rara, 1971. — 4to.
Score (28p.) & 8 parts.
Unpriced

(B72-50226)

Molter, Johann Melchior
[Concerto for trumpet, strings & basso continuo, no.3 in D major.
MWV IV/14]. Concerto no.3: for solo trumpet, strings and
continuo (bassoon ad lib.)/ by J.M. Molter; [edited by] Michael
Talbot. — London: Musica rara, 1971. — 4to.
Score (28p.) & 7 parts.
Unpriced

(B72-50227)

Stadlmair, Hans
[Concerto for trumpet & string orchestra]. Konzert für Trompete
in D und Streicher/ von Hans Stadlmair. — Frankfurt: Litolff;
[London]: [Hinrichsen], 1972. — 56p; 8vo.
Miniature score.
Unpriced

(B72-51105)

**RXMPWSPLSRE — Trumpet, cello & string orchestra. Sonatas**
Gabrielli, Domenico
[Sonata for trumpet, cello & string orchestra in D major]. Sonata
no.4 in D: for trumpet, strings and basso continuo/ by Domenico
Gabrielli; edited by Edward H. Tarr. — London: Musica rara,
1972. — 4to.
The numbering of this work is the editor's. — Score (7p.) & 9 parts.
y2.50

(B72-51106)

**RXMPWSPLVTF — Trumpet, oboe & string orchestra. Concertos**
Hertel, Johann Wilhelm
[Concerto for trumpet, oboe & string orchestra in E flat major].
Concerto à 6: for trumpet, oboe, strings and continuo/ by Johann
Wilhelm Hertel; edited by R.L. Minter. — London: Musica rara,
1972. — 4to.
Score (48p.) & 3 parts.
Unpriced

(B72-51107)

**RXNS — Quartets**
Beethoven, Ludwig van
[Quartet for strings in C major. Op.59, no.3]. String quartet in C
major. Op.59/3/ by Ludwig van Beethoven; edited by Paul Mies.
— Cassel; London: Bärenreiter, 1970. — vi,30p; 8vo.
Miniature score. — Duration 30 min.
£0.45

(B72-50662)

Beethoven, Ludwig van
[Quartet for strings in E flat major. Op.74]. String quartet in E
flat major. Op.74/ by Ludwig van Beethoven; edited by Paul
Mies. — Cassel; London: Bärenreiter, 1970. — v,28p; 8vo.
Miniature score. — Duration 32 min.
£0.45

(B72-50663)

Beethoven, Ludwig van
[Quartet for strings in E minor. Op.59, no.2]. String quartet in E
minor. Op.59/2/ by Ludwig van Beethoven; edited by Paul Mies.
— Cassel; London: Bärenreiter, 1970. — vi,28p; 8vo.
Miniature score.
£0.45

(B72-50664)

Beethoven, Ludwig van
[Quartet for strings in F major. Op.59, no.1]. String quartet in F
major. Op.59/1/ by Ludwig van Beethoven; edited by Paul Mies.
— Cassel; London: Bärenreiter, 1970. — vi,38p; 8vo.
Miniature score. — Duration 38 min.
£0.60

(B72-50665)

Beethoven, Ludwig van
[Quartet for strings in F minor. Op.95]. String quartet in F minor.
Op.74/ by Ludwig van Beethoven; edited by Paul Mies. — Cassel;
London: Bärenreiter, 1970. — vi,24p; 8vo.
Miniature score. — Duration 20 min.
£0.45

(B72-50666)

Debussy, Claude
[Quartet for strings. Op. 10]. Streichquartett. Op. 10/ von Claude
Debussy; nach den Quellen herausgegeben von Reiner
Zimmermann. — Leipzig: Peters; [London]: [Hinrichsen], 1971. —
viii,59p; 8vo.
Miniature score.
Unpriced

(B72-51108)

## Gal, Hans
[Quartet for strings , no.4]. String quartet 4/ by Hans Gal. — Hamburg; London: Simrock, 1972. — 4pt; 4to.
Contents: Legend. — Burlesque. — Elegy. — Capricio fugato.
Unpriced

(B72-50228)

## Gerhard, Roberto
[Quartet for strings, no.2]. String quartet, no.2/ by Roberto Gerhard. — London: Oxford University Press, 1972. — 36p; 8vo.
ISBN 0 19 356754 7 : £2.00

(B72-50229)

## Hessenberg, Kurt
[Quartet for strings, no.5]. Streichquartett No.5 (in einem Satz)/ [by] Kurt Hessenberg. — Regensberg: Bosse; [London]: [Bärenreiter], 1967. — 17p; 8vo.
Miniature score.
£1.05

(B72-50667)

## Horovitz, Joseph
[Quartet for strings no.5]. String quartet no.5/ by Joseph Horovitz. — Sevenoaks: Novello, 1971. — 4pt; 4to.
Unpriced

(B72-50230)

## Kelterborn, Rudolf
[Quartet for strings, no.4]. String quartet no.4/ by Rudolf Kelterborn. — Cassel; London: Bärenreiter, 1970. — 33p; 8vo.
Miniature score.
£1.15

(B72-50668)

## Lendvay, Kamilló
[Quartet for strings]. String quartet/ by Kamilló Lendvay. — London: Boosey and Hawkes, 1971. — 4to.
Score (20p.) & 4 parts.
£2.00

(B72-50231)

## Wolff, Christian
Lines: for string quartet, or quartet of stringed instruments/ by Christian Wolff. — New York; London: Peters, 1972. — 8ff; 4to.
'Four or more may play: versions for one to three are also possible.' - Composer's note.
Unpriced

(B72-51109)

## RXNS/T — Quartets. Variations
### Sigmund, Oskar
La Folia: neue Variationen nach Farinelli - Corelli, für 4 Soloviolinen/ [by] Oskar Sigmund. — Regensburg: Bosse; [London]: [Bärenreiter], 1970. — 11p; 8vo.
Miniature score.
£1.20

(B72-50669)

## RXNT — Trios
### Maconchy, Elizabeth
4 easy trios: for two violins and viola, or violin and two violas/ by Elizabeth Maconchy. — London: Faber Music, 1972. — 4to.
Score (9p.) & part for second violin or viola.
Unpriced

(B72-51110)

### Wuorinen, Charles
Trio: violin, viola, violoncello/ by Charles Wuorinen. — New York; London: Peters, 1971. 48p, 4to.
Duration 15 min.
£3.40

(B72-50670)

## S — VIOLIN
## S/AL — Examinations
### Associated Board of the Royal Schools of Music
Violin examinations, 1973 and 1974/ Associated Board of the Royal Schools of Music. — London: Associated Board of the Royal Schools of Music. —
Grade 1: Lists A and B (primary). — 1972. — 4to.
Score (13p.) & part.
£0.35

(B72-51111)

### Associated Board of the Royal Schools of Music
Violin examinations, 1973/ Associated Board of the Royal Schools of Music. — London: Associated Board of the Royal Schools of Music. —
Grade 2: Lists A and B (elementary). — 1972. — 4to.
Score (23p.) & part.
£0.35

(B72-51112)

Grade 3: Lists A and B (transitional). — 1972. — 4to.
Score (18p.) & part.
£0.35

(B72-51113)

Grade 4: Lists A and B (lower). — 1972. — 4to.
Score (21p.) & part.
£0.35

(B72-51114)

Grade 5: Lists A and B (higher). — 1972. — 4to.
£0.35

(B72-51115)

Grade 6: Lists A and B (intermediate). — 1972. — 4to.
Score (34p.) & part.
£0.40

(B72-51116)

Grade 7: Lists A & B (advanced). — 1972. — 4to.
Score (45p.) & part.
£0.50

(B72-51117)

## SNT — VIOLIN TRIOS
## SNTK/DW/G/AY — Violin trios. Arrangements. Folk songs.
### Collections
### Bryan, Rosamond
Ten violin trios/ arranged by Rosamond Bryan. — London: Oxford University Press, 1972. — 4to.
Score (11p.) & 2 parts.
ISBN 0 19 355736 3 : £0.50

(B72-50671)

## SP — VIOLIN & PIANO
## SP/AY — Collections
### Doflein, Elma
Music for violin and piano: a collection in 4 books in progressive order/ [compiled by] Elma and Erich Doflein. — Mainz; London: Schott. —
Score (48p.) & part.
4: Duos for piano and violin. — 1972. — 4to.
£1.50

(B72-50672)

## SP/T — Variations
### Cooper, Paul
Variations: violin and piano, 1967/ by Paul Cooper. — London: Chester, 1972. — 4to.
Score (19p.) & part.
Unpriced

(B72-50232)

## SPE — Sonatas
### Hoddinott, Alun
[Sonata for violin & piano, no.2. Op.73, no.1]. Sonata no.2, Op.73, no.1: for violin and piano/ by Alun Hoddinott. — London: Oxford University Press, 1972. — 4to.
ISBN 0 19 357152 8 : £2.00

(B72-50673)

### Hungar, Paul
[Sonata for violin & piano, no.2, in C major]. Sonate Nr.2, C-Dur: für Violine und Klavier/ [by] Paul Hungar. — Leipzig: Peters; [London]: [Hinrichsen], 1971. — 4to.
Score (24p.) & part.
£1.50

(B72-50674)

### Kadosa, Pál
[Sonata for violin & piano, no.1. Op.5]. Sonata no.1. Op.5: for violin and piano/ by Pál Kadosa. — London: Boosey and Hawkes, 1971. — 4to.
Score (18p.) & part.
£1.00

(B72-50233)

### Schwaen, Kurt
[Sonatina for violin & piano]. Sonatine für Violine und Klavier/ [by] Kurt Schwaen. — Leipzig: Peters; [London]: [Hinrichsen], 1972. — 4to.
Score (11p.) & part.
£0.80

(B72-50675)

### Shostakovich, Dmitri
[Sonata for violin & piano. Op.134]. Sonate für Violine und Klavier. Opus 134/ von Dmitri Schostakowitsch; Bezeichnung der Violinstimme von David Oistrach. — Leipzig; London: Peters, 1971. — 4to.
Score (60p.) & part.
Unpriced

(B72-51118)

### Srebotnjak, Alojz
Sonatina for violin and piano/ by Alojz Srebotnjak. — New York: Schirmer; [London]: [Chappell], 1971. — 4to.
Score (16p.) & part.
Unpriced

(B72-50234)

**Stanley, John**
English solos for flute (violin) and harpsichord, (v'c/va. da gamba ad lib.). Opus 1/ by John Stanley; edited with a keyboard realisation by George Pratt. — London: Peters, 1972. — 4to.
Score (54p.) & 2 parts.
Unpriced
*Primary classification VRPE*

**Veracini, Francesco Maria**
[Sonatas for violin & harpsichord. Op.2]. Sonata accademiche. Op.2: für Violine und beziffertem Bass, Violine und Klavier (Cembalo, Orgel) mit Violoncello ad libitum/ [by] Francesco Maria Veracini; herausgegeben von Walter Kolneder. — Leipzig: Peters; [London]: [Hinrichsen]. —
Sonata 10, F-Dur. — 1971. — 4to.
Score (12p.) & 2 parts.
£0.90
(B72-50676)

Sonata 11, E-Dur. — 1971. — 4to.
Score (23.) & 2 parts.
£0.90
(B72-50677)

**SPFL — Concertinos**
**Hertel, Klaus**
Concertino: für Violine (1.Lage) und Klavier/ [by] Klaus Hertel. — Leipzig: Peters; [London]: [Hinrichsen], 1971. — 4to.
Score (7p.) & part.
£0.75
(B72-50678)

**SPG — Suites**
**Kadosa, Pál**
Suite for violin and piano. Op.6/ by Pál Kadosa. — London: Boosey and Hawkes, 1972. — 4to.
Score (16p.) part.
£1.00
(B72-50679)

**SPHJN — Chaconnes**
**Vitali, Tomaso**
Chaconne: for violin and harpsichord/ [attributed to Tomaso Vitali]; edited and realized by Lionel Salter. — London: Oxford University Press, 1972. — 4to.
Score (12p.) & part.
ISBN 0 19 359210 x : £0.70
(B72-50680)

**SPJ — Miscellaneous works**
**Hovhaness, Alan**
Varak. Opus 47: violin and piano/ by Alan Hovhaness. — New York; London: Peters, 1971. — 4to.
Score (9p.) & part.
£1.00
(B72-50681)

**Schubert, Franz**
6 divertimenti da camera: for harpsichord (piano) and violin/ by Franz Schubert; edited by Wolfgang Plath. — Cassel; London: Nagel. —
Score (36p) & part.
Vol.2: Nos.4 - 6. — 1971. — 4to.
SPJ
(B72-50682)

**Schuster, Joseph**
6 divertimenti da camera: for harpsichord (piano) and violin/ by Joseph Schuster; edited by Wolfgang Plath. — Cassel; London: Nagel. —
Score (36p) & part.
Volume 1: Divertimenti 1 & 2. — 1971. — 4to.
£1.75
(B72-50683)

**SPK — Arrangements**
**Liszt, Franz**
[Selections]. Grand duo concertant. R.462; based on the romance 'Le Marin' by Philippe Lafont; [with], Epithalam. (Wedding Music). R.466: for piano and violin/ by Franz Liszt; edited by Zoltán Gárdonyi. — Cassel; London: Bärenreiter, 1971. — 4to.
Score (36p.) & part.
£2.00
(B72-50684)

**Routh, Francis**
Dialogue. Op. 16: for violin and orchestra/ by Francis Routh; arranged for violin and piano by the composer. — South Croydon: Lengnick, 1972. — 4to.
Score (23p.) & part.
£1.00
(B72-51119)

**SPK/LF — Arrangements. Concertos**
**Françaix, Jean**
[Concerto for violin]. Concerto: violin et orchestre/ [by] Jean Françaix. — Mainz; London: Schott, 1972. — 4to.
Reduction for violin and piano. Score (69p.) & part.
£5.00
(B72-50685)

**Mozart, Wolfgang Amadeus**
[Concerto for violin in D major. K.218]. Konzert, D-dur: f'ur Violine und Orchester/ von W.A. Mozart; Ausgabe f'ur Violine und Klavier von David Oistrach, [with cadenzas by Joseph Joachim and Ferdinand David]. — Leipzig; [London]: Peters, 1972. — 4to.
Klavierauszug von Wilhelm Weismann.
Unpriced
(B72-51120)

**SPLR — Violin & organ**
**Genzmer, Harald**
Introduzione, aria e finale: für Violine und Orgel/ [by] Harald Genzmer. — Frankfurt: Litolff; London: Peters, 1971. — obl.4to.
Score (12p.) & part.
£1.80
(B72-50235)

**SPLSQ — VIOLIN & VIOLA**
**Glasser, Stanley**
Four inventions: for violin and viola/ by Stanley Glasser. — Banbury: Piers Press, 1972. — 2pt.; 4to.
Unpriced
(B72-50686)

**Maconchy, Elizabeth**
3 easy pieces: for violin and viola/ by Elizabeth Maconchy. — London: Faber Music, 1972. — 7p; 4to.
Unpriced
(B72-51121)

**SPLSR — VIOLIN & CELLO**
**Joubert, John**
Duo for violin and cello. Op.65/ by John Joubert. — Sevenoaks: Novello, 1972. — 4to.
Score (38p.) & 2 parts.
£2.00
(B72-50687)

**SQNU — VIOLA DUETS**
**Maconchy, Elizabeth**
3 easy duets: for two violas/ by Elizabeth Maconchy. — London: Faber Music, 1972. — 7p; 4to.
Unpriced
(B72-51122)

**SQNUH — Duets. Dances**
**Hoffmann, Adolf**
Tanzbüchlein für zwei Bratschen: Tanzlieder und Volkstänze/ [by] Adolf Hoffmann; eingerichtet von Eva Wiesenfeldt. — Mainz; London: Schott, 1972. — 24p; obl.8vo.
£0.80
(B72-50688)

**SQP — VIOLA & PIANO**
**SQP/AY — Collections**
**Associated Board of the Royal Schools of Music**
New pieces for viola/ Associated Board of the Royal Schools of Music. — London: Associated Board of the Royal Schools of Music. —
Grades 2, 3. — 1972. — 4to.
Score (15p.) & part.
£0.95
(B72-51123)

Grades 2,3. — 1972. — 4to.
Score (15p.) & part.
£0.95
(B72-51124)

Grades 4, 5. — 1972. — 4to.
Score (35p.) & part.
£0.95
(B72-51125)

**SQPE — Sonatas**
**Corrette, Michel**
[Méthodes pour apprendre à jouer de la contre-basse. *Excerpts*]. Sonate für Viola und Klavier/ von Michel Corrette; herausgegeben von Erich Doflein. — Mainz; London: Schott, 1972. — 4to.
Score (11p.) & part.
Unpriced
(B72-51126)

**Finney, Ross Lee**
[Sonata for viola & piano no.1, in A minor]. Sonata in A minor: viola and piano/ by Ross Lee Finney; edited by Robert Courte. — New York; London: Peters, 1971. — 4to.
Score (27p.) & part.
£2.50
(B72-50689)

**Finney, Ross Lee**
[Sonata for viola & piano no.2]. Second sonata: viola and piano/ by Ross Lee Finney/ edited by Robert Courte. — New York; London: Peters, 1972. — 4to.
Score (35p.) & part.
£2.05
(B72-50690)

**Geissler, Fritz**
[Sonata for viola & piano]. Sonate für Viola und Klavier/ [by]
Fritz Geissler. — Leipzig: Peters; [London]: [Hinrichsen], 1971. —
4to.
Score (32p.) & part.
£1.80

(B72-50691)

**Haidmayer, Karl**
[Sonata for viola and piano, no.1]. Sonate 1 for viola and piano/
by Karl Haidmayer. — Cassel; London: Bärenreiter, 1971. — 4to.
Score (20p.) & part.
£1.25

(B72-50692)

## SQPJ — Miscellaneous works
**Corrette, Michel**
Zwei Sonaten und ein Menuett: für 2 Bratschen (Alto 1,2)/ von
Michel Corrette; herausgegeben von Erich Doflein. — Mainz;
London: Schott, 1972. — 15p; 4to.
£1.00

(B72-51127)

**Feldman, Morton**
The viola in my life/ by Morton Feldman. — New York;
[London]: Universal. —
3: Viola and piano. — 1972. — 4to.
Score (3p.) & part.
Unpriced

(B72-51128)

**Murray, Eleanor**
Tunes for my viola: fourteen pieces for viola and piano/ by
Eleanor Murray and Sebastian Brown. — London: Boosey and
Hawkes, 1972. — 4to.
Score (38p.) & part.
£0.75

(B72-50236)

## SQPK — Arrangements
**Bruch, Max**
Kol Nidrei. Opus 47/ by Max Bruch; arranged for viola and
piano by Robin de Smet. — London: Peters, 1972. — 4to.
Score (11p.) & part. — The score is another copy of that in the arrangement
for clarinet and piano.
Unpriced

(B72-51129)

**Holst, Gustav**
Lyric movement: for viola and small orchestra/ by Gustav Holst;
arranged for viola and piano by Imogen Holst. — London: Oxford
University Press, 1971. — 15p; 4to.
Reduction for viola & piano.
ISBN 0 19 357254 0 : £0.75

(B72-50237)

## SQPK/AEM — Arrangements. Sonatinas
**Hummel, Bertold**
[Sonatina for violin & piano (1969)]. Sonatina for viola and piano/
by Bertold Hummel. — Hamburg; London: Simrock, 1972. — 4to.
Score (11p.) & part. — After the Sonatina for violin and piano (1969).
Unpriced

(B72-50693)

## SQPLSR — VIOLA & CELLO
**Musgrave, Thea**
Elegy: for viola and cello/ by Thea Musgrave. — London:
Chester, 1971. — 19p; 4to.
Unpriced

(B72-50238)

## SQPM — UNACCOMPANIED VIOLA SOLOS
## SQPMG — Suites
**Williamson, Malcolm**
Partita for viola on themes of Walton/ by Malcolm Williamson;
edited by Yehudi Menuhin. — London: Weinberger, 1972. — 4p;
4to.
Unpriced

(B72-51130)

## SQPMJ — Miscellaneous works
**Tate, Phyllis**
Variegations: for solo viola/ by Phyllis Tate. — London: Oxford
University Press, 1971. — [11]p; 4to.
ISBN 0 19 359027 1 : £0.75

(B72-50239)

## SR — CELLO
## SRNRK/DW/AY — Quintets. Songs. Collections
**Thomas, Susanna**
Pieces for three, four and five cellos/ arranged by Susanna
Thomas. — London: Schott, 1972. — 4to.
Score (17p.) & 5 parts.
Unpriced

(B72-51131)

## SRNT — CELLO TRIOS
## SRNTK/AAY — Trios. Arrangements. Collections
**Thomas, Susanna**
Pieces for two and three cellos/ arranged by Susanna Thomas. —
London: Schott, 1972. — 4to.
Score (7p.) & 3 parts.
Unpriced

(B72-51132)

## SRNU — CELLO DUETS
**Maconchy, Elizabeth**
3 easy duets: for two cellos/ by Elizabeth Maconchy. — London:
Faber Music, 1972. — 7p; 4to.
Unpriced

(B72-51133)

## SRP — CELLO & PIANO
## SRP/AY — Collections
**Associated Board of the Royal Schools of Music**
The contemporary 'cellist: a collection of graded pieces for
violoncello and pianoforte/ Associated Board of the Royal Schools
of Music. — London: Associated Board of the Royal Schools of
Music. —
Book 1: Grades 1,2,3. — 1972. — 4to.
Score (31p.) & part.
£0.95

(B72-51134)

Book 2: Grades 4,5. — 1972. — 4to.
Score (27p.) & part.
£0.95

(B72-51135)

## SRPE — Sonatas
**Boismortier, Joseph Bodin de**
[Sonata for cello & basso continuo in D major, Op.26, no.1].
Sonata for cello and piano/ by J.B. de Boismortier; edited and
realised from the figured bass by A.D. Harris. — London: British
and Continental, 1972. — 4to.
Score (8p.) & part.
Unpriced

(B72-51136)

**Coke, Roger Sacheverell**
[Sonata for cello & piano, no.2, in C major. Op.29]. Sonata no.2
(in C major). Opus 29: for violoncello and piano, by R.
Sacheverell Coke. — London: Chappell, 1972. — 47p; 4to.
Unpriced

(B72-50240)

**Mercy, Louis**
[Sonata for cello & basso continuo in A minor. Op.3, no.6].
Sonata in A minor: for cello (or bassoon) and continuo
(harpsichord or piano)/ by Luidgi Merci; edited with realisation of
the figured bass by Walter Bergmann and Joan Dickson. —
London: Schott, 1972. — 4to.
Score (10p.) & part.
Unpriced

(B72-50241)

**Paxton, Stephen**
[Sonata for cello & harpsichord in A major. Op.l, no.1]. Sonata in
A. Op.l, no.1: for cello and harpsichord (or piano)/ by Stephen
Paxton; edited by Frank Dawes. — London: Schott, 1972. — 4to.
Score (20p.) & part.
£0.75

(B72-50694)

**Treibmann, Karl Ottomar**
[Sonata for cello & piano]. Sonate für Violoncello und Klavier/
[by] Karl Ottomar Treibmann. — Leipzig: Peters; [London]:
[Hinrichsen], 1971. — 4to.
Score (23p.) & part.
£1.80

(B72-50695)

## SRPJ — Miscellaneous works
**Bassett, Leslie**
Music for violoncello and piano/ by Leslie Bassett. — New York;
London: Peters, 1971. — 4to.
Score (15p.) & part.
£2.20

(B72-50696)

**Lidholm, Ingvar**
Quattro pezzi per violoncello & pianoforte/ [by] Ingvar Lidholm.
— London: Universal, 1972. — 4to.
Score (16p.) & part.
Unpriced

(B72-51137)

**Swayne, Giles**
Four lyrical pieces: for cello & piano/ by Giles Swayne. —
London: Oxford University Press, 1972. — 4to.
Score (17p.) & part.
ISBN 0 19 358935 4 : £1.20

(B72-51138)

**SRPK — Arrangements**
**Khachaturian, Aram**
[Concerto-rhapsody for cello]. Konzert-Rhapsodie: für Violoncello
und Orchester,/ [by] Aram Chatschaturjan; Ausgabe für
Violoncello und Klavier. — Leipzig: Peters; [London]:
[Hinrichsen], 1970. — 4to.
Score (40p.) & part.
£2.00

(B72-50697)

**Senaillé, Jean Baptiste**
[Sonata for violin & basso continuo, no.4, in D minor. Liv. 4. -
Allegro spirituoso]. Allegro/ by Jean Baptiste Senaillé; arranged
for 'cello and piano by Eric Gritton. — London: Associated Board
of the Royal Schools of Music, 1972. — 4to.
Score (6p.) & part.
£0.25

(B72-51139)

**SRPK/AEM — Arrangements. Sonatinas**
**Hummel, Bertold**
[Sonatina for violin & piano (1969)]. Sonatina for violoncello and
piano/ by Bertold Hummel. — Hamburg; London: Simrock, 1972.
— 4to.
Score (11p.) & part. — Arrangement of the Sonatina for violin and piano
(1969).
Unpriced

(B72-50698)

**SRPK/LF — Arrangements. Concertos**
**Stamitz, Carl**
[Concerto for cello, no.1, in G major]. Concerto 1, G major,
violoncello - small orchestra/ by Carl Stamitz; edited by Karlheinz
Füssl. — Cassel; London: Bärenreiter, 1971. — 4to.
Piano score (26p.) & part.
£1.00

(B72-50699)

**Stamitz, Carl**
[Concerto for cello, no.3, in C major]. Concerto 3, C major,
violoncello - small orchestra/ by Carl Stamitz; [edited by
Karlheinz] Füssel. — Cassel; London: Bärenreiter, 1971. — 4to.
Piano score (24p) & part.
£1.05

(B72-50700)

**Wood, Hugh**
Concerto for violoncello and orchestra. Op.12/ by Hugh Wood;
piano reduction by the composer. — London: Universal, 1971. —
4to.
Score (33p.) & part.
Unpriced

(B72-50242)

**SRPLTS — Harp & cello**
**Rubbra, Edmund**
Discourse. Op.27: for harp & cello/ by Edmund Rubbra. — South
Croydon: Lengnick, 1971. — 5p; 4to.
£0.25

(B72-50243)

**SRPLX — Cello & percussion**
**Braun, Gerhard**
Portrait 3: für Violoncello und kleiner Schlagzeug/ [by] Gerhard
Braun. — Regensburg: Bosse; [London]: [Bärenreiter], 1970. —
12ff.; obl.4to.
With a leaf explaining the lay-out of the instruments.
£1.25

(B72-50701)

**SRPM — UNACCOMPANIED CELLO SOLOS**
**SRPMJ — Miscellaneous works**
**Finney, Ross Lee**
Chromatic fantasy in E major: violoncello/ by Ross Lee Finney;
edited by Jerome Jelinek. — New York; London: Peters, 1971. —
7p; 4to.
Duration 10 min.
£1.10

(B72-50702)

**SS — DOUBLE BASS**
**SS/AF — Exercises**
**Slatford, Rodney**
Yorke studies for double bass/ [edited by Rodney Slatford]. —
London: Yorke. —
Vol.1: Half and first positions. — 1972. — 40p; 4to. —
Unpriced

(B72-51140)

**SSP — DOUBLE BASS & PIANO**
**SSPJ — Miscellaneous works**
**Berkeley, Lennox**
Introduction and allegro: for double bass and piano/ by Lennox
Berkeley. — London: Yorke, 1972. — 10p; 4to.
Unpriced

(B72-50244)

**SSPK/DW/AY — Arrangements. Songs, etc. Collections**
**Bottesini, Giovanni**
[Grande méthode complète de contre basse, pt.2; and, 'Etudes
mélodiques - Excerpts]. Arias for double bass and piano/ by
Giovanni Bottesini. — London (8 Cecil Rd, W.3): Yorke, 1972. —
4to.
Free arrangements of arias by Rossini, Verdi, and Bellini.
Unpriced

(B72-50703)

**ST — VIOL**
**STN/AZ — Viol consorts. Collected works of individual composers**
**Musica** Britannica: a national collection of music. — London:
Published for the Royal Music Association by Stainer and Bell. —
Vol.31: Matthew Locke: Chamber music 1/ transcribed and edited by
Michael Tilmouth. — 1971. — xxiii,146p; fol.
£10.00
*Primary classification C/AYD*

(B72-50007)

Vol.32: Matthew Locke: Chamber music 2/ transcribed and edited by
Michael Tilmouth. — 1971. — xxiii,109p; fol.
£10.00
*Primary classification C/AYD*

(B72-50008)

**STNU — VIOL DUETS**
**STUNTPW — Two bass viols & keyboard**
**Durkó, Zsolt**
Iconography no. 1: for two bass viols and harpsichord or two
violoncellos and piano (or harpsichord)/ by Zsolt Durkó. —
London: Boosey and Hawkes, 1972. — 4to.
Score (12p.) & 2 parts.
£1.00

(B72-51141)

**TQ — HARP**
**TQ/AC — Tutors**
**Watkins, David**
Complete method for the harp/ by David Watkins. — London:
Boosey and Hawkes, 1972. — 82p; 4to.
Unpriced

(B72-50704)

**TQPM — UNACCOMPANIED HARP SOLOS**
**TQPMJ — Miscellaneous works**
**Hoddinott, Alun**
Fantasy for harp. Opus 68, no.2/ by Alun Hoddinott. — London:
Oxford University Press, 1972. — 7p; 4to.
ISBN 0 19 357154 4 : £0.70

(B72-51142)

**Patachich, Ivan**
Contorni: per arpa/ d'Ivan Patachich. — London: Boosey and
Hawkes, 1971. — 12p; 4to.
£0.60

(B72-51143)

**TQPMK/AYD — Arrangements. Collections. England**
**Watkins, David**
Anthology of English music for the harp/ edited by David
Watkins. — London: Stainer and Bell. —
Vol.1. — 1972. — 25p; 4to. —
£1.00

(B72-51144)

Vol.4. — 1972. — 31p; 4to. —
£1.00

(B72-51145)

**TS — GUITAR**
**TS/AC — Tutors**
**Quine, Hector**
Introduction to the guitar/ by Hector Quine. — London: Oxford
University Press, 1971. — 33p; 4to.
ISBN 0 19 322325 2 : £0.80

(B72-50245)

**TS/AF — Exercises**
**Associated Board of the Royal Schools of Music**
Official book of scales & erpeggios for guitar/ Associated Board of
the Royal Schools of Music. — London: Associated Board of the
Royal Schools of Music, 1972. — 20p; 4to.
£0.25

(B72-50705)

**Roberts, Don**
An album of classical guitar studies/ composed and edited by Don
Roberts. — London: Francis, Day and Hunter, 1972. — 16p; 4to.
£0.40

(B72-51146)

**Roberts, Don**
Preset chords for guitar/ by Don Roberts. — London: Francis,
Day and Hunter, 1972. — 37p; 4to.
£0.75

(B72-50706)

**TS/EG — Sight reading**
**Associated Board of the Royal Schools of Music**
Specimen sight reading tests: guitar, grades 3,4,5,6 & 8/
Associated Board of the Royal Schools of Music. — London:
Associated Board of the Royal School of Music, 1972. — 4p; 4to.
£0.10

(B72-50246)

**TSNT — GUITAR TRIOS**
**TSNTK — Trios. Arrangements**
**Byrd, William**
The carman's whistle/ by William Byrd; arranged for 3 guitars by
Ivor Mairants. — London: Fenette Music: Breitkopf and Härtel,
1972. — 4to.
Score (8p.) & 3 parts.
Unpriced

(B72-50247)

**TSNTK/AAY — Trios. Arrangements. Collections**
**Wölki, Konrad**
Alte Lautenmusik: für drei Gitarren;/ herausgegeben von Konrad
Wölki. — Mainz; London: Schott, 1972. — 23p; 8vo.
£0.80

(B72-50707)

**TSPM — UNACCOMPANIED GUITAR SOLOS**
**TSPMG — Suites**
**Mairants, Ivor**
Six part suite: for solo guitar/ by Ivor Mairants. — London:
Fenette Music, Breitkopf and Härtel, 1972. — 15p; 4to.
Unpriced

(B72-51147)

**TSPMH — Dances**
**Brouwer, Leo**
Danza caracteristica para el "Quítate de la Acera": gitarre solo/
[by] Leo Brouwer. — Mainz; [London]: Schott, 1972. — 4p; 4to.
£0.08

(B72-51148)

**TSPMJ — Miscellaneous works**
**Arnold, Malcolm**
Fantasy. Op.107: for solo guitar/ by Malcolm Arnold; edited by
Julian Bream. — London: Faber Music, 1971. — 14p; 4to.
Unpriced

(B72-50248)

**Bennett, Richard Rodney**
Impromptus/ by Richard Rodney Bennett; fingering by Julian
Bream. — London: Universal, 1971. — 8p; 4to.
Unpriced

(B72-50249)

**Brouwer, Leo**
Canticum para guitarra/ [by] Leo Brouwer. — Mainz; [London]:
Schott, 1972. — 4p; 4to.
£0.80

(B72-51149)

**Brouwer, Leo**
Elogio de la danza: para guitarra/ [by] Leo Brouwer. — Mainz;
[London]: Schott, 1972. — 6p; 4to.
£0.90

(B72-51150)

**Brouwer, Leo**
Tres apuntes — Three sketches/ by Leo Brouwer. — Mainz,
[London]: Schott, 1972. — 7p; 4to.
£0.90

(B72-51151)

**Fricker, Peter Racine**
Paseo: for solo guitar/ by Peter Racine Fricker; edited by Julian
Bream. — London: Faber Music, 1971. — 12p; 4to.
Unpriced

(B72-50250)

**Hartig, Heinz Friedrich**
Solo for guitar (1951)/ by Heinz Friedrich Hartig; fingered by
Siegfried Behrend. — Sevenoaks: Novello, 1972. — 3p; 4to.
£0.25

(B72-50708)

**Stingl, Anton**
Improvisation über ein mittelalterliches Lied 'Es sass ein edly
maget schön'. Op 46: fur Gitarre/ [by] Anton Stingl. — Mainz;
London: Schott, 1972. — 4to.
Unpriced

(B72-50709)

**Wilson, Thomas**
Soliloquy/ by Thomas Wilson. — London: Stainer & Bell, 1972.
— 14p; 4to.
£0.66

(B72-50710)

**TSPMK/AAY — Arrangements. Collections**
**Pearse, John**
The first book of solos for the classical guitar/ edited by John
Pearse, arranged by Alan Hall. — London: Scatchwood Music,
1971. — 16p; 4to.
Unpriced

(B72-50251)

**Renbourn, John**
Guitar pieces/ [composed, compiled and arranged] John
Renbourn. — New York: Oak Publications; London: Pentangle,
Music Sales, 1972. — 48p; 4to.
Unpriced

(B72-51152)

**TSPMK/AHW — Arrangements. Waltzes**
**Granados, Enrique**
Valses poéticas/ by E. Granados; arranged for solo guitar by Ivor
Mairants. — London: British and Continental, 1972. — 8p; 4to.
Unpriced

(B72-51153)

**TSPMK/DW — Arrangements. Songs, etc**
**Beatles** complete: guitar edition. — London: Wise, Music Sales,
1972. — 205p; 4to.
ISBN 0 02 976930 2 : £2.50

(B72-50711)

**Mozart, Wolfgang Amadeus**
[Die Zauberflöte. - *Excerpts*]. Six airs/ by Wolfgang Amadeus
Mozart; arranged for guitar by Fernando Sor, new edition by
Martyn Hodgson. — Leeds: Regina Music, 1972. — 8p; 4to.
Fernando Sor's Opus 19.
Unpriced

(B72-50712)

**TT — BANJO**
**TT/AC — Tutors**
**Scruggs, Earl**
Earl Scruggs and the five-string banjo/ by Earl Scruggs; [assisted
by] Billy Keith and Burt Brent. — London: Music Sales, 1972. —
156p; 4to.
£1.75

(B72-51154)

**TWTPM — UNACCOMPANIED PSALTERY SOLOS**
**TWTPMJ — Miscellaneous works**
**Nicholson, Roger**
Nonesuch for dulcimer/ by Roger Nicholson; edited and
transcribed by John Pearse. — London: Scratchwood Music:
[Feldman], 1972. — 33p; 4to.
Unpriced

(B72-50252)

**UM — WIND BAND**
**UMG — Suites**
**Street, Allan**
Nott'num town: suite for symphonic band/ by Allan Street. —
London: Boosey and Hawkes, 1972. — 4to.
Score (53p.) conductor & 68 parts.
£5.25

(B72-50253)

**UMGM — Marches**
**Rodgers, Richard**
Symphonic marches for concert band/ by Richard Rodgers;
arranged by Robert Farnon. — London: Williamson, 1972. — 4to.
Conductor (24p.) & 34 parts.
Unpriced

(B72-50254)

**UMJ — Miscellaneous works**
**Hindemith, Paul**
Konzertmusik. Op.41: für Bläsorchester/ by Paul Hindemith. —
Mainz; London: Schott, 1972. — 51p; 8vo.
Study score.
£1.60

(B72-50713)

**Pennington, John**
Apollo: aleatoric piece for band/ by John Pennington. — New
York: Schirmer; [London]: [Chappell], 1971. — 4to.
Score (7p.) & 61 parts.
Unpriced

(B72-50255)

**UMK — Arrangements**
**Coates, Eric**
[Selections]. The music of Eric Coates/ arranged for concert band
by Trevor L. Sharpe. — London: Chappell, 1971. — 4to.
Conductor (16p.) & 35 parts.
Unpriced

(B72-50256)

**Hovhaness, Alan**
[Symphony no.2. Op.132. - Andante con moto]. Mysterious mountain/ Alan Hovhaness; transcribed for concert band by Frank Erickson. — New York; London: Associated Music, 1972. — 23p; 4to.
Unpriced

(B72-50257)

## UMM — MILITARY BAND
## UMM/AY — Collections
**Pätzig, Gerhard**
Historische Bläsermusiken: 25 Militärmärsche des 18, Jahrhunderts; erste Urtextausgabe nach den Originalhandschriften für den praktischen Gebrauch/ herausgegeben von Gerhard Pätzig. — Cassel; London: Bärenreiter. —
Score (32p.) & 7 parts.
Heft 1. — 1971. — 8vo.
£2.50

(B72-50714)

Heft 2. — 1971. — 8vo.
£3.00

(B72-50715)

Heft 3. — 1971. — 8vo.
£2.00

(B72-50716)

## UMMGM — Marches
**Elms, Albert**
Wembley way: quick march/ by Albert Elms. — London: Boosey and Hawkes, 1972. — 25pt.; obl.8vo.
With several copies of various parts.
£0.55

(B72-50717)

## UMMHW — Waltzes
**Ewing, Montague**
Purple heather/ by Montague Ewing. — Bognor Regis: Norman Richardson Band Arrangements, 1972. — 8vo & obl. 8vo.
Short score (4p.) & 40 parts.
Unpriced

(B72-50718)

## UMMJ — Miscellaneous works
**Chance, John Barnes**
Elegy/ by John Barnes Chance. — New York; [London]: Boosey and Hawkes, 1972. — 4to.
Score (19p.) Condensed score (12p.) & 67 parts.
£4.50

(B72-51155)

**Grundman, Clare**
A classical overture/ by Clare Grundman. — New York; [London]: Boosey and Hawkes, 1972. — 30p; 4to.
£1.50

(B72-51156)

**Grundman, Clare**
Festive piece/ by Clare Grundman. — New York; [London]: Boosey and Hawkes, 1972. — 36p; 4to.
£2.00

(B72-51157)

**Tull, Fisher**
Antiphon/ by Fisher Tull. — New York; [London]: Boosey and Hawkes, 1972. — 4to.
Full score (16p.), Condensed score (8p.) & 72 parts.
£30.00

(B72-51158)

**Tull, Fisher**
Terpsichore/ by Fisher Tull. — New York; [London]: Boosey and Hawkes, 1972. — 4to.
Full score (32p.), condensed score (12p.) & 69 parts.
£33.95

(B72-51159)

## UMMK — Arrangements
**Gray, Jerry**
American patrol/ original arrangement by Jerry Gray; arranged for band by W.J. Duthoit. — London: Chappell, 1972. — 4to.
Conductor (8p.) & 34 parts.
Unpriced

(B72-50719)

## UMMK/DW — Military band. Arrangements. Songs, etc
**Regney, Noel**
Do you hear what I hear?: Stadium dimension for marching bands/ by Noel Regney and Gloria Shayne; arranged by Dick Thomas. — London: Jewel Music, 1971. — 8vo.
Conductor & 54 parts.
Unpriced

(B72-50258)

## UMMK/DW/JS — Arrangements. Songs, etc. Television music
**Cole, Tony**
Beg, steal or borrow: Britain's Eurovision song 1972/ composed by Tony Cole, Graeme Hall and Steve Wolfe; arranged by William Relton. — London: Valley Music, 1972. — 8vo & obl 8vo.
Short score (2p.) & 24 parts.
Unpriced

(B72-50259)

## UMMK/JR — Arrangements. Films
**Gold, Ernest**
[Exodus. - *Excerpts*]. Main theme/ by Ernest Gold; arranged for military band by K. Griffin. — London: Chappell, 1972. — 32pt.; 4to.
Various parts are in duplicate.
Unpriced

(B72-50720)

## UMMK/JS — Arrangements. Television music
**Pearson, Johnny**
Sleepy shores: theme from the BBC TV series Owen M.D./ by Johnny Pearson; arranged by Edrich Siebert. — London: Keith Prowse Music, 1971. — obl.8vo.
Unpriced

(B72-50260)

## UMP — WORKS FOR SOLO INSTRUMENT (S) & WIND BAND
## UMPSRF — Cello and wind band. Concertos
**Genzmer, Harald**
[Concerto for cello and wind band]. Konzert für Violoncello und Bläser/ [by] Harald Genzmer. — Frankfurt: Litolff; [London]: [Hinrichsen], 1971. — 102p; 8vo.
£3.50

(B72-50261)

## UN — WIND ENSEMBLE
## UNN — Octets
**Mozart, Wolfgang Amadeus**
Divertimento, E flat major. KV App, 182: 2 oboes, 2 clarinets in B flat, 2 bassoons, 2 horns in E flat/ by W.A. Mozart; edited by Alfred Einstein. — New York; London: Peters, 1971. — 30p; 8vo.
£1.80

(B72-50721)

**Mozart, Wolfgang Amadeus**
[Divertimento for wind octet in B flat major. K. Anh. 227]. Divertimento, B flat major, KV app. 227: 2 oboes, 2 clarinets in B flat, 2 bassoons, 2 horns in E flat/ by W.A. Mozart; edited by Alfred Einstein. — New York; London: Peters, 1971. — 18p; 8vo.
£1.50

(B72-50722)

**Mozart, Wolfgang Amadeus**
[Divertimento for wind octet in E flat major. K. Anh. 226]. Divertimento, E flat major. KV App, 226: 2 oboes, 2 clarinets in B flat, 2 bassoons, 2 horns in E flat,/ by W.A. Mozart; edited by Alfred Einstein. — New York; London: Peters, 1971. — 31p; 8vo.
£1.80

(B72-50723)

## UNR — Quintets
**David, Gyula**
[Quintet for wind instruments, no.4]. Quintetto a fiati no.4/ by Gyula David. — London: Boosey and Hawkes, 1971. — 4to.
Score (16p.) & 5 parts.
£1.50

(B72-50262)

**Gebauer, François René**
[Quintet for wind instruments in E flat major]. Quintet in E flat major: for flute, oboe, clarinet, horn and bassoon/ by Francis René Gebauer; edited by Frans Vester. — London: Universal, 1972. — 4to.
Score (42p.) & 5 parts.
Unpriced

(B72-51160)

## UNRK/DW — Quintets. Arrangements. Songs, etc
**Grainger, Percy Aldridge**
Lisbon: for wind five-some (flute, oboe, clarinet, horn and bassoon)/ English folksong noted down from the singing of Mr. Deane by Percy Aldridge Grainger. — London: Schott, 1971. — 4to.
Score (3p.) & 5 parts.
£0.65

(B72-50724)

UNSK/AE — Quartets. Arrangements, Symphonies
Vivaldi, Antonio
Sinfonia 'Al santo sepulcro'. [Rinaldi Op.50]/ by Antonio Vivaldi;
arranged for recorder quartet (tr.1 & 2, T, B) or wind quartet fl.,
ob., clar., 1 horn, bn.,) by Richard Coles. — Banbury (c/o Stanley
Glasser, Goldsmiths' College, S.E.14): Piers Press, 1972. — 4to.
Score (5p.) & 5 parts. — An errata slip is inserted. — The alternative part
for clarinet is printed on the verso of the last page of the score.
Unpriced
*Primary classification VSNSK/AE*

(B72-50744)

VN — WOODWIND ENSEMBLE
VNRG — Quintets. Suites
Le Fleming, Christopher
Homage to Beatrix Potter: six short pieces for wind ensemble
(flute, oboe, 2 clarinets and bassoon)/ by Christopher le Fleming.
— London: Chester, 1971. — 8vo.
Score (15p.) & 5 parts.
Unpriced

(B72-50263)

VNT — Trios
Stoker, Richard
Trio for flute, oboe, clarinet/ by Richard Stoker. — London:
Leeds Music, 1971. — 8vo.
Score (16p.) & 3 parts.
Unpriced

(B72-50264)

VR — FLUTE
VR/AC — Tutors
Rendell, Don
Robbins flute tutor: a contemporary method/ by Don Rendell. —
London: Robbins. —
Part 1. — 1972. — 44p; 4to.
£1.50

(B72-50725)

VR/ELM — Fingering
Schaeffer, Burghard
Annotated fingering tables for the Boehm flute/ by Burghard
Schaeffer. — Hamburg; London: Rahter, 1972. — 61p; 4to.
Unpriced

(B72-50726)

VRNS — FLUTE QUARTETS
Braun, Gerhard
Portrait 1: für 4 Querflöten/ [by] Gerhard Braun. — Regensburg:
Bosse; [London]: [Bärenreiter], 1970. — 9ff; obl.fol.
With a separate leaf of instructions.
£1.50

(B72-50727)

Kuhlau, Friedrich
[Quartet for four flutes in E major. Op.103]. Quartett, E-dur: für
vier Flöten/ [by] Friedrich Kuhlau; herausgegeben von Frank
Nagel. — Frankfurt: Litolff; London: Peters, 1971. — 4pt; 4to.
£3.00

(B72-50265)

VRNTPW — TWO FLUTES & KEYBOARD
VRNTPWE — Two flutes & keyboard. Sonatas
Handel, George Frideric
[Sonata for two flutes & basso continuo in E minor]. Sonata in E
minor: 2 flutes and continuo, (v'c ad libitum)/ by G.F. Handel;
edited by A. Craig Bell, continuo realisation by Alan Cuckston. —
London: Peters, 1972. — 4to.
Score (20p.) & 3 parts.
£1.40

(B72-50728)

VRNU — FLUTE DUETS
Zehm, Friedrich
Neue Duettstudien: für Querflöten/ von Friedrich Zehm. —
Mainz; London: Schott, 1972. — 23p; 4to.
Unpriced

(B72-51161)

VRNU/T — Duets. Variations
Reicha, Anton
Variations for two flutes. Op.20/ by Anton Reicha; edited by F.F.
Polnauer. — New York; London: Peters, 1971. — 9p; 4to.
£1.60

(B72-50729)

VRP — FLUTE & PIANO
VRP/T — Variations
Kuhlau, Friedrich
Introduction and variations on a theme from Carl Maria von
Weber's 'Euryanthe' Op.63/ by Friedrich Kuhlau; edited by Hans
Peter Schmitz. — Cassel; London: Bärenreiter, 1971. — 4to.
Score (23p) & part.
£1.50

(B72-50730)

VRPE — Sonatas
Abel, Carl Friedrich
[Sonata for flute & basso continuo in E minor. Op.6, no.3]. Sonata
in E minor: for flute and continuo/ by C.F. Abel; edited by
Gwilym Beechey. — London: Oxford University Press, 1972. —
4to.
Score (10p.) & part.
ISBN 0 19 355081 4 : £0.75

(B72-50731)

Abel, Carl Friedrich
[Sonata for flute & basso continuo in G major. Op.6, no.6]. Sonata
in G major. Op 6, no.6: for flute and basso continuo/ by Carl
Friedrich Abel; edited by Gwilym Beechey. — Cassel; London:
Bärenreiter, 1971. — 4to.
Score (14p.) & 2 parts.
£1.20

(B72-50732)

Kalmár, Lászlo
[Sonata for flute & piano]. Sonate per flauto e pianoforte/ di
Lászlo Kalmár. — London: Boosey and Hawkes, 1971. — 9p; 4to.
£0.60

(B72-51162)

Ries, Ferdinand
[Sonata sentimentale for flute & piano in E flat major. Op.169].
Sonata in E flat major for flute or clarinet and piano/ by
Ferdinand Ries; edited by Hans-Peter Schmitz. — Cassel; London:
Bärenreiter, 1970. — 4to.
Score (53p.) & 2 parts.
£2.45
*Also classified at VVPE*

(B72-50733)

Stanley, John
[Selections]. Vier Sonaten: für Querflöte und Basso continuo,
Cembalo (Pianoforte, Violoncello, Viola da gamba), ad lib./ [von]
John Stanley; herausgegeben von Bernhard Weigart. — Mainz;
London: Schott. —
Band 1: Sonate 1, G-Dur. [Op.4, no.3]; Sonate 2, G-Moll. [Op.1, no.2]. —
1972. — 4to.
Score (20p.) & 2 parts.
£1.20

(B72-51163)

Stanley, John
[Selections]. Vier Sonaten: für Querflöte und Basso continuo,
Cembalo (Pianoforte, Violoncello, Viola da gamba), ad lib./ [by]
John Stanley; herausgegeben von Bernhard Weigart. — Mainz;
London: Schott. —
Band 2: Sonate 3, D-Dur. [Op.1, no.4]; Sonate 4, D-Moll. [Op.1, no.7]. —
1972. — 4to.
Score (20p.) & 2 parts.
£1.20

(B72-51164)

Stanley, John
English solos for flute (violin) and harpsichord, (v'c/va. da gamba
ad lib.). Opus 1/ by John Stanley; edited with a keyboard
realisation by George Pratt. — London: Peters, 1972. — 4to.
Score (54p.) & 2 parts.
Unpriced
*Also classified at SPE*

(B72-51165)

VRPG — Suites
Copland, Aaron
Duos for flute and piano/ by Aaron Copland. — London: Boosey
and Hawkes, 1971. — 4to.
Score (21p.) & part.
£1.25

(B72-50266)

VRPJ — Miscellaneous works
Fekete Györ, István
Three duos for flute and piano/ by István Fekete Györ. —
London: Boosey and Hawkes, 1971. — 4to.
Score (18p.) & part.
£0.55

(B72-51166)

Golle, Jürgen
Vier leichte Stücke: für Flote und Klavier/ [by] Jürgen Golle. —
Leipzig: Peters; [London]: [Hinrichsen], 1971. — 4to.
Score (13p.) & part.
£0.80

(B72-50734)

Guy, Barry
4 miniatures: for flute and piano/ by Barry Guy. — Sevenoaks:
Novello, 1972. — 6p; 4to.
£1.50

(B72-50735)

**Kocs'ar, Miklos**
Repliche: per flauto e zimbalo ungherese (o clavicembalo) [by]
Miklos Kocs'ar. — London: Boosey and Hawkes, 1971. — 10p;
4to.
£0.85
*Primary classification VRPLTWT*

(B72-50738)

**Sári, József**
Contemplazione: per flauto e pianoforte/ [by] József Sári. —
London: Boosey and Hawkes, 1971. — 4to.
Score (12p.) & part.
£1.00

(B72-50736)

**Veal, Arthur**
Three Greek pastorals: flute and piano/ by Arthur Veal. —
London: Peters, 1972. — 4to.
Score (12p.) & part.
Unpriced

(B72-51167)

**Wilson, John**
Three Westmorland sketches: oboe and piano/ by John Wilson. —
London: Forsyth, 1972. — 4to.
Score (13p.) & 2 parts.
Unpriced
*Primary classification VTPJ*

(B72-50283)

**VRPK/AAY — Arrangements. Collections**
**Kovács, Imre**
Flute music for beginners/ edited by Imre Kovács and Vilmos
Bántai. — London: Boosey and Hawkes, 1971. — 4to.
£0.85

(B72-50737)

**Phillips, Ivan Clarence**
The beginner's repertoire for flute/ selected and adapted by Ivan
C. Phillips. — London: Oxford University Press. —
Vol.1. — 1971. — 4to.
Score (13p.) & part.
ISBN 0 19 358220 1 : £0.50

(B72-50267)
Vol.2. — 1971. — 4to.
Score (18p.) & part.
ISBN 0 19 358221 x : £0.65

(B72-50268)

**VRPK/LF — Arrangements. Concertos**
**Mozart, Wolfgang Amadeus**
[Concerto for flute, no.2, in D major. K.314]. Konzert Nr.2, D
dur, für Flöte and Orchester. K.314/ von W.A. Mozart; Ausgabe
für Flöte und Klavier (mit Kadenzen) von Erich List. — London:
Peters, 1972. — 4to.
Klavierauszug von Siegfried Thiele. Score (24p.) & part.
Unpriced

(B72-51168)

**VRPLTWT — Flute & psaltery**
**Kocsár, Miklos**
Repliche: per flauto e zimbalo ungherese (o clavicembalo) [by]
Miklos Kocsár. — London: Boosey and Hawkes, 1971. — 10p;
4to.
£0.85
*Also classified at VRPJ*

(B72-50738)

**VRPM — UNACCOMPANIED FLUTE SOLOS**
**VRPMJ — Miscellaneous works**
**Neubert, Günter**
Musik für Flöte solo/ [by] Günter Neubert. — Leipzig: Peters;
[London]: [Hinrichsen], 1971. — 5p; 4to.
£0.50

(B72-50739)

**VS — RECORDER**
**VS/AC — Tutors**
**Blackburn, Marie**
Let's play recorders: a simple recorder tutor for very young
children, including 28 folk songs to play/ by Marie Blackburn. —
London: Feldman, 1971. — 13p; 4to.
£0.20

(B72-50269)

**VSK/DW/AY — Arrangements. Songs. Collections**
**Dinn, Freda**
Sing a son, play a song: a recorder book for sixes and sevens/ by
Freda Dinn. — London: Schott, 1972. — 4to.
Teacher's book (20p.) & class book (16p.).
£0.95

(B72-50740)

**VSNN — RECORDER OCTETS**
**Viadana, Lodovico**
[Sinfonie musicali. Op.18. - *Excerpts*]. Canzona - La Padovana: 8
recorders/ by Ludovico Grossi da Viadana; edited and arranged
by Reginald Johnson. — London: Universal, 1972. — 4to.
Score (11p.) & 8 parts.
Unpriced

(B72-51169)

**VSNR — RECORDER QUINTETS**
**VSNRK — Quintets. Arrangements**
**Elgar, *Sir* Edward, *bart***
Chanson de matin. Op.15, no.2/ by Edward Elgar; arranged for
recorder quintet by Gregory Murray. — London: Novello, 1971.
— 4to.
Score (8p.) & 5 parts.
Unpriced

(B72-50270)

**Lawes, William**
Fantasia and air/ by William Lawes; arranged for recorder
quintet, 2D., Tr. T.B., by Ian Lawrence. — London: Faber, 1972.
— 4to.
Score (9p.) & 5 parts.
Unpriced

(B72-50741)

**VSNS — RECORDER QUARTETS**
**Gabrieli, Andrea**
[Madrigali et ricercari a quattro voci. - *Excerpts*]. Ricercari a
quattro, nos.6 & 7: for four recorders (descant, treble, tenor and
bass)/ by Andrea Gabrieli; edited by Walter Lebermann. —
Mainz; London: Schott, 1972. — 24p; 4to.
£1.20

(B72-51170)

**Jacques, Michael**
[Divertimento for recorder quartet, no.3]. Divertimento no.3: for
recorder quartet (2 descant, treble & tenor)/ by Michael Jacques.
— London: Schott, 1972. — 4to.
Score (13p.) & 4 parts.
£1.00

(B72-50742)

**VSNSK — Arrangements**
**Gibbons, Orlando**
[Selections]. Two fantasias/ by Orlando Gibbons; arranged for
descant, treble, tenor and bass [recorders] by Ward Gardner. —
London: Schott, 1972. — 4to.
Score (8p.) & 4 parts.
£0.75

(B72-51171)

**VSNSK — Quartets. Arrangements**
**Mozart, Wolfgang Amadeus**
[Divertimento for wind sextet in B flat major. K. 240. - Excerpts].
Allegro: for descant, 2 treble and tenor recorders/ by Wolfgang
Amadeus Mozart; arranged by Tony Frost. — London: Chester,
1972. — 4to.
Score (8p.) & 4 parts. — Arranged in the key of G.
Unpriced

(B72-50743)

**VSNSK/AAY — Quartets. Arrangements. Collections**
**Attaingnant, Pierre**
[Vingt et sept chansons musicales à quatre parties. - *Excerpts*].
Fourteen chansons: for four recorders or voices, ATTB,/
[compiled by] Pierre Attaingnant; edited by Bernard Thomas,
texts edited and translated by Alan Robson. — London: Pro
musica, 1972. — 4to.
Unpriced
*Primary classification EZDU/AY*

**VSNSK/AE — quartets. Arrangements. Symphonies**
**Vivaldi, Antonio**
Sinfonia 'Al santo sepulcro'. [Rinaldi Op.50]/ by Antonio Vivaldi;
arranged for recorder quartet (tr.1 & 2, T, B) or wind quartet fl.,
ob., clar., 1 horn, bn.,) by Richard Coles. — Banbury (c/o Stanley
Glasser, Goldsmiths' College, S.E.14): Piers Press, 1972. — 4to.
Score (5p.) & 5 parts. — An errata slip is inserted. — The alternative part
for clarinet is printed on the verso of the last page of the score.
Unpriced
*Also classified at UNSK/AE*

(B72-50744)

**VSNT — Trios**
**Gál, Hans**
Divertimento. Op.98: for 3 recorders (descant, treble, tenor)/ by
Hans Gál. — Mainz; London: Schott, 1972. — 13p; 4to.
£0.80

(B72-50745)

**VSNTG — Trios. Suites**
**Clements, John**
A suite: for recorder trio, one descant and two trebles/ by John
Clements. — London: Ashdown, 1971. — 10p; 4to.
Unpriced

(B72-50271)

**Gubby, Roy**
Suite for three recorders: treble (tenor 1), tenor 2 and bass (or cello)/ by Roy Gubby. — London: Boosey and Hawkes, 1972. — 12p; 4to.
Duration 7 min.
£0.50
*Also classified at NVSNTG*
(B72-50746)

**Simpson, John**
A little suite: for two descant recorders & treble recorders/ by John Simpson. — London: Feldman, 1972. — 4to.
Score (6p.) & part.
Unpriced
(B72-50272)

**VSNTPWK/AAY — Arrangements. Collections**
**Wohlgemuth, Gerhard**
Classisches Spielbuch: für Sopran-Blockflöte, Alt-Blockflöte und Klavier/ herausgegeben von Gerhard Wohlgemuth.. — Leipzig: Peters; [London]: [Hinrichsen], 1971. — 4to.
Score (18p.) & part.
Unpriced
(B72-51172)

**VSNU — RECORDER DUETS**
**VSNUK/AH — Duets. Dances**
**Arbeau, Thoinot**
[Orchésographie. - *Excerpts*]. Twelve dances/ by Arbeau; arranged for descant & treble recorders by Freda Dinn. — London: Schott, 1972. — 13p; 8vo.
Unpriced
(B72-50273)

**VSPM — UNACCOMPANIED RECORDER**
**VSPMK/AHM/AY — Arrangements. Ballet. Collections**
**Sadleir, Richard**
A book of ballet: [arranged] and compiled for recorder by Richard Sadleir. — London: British & Continental, 1972. — 11p; 8vo.
Unpriced
(B72-50747)

**VSPMK/DW/G/AY — Arrangements. Folk songs. Collections**
**Sansom, Clive A**
Favourites for recorder/ arranged by Clive A. Sansom. — London: Feldman. —
No.1. — 1971. — 25p; 8vo.
£0.25
(B72-50274)

**VSR/AC — Descant recorder. Tutors**
**Salkeld, Robert**
Play the recorder/ by Robert Salkeld. — London: Chappell, 1971. — 4to.
Accompaniments for book2. — Score (44p.) & part.
£1.40
(B72-50275)

**Slaney, Ivor**
The recorder: how to play the descant recorder, complete with rudiments of music, fingering and studies/ by Ivor Slaney. — London: Campbell, Connelly, 1972. — 40p; 8vo.
This tutor is also suitable for the tenor recorder.
£0.40
*Also classified at VST/AC*
(B72-51173)

**VSRNTK/DW/AY — Descant recorder trios. Arrangements. Songs. Collections**
**Draths, Willi**
Aus fremden Ländern: Lieder und Tänze für drei Sopranblockflöten der andere Melodie - Instrumente, Gitarre und Schlagwerk ad lib/ bearbeitet von Willi Draths. — London: Schott. —
Band 2. — 1972. — 32p; obl.8vo.
£0.70
(B72-50748)

**VSRNTQK — Two descant recorders & piano. Arrangements**
**Debussy, Claude**
[Petite suite. - *Excerpts*]. En bateau by Claude Debussy; arranged for two descant recorders and piano (with optional treble recorder) by A.W. Benoy. — London: Oxford University Press, 1972. — 4to.
Score (9p.) & 6 parts.
ISBN 0 19 356150 6 : £0.50
(B72-50276)

**VSRNU — Descant recorder ensemble. Duets**
**Böhn, Liselotte**
Spiel im Duett: leichte Stücke für zwei Sopran-Blockflöten/ [by] Liselotte Böhn. — Mainz; London: Schott, 1972. — 16p; obl.8vo.
£0.60
(B72-51174)

**VSRP/AYJV(XE) — Descant recorder & piano. Collections. Venice, 1600**
**Linde, Hans Martin**
Venezianische Musik um 1600: Stücke von Frescobaldi, Castello und Fontana, für Sopran - oder Tenorblockflöte oder andere Melodieinstrumente und Basso continuo/ herausgegeben von Hans-Martin Linde. — Mainz; London: Schott, 1972. — 4to.
Score (20p.) & 2 parts.
£1.10
(B72-51175)

**VSRPEM — Descant recorder & piano. Sonatinas**
**Lerich, Rudolf**
[Sonatina for descant recorder & piano]. Sonatine in F major: for descant recorder or oboe and piano/ by Rudolf Lerich. — Cassel; London: Barenreiter, 1971. — 4to.
Score (14p) & part.
£0.60
*Also classified at VTPEM*
(B72-50749)

**VSRPJ — Miscellaneous works**
**Enfield, Patrick**
Descants' delight: three pieces for descant recorder(s) and piano/ by Patrick Enfield. — London: Elkin, 1972. — 4to.
Score (11p.) & part.
£0.50
(B72-51176)

**VSRPMHVG/T — Unaccompanied descant recorder. Pavanes. Variations**
**Eyk, Jacob van**
[Der Fluyten Lust-Hof. Deel 1. - *Excerpts*]. Pavane lachrymae: two settings with variations for solo decant recorder/ by Jacob van Eyk; edited by Edgar Hunt. — London: Schott, 1971. — 11p; obl.8vo.
Melody by John Dowland.
£0.45
(B72-50750)

**VSRPMK/DW/G/AY — Arrangements. Folk songs. Collections**
**Dinn, Freda**
More tunes for my recorder: for the descant recorder/ collected by Freda Dinn. — Revised ed. — London: Schott, 1971. — 24p; 8vo.
£0.15
(B72-50277)

**VSS/AF — Treble recorder. Exercises**
**Dinn, Freda**
Eighteen short studies: for treble recorder/ by Freda Dinn. — London: Schott, 1972. — 16p; obl.8vo.
£0.35
(B72-50278)

**VSSNUE — Treble recorder duets. Sonatas**
**Gorton, William**
[Sonata for two treble recorders, nos.1 & 2]. Two sonatas for two treble recorders/ by William Gorton; edited by Brian Davey. — London: Schott, 1972. — 8p; 4to.
£0.40
(B72-50751)

**VSSPE/AYD — Treble recorder & piano. Sonatas. Collections. England**
**Ruf, Hugo**
Sonatas by old English masters: for treble recorder and basso continuo/ edited by Hugo Ruf. — Cassel; London: Bärenreiter —
Vol.1. 1971. — 4to.
Score (24p) & 2 parts.
£1.50
(B72-50752)

Vol.2. — 1971. — 4to.
Score (22p) & 2 parts.
£1.50
(B72-50753)

**VSSPJ — Treble recorder & piano. Miscellaneous works**
**Schäfer, Gerhart**
Akuomenon: drei Sätze für Alt-Blockflöte und Klavier/ [by] Gerhart Schäfer. — Regensburg: Bosse; [London]: [Bärenreiter], 1972. — 4to.
Score (16p.) & part.
£1.50
(B72-50754)

**VSSPK/AE — Treble recorder & piano. Arrangements. Sonatas**
**Corelli, Arcangelo**
[Sonata for violin & basso continuo in D minor. Op.5 no.12]. La Follia: for treble recorder and basso continuo/ by Arcangelo Corelli; edited by Hans-Martin Linde. — Mainz; London: Schott, 1972. — 4to.
Score (20p.) & 2 parts. 'Corelli's 'La Follia', Op.5, no.12, was published by John Walsh (London, 1702) in a version for recorder transposed from d to g. It follows the original version for violin exactly, except for the double-stop parts' - Editor's note.
£1.00
(B72-51177)

**VSSPK/LF — Treble recorder & piano. Concertos**
Boismortier, Joseph Bodin de
[Concerto for treble recorder & string orchestra in G major. Op.21, no.3]. Konzert für Altblockflöte mit Violinen oder Querflöten und Generalbass, G-Dur/ [by] Joseph Bodin de Boismortier; herausgegeben [with] Klavierauszug von Erich Doflein. — Mainz; London: Schott, 1972. — 4to.
Score (12p.) & part.
£0.90

(B72-50755)

**VSSPK/LG — Treble recorder & piano. Arrangements. Suites**
Telemann, Georg Philipp
[Suite for treble recorder & string orchestra in A minor]. Suite in A minor: for treble recorder and string orchestra/ by Georg Philipp Telemann. — London: Schott, 1971. — 4to.
Reduction for treble recorder & piano by Edgar Hunt. — Score (27p.) & part.
£1.25

(B72-50279)

**VSSPMJ — Unaccompanied treble recorder. Miscellaneous works**
Andriessen, Louis
Sweet: for alto (treble) recorder/ by Louis Andriessen. — London: Schott, 1972. — 6p; 4to.
Unpriced

(B72-51179)

Du Bois, Rob
Muziek voor altblokfluit = Music for alto recorder/ by Rob du Bois. — London: Schott, 1971. — 5p; 4to.
Unpriced

(B72-50280)

Hotteterre Le Romain, Jacques
[L'Art de préluder sur la flûte. Op.7. - Excerpts]. 48 Préludes in 24 keys: for treble recorder, (flute oboe)/ [by] Jacques Hotteterre; edited by Erich Doflein and Nikolaus Delius. — Mainz; London: Schott, 1972. — 23p; 4to.
£0.90

(B72-51178)

**VST/AC — Tenor recorder. Tutors**
Slaney, Ivor
The recorder: how to play the descant recorder, complete with rudiments of music, fingering and studies/ by Ivor Slaney. — London: Campbell, Connelly, 1972. — 40p; 8vo.
This tutor is also suitable for the tenor recorder.
£0.40
*Primary classification VSR/AC*

**VT — OBOE**
**VT/AC — Tutors**
Hinke, Gustav Adolf
[Praktische Elementar-Schule für die Oboe]. Elementary method for oboe/ by Gustav Adolf Hinke. — London: Peters, 1971. — 38p; 4to.
£0.70

(B72-50281)

Sous, Alfred
Neue Oboenschule/ [by] Alfred Sous; unter Einbeziehung der Elementarschule für Oboe von Gustav Adolf Hinke. — Frankfurt: Litolff; London: Peters, 1971. — 98p; 4to.
£3.80

(B72-50282)

**VT/AF — Exercises**
Beaumont, Adrian
Preliminary exercises for the oboe/ by Adrian Beaumont. — London: Schott, 1972. — 15p; 8vo.
£0.40

(B72-51180)

**VTN — Ensembles**
Amy, Gilbert
Jeux: pour (1 à 4) hautbois/ de Gilbert Amy. — London: Universal, 1972. — 12pt; obl. fol.
Unpriced

(B72-51181)

**VTP — OBOE & PIANO**
**VTPEM — Sonatinas**
Lerich, Rudolf
[Sonatina for descant recorder & piano]. Sonatine in F major: for descant recorder or oboe and piano/ by Rudolf Lerich. — Cassel; London: Barenreiter, 1971. — 4to.
Score (14p) & part.
£0.60
*Primary classification VSRPEM*

(B72-50749)

**VTPJ — Miscellaneous works**
Wilson, John
Three Westmorland sketches: oboe and piano/ by John Wilson. — London: Forsyth, 1972. — 4to.
Score (13p.) & 2 parts.
Unpriced
*Also classified at VRPJ; VVPJ*

(B72-50283)

**VTPK — Arrangements**
Grieg, Edvard
[Selections]. Four pieces/ by Edward Grieg; [nos.1-3] edited and arranged for oboe and piano by Nicholas Blake, [no.4] edited and arranged for oboe and piano by Janet Craxton. — London: Chester, 1972. — 4to.
Score & part.
Unpriced

(B72-51182)

**VTPK/LF — Arrangements, Concertos**
Albinoni, Tommaso
[Concerto for oboe & string orchestra in G minor. Op. 9 no.8]. Concerto á 5: for oboe and strings/ by Tommaso Albinoni; edited by Franz Giegling. — London: Musica rara, 1972. — 4to.
Reduction for oboe & piano. — Score (14p.) & part.
Unpriced

(B72-51183)

Besozzi, Alessandro
[Concerto for oboe & string orchestra in G major]. Concerto in G major: for oboe, strings and basso continuo/ by Alessandro Besozzi; [edited by] David Lasocki. — London: Musica rara, 1972. — 4to.
Reduction for oboe & piano. — Score (20p.) & part.
£1.00

(B72-51184)

**VTPLWSK/LF — Oboe & trumpet. Arrangements. Concertos**
Hertel, Johann Wilhelm
[Concerto for trumpet, oboe & string orchestra in E flat major]. Concerto à 6: for trumpet, oboe, strings and continuo/ by Johann Wilhelm Hertel; edited by R.L. Minter, piano reduction by Barry Cooper. — London: Musica rara, 1972. — 4to.
Score (27p.) & 3 parts.
Unpriced

(B72-51185)

**VTPM — UNACCOMPANIED OBOE SOLOS**
**VTPMJ — Miscellaneous works**
Barkauskas, Vytantas
Monolog: für Oboe solo/ von Vytantas Barkauskas. — Leipzig; [London]: Peters, 1972. — 5p; 4to.
Unpriced

(B72-51186)

Berio, Luciano
Sequenza 7: per oboe solo/ [by] Luciano Berio. — London: Universal, 1971. — s.sh; obl.fol.
Unpriced

(B72-50284)

Berio, Luciano
Sequenza 7: per oboe solo/ [by] Luciano Berio. — London: Universal, 1971. — s.sh; obl.fol.
Unpriced

(B72-50285)

Exton, John
Three pieces for solo oboe/ by John Exton. — London: Chester, 1972. — 5p; 4to.
Unpriced

(B72-50756)

Jacob, Gordon
Seven bagatelles: for solo oboe/ by Gordon Jacob. — London: Oxford University Press, 1971. — 5p; 4to.
Duration 7 1/2 min.
ISBN 0 19 357366 0 : £0.35

(B72-50286)

**VTTP — COR ANGLAIS & PIANO**
Stoker, Richard
Three epigrams: for cor anglais and piano (or horn in F and piano)/ by Richard Stoker. — London: Leeds Music, 1972. — 4to.
Score (7p.) & part.
Unpriced
*Also classified at VWPJ*

(B72-50287)

**VTW — CRUMHORN**
**VTWNSK/AAY — Quartets. Arrangements. Collections**
Thomas, Bernard
  Crumhorn consort anthology/ [edited by] Bernard Thomas. —
  London: Musica rara. —
  Vol.1. — 1972. — 4to. —
  Unpriced

(B72-51187)

**VVNS — CLARINET QUARTETS**
**VVNSQK/DM/AY — Arrangements. Hymns. Collections**
Clelland, Lamont
  Hymns arranged for B flat instruments/ by Lamont Clelland. —
  London: Feldman, 1971. — 4to.
  Score (8p.) & 3 parts.
  Unpriced

(B72-50288)

**VVNT — CLARINET TRIOS**
Brooks, Keith
  Ten trios for developing clarinet technique: for 3 clarinets/ by
  Keith Brooks. — London: Boosey and Hawkes, 1972. — 15p; 4to.
  £0.60

(B72-51188)

Verrall, Pamela
  Cameos for clarinets/ by Pamela Verrall. — London: Feldman,
  1971. — 13p; 4to.
  £0.40

(B72-50289)

**VVP — CLARINET & PIANO**
**VVPE — Sonatas**
Ries, Ferdinand
  [Sonata sentimentale for flute & piano in E flat major. Op.169].
  Sonata in E flat major for flute or clarinet and piano/ by
  Ferdinand Ries; edited by Hans-Peter Schmitz. — Cassel; London:
  Bärenreiter, 1970. — 4to.
  Score (53p.) & 2 parts.
  £2.45
  *Primary classification VRPE*

(B72-50733)

Stoker, Richard
  Sonatina: for clarinet and piano/ by Richard Stoker. — London:
  Leeds Music, 1972. — 9p; 4to.
  Unpriced

(B72-50290)

**VVPG — Suites**
Collis, James
  Tom Sawyer suite: for B flat clarinet and piano/ by James Collis;
  piano part edited by Julius Mattfield. — New York; [London]:
  Boosey and Hawkes, 1972. — 4to.
  £1.25

(B72-50757)

**VVPJ — Miscellaneous works**
Banks, Don
  Prologue, Night piece and Blues for two: for clarinet (B flat) and
  piano/ by Don Banks. — London: Schott, 1971. — 4to.
  Score (9p.) & part.
  Unpriced

(B72-51189)

Carr, Edwin
  Aubade: for clarinet and piano/ by Edwin Carr. — Chesham:
  Ricordi, 1972. — 4to.
  Score (12p.) & part.
  £1.00

(B72-50291)

Fly, Leslie
  Sea tang: 3 pieces for clarinet and piano/ by Leslie Fly. —
  Manchester; London: Forsyth, 1972. — 4to.
  Score & part.
  Unpriced

(B72-50292)

Foster, Ivor Reginald
  An evening song: for clarinet (B flat) and piano/ by Ivor R.
  Foster. — London: Schott, 1971. — 4to.
  Score & part.
  Unpriced

(B72-50293)

Wilson, John
  Three Westmorland sketches: oboe and piano/ by John Wilson. —
  London: Forsyth, 1972. — 4to.
  Score (13p.) & 2 parts.
  Unpriced
  *Primary classification VTPJ*

(B72-50283)

**VVPK — Arrangements**
Bruch, Max
  Kol Nidrei. Opus 47/ by Max Bruch; arranged for clarinet and
  piano by Robin de Smet. — London: Peters, 1972. — 4to.
  Score (11p.) & part. — The clarinet part is set for A and B flat instruments.
  Unpriced

(B72-51190)

**VVPK/AE — Arrangements. Sonatas**
Marcello, Benedetto
  [Sonata for cello & basso continuo in C major]. Sonata no.6/ by
  Benedetto Marcello; transcribed and edited for B flat clarinet and
  piano, by Robin de Smet. — London: Peters, 1972. — 4to.
  Score (8p.) & part.
  Unpriced

(B72-51191)

**VVPK/LF — Arrangements. Concertos**
Molique, Bernhard
  [Concertino for clarinet in F minor]. Concertino in F minor for
  clarinet and orchestra/ by Bernhard Molique; first edition edited
  by Jost Michaels. — Cassel; London: Bärenreiter, 1970. — 4to.
  Piano score (36p.) & part.
  £1.50

(B72-50758)

**VW — BASSOON**
**VW/AF — Exercises**
Bianchi, Virginia
  Twelve études for bassoon/ by Virginia Bianchi. — New York:
  Schirmer; [London]: [Chappell], 1971. — 25p; 4to.
  Unpriced

(B72-50294)

**VWNU — BASSOON DUETS**
**VWPE — Sonatas**
Buttkewitz, Jürgen
  [Sonata for bassoon & piano]. Sonate für Fagott und Klavier/ by
  Jürgen Buttkewitz. — Leipzig: Peters; [London]: [Hinrichsen],
  1971. — 4to.
  Score (23p.) & part.
  £1.60

(B72-50759)

**VWPJ — Miscellaneous works**
Bishop, Jeffrey
  Spells and incantations: for horn and piano/ by Jeffrey Bishop. —
  Sevenoaks: Novello, 1972. — 4to.
  Score (19p.) & part.
  £0.90

(B72-50295)

Stoker, Richard
  Three epigrams: for cor anglais and piano (or horn in F and
  piano)/ by Richard Stoker. — London: Leeds Music, 1972. —
  4to.
  Score (7p.) & part.
  Unpriced
  *Primary classification VTTPJ*

(B72-50287)

**VWPK/AH — Arrangements. Dances**
Bach, Johann Sebastian
  [Suites for cello, nos.1-3. S.1007-9. - *Excerpts]*. Three movements
  from the solo cello suites/ by J.S. Bach; arranged for bassoon by
  Martin Gatt. — London: Associated Board of the Royal Schools
  of Music, 1972. — 3p; 4to.
  Gigue from Suite no.1 - Bourrée 1 from Suite no.3 - Menuet 2 from Suite
  no.2.
  £0.15

(B72-51192)

**VWPK/LF — Arrangements. Concertos.**
Hummel, Johann Nepomuck
  [Concerto for bassoon in F major]. Grand concerto: for bassoon
  and orchestra/ by Johann Nepomuck Hummel; [edited by] Ronald
  Tyree. — London: Musica rara, 1971. — 4to.
  Catalogues of Hummel's works omit any reference to it, and the autograph,
  located in the British Museum (Add. MS. 32218), gives no opus number or
  date. — Reduction for bassoon & piano. Score (38p.) & part.
  £2.50

(B72-51193)

**VWPM — UNACCOMPANIED BASSOON SOLOS**
**VWPMG — Suites**
Jacob, Gordon
  Partita: for solo bassoon/ by Gordon Jacob. — London: Oxford
  University Press, 1971. — 4p; 4to.
  ISBN 0 19 357364 4 : £0.35

(B72-50296)

## VY — BAGPIPES
### VY/AY — Collections
**MacLellan, John A**
Ceol beag agus ceol mor = Little music and big music/ arranged, compiled and composed by John A. MacLellan. — London: Paterson, 1972. — 40p; 8vo.
Unpriced

(B72-50297)

## WM — BRASS BAND
### WM/AC — Tutors
**Schneider, Willy**
[Chorische Bläserschule]. Method for brass/ by Willy Schneider; translated from the German by Edgar Hunt. — London: Schott, 1972. — 28p; obl.8vo.
£0.50

(B72-51194)

### WM/AY — Collections
**Salvation Army**
Salvation Army Brass Band Journal (General series). — London: Salvationist Publishing and Supplies. —
Nos.1625-1628: Gospel bells: song arrangement, by Ray Steadman-Allen; and, Calling to-day: flugel horn solo, by Ken James; Songs of the faith: selection, by Dean Goffin; Contemplation: meditation, by Philip Catelinet; The fight of faith: march, by Charles Skinner. — 1971. — 37p; obl.8vo. —
Unpriced

(B72-50298)

**Salvation** Army Brass Band Journal (Festival series). — London: Salvationist Publishing & Supplies. —
Nos.341-344: Lift up your heads '(Gopsal): variations, by Dean Goffin. The present age: tone poem/ by Leslie Condon. My Christ (is all in all): euphonium solo/ by William Himes. Pledge for service: festival march/ by Eric Ball. — 1972. — 61p; obl.8vo. —
Unpriced

(B72-50760)

The **Salvation** Army Brass Band Journal (Triumph series). — London: Salvationist Publishing and Supplies. —
Nos 741-744: Never alone; selection, by Eiliv Herikstad. Variations on 'Nativity new', by Michael Kenyon. O return unto God; cornet solo, by Paul Marti. Mancunian; march, by Norman Hall. — 1971. — 32p; obl.8vo. —
Unpriced

(B72-50299)

**Salvation** Army Brass Band Journal (Triumph series).. — London: Salvationist Publishing & Supplies. —
Nos.745-748. God is love: cornet solo/ by Ray Steadman-Allen. Songs of friendship; selection/ by Kenneth Ketteringham. With gladsome mind:/ song arrangement by Derek Jordan. The harvest home. — 1972. — 29p; obl.8vo. —
Unpriced

(B72-50761)

### WMG — Suites
**Hanmer, Ronald**
The four corners of the world/ by Ronald Hanmer. — London: Studio Music, 1971. — 40p; 4to.
Contents: 1.This sceptered isle - 2.Mystic east - 3.Pacific paradise - 4.Way out west.
Unpriced

(B72-50300)

**Stephens, Denzil**
Lindum suite/ by Denzil Stephens. — Sevenoaks: Novello, 1972. — 4to.
Score (50p.) & 21 parts.
£3.50

(B72-50762)

**Street, Allan**
Doon valley: a suite for brass/ by Allan Street. — London: Boosey and Hawkes, 1972. — obl, 8vo & 8vo.
Score (37p.) & 25 parts.
£3.30

(B72-51195)

### WMGM — Marches
**Allan, Geoffrey**
Räby/ by G. Allan. — London: Peter Maurice, 1972. — obl.8vo.
Conductor & 24 parts.
Unpriced

(B72-50301)

**Bryce, Frank**
Ground bass/ by Frank Bryce. — Sevenoaks: Paxton Music, 1972. — 23p; 8vo.
With several copies of various parts.
Unpriced

(B72-50763)

**Jacob, Gordon**
Sospan fach = The little saucepan: march: a prelude to a Welsh football match, for brass band/ by Gordon Jacob. — Sevenoaks: Novello, 1972. — 4to.
Score (18p.) & 25 parts.
£1.75

(B72-51196)

**New, Derek**
Bugle call blues/ by Derek New. — London: Studio Music, 1971. — 8vo.
Conductor & 24 parts.
Unpriced

(B72-50302)

### WMHR — Minuets
**Schubert, Franz**
Six minuets for wind instruments/ by Franz Schubert; edited by Christa Landon. — Cassel; London: Bärenreiter. —
First edition; newly discovered in this form. A 'piano draft' of minuets nos. 1 and 2 is included in Deutsch as D.995 under the heading 'Two minuets for pianoforte.' Minuets nos. 3 - 6 are not found in Deutsch.
Vol.1: Nos.1 - 3. — 1970. — 14p; 4to.
£1.20

(B72-50764)

### WMHVH — Polkas
**Siebert, Edrich**
The Louisiana polka/ by Edrich Siebert. — London: Studio Music, 1972. — 25pt.; 8vo.
With several copies of various parts.
Unpriced

(B72-50765)

### WMHW — Waltzes
**Ewing, Montague**
Purple heather/ by Montague Ewing. — Bognor Regis: Norman Richardson Band Arrangements, 1972. — 8vo & obl. 8vo.
Short score (4p.) & 27 parts.
Unpriced

(B72-50766)

**Siebert, Edrich**
The Delaware waltz/ by Edrich Siebert. — London: Studio Music, 1972. — 25pt.; 8vo.
With several copies of various parts.
Unpriced

(B72-50767)

### WMJ — Miscellaneous works
**Antegnati, Costanzo**
Canzon 20: for 2 trumpets and 3 trombones (2 trumpets, horn and 2 trombones)/ by Costanzo Antegnati; [edited by] Robert Paul Block. — London: Musica rara, 1970. — 4to.
Numbering of canzoni refers to Alessandro Rauerij's collection of 1608. —
Score (4p.) & 6 parts.
£0.70

(B72-50303)

**Ball, Eric**
A Kensington concerto for brass band/ by Eric Ball. — London: Boosey and Hawkes, 1972. — obl.8vo & 8vo.
Score (41p.), Conductor (6p.) & 24 parts.
£3.75

(B72-50768)

**Barsotti, Roger**
Fantasia on British airs/ by Roger Barsotti. — London: Boosey and Hawkes, 1972. — 8vo.
Condensed score (19p.) & 18 parts.
Unpriced

(B72-50769)

**Bevan, Clifford**
Meditation on 'Austria' [by Haydn]: for brass band/ by Clifford Bevan. — London: Feldman, 1972. — 8vo.
Score & 24 parts.
Unpriced

(B72-50304)

**Butterworth, Arthur**
Processional prelude/ by Arthur Butterworth; based on the hymn tune 'Saint Gertrude' by A.S. Sullivan. — Sevenoaks: Novello, 1972. — 4to.
Score (20p.) & 24 parts.
£1.00

(B72-51197)

**Carr, John**
The gay Delavals: portrait in music, for brass band/ by John Carr. — London: Paxton, 1971. — obl. 4to & 8vo.
Score (28p.) & 25 parts.
£2.50

(B72-50305)

**Chilese, Bastian**
Canzon 22: for 3 trumpets and 2 trombones (2 trumpets, horn and 2 trombones)/ by Bastian Chilese; [edited by] Robert Paul Block. — London: Musica rara, 1970. — 4to.
Numbering of canzoni refers to Alessandro Rauerij's collection of 1608. —
Score (4p.) & 6 parts.
Unpriced

(B72-50306)

**Elms, Albert**
Wembley way: quick march/ by Albert Elms. — London: Boosey and Hawkes, 1972. — 21pt; obl.8vo.
With several copies of various parts.
£0.45

(B72-50770)

**Gabrieli, Giovanni**
Canzoni 1 & 2: for 2 trumpets and 2 trombones (2 trumpets, horn & trombone)/ by Giovanni Gabrieli; edited by Alan Lumsden. — London: Musica rara, 1966. — 4to.
Numbering of canzoni refers to Alessandro Rauerij's collection of 1608. — Score (8p.) & 5 parts.
£0.90

(B72-50307)

**Gabrieli, Giovanni**
Canzoni 3 and 4: for 2 trumpets and 2 trombones (2 trumpets, horn & trombone)/ by Giovanni Gabrieli; edited by Alan Lumsden. — London: Musica rara, 1966. — 4to.
Numbering of canzoni refers to Alessandro Rauerij's collection of 1608. — Score (10p.) & 5 parts.
£0.90

(B72-50308)

**Gabrieli, Giovanni**
[Sacrae symphoniae. Bk. 1]. Symphoniae sacrae/ by Giovanni Gabrieli; edition for brass ensembles, edited by R.P. Block. — London: Musica rara. —
Vol.1: Canzon primi toni à 8: for 4 trumpets and 4 trombones. — 1972. — 4to.
Score (7p.) & 12 parts.
Unpriced

(B72-51198)

Vol.2: Canzon septimi toni à 8 (no.1): for 4 trumpets and 4 trombones. — 1972. — 4to.
Score (8p.) & 12 parts.
Unpriced

(B72-51199)

Vol.3: Canzon septimi toni à 8 (no.2): for 4 trumpets and 4 trombones. — 1972. — 4to.
Score (7p.) & 12 parts.
Unpriced

(B72-51200)

Vol.4: Canzon noni toni à 8: for 4 trumpets and 4 trombones. — 1972. — 4to.
Score (6p.) & 12 parts.
Unpriced

(B72-51201)

Vol.5: Canzon duo decimi toni à 8: for 4 trumpets and 4 trombones. — 1972. — 4to.
Score (7p.) & 12 parts.
£2.00

(B72-51202)

Vol.6: Sonata pian e forte à 8: for 2 trumpets and 6 trombones. — 1972. — 4to.
Score (4p.) & 10 parts.
£1.80

(B72-51203)

Vol.7: Canzon primi toni à 10: for 7 trumpets and 3 trombones, (5 trumpets and 5 trombones). — 1972. — 4to.
Score (11p.) & 17 parts.
£2.50

(B72-51204)

Vol.8: Canzon duo decimi toni à 10 (no.1): for 6 trumpets and 4 trombones. — 1972. — 4to.
Score (12p.) & 16 parts.
£2.85

(B72-51205)

Vol.9: Canzon duo decimi toni à 10 (no.2): for 6 trumpets and 4 trombones. — 1972. — 4to.
Score (16p.) & 16 parts.
£3.00

(B72-51206)

Vol.10: Canzon duo decimi toni à 10 (no.3): for 5 trumpets and 5 trombones. — 1972. — 4to.
Score (12p.) & 15 parts.
£2.50

(B72-51207)

Vol.11: Canzon duo decimi toni à 10 (no.4): for 6 trumpets and 4 trombones. — 1972. — 4to.
Score (14p.) & 16 parts.
£3.50

(B72-51208)

Vol.12: Canzon in echo duo decima toni à 10: for 6 trumpets, 4 trombones and 2 organs (4 trumpets, 2 horns, 4 trombones and 2 organs). — 1972. — 4to.
Score (32p.) & 19 parts.
£3.00

(B72-51209)

Vol.13: Canzon septimi octavi toni à 12: for 6 trumpets and 6 trombones. — 1972. — 4to.
Score (8p.) & 18 parts.
Unpriced

(B72-51210)

Vol.14: Canzon noni toni à 12: for 6 trumpets and 6 trombones. — 1972. — 4to.
Score (11p.) & 18 parts.
Unpriced

(B72-51211)

Vol.15: Sonata octavi toni `a 12: for 2 trumpets and 10 trombones (2 trumpets, 2 horns and 8 trombones). — 1972. — 4to.
Score (17p.) & 16 parts.
Unpriced

(B72-51212)

Vol.16: Canzon quarti toni à 15: for 3 trumpets and 12 trombones. — 1972. — 4to.
Score (15p.) & 18 parts.
Unpriced

(B72-51213)

**Humperdinck, Engelbert**
[Hansel und Gretel. - *Excerpts*]. Prelude/ by Engelbert Humperdinck; arranged for brass band by Eric Ball. — London: Weinberger, 1972. — 28p; obl.8vo.
Unpriced

(B72-51214)

**Jacob, Gordon**
A Swedish rhapsody: for brass band/ by Gordon Jacob. — Sevenoaks: Novello, 1972. — 4to.
Score (55p.) & 26 parts.
£3.40

(B72-51215)

**Kelly, Bryan**
Divertimento/ by Bryan Kelly. — Sevenoaks: Novello, 1972. — 4to.
Score (67p) & 26 parts.
£3.80

(B72-50771)

**Richardson, Norman**
The white company - overture/ by Norman Richardson. — London: Boosey and Hawkes, 1972. — obl.8vo & 8vo.
Score (38p.) & 25 parts.
£3.30

(B72-51216)

**Turok, Paul**
Elegy in memory of Karol Rathaus. Op. 23: for 3 trumpets, 2 horns, 3 trombones and baritone and tuba/ by Paul Turok. — London: Musica rara, 1972. — 4to.
Score (23p.) & 10 parts.
Unpriced

(B72-51217)

**WMK — Arrangements**
**Borodin, Alexander**
[Prince Igor. - Overture]. Price Igor overture/ by A. Glazounov, based on themes by A. Borodin; arranged by Roger Barsotti. — London: Boosey and Hawkes, 1972. — obl.8vo & 8vo.
Score (47p.) & 25 parts.
£3.90

(B72-51218)

**Khachaturian, Aram**
[Spartak-Adagio]. The Adagio from Spartacus. (For my love)/ by Aram Khachaturian; [adapted] by E. Charles and N. Newell, arranged for brass band by Edrich Siebert. — London: Feldman, 1971. — 4to.
Conductor & 24 parts.
Unpriced

(B72-50309)

**Stone, Pol**
Mexican shuffle/ by Pol Stone; arranged by Edrich Siebert. — London: Peter Maurice, 1972. — 27pt; 8vo.
With several copies of various parts.
Unpriced

(B72-50772)

**WMK/AHVH — Arrangements. Polkas**
**Strauss, Johann, b.1825**
Explosions - Polka. Op.43/ by Johann Strauss; arranged by Roy Newsome. — London: Studio Music, 1972. — 26pt.; 8vo.
With several copies of various parts.
Unpriced

(B72-50773)

**WMK/CC — Arrangements. Opera**
**Humperdinck, Engelbert**
Hänsel and Gretel/ by Englebert Humperdinck; selection, arranged by Ronald Hanmer. — London: Studio Music, 1972. — 26pt.; 8vo.
With several copies of various parts.
Unpriced

(B72-50774)

**WMK/DM — Arrangements. Hymns**
**Siebert, Edrich**
Two vesper hymns/ arranged by Edrich Siebert. — London: Studio Music, 1972. — 24pt; obl.8vo.
Contents: Lord, keep us safe this night/ by Sir Arthur Sullivan - God be with you (till we meet again)/ by W.G. Turner.
Unpriced

(B72-50775)

**WMK/DW — Arrangements. Songs**
**Verdi, Giuseppe**
[Nabucodonosor. - Va pensiero]. The chorus of Hebrew slaves/ by
Verdi; [arranged by] Norman Richardson. — Bognor: Norman
Richardson Band Arrangements, 1971. — 27pt.
Short score & 26 parts.
Unpriced

(B72-50310)

**WMK/DW — Arrangements. Songs, etc**
**Barratt, Bob**
Ballycastle Bay: for brass band/ by Bob Barratt & Edrich Siebert.
— London: Ambleside: Keith Prowse, 1971. — obl.8vo.
Conductor & 24 parts.
Unpriced

(B72-50311)

**Danvers, Charles**
Till/ by Charles Danvers; arranged for brass by Allan Street. —
London: Chappell, 1972. — 27pt.; 8vo.
With several copies of several parts.
Unpriced

(B72-50776)

**Luboff, Norman**
Yellow bird/ by Norman Luboff; arranged for brass by Allan
Street. — London: Frank Music, 1972. — 27 pt.; 8vo.
With several copies of various parts.
Unpriced

(B72-50777)

**Siebert, Edrich**
We shall not be moved: traditional/ arranged by Edrich Siebert.
— London: Studio Music, 1972. — 25pt; obl. 8vo.
With several copies of various parts.
Unpriced

(B72-50778)

**Smith-Masters, Stanley**
Cum Baija: African folk song/ arranged for brass band by Stanley
Smith-Masters. — London: Studio Music, 1972. — 24pt.; obl.8vo.
With several copies of various parts.
Unpriced

(B72-50779)

**WMK/JR — Arrangements. Film music**
**Prokofiev, Sergei**
[Lieutenant Kije. Op.60. - Wedding of Kije, Troika]. Two pieces/
by Serge Prokofiev; arranged by Fisher Tull. — New York;
[London]: Boosey and Hawkes, 1971. — 4to.
Score (14p.) & 22 parts.
£3.00

(B72-50312)

**WMK/JR — Arrangements. Films**
**Rota, Nina**
The godfather: selection of themes from the film/ by Nina Rota;
arranged for brass and reed band by Allan Street. — London:
Chappell, 1972. — 8vo.
Conductor (8p.) & 26 parts.
Unpriced

(B72-51219)

**WMK/JS — Arrangements. Television music**
**Pearson, Johnny**
Sleepy shores: theme from the BBC TV series Owen M.D./ by
Johnny Pearson; arranged by Edrich Siebert. — London: Keith
Prowse Music, 1971. — obl.8vo.
Conductor & 26 parts.
Unpriced

(B72-50313)

**WMPWSVN — Fanfare trumpets & brass band**
**Dunn, F Vivian**
Supreme command: for fanfare trumpets and brass band/ by F.
Vivian Dunn. — London: Boosey and Hawkes, 1972. — 28pt.;
obl.8vo.
With several copies of various parts.
£0.45

(B72-50780)

**WN — BRASS ENSEMBLE**
**WNGN — Fanfares**
**Walton, *Sir* William**
A Queen's fanfare: for trumpets and trombones/ by William
Walton. — London: Oxford University Press, 1972. — 8vo.
Score (5p.) & 12 parts.
ISBN 0 19 368186 2 : £0.40

(B72-50781)

**WNN — Octets**
**Grillo, Giovanni Battista**
[Sacrae concentus ac symphoniae. - *Excerpts*]. Canzona quarta: for
4 trumpets and 4 trombones (4 trumpets, 2 horns and 2
trombones)/ by Giovanni Battista Grillo; [edited by] Bernard
Thomas. — London: Musica rara, 1972. — 4to.
Score (6p.) & 10 parts.
£1.50

(B72-51220)

**Viadana, Lodovico**
[Sinfonia musicale. - *Excerpts*]. Sinfonia, 'La Bergamasca': for 4
trumpets and 4 trombones, (4 trumpets, 2 horns and 2
trombones)/ by Ludovico Grossi da Viadana; [edited] by Bernard
Thomas. — London: Music rara, 1972. — 4to.
Score (7p.) & 10 parts.
£2.00

(B72-51221)

**Viadana, Lodovico**
[Sinfonia musicale. - *Excerpts*]. Sinfonia, 'La Padovana': for 4
trumpets and 4 trombones (4 trumpets, 2 horns and 2
trombones)/ by Ludovici Viadana; edited by Bernard Thomas. —
London: Musica rara, 1972. — 4to.
Score (6p.) & 10 parts.
£1.50

(B72-51222)

**WNR — Quintets**
**Buonamente, Giovanni Battista**
[Sonate & canzone. Lib. 6. - *Excerpts*]. Canzon à 5: for 2 cornetti
and 3 trombones (2 trumpets/oboes and 3 trombones)/ by
Giovanni Battista Buonamente; [edited by] Bernard Thomas. —
London: Musica rara, 1972. — 4to.
Score (10p.) & 5 parts.
Unpriced

(B72-51223)

**Maurer, Ludwig**
[12 kleine Stücke]. Twelve little pieces for brass quintet/ edited by
Brian Gay. — Sevenoaks: Novello. —
Book 1. — 1972 — 4to.
Score (28p.) & 10 parts.
£2.70

(B72-51224)

**Newsome, R**
Two London sketches/ by R. Newsome. — London: Feldman,
1971. — 8vo.
Score (11p.) & 5 parts.
Unpriced

(B72-50314)

**Orr, Buxton**
Divertimento for brass quintet (1969)/ by Buxton Orr. —
Sevenoaks: Novello, 1972. — 4to.
Score (34) & 7 parts.
Unpriced

(B72-50782)

**Polin, Claire**
Cader Idris: landscape for brass quintet/ by Claire Polin. — New
York: Schirmer; [London]: [Chappell], 1971. — 4to.
Score (10p.) & 5 parts.
Unpriced

(B72-50315)

**WNRHG — Quintets. Dance suites**
**Hartmann, Karl Amadeus**
Dance suite: for wind quintet, clarinet, bassoon, horn, trumpet and
trombone/ by Karl Amadeus Hartmann. — Mainz; London:
Schott, 1972. — 4to.
Score (24p.) & 5 parts.
£4.40

(B72-51225)

**WNS — Quartets**
**Banchieri, Adriano**
[Canzoni alla francese a quatro voci, nos.10, 11]. Two canzonas:
for 2 trumpets and 2 trombones, (2 trumpets, horn and
trombone)/ by Adriano Banchieri; [edited by] Bernard Thomas. —
London: Musica rara, 1972. — 4to.
Score (6p.) & 5 parts. — Contents: La Feliciana - La Organistina bella.
£0.90

(B72-51226)

**Banchieri, Adriano**
[Canzoni alla francese a quattro voci, nos.6, 8]. Two canzonas: for
2 trumpets and 2 trombones, (2 trumpets, horn and trombone)/
by Adriano Banchieri; [edited by] Bernard Thomas. — London:
Musica rara, 1972. — 4to.
Score (7p.) & 5 parts. — Contents: L'Alcenagina - La Banchieriana.
£0.90

(B72-51227)

**Bargagni, Ottavio**
[Secondo libro delle canzoni da suonare. - *Excerpts*]. Canzona 'La Monteverde': for 2 trumpets and 2 trombones (2 trumpets, horn and trombone)/ by Ottavio Bargagni; edited by Bernard Thomas. — London: Musica rara, 1972. — 4to.
Score (4p.) & 5 parts.
£0.70

(B72-51228)

**Bogar, István**
Three movements: for brass quartet/ by István Bogár. — London: Boosey and Hawkes, 1972. — 4to.
Score (15p.) & 4 parts.
£1.25

(B72-51229)

**Cavaccio, Giovanni**
[Musica a quattro voci. - *Excerpts*]. Two canzonas: for 2 trumpets and 2 trombones (2 trumpets, horn and trombone)/ by Giovanni Cavaccio; [edited by] Bernard Thomas. — London: Musica rara, 1972. — 4to.
Score (6p.) & 5 parts. — Contents: La Fina - La Foresta.
£0.80

(B72-51230)

**Guami, Gioseffo**
La Guamina: for 2 trumpets and 2 trombones, (2 trumpets, horn and trombone)/ by Gioseffo Guami; [edited by] Bernard Thomas. — London: Musica rara, 1972. — 4to.
Score (4p.) & 5 parts.
£0.70

(B72-51231)

**Maschera, Florentino**
[Libro primo de canzoni da sonare, nos.5, 7]. Two canzonas: for 2 trumpets and 2 trombones (2 trumpets, horn and trombone)/ by Florentio Maschera; [edited by] Bernard Thomas. — London: Musica rara, 1972. — 4to.
Score (6p.) & 5 parts.
£0.70

(B72-51232)

**Maschera, Florentio**
[Libro primo de canzoni da sonare, nos.13, 12]. Two canzonas: for 2 trumpets and 2 trombones (2 trumpets, horn and trombone)/ by Florentio Maschera; [edited by] Bernard Thomas. — London: Musica rara, 1972. — 4to.
Score (7p.) & 5 parts. — Contents: La Girella - L'Uggieva.
£0.80

(B72-51233)

**WNSG — Quartets. Suites**
**Zehm, Friedrich**
Neue Bläserstücke. Partitur in C: für 4 Blechbläser (Trompeten Posaunen)/ [by] Friedrich Zehm. — Mainz; London: Schott, 1972. — 15p; 4to.
£0.80

(B72-50783)

**WNT — Trios**
**Muczynski, Robert**
Voyage. Op.27: seven pieces for brass trio (B flat trumpet, F horn, trombone)/ by Robert Muczyinski. — New York: Schirmer; [London]: [Chappell], 1970. — 4to.
Score (15p.) & 3 parts.
Unpriced

(B72-50316)

**WRP — CORNET & PIANO**
**WRPK/AAY — Arrangements. Collections**
**Borst, Rudolf**
Cornet (trumpet) music for beginners/ edited by Rudolf Borst and István Bogár. — 4to.
Score (39p.) & part.
£0.85

(B72-50784)

**WS — TRUMPET**
**WS/AF — Exercises**
**Reynolds, Vernon**
[48 études for French horn]. 48 études for trumpet: transcribed from 48 études for French horn/ by Vernon Reynolds. — New York: Schirmer; [London]: [Chappell], 1971. — 53p; 4to.
Unpriced

(B72-50317)

**WSLRE — Trumpet & organ. Sonatas**
**Fantini, Girolamo**
[Modo per imparare a sonare di tromba. - *Excerpts*]. Eight sonatas: for trumpet & organ/ by Girolamo Fantini; edited by E.H. Tarr. — London: Musica rara, 1971. — 4to.
Score (18p.) & part.
Unpriced

(B72-50318)

**WSM — TRUMPET BAND**
**WSN/AZ — Trumpet ensemble. Collected works of individual composers**
**Bach, Johann Sebastian**
Complete trumpet repertoire/ [by] J.S. Bach; revised and [edited by] Ludwig Guttler. — London: Musica rara. —
Vol.1. — 1971. — 70p; 4to.
£2.75

(B72-50319)

Vol.2. — 1971. — 64p; 4to.
£2.75

(B72-50320)

**Bach, Johann Sebastian**
Complete trumpet repertoire/ [by] J.S. Bach; revised and [edited by] Ludwig Guttler. — London: Musicara rara. —
Vol.3. — 1971. — 76p; 4to.
£2.75

(B72-50321)

**WSNS — TRUMPET QUARTETS**
**WSNSGN — Quartets. Fanfares**
**Roe, Betty**
A flourish of fanfares: for 4 flat trumpets/ by Betty Roe. — London: Thames, 1972. — 3p; 8vo.
Unpriced

(B72-50322)

**WSNT — TRUMPET TRIOS**
**WSNT/X — Trios. Canons**
**Benger, Richard**
Preludes and canons for three trumpets/ by Richard Benger. — London: Chester, 1972. — 8vo.
Score (14p.) & 3 parts.
Unpriced

(B72-50785)

**WSNTQ — TWO TRUMPETS & PIANO**
**WSNTQG — Two trumpets & piano. Suites**
**Benger, Richard**
Miniature suite: for two B flat trumpets or cornets and piano/ by Richard Benger. — London: Chester, 1972. — 4to.
Score (22p.) & 2 parts.
Unpriced

(B72-51234)

**WSP — TRUMPET & PIANO**
**WSPJ — Miscellaneous works**
**Burgon, Geoffrey**
Toccata: for trumpet and piano/ by Geoffrey Burgon. — London: Stainer and Bell, 1972. — 4to.
Score (6p.) & part.
£0.40

(B72-51235)

**WSPK — Arrangements**
**Stradella, Alessandro**
[Il Barcheggio. - Sinfonia to part 2]. Sinfonia: for trumpet, 2 violins and continuo/ by Allessandro Stradella; edited by Robert Paul Block. — London: Musica rara, 1971. — 4to.
Reduction for trumpet & piano. — Score (7p.) & part.
£1.00

(B72-51236)

**WSPK/AAY — Arrangement. Collections**
**Lawton, Sidney Maurice**
Old English trumpet tunes: for trumpet in B flat/ piano accompaniments by Sidney M. Lawton. — London: Oxford University Press, 1971. — 4to.
Score (28p.) & part.
£0.80

(B72-50323)

**WSPK/AAY — Arrangements. Collections**
**Siebert, Edrich**
Latin American album: for B flat trumpet(s) and piano/ selected and arranged by Edrich Siebert. — London: Boosey and Hawkes, 1972. — 4to.
Score (13p.) & part.
£0.95

(B72-50324)

**WSPK/AG — Arrangements. Suites**
**Clarke, Jeremiah**
[Suite for trumpet & orchestra in D major]. Suite in D major: for trumpet, 2 oboes, bassoon, strings and continuo/ by Jeremiah Clarke; edited [as a reduction] by R.L. Minter. — London: Musica rara, 1971. — 4to.
Score (11p.) & part.
Unpriced

(B72-50325)

## WSPK/LE — Arrangements Sonatas
**Baldassare, Pietro**
[Sonata for trumpet & string orchestra, no.1, in F major]. Sonata in F, no.1: for cornetto (trumpet), strings and continuo/ by Pietro Baldassare; edited by R.P. Block and John Beer. — London: Musica rara, 1972. — 4to.
Reduction for trumpet & piano. — Score (11p.) & part.
Unpriced

(B72-51237)

**Baldassare, Pietro**
[Sonata for trumpet & string orchestra, no.2, in F major]. Sonata in F, no.2: for solo trumpet (cornetto) and strings/ by Pietro Baldassare; edited by R.P. Block and John Beer. — London: Musica rara, 1972. — 4to.
Reduction for trumpet & piano. — Score (8p.) & part.
Unpriced

(B72-51238)

**Cazzati, Mauritio**
[Sonata for trumpet & string orchestra. Op.35, no.10, 'La Cappara']. Sonata à 5, 'La Cappara': for trumpet and strings/ by Mauritio Cazzati. Op.35, no.10; [edited by] Robert Paul Block and Edward H. Tarr. — London: Musica rara, 1972. — 4to.
This work is issued with op.35, nos 11-12. — Reduction for trumpet and piano. — Score (6p.) & part.
£1.00

(B72-51239)

**Cazzati, Mauritio**
[Sonata for trumpet & string orchestra. Op.35, no.12, 'La Zambecari']. Sonata à 5, 'La Zambecari': for trumpet and strings/ by Mauritio Cazzati. Op.35, no.12; [edited by] Robert Paul Block and Edward H. Tarr. — London: Musica rara, 1972. — 4to.
This work is issued with Opus 35, nos 10-11. Reduction for trumpet and piano. Score (tp.) & part.
£1.00

(B72-51240)

**Cazzati, Mauritio**
[Sonata for trumpets & string orchestra. Op.35, no.11, 'La Bianchina']. Sonata à 5, 'La Bianchina': for trumpet and strings/ by Mauritio Cazzati. Op.35, no.11; [edited by] Robert Paul Block and Edward H. Tarr. — London: Musica rara, 1972. — 4to.
This work is issued with opus 35, nos 10 and 12. — Reduction for trumpet and piano. — Score (10p.) & part.
£1.00

(B72-51241)

**Grossi, Andrea**
[Sonata for trumpet & string orchestra in D major. Op.3, no.10]. Sonata decima: for trumpet and strings/ by Andrea Grossi; edited by Robert Paul Block. — London: Musica rara, 1972. — 4to.
Reduction for trumpet & piano. — Score (8p.) & 2 parts.
£1.00

(B72-51242)

## WSPK/LF — Arrangements. Concertos
**Haydn, Michael**
[Concerto for trumpet, no.2, in C major]. Trumpet concerto no.2 in C major: for trumpet, 2 flutes, strings and continuo/ by Michael Haydn; edited [as a reduction] by E.H. Tarr. — London: Musica rara, 1971. — 4to.
Score (12p.) & 2 parts.
Unpriced

(B72-50326)

**Hertel, Johann Wilhelm**
[Concerto for trumpet & string orchestra in E flat major]. Concerto no.2 in E flat: for trumpet, strings and continuo/ by Johann Wilhelm Hertel; edited by Edward H. Tarr. — London: Musica rara, 1972. — 4to.
The numbering of this work is the editor's. — Reduction for trumpet and piano score (15p.) & 2 parts.
Unpriced

(B72-51243)

**Molter, Johann Melchior**
[Concerto for trumpet, strings & basso continuo, no.1 in D major. MWV IV/12]. Concerto no.1: for solo trumpet, strings and continuo (bassoon ad lib.)/ by J.M. Molter; [edited as a reduction by] Michael Talbot. — London: Musica rara, 1971. — 4to.
Score (11p.) & 2 parts.
Unpriced

(B72-50327)

**Molter, Johann Melchior**
[Concerto for trumpet, strings & basso continuo, no.2 in D major. MWV IV/13]. Concerto no.2: for solo trumpet, strings and continuo (bassoon ad lib.)/ by J.M. Molter; [edited as a reduction by] Michael Talbot. — London: Musica rara, 1971. — 4to.
Score (12p.) & 2 parts.
Unpriced

(B72-50328)

**Molter, Johann Melchior**
[Concerto for trumpet, strings & basso continuo, no.3 in D major. MWV IV/14]. Concerto no.3: for solo trumpet, strings and continuo (bassoon ad lib.)/ by J.M. Molter; [edited as a reduction by] Michael Talbot. — London: Musica rara, 1971. — 4to.
Score (12p.) & 2 parts.
Unpriced

(B72-50329)

**Patterson, Paul**
[Concerto for trumpet]. Trumpet concerto/ by Paul Patterson. — London: Weinberger, 1972. — 4to.
Reduction for trumpet & piano. — Score (24p.) & part.
Unpriced

(B72-51244)

## WSPLR — TRUMPET & ORGAN
### WSPLRE — Trumpet & organ. Sonatas
**Fantini, Girolamo**
Eight sonatas: for trumpet and organ/ by Girolamo Fantini; edited by Edward H. Tarr. — London: Musica rara, 1971. — 4to.
Score (18p.) & 2 parts.
Unpriced

(B72-51245)

## WSPLWU — TRUMPET & TROMBONE
**Hader, Widmar**
[Duet for trumpet and trombone (1960)]. Duett für Trompete in C und Posaune/ [by] Widmar Hader. — Regensburg: Bosse; [London]: [Bärenreiter], 1970. — 11p; 4to.
£0.85

(B72-50786)

## WT — HORN
**Mahler, Gustav**
[Selections]. Complete horn parts [to] 1st & 2nd symphonies [and] Lieder eines fahrenden Gesellen/ by Gustav Mahler; compiled by Richard Merewether. — London: Paxman, 1972. — 40p; 4to.
£1.50

(B72-50787)

## WT/AC — Tutors
**Burden, John**
Horn playing: a new approach/ by John Burden. — London: Paterson, 1972. — 40p; 4to.
With duets for horn and piano inserted (4p.).
Unpriced

(B72-51246)

## WTP — HORN & PIANO
### WTPK/LF — Arrangements. Concertos
**Amram, David**
Concerto for horn and orchestra/ by David Amram; piano reduction by Paul Turok. — New York; London: Peters, 1971. — 4to.
Score (16p.) & part.
£1.60

(B72-50788)

## WUNS — TROMBONE QUARTETS
### WUNS/T — Quartets. Variations
**Premru, Raymond**
Tissington variations: for four trombones/ by Raymond Premru. — London: Musica rara, 1972. — 4to.
Score (15p.) & 4 parts.
Unpriced

(B72-51247)

## WUP — TROMBONE & PIANO
### WUPE — Sonatas
**Kalabis, Viktor**
[Sonata for trombone & piano. Op.32]. Sonate für Posaune und Klavier. Opus 32/ [by] Viktor Kalabis. — Mainz; London: Schott, 1972. — 4to.
Score (29p.) & part.
£2.00

(B72-51248)

## WWP — EUPHONIUM & PIANO
### WWPK/LF — Arrangements. Concertos
**Horovitz, Joseph**
[Concerto for euphonium]. Euphonium concerto/ by Joseph Horovitz; arranged for euphonium and piano by the composer. — Sevenoaks: Novello, 1972. — 4to.
Score (25p.) & part.
£1.25

(B72-51249)

## X — PERCUSSION INSTRUMENTS
### XDW — With percussion ensemble. Songs, etc
**Dennis, Brian**
Chant for Spike Milligan: for voices and instruments/ by Brian Dennis; text by Spike Milligan. — London: Universal, 1972. — s. sh; obl.fol.
Duration 5 min.
Unpriced

(B72-51250)

## XN — PERCUSSION ENSEMBLE
**Morgan, Robert**
L'Apr`es - midi du Dracoula for sound - producing instruments;
[and], Elegant journey with stopping points of interest: for
chamber orchestra or percussion ensemble/ by Robert Morgan. —
Mainz: Ars viva; [London]: [Schott], 1972. — 2p.; 4to.
£2.00
*Primary classification LJ*

                  (B72-50499)

## XNPK — Septets. Arrangements
**Liebermann, Rolf**
[Les Echanges]. Symphony, (Les Echanges): for
percussion-ensemble (7 players)/ by Rolf Liebermann; arranged by
Siegfried Fink. — Hamburg; London: Simrock, 1971. — 4to.
Score (24p.) & 7 parts.
Unpriced

                  (B72-50330)

## XNSEM — Quartets. Sonatinas
**Tull, Fisher**
Sonatina for percussion ensemble/ by Fisher Tull. — New York;
[London]: Boosey and Hawkes, 1971. — 4to.
Score (16p.) & 4 parts.
£1.75

                  (B72-50331)

## XNU — Duets
**Fink, Siegfried**
Mini Musik: for two percussionists/ by Siegfried Fink. — Mainz;
London: Schott, 1972. — 15p; 4to.
£1.00

                  (B72-51251)

**Regner, Hermann**
Percussion-Duos/ [by] Herman Regner, Rudolf Schingerlin,
Werner Stadler. — Mainz; London: Schott, 1972. — 40p; 4to.
Unpriced

                  (B72-50789)

## XPQ — MELODIC PERCUSSION
## XPQMJ — Melodic percussion band. Miscellaneous works
**Balázs, Oszkár**
Three burlesques: children's chamber music for percussion/ by
Oszkár Balázs. — London: Boosey and Hawkes, 1971. — 4to.
Score (40p.) & 8 parts.
£2.25

                  (B72-50332)

## XQ — DRUMS
## XQ/AF — Drum. Studies
**Fink, Siegfried**
Studies for snare drum/ by Siegfried Fink. — Hamburg; London:
Simrock. —
Vol.6: Studies for 2-3-4 snare drums. — 1972. — 31p; 4to.
Unpriced

                  (B72-50790)

## XQ/AF — Exercises
**Fink, Siegfried**
Beat the beat: solo for beat percussion/ by Siegfried Fink. —
Mainz; London: Schott, 1972. — 7p; 4to.
£0.80

                  (B72-51252)

## XTQTPM — UNACCOMPANIED VIBRAPHONE SOLOS
## XTRNT — Vibrophone. Trios
**Blarr, Oskar Gottlieb**
Trinité: musica sacramenti, für drei Vibraphone/ [by] Oskar
Gottlieb Blarr. — Regensburg: Bosse; [London]: [Bärenreiter],
1970. — 18p; 4to.
£1.85

                  (B72-50791)

# COMPOSER AND TITLE INDEX

8, 4, 5: eight pieces in the five-finger position for beginner pianists of any age. (Pointon, Malcolm). *Boosey and Hawkes. £0.40* Q/AF (B72-50169)

14 ayres in tabletorie, 1598/ by Michael Cavendish; and, Ayres, 1609/ by Alfonso Ferrabosco; and, Musicke of sundrie kindes, 1607/ by Thomas Ford; and, Songes of sundrie kindes, 1604/ by Thomas Greaves; and, Ayres to be sung to the lute, ca.1609/ by George Handford. (Cavendish, Michael). *Scolar Press. £12.00* ADW(YD/XDZT12) (B72-05572) ISBN 0 85417 561 x

35 songs from 35 counties. (Brace, Geoffrey). *Cambridge University Press. £1.60* JFDW/G/AY (B72-50907)

48 études for French horn. 48 études for trumpet: transcribed from 48 études for French horn. (Reynolds, Vernon). *Schirmer: Chappell. Unpriced* WS/AF (B72-50317)

5,000 nights at the opera. (Bing, *Sir* Rudolf). *Hamilton. £4.00* AC(WB/P) (B72-26658) ISBN 0 241 02201 0

A la bataglia: for four instruments, ATTB, by Heinrich Isaac. (Isaac, Heinrich). *Pro musica. Unpriced* LNS (B72-50950)

A meno vesedá: polca. (Nazareth, Ernesto). *Arthur Napoleão: Essex Music. Unpriced* QPHVH (B72-50577)

A travers chants: études musicales, adorations, boutades et critiques. (Berlioz, Hector). *Gregg. £9.60* A(D) (B72-06100) ISBN 0 576 28422 x

Ab irato; and, Two concert studies for piano solo. (Liszt, Franz). *Bärenreiter. £0.90* QPJ (B72-50590)

Abel, Carl Friedrich.

Sonata for flute & basso continuo in E minor. Op.6, no.3. Sonata in E minor: for flute and continuo. *Oxford University Press. £0.75* VRPE (B72-50731) ISBN 0 19 355081 4

Sonata for flute & basso continuo in G major. Op.6, no.6. Sonata in G major. Op 6, no.6: for flute and basso continuo. *Bärenreiter. £1.20* VRPE (B72-50732)

Acquaint thyself with God: anthem for alto (or tenor) solo, chorus, and organ. (Greene, Maurice). *Novello. £0.17* DK (B72-50031)

Acton, Thomas. The Romano Drum song book

Vol.1. (Hurley, Bernard). *Romanestan Publications. £0.25* JFEZDW/GJ/AYCG (B72-50105)

Adagio from Spartacus. (For my love). (Khachaturian, Aram). *Feldman. Unpriced* WMK (B72-50309)

Adams-Jeremiah, Dorothy. Sing, say and play: a book of junior music making and poetry for primary and junior schools. *Lengnick. £0.45* JFE/LDW (B72-50104)

Addison, Joseph. The spacious firmament: SSATTBB. (Drayton, Paul). *Oxford University Press. Unpriced* DH (B72-50024)

Adler, Guido.

Methode der Musikgeschichte. *Gregg. £6.60* A(VX) (B72-03925) ISBN 0 576 28180 8

Musikalische Werke der Kaiser Ferdinand III, Leopold I und Joseph I im Aufrage des K.K. Ministeriums für Cultur und Unterricht. (Ferdinand, *III, Emperor*). *Gregg. £18.00* C/AZ (B72-50335)

Adrio, Adam. Diletti pastorali, nos.1, 5, 6, 13, 15. Hirten last: funf weltliche Madrigale, für fünf stimmen und Basso Continuo. (Schein, Johann Hermann). *Bärenreiter. £0.95* DU (B72-50377)

After the ball. (Whitcomb, Ian). *Allen Lane. £3.00* A/GB(X) (B72-28006) ISBN 0 7139 0308 2

Ager, Laurence.

Book of birthdays. *Forsyth. Unpriced* QPJ (B72-50183)

London sparrow: unison song for children. *Cramer. £0.06* JFDW/GJ (B72-50451)

Ainslie, John. Praise the Lord. Revised ed. *Chapman. Unpriced* DM/LSB/AY (B72-50822) ISBN 0 225 65838 0

Akuomenon: drei Sätze für Alt-Blockflöte und Klavier. (Schäfer, Gerhart). *Bosse: Bärenreiter. £1.50* VSSPJ (B72-50754)

Al Jolson. (Freedland, Michael). *W.H. Allen. £3.00* AKG/E(P) (B72-28010) ISBN 0 491 00633 0

Alberti, Rafael. El mar la mar: per soprano, mezzo-soprano e 7 strumenti. (Berio, Luciano). *Universal. Unpriced* JNEE/NVPNPDW (B72-50106)

Albertini, Sergio. Contredanses: für Orchester. (Cherubini, Luigi). *Peters. £3.00* MRH (B72-50530)

Albinoni, Tommaso.

Concerto for oboe & string orchestra in G minor. Op. 9 no.8. Concerto á 5: for oboe and strings. *Musica rara. Unpriced* VTPK/LF (B72-51183)

Concerto for oboe & string orchestra in G minor. Op.9, no.8. Concerto a 5: for oboe and strings. *Musica rara. Unpriced* RXMPVTF (B72-51091)

'Album of classical guitar studies. (Roberts, Don). *Francis, Day and Hunter. £0.40* TS/AF (B72-51146)

Alive!. - *Excerpts.* Five new songs. (Maddox, Hugh). *Galliard. £0.27* JE/TSDW (B72-50445) ISBN 0 85249 141 7

Alive! (Maddox, Hugh). *Queen Anne's Rd, Southtown, Great Yarmouth, Norfolk: Distributed by Publishing Services Partnership for Galliard Ltd. £0.17* BMDACM/LGZ (B72-10329) ISBN 0 85249 122 0

Alkan, Charles Henri Valentin. Marcia funèbre d'un Pappagallo. Funeral march on the death of a parrot: for four-part chorus of mixed voices with organ, or piano, or woodwind accompaniment. *Schirmer: Chappell. Unpriced* D (B72-50015)

All seasons shall be sweet. Opus 6: for treble voices, percussion and piano. (Platts, Kenneth). *Ashdown. Unpriced* FLE/NYLNSDX (B72-50433)

Allan, Geoffrey. Räby. *Peter Maurice. Unpriced* WMGM (B72-50301)

Allan, Thomas. Allan's illustrated edition of Tyneside songs. 6th ed. reprinted. *Graham. £3.50* ADW/G(YDJHT) (B72-28011) ISBN 0 902833 75 8

Allan's illustrated edition of Tyneside songs. (Allan, Thomas). 6th ed. reprinted. *Graham. £3.50* ADW/G(YDJHT) (B72-28011) ISBN 0 902833 75 8

'Allein Gott in der Hör sei Ehr'. T.3, no.11, T1.9, no.54, T1.5, no.21: chorale arrangements for three, four and eight voices. (Praetorius, Michael). *Bärenreiter. £0.60* EZDM (B72-50402)

Alleluia, now may we mirthës make: SATB(unacc.). (Pope, Alan). *Oxford University Press. Unpriced* EZDP/LF (B72-50853) ISBN 0 19 343035 5

Allin, Stuart. Tutankhamun. (Odam, George). *Chester. Unpriced* CQN (B72-50806)

Altamira: for chamber choir and orchestra. (Durkó, Zsolt). *Boosey and Hawkes. £1.50* EMDX (B72-50051)

Am Ende des Jahrhunderts, 1895-1899: musikalische Kritiken und Schilderungen. (Hanslick, Eduard). 2. Aufl. reprinted. *Gregg. £7.20* A (B72-07355) ISBN 0 576 28188 3

Amazing grace: early American melody, SATB and piano; words by John Newton. *Keith Prowse. Unpriced* DM (B72-50362)

Amazing grace: traditional melody arranged with piano or organ accompaniment. (Burt, James). *Chappell. £0.20* KDW (B72-50459)

Ameln, Konrad.

Biblische Motetten: für das Kirchen jahr

Band 1: Erster Advent bis letzter Sonntag nach Epiphanias. *Bärenreiter. £2.00* EZDH/AYE (B72-50398)

Fürchte dich nicht, ich bin bei dir. S.228: motet for two four - part mixed choirs. (Bach, Johann Sebastian). *Bärenreiter. £0.35* EZDH (B72-50392)

Komm, Jesu, komm. S.229: motet for two four-part mixed choirs. (Bach, Johann Sebastian). *Bärenreiter. £0.40* EZDH (B72-50393)

Singet dem herrn ein neues Lied. S.225: motet for two four-part mixed choirs. (Bach, Johann Sebastian). *Bärenreiter. £0.50* EZDH (B72-50394)

American patrol. (Gray, Jerry). *Chappell. Unpriced* UMMK (B72-50719)

Ammer, Christine. Harper's dictionary of music. *Hale. £4.00* A(C) (B72-10997) ISBN 0 7091 3064 3

Amram, David. Concerto for horn and orchestra. *Peters. £1.60* WTPK/LF (B72-50788)

Amy, Gilbert. Jeux: pour (1 à 4) hautbois. *Universal. Unpriced* VTN (B72-51181)

Ancient voices of children: a cycle of songs for soprano, boy soprano, oboe, mandolin, harp, electric piano, percussion. (Crumb, George). *Peters: Hinrichsen. £6.00* JNFLEE/NYDTNPDW (B72-50457)

And music at the close: Stravinsky's last years: a personal memoir. (Libman, Lillian). *Macmillan. £3.50* BSV(N/XPU13) (B72-30741) ISBN 0 333 14304 3

And so it was (Christmas): for SATB chorus and piano. (Rocherolle, Eugénie R). *Warner: Blossom Music. Unpriced* EZDH/LF (B72-50055)

Andernaken: anon., for five instruments, ATTBB. (Thomas, Bernard). *Pro musica. Unpriced* LNR (B72-50948)

Andriessen, Louis. Sweet: for alto (treble) recorder. *Schott. Unpriced* VSSPMJ (B72-51179)

Angelo, Bacchi. Symphony for string orchestra in D major. Sinfonia, D-Dur: für Streichorchester und zwei Hörner ad lib. *Peters: Hinrichsen. £1.20* RXME (B72-50647)

Angel's carol: SATB a capella. (Billings, William). *Peters Hinrichsen. £0.50* EZDP/LF (B72-50404)

Anglo-American Primary Education Project. Music. (Horton, John). *Macmillan for the Anglo-American Primary Education Project. £0.60* A(VG) (B72-13853) ISBN 0 333 13332 3

Anna Karenina: ballet in three acts. (Schedrin, Rodion). *Anglo-Soviet Music: Distributed by Boosey and Hawkes. £10.00* MM/HM (B72-50961)

Annotated fingering tables for the Boehm flute. (Schaeffer, Burghard). *Rahter. Unpriced* VR/ELM (B72-50726)

Antegnati, Costanzo. Canzon 20: for 2 trumpets and 3 trombones (2 trumpets, horn and 2 trombones). *Musica rara. £0.70* WMJ (B72-50303)

Anthology of English music for the harp

Vol.1. (Watkins, David). *Stainer and Bell. £1.00* TQPMK/AYD (B72-51144)

Vol.4. (Watkins, David). *Stainer and Bell. £1.00* TQPMK/AYD (B72-51145)

Anthology of organ music: works for two manuals and pedals

Vol.7: Works by Boyvin, Couperin, Reichardt, Adams, Merkel, Beechey. (Phillips, Gordon). *Hinrichsen. £0.90* R/AY (B72-50199)

Vol.8: Works by Le Bègue, J.S. Bach, Albrechtsberger, Rembt, S.S. Wesley, Guilmant, Spooner. (Phillips, Gordon). *Hinrichsen. £0.90* R/AY (B72-50200)

Vol.9: Works by Marchand, Guilain, Vivaldi, A.W. Bach, Karg-Elert, Eberlin, Stevens, Guilmant. (Phillips, Gordon). *Hinrichsen. £0.90* R/AY (B72-50201)

Vol.10: Works by J.S. Bach, Russell, Merkel, Rheinberger, Sowerby. (Phillips, Gordon). *Hinrichsen. £0.90* R/AY (B72-50202)

Vol.11: Works by Boyvin, du Mage, Raison, J.S. Bach, Martini, Rinck, Cooke. (Phillips, Gordon). *Hinrichsen. £0.90* R/AY (B72-50203)

Vol.12: Works by de Grigny, J.S. Bach, Krebs, Vierling, Chipp, Phillips. (Phillips, Gordon). *Hinrichsen. £0.90* R/AY (B72-50204)

Antiphon. (Tull, Fisher). *Boosey and Hawkes. £30.00* UMMJ (B72-51158)

Apocalypse: for orchestra. (Brindle, Reginald Smith). *Hinrichsen. £7.50* MMJ (B72-50142)

Apollo: aleatoric piece for band. (Pennington, John). *Schirmer: Chappell. Unpriced* UMJ (B72-50255)

Appalachian spring. (Ballet for Martha): suite; version for 13 instruments. (Copland, Aaron). *Boosey and Hawkes. £6.00* MRG (B72-50527)

Appalachian spring. (Ballet for Martha): suite; version for 13 instruments. (Copland, Aaron). *Boosey and Hawkes. £1.25* MRG (B72-50528)

Apparitions: a ballad sequence for tenor, harmonica, string quartet and piano. (Tate, Phyllis). *Oxford University Press. £2.50* KGHE/NUPNQDX (B72-50132) ISBN 0 19 345822 5

Apple: unison song. (Cope, Cecil). *Boosey and Hawkes. £0.09* JFDP (B72-50904)

Après - midi du Dracoula for sound - producing instruments; and, Elegant journey with stopping points of interest: for chamber orchestra or percussion ensemble. (Morgan, Robert). *Ars viva: Schott. £2.00* LJ (B72-50499)

Aquinas, Thomas, *Saint.* Thee we adore. (Holman, Derek). *Royal School of Church Music. Unpriced* FLDH (B72-50081)

Arbeau, Thoinot. Orchésographie. - *Excerpts.* Twelve dances. *Schott. Unpriced* VSNUK/AH (B72-50273)

Arch, Gwyn.

A golden legend. *British and Continental. Unpriced* CQN/L (B72-50808)

The promised land. *Feldman. £0.40* FDE (B72-50069)

Robert Brown - instant hero: for voices, glockenspiels or chime-bars and piano. *Feldman. Unpriced* JFE/XPQDX (B72-50454)

Archer, G Scott-. *See* Scott-Archer, G.

Archer, William. Margrete's cradle-song. Op.4, no.2. (Holst, Gustav). *Bosworth. £0.20* KDW (B72-50925)

Argento, Dominick.

Postcard from Morocco: an opera. *London: Boosey and Hawkes. £10.00* CC (B72-50336)

The shoemakers' holiday: a ballad-opera based on the play by Thomas Dekker. *Boosey and Hawkes. £6.00* CLM (B72-50343)

Arianna: Kantate für Sopran, zwei Violinen und Basso continuo. (Scarlatti, Alessandro). *Peters. £2.00* KFLE/SNTPWDX (B72-50477)

Arias for double bass and piano. (Bottesini, Giovanni). *8 Cecil Rd, W.3: Yorke. Unpriced* SSPK/DW/AY (B72-50703)

Arias from famous operas: for all-organs. (Bayford, Dudley Escott). *Francis, Day & Hunter. £0.60* RK/DW/AY (B72-50645)

Ariodante. - Overture, 3rd section. Rigaudon. (Handel, George Frideric). *Bosworth. £1.80* MJ (B72-50958)

Arion and the dolphins: for unison choir and instruments. (Marshall, Nicholas). *Chester. Unpriced* CQN (B72-50348)

Arma, Paul. The Faber book of French folk songs. *Faber Music. £3.00* JDW/G/AYH (B72-50899) ISBN 0 571 09944 0

Armenian rhapsody, no.3. Op.189: for string orchestra,. (Hovhaness, Alan). *Peters. £1.50* RXMJ (B72-50652)

Arms of Hungary: SATB unaccompanied. (Kodály, Zoltán). *Boosey and Hawkes. £0.05* EZDW (B72-50412)

Armstrong, Robert.

Five Finnish Christmas songs: for mixed chorus and orchestra (or piano)

1: Christmas = No, onkos tullut kesä. (Head, Michael). *Boosey and Hawkes. £0.14* DW/LF (B72-50830)

2: When it is Christmas = Kun joulu on. (Head, Michael). *Boosey and Hawkes. £0.14* DW/LF (B72-50831)

3: A sparrow on Christmas morning = Varpunen jouluaamuna. (Head, Michael). *Boosey and Hawkes. £0.09* DW/LF (B72-50832)

4: Christmas bells = Joulun kellot. (Head, Michael). *Boosey and Hawkes. £0.14* DW/LF (B72-50833)

5: Uncle Frost = Halla. (Head, Michael). *Boosey and Hawkes. £0.14* DW/LF (B72-50834)

Arnell, C P. Symphony in D major. Op.5, no.5. Rococo symphony. (Stamitz, Johann). *Bosworth. £2.25* ME (B72-50957)

Arnold, Malcolm.

Fantasy. Op.107: for solo guitar. *Faber Music. Unpriced* TSPMJ (B72-50248)

Song of freedom. Op.109: for chorus of sopranos and altos, and piano. *Henrees Music. Unpriced* FDX (B72-50879)

Arnold, Matthew. A Victorian garland: three poems by Matthew Arnold set for soprano and contralto solo voices, horn, and piano by Phyllis Tate. (Tate, Phyllis). *Oxford University Press. £1.80* JNFEE/WTPDW (B72-50921) ISBN 0 19 345824 1

Arnold Bax, a catalogue of his music. (Parlett, Graham). *10e Prior Bolton St., N.1: Triad Press. £1.50* BBH(WJ) (B72-24473) ISBN 0 902070 04 5

Arnold Schoenberg. (Wellesz, Egon). 1st ed. reprinted. *Queen Anne's Rd, Great Yarmouth, Norfolk: Galliard*

*Ltd. Unpriced* BSET (B72-01561) ISBN 0 85249 104 2
Arsinda: Rezitativ und Arie, für Sopran und Orchester. (Bach, Johann Christian). *Peters. £3.50* KFLE/MDW (B72-50475)
Art de préluder sur la flûte. Op.7. - *Excerpts.* 48 Préludes in 24 keys: for treble recorder, (flute oboe). (Hotteterre Le Romain, Jacques). *Schott. £0.90* VSSPMJ (B72-51178)
Art of record buying: a list of recommended microgroove recordings
1972. *E.M.G. £1.75* A/FD(WT) (B72-01805) ISBN 0 900982 03 9
Arts second level course: Renaissance and Reformation. *(Open University Press)* Hendrie, Gerald. Renaissance music. *Walton Hall, Bletchley, Bucks.: Open University Press. £1.10* A(XRE201) (B72-50334) ISBN 0 335 00657 4
Arts second level course: the age of revolutions. *(Open University Press)* Edwards, Owain Tudor. Beethoven. *Walton Hall, Bletchley, Bucks.: Open University Press. Unpriced* BBJ (B72-22483) ISBN 0 335 00572 1
Aspects of whiteness: cantata for SSAATTBB and piano, by John McCabe. (McCabe, John). *Novello. £1.75* DX (B72-50380)
Associated Board of the Royal Schools of Music.
The contemporary 'cellist: a collection of graded pieces for violoncello and pianoforte
Book 1: Grades 1,2,3. *Associated Board of the Royal Schools of Music. £0.95* SRP/AY (B72-51134)
Book 2: Grades 4,5. *Associated Board of the Royal Schools of Music. £0.95* SRP/AY (B72-51135)
New pieces for viola
Grades 2, 3. *Associated Board of the Royal Schools of Music. £0.95* SQP/AY (B72-51123)
Grades 4, 5. *Associated Board of the Royal Schools of Music. £0.95* SQP/AY (B72-51125)
Grades 2,3. *Associated Board of the Royal Schools of Music. £0.95* SQP/AY (B72-51124)
Official book of scales & erpeggios for guitar. *Associated Board of the Royal Schools of Music. £0.25* TS/AF (B72-50705)
Pianoforte examinations, 1973
Grade 1: Lists A and B (primary). *Associated Board of the Royal Schools of Music. £0.35* Q/AL (B72-51007)
Pianoforte examinations 1973
Grade 2: lists A and B (elementary). *Associated Board of the Royal Schools of Music. £0.35* Q/AL (B72-51008)
Pianoforte examinations, 1973
Grade 3: Lists A and B (transitional). *Associated Board of the Royal Schools of Music. £0.35* Q/AL (B72-51009)
Grade 4: Lists A and B lower. *Associated Board of the Royal Schools of Music. £0.35* Q/AL (B72-51010)
Grade 5: List A (higher). *Associated Board of the Royal Schools of Music. £0.35* Q/AL (B72-51011)
Grade 5: List B (higher). *Associated Board of the Royal Schools of Music. £0.35* Q/AL (B72-51012)
Grade 6: List A (intermediate). *Associated Board of the Royal Schools of Music. £0.35* Q/AL (B72-51013)
Grade 6: List B (intermediate). *Associated Board of the Royal Schools of Music. £0.35* Q/AL (B72-51014)
Grade 7: List A (advanced). *Associated Board of the Royal Schools of Music. £0.35* Q/AL (B72-51015)
Grade 7: List B (advanced). *Associated Board of the Royal Schools of Music. £0.35* Q/AL (B72-51016)
Specimen sight reading tests: guitar, grades 3,4,5,6 & 8. *Associated Board of the Royal School of Music. £0.10* TS/EG (B72-50246)
Violin examinations, 1973 and 1974
Grade 1: Lists A and B (primary). *Associated Board of the Royal Schools of Music. £0.35* S/AL (B72-51111)
Violin examinations, 1973
Grade 2: Lists A and B (elementary). *Associated Board of the Royal Schools of Music. £0.35* S/AL (B72-51112)
Grade 3: Lists A and B (transitional). *Associated Board of the Royal Schools of Music. £0.35* S/AL (B72-51113)
Grade 4: Lists A and B (lower). *Associated Board of the Royal Schools of Music. £0.35* S/AL (B72-51114)
Grade 5: Lists A and B (higher). *Associated Board of the Royal Schools of Music. £0.35* S/AL (B72-51115)
Grade 6: Lists A and B (intermediate). *Associated Board of the Royal Schools of Music. £0.40* S/AL (B72-51116)
Grade 7: Lists A & B (advanced). *Associated Board of the Royal Schools of Music. £0.50* S/AL (B72-51117)
Aston, Peter. The music of York Minster. *29 Newman St., W.1: Stainer and Bell. £0.50* AD/LE(YDJGYB) (B72-22491) ISBN 0 903000 07 5
At the piano with Debussy. (Long, Marguerite). *Dent. £2.75* BDJAQ (B72-03316) ISBN 0 460 03821 4
Attaingnant, Pierre. Vingt et sept chansons musicales à quatre parties. - *Excerpts.* Fourteen chansons: for four recorders or voices, ATTB,. *Pro musica. Unpriced* EZDU/AY (B72-50857)
Aubade: for clarinet and piano. (Carr, Edwin). *Ricordi. £1.00* VVPJ (B72-50291)
Aubade. (Study no.4): for piano. (McCabe, John). *Novello. £0.45* QPJ (B72-50600)
Aus alten Spielbüchern: 32 Tänze und Stücke aus dem 16, und 17. Jahrhundert, für Tasteninstrumente. (Speckner, Anna Barbara). *Schott. £1.20* PWP/AY(XD126) (B72-51002)
Aus dem Opernleben der Gegenwart: neue Kritiken und Studien. (Hanslick, Eduard). *Gregg. £6.00* AC (B72-07360) ISBN 0 576 28183 2
Aus dem Tagebuche eines Musikers: Kritiken und Schilderungen. (Hanslick, Eduard). *Gregg. £6.00* A (B72-07353) ISBN 0 576 28186 7
Aus fremden Ländern: Lieder und Tänze für drei Sopranblockflöten der andere Melodie - Instrumente, Gitarre und Schlagwerk ad lib
Band 2. (Draths, Willi). *Schott. £0.70* VSRNTK/DW/AY (B72-50748)
Aus meinem Leben. (Hanslick, Eduard). *Gregg. £10.20* A/CC(P) (B72-07348) ISBN 0 576 28225 1
Aus neuer und neuester Zeit: musikalische Kritiken und Schilderungen. (Hanslick, Eduard). 3. Aufl. reprinted. *Gregg. £7.20* A (B72-07356) ISBN 0 576 28189 1
Austin, William. Prélude à l'après-midi d'un faune. Prelude to 'The afternoon of a faun'. (Debussy, Claude). *Chappell. Unpriced* MMJ (B72-50967)
Autobiography of a New Orleans Jazzman. (Foster, Pops). *2 Brook St., W1Y 1AA: University of California Press. £4.25* AMT/E(P) (B72-02170) ISBN 0 520 01826 5
Autumn: for voices and instruments. (Paynter, John). *Universal. Unpriced* JFE/XPQDW (B72-50915)
Ave Maria and Pater noster. (Wilson, Thomas). *Galliard. £0.10* EZDJ (B72-50057)
Ave Maria. Op.52, no.6. (Schubert, Franz). *Gould & Bolttler. £0.89* FDW (B72-50422)
Awake, awake my lyre: for soprano (or tenor), solo optional baritone, chorus, strings and continuo. (Blow, John). *Hinrichsen. Unpriced* DX (B72-50047)
Awake awake my lyre: for soprano (or tenor) solo, optional baritone, chorus, strings and continuo. (Blow, John). *Hinrichsen. Unpriced* ERXMDX (B72-50053)
Ayre, Leslie. The Gilbert and Sullivan companion. *W.H. Allen. £4.50* BSWACF(C) (B72-26093) ISBN 0 491 00832 5
Ayres, Reginald Barrett-. *See* Barrett-Ayres, Reginald.
Babe is born. Op.55: S.A.T.B. (Mathias, William). *Oxford University Press. Unpriced* DP/LF (B72-50039) ISBN 0 19 343023 1
Babe of Bethlehem: a nativity, for unison voices, piano, recorders, tuned and untuned percussion. (Burtch, Mervyn). *Chappell. £0.50* JFE/NYFSDP/LF (B72-50911)
Baby's song book. (Poston, Elizabeth). *Bodley Head. £4.20* JFDW/GJ/AY (B72-50452)
Bach, Anna Magdalena. Die Gesänge zu Georg Christian Schmellis 'Musicalischen Gesang-Buch' S.439-507 sowie sechs Lieder aus dem 'Klavierbüchlein für Anne Magdalena Bach'. S.511-14, 516, 517. (Bach, Johann Sebastian). *Bärenreiter. Unpriced* KFXDH/AY (B72-50490)
Bach, Carl Philipp Emanuel. Sonatas for piano. Sechs Klavier-Sonaten. Neu revidierte Ausgabe. *Peters. £1.25* QPE (B72-50176)
Bach, Johann Christian.
La Clemenza di Scipione. - Infelice! in van m'affano. Arsinda: Rezitativ und Arie, für Sopran und Orchester. *Peters. £3.50* KFLE/MDW (B72-50475)
La Clemenza di Scipione. Op. 14. *Gregg. £9.60* CQC (B72-50802)
Symphony in B flat major. (Overture, Lucio Silla). Op.18, no.2. *Eulenburg. £0.40* MRE (B72-50525)
Bach, Johann Sabastian. Fifteen 2-part inventions. S.772-786. *Peters. £0.45* PWPJ (B72-50554)
Bach, Johann Sebastian.
Clavierübung. Tl.3. - *Excerpts.* Duets. S.802-805. *Bärenreiter. £0.50* RJ (B72-50634)
Come, let us all this day/ melody and bass by J.S. Bach words by J. Troutbeck interludes and inner parts by Gerald H. Knight; and, Prepare thyself, Zion, from the Christmas Oratorio. *Royal School of Church Music. Unpriced* JDH (B72-50439)
Complete trumpet repertoire
Vol.1. *Musica rara. £2.75* WSN/AZ (B72-50319)
Vol.2. *Musica rara. £2.75* WSN/AZ (B72-50320)
Vol.3. *Musicara rara. £2.75* WSN/AZ (B72-50321)
Concerto for harpsichord in A major. S.1055. Concerto in A major for oboe d'amore, strings and basso continuo. *Bärenreiter. £1.50* RXMPVTQK/LF (B72-50661)
Concerto for harpsichord in F minor. S.1056. Concerto in G minor for violin, strings and basso continuo. *Bärenreiter. £1.25* RXMPSK/LF (B72-50658)
Concerto for three harpsichords in D major. S.1064. Concerto in D major for three violins, strings and basso continuo. *Bärenreiter. £1.85* RXMPSNTK/LF (B72-50659)
Er rufet seinen Schafen mit Namen = He calleth his own sheep each by name: cantata for Whit Tuesday. *Bärenreiter. £0.65* DE/LN (B72-50353)
Fifteen 3-part inventions (sinfonias). S.787-801. *Peters. £0.45* PWPJ (B72-50555)
Fürchte dich nicht, ich bin bei dir. S.228: motet for two four - part mixed choirs. *Bärenreiter. £0.35* EZDH (B72-50392)
Die Gesänge zu Georg Christian Schmellis 'Musicalischen Gesang-Buch' S.439-507 sowie sechs Lieder aus dem 'Klavierbüchlein für Anne Magdalena Bach'. S.511-14, 516, 517. *Bärenreiter. Unpriced* KFXDH/AY (B72-50490)
Gleich wie der Regen und Schnee von Himmel fällt = Like as the raindrops and snow from heaven fall, S.18: cantata for Sunday, sexagesimae. *Bärenreiter. £0.65* DE/LG (B72-50352)
Jesu, der du meine Seele = Jesus, by thy Cross and Passion, S.78: cantata for 14. Sunday after Trinity. *Bärenreiter. £0.90* DE (B72-50349)
Komm, Jesu, komm. S.229: motet for two four-part mixed choirs. *Bärenreiter. £0.40* EZDH (B72-50393)
Singet dem herrn ein neues Lied. S.225: motet for two four-part mixed choirs. *Bärenreiter. £0.50* EZDH (B72-50394)
Suites for cello, nos.1-3. S.1007-9. - *Excerpts.* Three movements from the solo cello suites. *Associated Board of the Royal Schools of Music. £0.15* VWPK/AH (B72-51192)
Toccata and fugue in D minor. *Peters. £0.40* QPK (B72-50606)
Wachet auf ruft uns die Stimme = Wake ye maids! hark, strikes the hour. S.140: cantata for 27. Sunday after Trinity. *Bärenreiter. £1.00* DE (B72-50350)
Das wohltemperierte Klavier. S.846-893
Band 1. *Peters: Hinrichsen. Unpriced* PWP/Y (B72-51003)
Band 2. *Peters: Hinrichsen. Unpriced* PWP/Y (B72-51004)
Bach, Wilhelm Friedemann. Fantasias for keyboard. Klavier fantasien. *Schott. £2.00* PWPJ (B72-50556)
Bach organ music. (Williams, Peter, *b.1937*). *British Broadcasting Corporation. £0.45* BBCAR (B72-15429) ISBN 0 563 10348 5
Bache, Constance. Hänsel and Gretel. - *Excerpts.* Hänsel and Gretel song book
by Engelbert Humperdinck. (Humperdinck, Engelbert). *Francis, Day and Hunter. £0.35* KDW (B72-50461)
Backgrounds and traditions of opera. (Berges, Ruth). 2nd., enlarged, ed.. *Barnes: Yoseloff. £3.25* AC(XA1900) (B72-04571) ISBN 0 498 07672 5
Bahk, Junsang. Mark: für Klavier. *Peters. £2.80* QPJ (B72-50579)
Bailey, George. The Strauss family: the era of the Great Waltz. *Pan Books. £0.50* BSQB(N) (B72-29417) ISBN 0 330 23437 4
Baird, Tadensz. Goethe-Briefe: Kantate für Bariton, gemischten Chor und Orchester nach Texten von Johann Wolfgang von Goethe und Charlotte von Stein in einer Auswahl des Komponisten. *Peters. £2.20* DX (B72-50379)
Baker, *Sir* Henry. Carols of King David: for unison choir, congregation and organ
No.5: The King of love: Psalm 23. (Williamson, Malcolm). *Weinberger. £0.05* JDR (B72-50092)
Balázs, Oszkár. Three burlesques: children's chamber music for percussion. *Boosey and Hawkes. £2.25* XPQMJ (B72-50332)
Baldassare, Pietro.
Sonata for trumpet & string orchestra, no.1, in F major. Sonata in F, no.1: for cornetto (trumpet), strings and continuo. *Musica rara. Unpriced* RXMPWSE (B72-51098)
Sonata for trumpet & string orchestra, no.1, in F major. Sonata in F, no.1: for cornetto (trumpet), strings and continuo. *Musica rara. Unpriced* WSPK/LE (B72-51237)
Sonata for trumpet & string orchestra, no.2, in F major. Sonata in F, no.2: for solo trumpet (cornetto) and strings. *Musica rara. Unpriced* RXMPWSE (B72-51099)
Sonata for trumpet & string orchestra, no.2, in F major. Sonata in F, no.2: for solo trumpet (cornetto) and strings. *Musica rara. Unpriced* WSPK/LE (B72-51238)
Ball, Eric.
Hansel und Gretel. - *Excerpts.* Prelude. (Humperdinck, Engelbert). *Weinberger. Unpriced* WMJ (B72-51214)
A Kensington concerto for brass band. *Boosey and Hawkes. £3.75* WMJ (B72-50768)
Ballet, W. Lute-book lullaby: for treble voices and organ. (Pehkonen, Elis). *Chappell. Unpriced* FLDP/LF (B72-50891)
Ballet music from the French operas. (Moore, Elizabeth). *Cramer. Unpriced* QPK/HM/AYH (B72-51046)
Ballycastle Bay: for brass band. (Barratt, Bob). *Ambleside: Keith Prowse. Unpriced* WMK/DW (B72-50311)
Banchieri, Adriano.
Canzoni alla francese a quatro voci, nos.10, 11. Two canzonas: for 2 trumpets and 2 trombones, (2 trumpets, horn and trombone). *Musica rara. £0.90* WNS (B72-51226)
Canzoni alla francese a quattro voci, nos.6, 8. Two canzonas: for 2 trumpets and 2 trombones, (2 trumpets, horn and trombone). *Musica rara. £0.90* WNS (B72-51227)
Band call: 76 tunes for folk dance musicians and bands. (Darke, Dennis). *English Folk Dance and Song Society. £0.40* LH/G/AYC (B72-50498)
Banks, Don. Prologue, Night piece and Blues for two: for clarinet (B flat) and piano. *Schott. Unpriced* VVPJ (B72-51189)
Banks, Eric. The Red Arrows march. *Robbins Music. £0.20* QPK/AGM (B72-50610)
Bántai, Vilmos. Flute music for beginners. (Kovács, Imre). *Boosey and Hawkes. £0.85* VRPK/AAY (B72-50737)
Bantock, Myrrha. Granville Bantock: a personal portrait. *Dent. £3.50* BBE(N) (B72-11534) ISBN 0 460 03971 7
Banyard, Edmund. One Friday in eternity. *82 High Rd, N.2: Galliard Ltd. £0.17* BBDNACM/LK (B72-10328) ISBN 0 85249 121 2
Banyard, Stephen. One Friday in eternity. (Banyard, Edmund). *82 High Rd, N.2: Galliard Ltd. £0.17* BBDNACM/LK (B72-10328) ISBN 0 85249 121 2
Barber, Samuel. The lovers. Op.43: for baritone, mixed chorus and orchestra. *Schirmer. Unpriced* DX (B72-50045)
Barbiere di Siviglia. - *Excerpts.* Largo al factotum. (Rossini, Gioacchino Antonio). *Charnwood Music. Unpriced* RSPMK/DW (B72-51083)
Barcheggio. - Sinfonia to part 2. Sinfonia: for trumpet, 2 violins and continuo. (Stradella, Alessandro). *Musica rara. £3.00* RXMPWS (B72-51097)
Barcheggio. - Sinfonia to part 2. Sinfonia: for trumpet, 2 violins and continuo. (Stradella, Alessandro). *Musica rara. £1.00* WSPK (B72-51236)
Baretti, Giuseppe. Lives of Haydn, Mozart and Metastasio. (Stendhal). *Calder and Boyars. £5.50* BHE(N) (B72-14734) ISBN 0 7145 0349 5
Baretti, Joseph. *See* Baretti, Guiseppe.

Bargagni, Ottavio. Secondo libro delle canzoni da suonare. - *Excerpts.* Canzona 'La Monteverde': for 2 trumpets and 2 trombones (2 trumpets, horn and trombone). *Musica rara. £0.70* WNS (B72-51228)
Barkauskas, Vytantas. Monolog: für Oboe solo. *Peters. Unpriced* VTPMJ (B72-51186)
Barnet, Miguel. El Cimarrón-Biography of the runaway slave Esteban Montejo: recital for four musicians. (Henze, Hans Werner). *Schott. £2.40* KE/NYERNSDX (B72-50933)
Barnett, David, *b.1907.* The performance of music: a study in terms of the pianoforte. *Barrie and Jenkins. £4.00* AQ/E (B72-12722) ISBN 0 214 65403 6
Barratt, Bob. Ballycastle Bay: for brass band. *Ambleside: Keith Prowse. Unpriced* WMK/DW (B72-50311)
Barrett-Ayres, Reginald. Communion service, series 3: for congregational use. *Novello. £0.14* JDGS (B72-50438)
Barry, John.
This way Mary: love theme from the film 'Mary, Queen of Scots'. *Leeds Music. £0.20* KDW/JR (B72-50121)
Wish now was then: from the film, 'Mary, Queen of Scots'. *Leeds Music. £0.20* KDW/JR (B72-50109)
Barsham, Dinah. Renaissance music. (Hendrie, Gerald). *Walton Hall, Bletchley, Bucks.: Open University Press. £1.10* A(XRE201) (B72-50334) ISBN 0 335 00657 4
Barsotti, Roger. Prince Igor. - Overture. Price Igor overture. (Borodin, Alexander). *Boosey and Hawkes. £3.90* WMK (B72-51218)
Barsotti, Roger. Fantasia on British airs. *Boosey and Hawkes. Unpriced* WMJ (B72-50769)
Bartlett, Ian J. Two songs for Feste. *Piers Press. £0.25* KDW (B72-50110)
Bartók, Béla.
Chorus music. 18 part songs: for unaccompanied choir Vol.1. *Boosey and Hawkes. £0.40* FEZDW (B72-50885)
Chorus music. 18 part songs: for unaccompanied choir Vol.2. *Boosey and Hawkes. £0.40* FEZDW (B72-50886)
Chorus music. 18 part songs: for unaccompanied choir Vol.3. *Boosey and Hawkes. £0.40* FEZDW (B72-50887)
Bassett, Leslie.
Moon canticle: large mixed chorus a cappella and violoncello obbligato. *Peters. £1.20* ESRDX (B72-50389)
Music for violoncello and piano. *Peters. £2.20* SRPJ (B72-50696)
Bate, H N. Weihnachtslieder Op.8. - Die Könige. The kings: SSATB (acc. or unacc.). (Cornelius, Peter). *Oxford University Press. Unpriced* DP/LF (B72-50373) ISBN 0 19 343029 0
Bawdy British folk songs. (McCarthy, Tony). *Wolfe. £0.60* KE/TSDW/K/G/KDX/AYC (B72-50938) ISBN 0 7234 0492 5
Bayco, Fredric. A Christmas alleluya: S.A.T.B. *Oxford University Press. Unpriced* DH/LF (B72-50027) ISBN 0 19 351111 8
Bayer, Bathja. Yuval: studies of the Jewish Music Research Centre
Vol.2. *Magnes Press: Distributed by Oxford University Press. £6.15* A(YBU) (B72-12719) ISBN 0 19 647627 5
Bayford, Dudley E. The music of Saint-Saëns. (Saint-Saens, Camille). *Francis, Day and Hunter. £0.35* QPK (B72-50607)
Bayford, Dudley Escott.
Arias from famous operas: for all-organs. *Francis, Day & Hunter. £0.60* RK/DW/AY (B72-50645)
Gilbert and Sullivan song book: for all-organs. (Sullivan, *Sir* Arthur). *Francis, Day & Hunter. £0.75* RK/DW (B72-50644)
Bayly, Ernie.
Catalogue of 'Red Label' gramophone records 1904. (Gramophone and Typewriter Limited). 1st ed. reprinted with September to November supplements. *19 Glendale Rd, Bournemouth BH6 4JA: E. Bayly. £0.85* A/FD(WM) (B72-30321) ISBN 0 902338 14 5
Catalogue of twelve-inch Monarch records ... March 1904. (Gramophone and Typewriter Limited). 1st ed. reprinted with supplements. *19 Glendale Rd, Bournemouth BH6 4JA: E. Bayly. £0.85* A/FD(WM) (B72-30322) ISBN 0 902338 15 3
B.B.C. *See* British Broadcasting Corporation.
Bears' dances: piano solo. (Field, John). *Bosworth. £0.15* QPH (B72-51032)
Beat the beat: solo for beat percussion. (Fink, Siegfried). *Schott. £0.80* XQ/AF (B72-51252)
Beatles complete: guitar edition. *Wise, Music Sales. £2.50* TSPMK/DW (B72-50711) ISBN 0 02 976930 2
Beatles year: piano vocal or easy organ. (Lennon, John). *Northern Songs. Unpriced* QPK/DW (B72-50612)
Beaumont, Adrian. Preliminary exercises for the oboe. *Schott. £0.40* VT/AF (B72-51180)
Beck, John Ness. Hyfrydol. Hymn for our time: for three-part chorus of mixed voices with piano (or organ) accompaniment. (Prichard, Rowland H). *Schirmer Chappell. Unpriced* DM (B72-50033)
Bedford, David.
Star clusters, Nebulae and Places in Devon. *Universal. Unpriced* DX (B72-50046)
Trona. *Universal. Unpriced* MRJ (B72-50154)
Beechey, Gwilym.
Sonata for flute & basso continuo in E minor. Op.6, no.3. Sonata in E minor: for flute and continuo. (Abel, Carl Friedrich). *Oxford University Press. £0.75* VRPE (B72-50731) ISBN 0 19 355081 4
Sonata for flute & basso continuo in G major. Op.6, no.6. Sonata in G major. Op 6, no.6: for flute and basso continuo. (Abel, Carl Friedrich). *Bärenreiter. £1.20* VRPE (B72-50732)
Symphony in B flat major. (Overture, Lucio Silla). Op.18, no.2. (Bach, Johann Christian). *Eulenburg. £0.40* MRE (B72-50525)
Beer, John.
Sonata for trumpet & string orchestra, no.1, in F major. Sonata in F, no.1: for cornetto (trumpet), strings and continuo. (Baldassare, Pietro). *Musica rara. Unpriced* RXMPWSE (B72-51098)
Sonata for trumpet & string orchestra, no.1, in F major. Sonata in F, no.1: for cornetto (trumpet), strings and continuo. (Baldassare, Pietro). *Musica rara. Unpriced* WSPK/LE (B72-51237)
Sonata for trumpet & string orchestra, no.2, in F major. Sonata in F, no.2: for solo trumpet (cornetto) and strings. (Baldassare, Pietro). *Musica rara. Unpriced* RXMPWSE (B72-51099)
Sonata for trumpet & string orchestra, no.2, in F major. Sonata in F, no.2: for solo trumpet (cornetto) and strings. (Baldassare, Pietro). *Musica rara. Unpriced* WSPK/LE (B72-51238)
Beethoven, Ludwig van.
Quartet for strings in C major. Op.59, no.3. String quartet in C major. Op.59/3. *Bärenreiter. £0.45* RXNS (B72-50662)
Quartet for strings in E flat major. Op.74. String quartet in E flat major. Op.74. *Bärenreiter. £0.45* RXNS (B72-50663)
Quartet for strings in E minor. Op.59, no.2. String quartet in E minor. Op.59/2. *Bärenreiter. £0.45* RXNS (B72-50664)
Quartet for strings in F major. Op.59, no.1. String quartet in F major. Op.59/1. *Bärenreiter. £0.60* RXNS (B72-50665)
Quartet for strings in F minor. Op.95. String quartet in F minor. Op.74. *Bärenreiter. £0.45* RXNS (B72-50666)
Symphony no.5 in C minor. Op. 67. *Chappell. £1.75* MME (B72-50962) ISBN 0 900277 08 4
Trio for piano, flute & bassoon in G major. K-H37. *Eulenburg. £0.60* NWPNT (B72-50166)
Beethoven. (Edwards, Owain Tudor). *Walton Hall, Bletchley, Bucks.: Open University Press. Unpriced* BBJ (B72-22483) ISBN 0 335 00572 1
Beg, steal or borrow: Britain's Eurovision song 1972. (Cole, Tony). *Valley Music. Unpriced* UMMK/DW/JS (B72-50259)
Beginner's repertoire for flute
Vol.1. (Phillips, Ivan Clarence). *Oxford University Press. £0.50* VRPK/AAY (B72-50267) ISBN 0 19 358220 1
Vol.2. (Phillips, Ivan Clarence). *Oxford University Press. £0.65* VRPK/AAY (B72-50268) ISBN 0 19 358221 x
Behrend, Siegfried. Solo for guitar (1951). (Hartig, Heinz Friedrich). *Novello. £0.25* TSPMJ (B72-50708)
Bell, A Craig. Sonata for two flutes & basso continuo in E minor. Sonata in E minor: 2 flutes and continuo, (v'c ad libitum). (Handel, George Frideric). *Peters. £1.40* VRNTPWE (B72-50728)
Bell, Arnold Craig. Chronological catalogue of Handel's works. *See* Bell, Arnold Craig. Handel - chronological thematic catalogue.
Bell, Arnold Craig. Handel - chronological thematic catalogue. 2nd ed.. *Darley, Harrogate, Yorkshire: Grian-aig Press. £12.00* BHC(TD) (B72-32113) ISBN 0 9500714 4 7
Bell 'popular' phonograph records, new catalogue no.9. (Edison-Bell Consolidated Phonograph Company). *19 Glendale Rd, Bournemouth, Hants. BH6 4JA: 'Talking Machine Review'. Unpriced* A/FE(WM) (B72-05227) ISBN 0 902338 13 7
Belloc, Hilaire. Rebecca. (Patterson, Paul). *Weinberger. Unpriced* KHYE/MPQ (B72-50946)
Benger, Richard.
Miniature suite: for two B flat trumpets or cornets and piano. *Chester. Unpriced* WSNTQG (B72-51234)
Preludes and canons for three trumpets. *Chester. Unpriced* WSNT/X (B72-50785)
Bennett, F Roy.
Evening. *Ashdown. £0.05* FDW (B72-50420)
The wind sings on the mountain. *Ashdown. £0.05* JDW (B72-50442)
Bennett, Richard Rodney.
Concerto for guitar and chamber ensemble. *Universal. Unpriced* MPTSF (B72-50150)
Concerto for piano. Piano concerto. *Universal. Unpriced* QNUK/LF (B72-50172)
Impromptus. *Universal. Unpriced* TSPMJ (B72-50249)
Nicholas and Alexandra: theme. *Columbia Music, Chappell. £0.20* QPK/JR (B72-50196)
Party piece: for piano and small orchestra. *Universal. Unpriced* MPQ (B72-50148)
Benoy, A W.
Petite suite. - *Excerpts.* En bateaus. (Debussy, Claude). *Oxford University Press. £0.50* VSRNTQK (B72-50276) ISBN 0 19 356150 6
Symphonic dance. Op.64, no.2. (Grieg, Edvard). *Oxford University Press. Unpriced* MH (B72-50505) ISBN 0 19 363819 3
Two waltzes. (Waldteufel, Emile). *Oxford University Press. £0.90* MHW (B72-50139) ISBN 0 19 368017 3
Berberian, Cathy. Morsicat(h)y: per la mano destra. *Universal. Unpriced* PWPR (B72-50168)
Berges, Ruth. The backgrounds and traditions of opera 2nd., enlarged, ed.. *Barnes: Yoseloff. £3.25* AC(XA1900) (B72-04571) ISBN 0 498 07672 5
Berges, Ruth. Opera - origins and side lights. *See* Berges, Ruth. The backgrounds and traditions of opera.
Bergmann, Walter.
Ode for Queen Mary's birthday, 1694. Come ye sons of art. (Purcell, Henry). *Schott. £0.75* DX (B72-50048)
Sonata for cello & basso continuo in A minor. Op.3, no.6. Sonata in A minor: for cello (or bassoon) and continuo (harpsichord or piano). (Mercy, Louis). *Schott. Unpriced* SRPE (B72-50241)
Berio, Luciano.
Chemins 2 su sequenza 6: per viola & 9 strumenti. *Universal. Unpriced* MPSQ (B72-50974)
Concertino for violin. Concertino per clarinetto, violino concertante, celesta, opera & archi. *Universal. Unpriced* MPSFL (B72-50973)
El mar la mar: per soprano, mezzo-soprano e 7 strumenti. *Universal. Unpriced* JNEE/NVPNPDW (B72-50106)
Sequenza 7: per oboe solo. *Universal. Unpriced* VTPMJ (B72-50284)
Sequenza 7: per oboe solo. *Universal. Unpriced* VTPMJ (B72-50285)
Berkeley, Lennox.
Counting the beats: song for high voice and piano. *Thames. Unpriced* KFTDW (B72-50131)
Introduction and allegro: for double bass and piano. *Yorke. Unpriced* SSPJ (B72-50244)
Windsor variations: for chamber orchestra. *Chester. Unpriced* MR/T (B72-50976)
Berlioz, Hector.
A travers chants: études musicales, adorations, boutades et critiques. *Gregg. £9.60* A(D) (B72-06100) ISBN 0 576 28422 x
Episode de la vie d'un artiste. Fantastic symphony. *Chappell. Unpriced* MME (B72-50507) ISBN 0 900277 02 5
Grand traité d'instrumentation et d'orchestration: opus 10. Traité d'instrumentation et d'orchestration: suivie de 'L'Art du chef d'orchestre'. Nouvelle éd., reprinted. *Gregg. £21.00* AM/DF (B72-06769) ISBN 0 576 28418 1
Les Grotesques de la musique. *Gregg. £8.40* A(D) (B72-06099) ISBN 0 576 28421 1
Mémoires de Hector Berlioz: comprenant ses voyages en Italie, en Allemagne, en Russie et en Angleterre, 1803-1865. *Gregg. £12.60* BBM(N) (B72-06102) ISBN 0 576 28423 8
Les Musiciens et la musique. *Gregg. £9.60* A(D/XFZ84) (B72-06101) ISBN 0 576 28424 6
Les Soirées de l'orchestre. *Gregg. £9.60* A(E) (B72-06098) ISBN 0 576 28420 3
Voyage musical en Allemagne et en Italie: études sur Beethoven, Gluck et Weber, mélanges et nouvelles. *Gregg. £18.60* A(D) (B72-06763) ISBN 0 576 28419 x
Berlioz, romantic and classic: writings by Ernest Newman. (Newman, Ernest). *Gollancz. £3.00* BBM(D) (B72-03314) ISBN 0 575 01365 6
Bernhard, Christoph. Geistlicher Harmonien, erster Teil. *Excerpts.* Jauchzet dem Herrn, alle Welt: für zwei Soprane, zwei Violinen und Basso continuo. *Bärenreiter. £1.00* JNFLEE/SNTRDE (B72-50458)
Bernhoff, John. A mass of life. Eine Messe des Lebens = A mass of life: für Sopran, Alt, Tenor, Bariton, gemischten Chor und grosses Orchester. (Delius, Frederick). *Boosey and Hawkes. £6.00* EMDX (B72-50384)
Bernstein, Leonard.
Mass: a theatre piece for singers, players and dancers. *Amberson: Chappell. Unpriced* CM (B72-50013)
West Side story: a musical. (Laurents, Arthur). *Heinemann Educational. £0.50* BBMMACM (B72-08533) ISBN 0 435 23529 x
Bernstein, Walter Heinz. Jesu, der du meine Seele = Jesus, by thy Cross and Passion, S.78: cantata for 14. Sunday after Trinity. (Bach, Johann Sebastian). *Bärenreiter. £0.90* DE (B72-50349)
Bertali, Antonio.
Sonata for two violins, trombone & organ continuo, no.1, in D minor. Sonata á 3, no.1 in D minor: for 2 violins, trombone and organ continuo. *Musica rara. £1.50* NUXUNSE (B72-50986)
Sonata for two violins, trombone & organ continuo, no.2 in D minor. Sonata á 3, no.2 in D minor: for 2 violins, trombone and organ continuo. *Musica rara. £1.50* NUXUNSE (B72-50987)
Sonatas for brass quintet & basso continuo, nos.1-6. Six sonatas: for 2 trumpets, 3 trombones and continuo (2 trumpets, horn, 2 trombones and continuo). *Musica rara. Unpriced* NWXPNRE (B72-50993)
Besozzi, Alessandro.
Concerto for oboe & string orchestra in G major. Concerto in G major: for oboe, strings and basso continuo. *Musica rara. Unpriced* RXMPVTF (B72-51092)
Concerto for oboe & string orchestra in G major. Concerto in G major: for oboe, strings and basso continuo. *Musica rara. £1.00* VTPK/LF (B72-51184)
Best music hall and variety songs. (Gammond, Peter). *Wolfe. £5.00* ADW/GM(YD) (B72-30743) ISBN 0 7234 0451 8
Besuch der alten Dame = The visit of the old lady. Op.35: Oper in drei Akten. (Einem, Gottfried von). *Boosey and Hawkes. £8.00* CC (B72-50339)
Besuch der alten Dame. The visit of the old lady. (Dürrenmatt, Friedrich). *Boosey and Hawkes. £0.55* BELAC (B72-19611) ISBN 0 85162 006 x
Besuch der alten Dame= The visit of the old lady. Op.35: opera in three acts after Friedrich Dürrenmatt's tragi-comedy. (Einem, Gottfried von). *Boosey and Hawkes. £10.00* CQC (B72-50803)
Bethlehem: SAATB a cappella. (Billings, William). *Peters Hinrichsen. £0.40* EZDP/LF (B72-50405)
Bevan, Clifford. Meditation on 'Austria' by Haydn: for brass band. *Feldman. Unpriced* WMJ (B72-50304)
Beyle, Marie Henri. *See* Stendhal.
Bezirk: für Klavier und Orchester. (Heider, Werner). *Peters. £3.50* MPQ (B72-50521)

Bianchi, Virginia. Twelve études for bassoon. *Schirmer Chappell. Unpriced* VW/AF (B72-50294)
Biblische Motetten: für das Kirchen jahr
Band 1: Erster Advent bis letzter Sonntag nach Epiphanias. (Ameln, Konrad). *Bärenreiter. £2.00* EZDH/AYE (B72-50398)
Biesantz, Clemens Schultze-. *See* Schultze-Biesantz, Clemens.
Big bands. (Simon, George Thomas). Revised enlarged ed. *Macmillan (N.Y.): Collier-Macmillan. £2.75* AMT/E(QB/XNQ12) (B72-12017) ISBN 0 02 610970 0
Billings, William.
The New England Psalm singer. - *Excerpts.* Chester: SATB a cappella. *Peters: Hinrichsen. £0.40* EZDM (B72-50400)
The psalm singer's amusement. - *Excerpts.* The angel's carol: SATBB a capella. *Peters: Hinrichsen. £0.50* EZDP/LF (B72-50404)
The psalm singer's amusement. - *Excerpts.* The bird: SATBB. *Peters: Hinrichsen. £0.40* DM (B72-50363)
The psalm-singer's amusement. - *Excerpts.* Modern music: SATB a cappella. *Peters: Hinrichsen. £0.75* EZDW (B72-50410)
The singing master's assistant. - *Excerpts.* Bethlehem: SAATB a cappella. *Peters: Hinrichsen. £0.40* EZDP/LF (B72-50405)
The singing master's assistant. - *Excerpts.* David's lamentation: SATBB a cappella. *Peters: Hinrichsen. £0.40* EZDM (B72-50401)
The singing master's assistant. - *Excerpts.* Lamentation over Boston; and, Jargon: SATB (or male chorus or mixed quartet). *Peters: Hinrichsen. £0.75* EZDW (B72-50411)
The singing master's assistant. - *Excerpts.* Peace be on earth = Retrospect: an anthem from sundry Scriptures for SATB (or male chorus or mixed chorus). *Peters Hinrichsen. Unpriced* DK (B72-50360)
Two Easter anthems: SATB a cappella. *Peters: Hinrichsen. £0.50* EZDH/LL (B72-50399)
Bing, *Sir* Rudolf. 5,000 nights at the opera. *Hamilton. £4.00* AC(WB/P) (B72-26658) ISBN 0 241 02201 0
Bird: SATBB. (Billings, William). *Peters: Hinrichsen. £0.40* DM (B72-50363)
Birkenshaw, F W. Selected Christian songs
Album 12. (Hathaway, W G). *Gospel Music. Unpriced* DM/AY (B72-50368)
Birtwistle, Harrison. Verses for ensembles: for 13 woodwind, brass and percussion instruments. *Universal. Unpriced* MRJ (B72-50979)
Biscogli, Francesco.
Concerto for trumpet, oboe, bassoon & string orchestra. Concerto for trumpet, oboe, bassoon, violins and continuo. *Musica rara. Unpriced* NWXPNSK/LF (B72-50995)
Concerto for trumpet, oboe, bassoon & string orchestra in D Major. Concerto for trumpet, oboe, bassoon, violins and continuo. *Musica rara. Unpriced* RXMPWNTE (B72-51095)
Bishop, Chiz.
Il Barbiere di Siviglia. - *Excerpts.* Largo al factotum. (Rossini, Gioacchino Antonio). *Charnwood Music. Unpriced* RSPMK/DW (B72-51083)
Bunty: musette waltz, for accordion solo. *Charnwood Music. Unpriced* RSPMHW (B72-51073)
La Ritrovata figlia. Op. 39. - *Excerpts.* Andantino. (Kozeluch, Leopold). *Charnwood Music. Unpriced* RSPMK (B72-51082)
El Salto de agna: accordion solo. *Charnwood Music. Unpriced* RSPMHW (B72-51074)
Bishop, Jeffrey. Spells and incantations: for horn and piano. *Novello. £0.90* VWPJ (B72-50295)
Bits and pieces for piano. (Pitfield, Thomas). *Forsyth. Unpriced* QPJ (B72-50603)
Bizet, Georges.
Carmen. - Avec la garde montante. Street boys' song = Choeur des gamins. *Schott. £0.60* JFE/NYFSRDW (B72-50913)
Te Deum: for mixed voices (with soprano and tenor solo) and orchestra. First edition. *Simrock. Unpriced* DH (B72-50356)
Black, Don.
This way Mary: love theme from the film 'Mary, Queen of Scots'. (Barry, John). *Leeds Music. £0.20* KDW/JR (B72-50121)
Wish now was then: from the film, 'Mary, Queen of Scots'. (Barry, John). *Leeds Music. £0.20* KDW/JR (B72-50109)
Blackburn, Marie. Let's play recorders: a simple recorder tutor for very young children, including 28 folk songs to play. *Feldman. £0.20* VS/AC (B72-50269)
Blair, Jimmy. La Mantilla: Spanish serenade: accordion solo. *Charnwood Music. Unpriced* RSPMJ (B72-51076)
Blake, Nicholas. Four pieces. (Grieg, Edvard). *Chester. Unpriced* VTPK (B72-51182)
Bland, William. Like a mad animal ...: for double bass, piano, violin, viola, alto flute and clarinet. *Yorke. Unpriced* NUPNQ (B72-50983)
Blarr, Oskar Gottlieb. Trinité: musica sacramenti, für drei Vibraphone. *Bosse: Bärenreiter. £1.85* XTRNT (B72-50791)
Blathmac. Celtic requiem: for soprano, children's choir, chorus and orchestra. (Tavener, John). *Chester. Unpriced* EMDGKAV (B72-50383)
Blaydon races. (Ridley, George). *Boosey and Hawkes. £0.30* KGXDW (B72-50944)
Bleiler, Ellen H. Lucia di Lammermoor. (Cammarano, Salvatore). *Dover Publications: Constable. £1.00* BDRAC (B72-22490) ISBN 0 486 22110 5
Blessed art thou Mary: Advent carol for soprano solo SA and piano or organ. (Harley, E Daker). *Novello. £0.07* FDP/LEZ (B72-50418)
Blessed be the God and Father. - *Excerpts.* Love one another/ by S.S. Wesley; words from I St Peter; and, O worship the Lord/ by John Travers; words from Psalm 96. (Wesley, Samuel Sebastian). *Royal School of Church Music. Unpriced* JDK (B72-50441)
Bliss, *Sir* Arthur.
Put thou thy trust in the Lord: introit for double choir (unaccompanied). *Novello. £0.07* EZDK (B72-50846)
Three songs. *Novello. Unpriced* KDW (B72-50923)
Triptych for piano. *Novello. £0.60* QPJ (B72-51033)
Block, Robert Paul.
Il Barcheggio. - Sinfonia to part 2. Sinfonia: for trumpet, 2 violins and continuo. (Stradella, Alessandro). *Musica rara. £3.00* RXMPWS (B72-51097)
Il Barcheggio. - Sinfonia to part 2. Sinfonia: for trumpet, 2 violins and continuo. (Stradella, Alessandro). *Musica rara. £1.00* WSPK (B72-51236)
Canzon 20: for 2 trumpets and 3 trombones (2 trumpets, horn and 2 trombones). (Antegnati, Costanzo). *Musica rara. £0.70* WMJ (B72-50303)
Canzon 22: for 3 trumpets and 2 trombones (2 trumpets, horn and 2 trombones). (Chilese, Bastian). *Musica rara. Unpriced* WMJ (B72-50306)
Concerto for oboe & string orchestra in G major. Concerto in G major: for oboe, strings and basso continuo. (Besozzi, Alessandro). *Musica rara. Unpriced* RXMPVTF (B72-51092)
Concerto for treble recorder in G minor. P.402. Concerto in G minor: for flute, (clarinet), oboe and bassoon or treble recorder, oboe and basso continuo ad lib. (Vivaldi, Antonio). *Musica rara. Unpriced* NWNSF (B72-50165)
Sacrae symphoniae. Bk. 1. Symphoniae sacrae
Vol.1: Canzon primi toni à 8: for 4 trumpets and 4 trombones. (Gabrieli, Giovanni). *Musica rara. Unpriced* WMJ (B72-51198)
Sacrae symphoniae. Bk. 1. Symphoniae sacrae
Vol.2: Canzon septimi toni à 8 (no.1): for 4 trumpets and 4 trombones. (Gabrieli, Giovanni). *Musica rara. Unpriced* WMJ (B72-51199)
Sacrae symphoniae. Bk. 1. Symphoniae sacrae
Vol.3: Canzon septimi toni à 8 (no.2): for 4 trumpets and 4 trombones. (Gabrieli, Giovanni). *Musica rara. Unpriced* WMJ (B72-51200)
Sacrae symphoniae. Bk. 1. Symphoniae sacrae
Vol.4: Canzon noni toni à 8: for 4 trumpets and 4 trombones. (Gabrieli, Giovanni). *Musica rara. Unpriced* WMJ (B72-51201)
Sacrae symphoniae. Bk. 1. Symphoniae sacrae
Vol.5: Canzon duo decimi toni à 8: for 4 trumpets and 4 trombones. (Gabrieli, Giovanni). *Musica rara. £2.00* WMJ (B72-51202)
Sacrae symphoniae. Bk. 1. Symphoniae sacrae
Vol.6: Sonata pian e forte à 8: for 2 trumpets and 6 trombones. (Gabrieli, Giovanni). *Musica rara. £1.80* WMJ (B72-51203)
Sacrae symphoniae. Bk. 1. Symphoniae sacrae
Vol.7: Canzon primi toni à 10: for 7 trumpets and 3 trombones, (5 trumpets and 5 trombones). (Gabrieli, Giovanni). *Musica rara. £2.50* WMJ (B72-51204)
Sacrae symphoniae. Bk. 1. Symphoniae sacrae
Vol.8: Canzon duo decimi toni à 10 (no.1): for 6 trumpets and 4 trombones. (Gabrieli, Giovanni). *Musica rara. £2.85* WMJ (B72-51205)
Sacrae symphoniae. Bk. 1. Symphoniae sacrae
Vol.9: Canzon duo decimi toni à 10 (no.2): for 6 trumpets and 4 trombones. (Gabrieli, Giovanni). *Musica rara. £3.00* WMJ (B72-51206)
Sacrae symphoniae. Bk. 1. Symphoniae sacrae
Vol.10: Canzon duo decimi toni à 10 (no.3): for 5 trumpets and 5 trombones. (Gabrieli, Giovanni). *Musica rara. £2.50* WMJ (B72-51207)
Sacrae symphoniae. Bk. 1. Symphoniae sacrae
Vol.11: Canzon duo decimi toni à 10 (no.4): for 6 trumpets and 4 trombones. (Gabrieli, Giovanni). *Musica rara. £3.50* WMJ (B72-51208)
Sacrae symphoniae. Bk. 1. Symphoniae sacrae
Vol.12: Canzon in echo duo decima toni à 10: for 6 trumpets, 4 trombones and 2 organs (4 trumpets, 2 horns, 4 trombones and 2 organs). (Gabrieli, Giovanni). *Musica rara. £3.00* WMJ (B72-51209)
Sacrae symphoniae. Bk. 1. Symphoniae sacrae
Vol.13: Canzon septimi octavi toni à 12: for 6 trumpets and 6 trombones. (Gabrieli, Giovanni). *Musica rara. Unpriced* WMJ (B72-51210)
Sacrae symphoniae. Bk. 1. Symphoniae sacrae
Vol.14: Canzon noni toni à 12: for 6 trumpets and 6 trombones. (Gabrieli, Giovanni). *Musica rara. Unpriced* WMJ (B72-51211)
Sacrae symphoniae. Bk. 1. Symphoniae sacrae
Vol.15: Sonata octavi toni à 12: for 2 trumpets and 10 trombones (2 trumpets, 2 horns and 8 trombones). (Gabrieli, Giovanni). *Musica rara. Unpriced* WMJ (B72-51212)
Sacrae symphoniae. Bk. 1. Symphoniae sacrae
Vol.16: Canzon quarti toni à 15: for 3 trumpets and 12 trombones. (Gabrieli, Giovanni). *Musica rara. Unpriced* WMJ (B72-51213)
Sonata for trumpet & string orchestra in D major. Op.3, no.10. Sonata decima: for trumpet and strings. (Grossi, Andrea). *Musica rara. £2.00* RXMPWSE (B72-51103)
Sonata for trumpet & string orchestra in D major. Op.3, no.10. Sonata decima: for trumpet and strings. (Grossi, Andrea). *Musica rara. £1.00* WSPK/LE (B72-51242)
Sonata for trumpet & string orchestra, no.1, in F major. Sonata in F, no.1: for cornetto (trumpet), strings and continuo. (Baldassare, Pietro). *Musica rara. Unpriced* RXMPWSE (B72-51098)
Sonata for trumpet & string orchestra, no.1, in F major. Sonata in F, no.1: for cornetto (trumpet), strings and continuo. (Baldassare, Pietro). *Musica rara. Unpriced* WSPK/LE (B72-51237)
Sonata for trumpet & string orchestra, no.2, in F major. Sonata in F, no.2: for solo trumpet (cornetto) and strings. (Baldassare, Pietro). *Musica rara. Unpriced* RXMPWSE (B72-51099)
Sonata for trumpet & string orchestra, no.2, in F major. Sonata in F, no.2: for solo trumpet (cornetto) and strings. (Baldassare, Pietro). *Musica rara. Unpriced* WSPK/LE (B72-51238)
Sonata for trumpet & string orchestra. Op. 35, no.10, 'La Cappara'. Sonata à 5, 'La Cappara': for trumpet and strings. (Cazzati, Mauritio). *Musica rara. £1.00* WSPK/LE (B72-51239)
Sonata for trumpet & string orchestra. Op.35, no.11, 'La Bianchina'. Sonata à 5, 'La Bianchina': for trumpet and strings. (Cazzati, Mauritio). *Musica rara.* RXMPWSE (B72-51101)
Sonata for trumpet & string orchestra. Op.35, no.12, 'La Zambecari. Sonata à 5, 'La Zambecari': for trumpet and strings. (Cazzati, Mauritio). *Musica rara. £2.50* RXMPWSE (B72-51102)
Sonata for trumpets & string orchestra. Op.35, no.11, 'La Bianchina'. Sonata à 5, 'La Bianchina': for trumpet and strings. (Cazzati, Mauritio). *Musica rara. £1.00* WSPK/LE (B72-51241)
Sonata for two trumpets, bassoon & string orchestra, in A minor. Lib.3. Op.8, 'La Buscha'. Sonata, 'La Buscha': for 2 trumpets (cornetti), bassoon, and strings. (Legrenzi, Giovanni). *Musica rara. £1.00* NWXPNSE (B72-50994)
Sonata for two trumpets, bassoon & string orchestra, in A minor. Lib.3, Op.8, 'La Buscha'. Sonata, 'La Buscha': for 2 trumpets (cornetti), bassoon, and strings. (Legrenzi, Giovanni). *Musica rara. £1.00* RXMPWNTE (B72-51096)
Sonata for two violins, trombone & organ continuo, no.1, in D minor. Sonata á 3, no.1 in D minor: for 2 violins, trombone and organ continuo. (Bertali, Antonio). *Musica rara. £1.50* NUXUNSE (B72-50986)
Sonata for two violins, trombone & organ continuo, no.2 in D minor. Sonata á 3, no.2 in D minor: for 2 violins, trombone and organ continuo. (Bertali, Antonio). *Musica rara. £1.50* NUXUNSE (B72-50987)
Sonatas for brass quintet & basso continuo, nos.1-6. Six sonatas: for 2 trumpets, 3 trombones and continuo (2 trumpets, horn, 2 trombones and continuo). (Bertali, Antonio). *Musica rara. Unpriced* NWXPNRE (B72-50993)
Block, R.P. Suite for trumpet & orchestra in D major. Suite in D major: for trumpet, 2 oboes, bassoon, strings and continuo. (Clarke, Jeremiah). *Musica rara. Unpriced* MPWSG (B72-50152)
Block, Robert Paul. Sonata for trumpet & string orchestra. Op.35, no.12, 'La Zambecari'. Sonata à 5, 'La Zambecari': for trumpet and strings. (Cazzati, Mauritio). *Musica rara. £1.00* WSPK/LE (B72-51240)
Bloodworth, Denis. Pictures at an exhibition. - *Excerpts.* Bydlo and two promenades. (Mussorgsky, Modest). *Oxford University Press. Unpriced* MK (B72-50506) ISBN 0 19 366175 6
Blow, John.
Awake, awake my lyre: for soprano (or tenor), solo optional baritone, chorus, strings and continuo. *Hinrichsen. Unpriced* DX (B72-50047)
Awake awake my lyre: for soprano (or tenor) solo, optional baritone, chorus, strings and continuo. *Hinrichsen. Unpriced* ERXMDX (B72-50053)
Service in F major. - Excerpts. Magnificat and Nunc dimittis: for SATB. *Novello. £0.17* DGPP (B72-50023)
Blower, Maurice. In midst of woods: part-song for SSA and piano. *Elkin. £0.10* FDW (B72-50073)
Bluette: continental accordion solo. (Staquet, Willy). *Charnwood Music. £0.19* RSPMHW (B72-51075)
Blume, Friedrich. Classic and Romantic music: a comprehensive survey. *3 Queen Sq., WC1N 3AU: Faber. £3.00* A(YB/XFY190) (B72-24250) ISBN 0 571 08215 7
Blunn, John Robert-. *See* Robert-Blunn, John.
Blyth, Alan. Colin Davis. *Allan. £1.50* A/EC(P) (B72-50792) ISBN 0 7110 0319 x
Bob Dylan. (Scaduto, Anthony). *30 Gray's Inn Rd, WC1X 8JL: Abacus. £0.60* AKG/E(P) (B72-23642) ISBN 0 349 13127 9
Bob Dylan. (Scaduto, Anthony). *W.H. Allen. £2.50* AKG/E(P) (B72-12015) ISBN 0 491 00662 4
Bock, Jerry. Fiddler on the roof: selection for all organs. *Valando. £0.60* RK/DW (B72-50643)
Bodleian Library. Felix Mendelssohn Bartholdy. *Bodleian Library. £1.00* BMJ(EM) (B72-19610) ISBN 0 900177 15 2
Bodleian picture books: special series. *(Bodleian Library)* Bodleian Library. Felix Mendelssohn Bartholdy. *Bodleian Library. £1.00* BMJ(EM) (B72-19610) ISBN 0 900177 15 2
Boersma, James G. Pat Boone rapture theme songs. (Mickelson, Paul). *Marshall, Morgan and Scott. £0.40* KDW/L/AY (B72-50123) ISBN 0 551 05159 0
Bogár, István. Cornet (trumpet) music for beginners. (Borst, Rudolf). *£0.85* WRPK/AAY (B72-50784)
Bogar, István. Three movements: for brass quartet. *Boosey and Hawkes. £1.25* WNS (B72-51229)
Böhn, Liselotte. Spiel im Duett: leichte Stücke für zwei Sopran-Blockflöten. *Schott. £0.60* VSRNU (B72-51174)
Bois, Rob du. *See* Du Bois, Rob.
Boismortier, Joseph Bodin de.
Concerto for treble recorder & string orchestra in G major. Op.21, no.3. Konzert für Altblockflöte mit Violinen oder

Querflöten und Generalbass, G-Dur. *Schott. £1.60* RXMPVSSF (B72-50660)
Concerto for treble recorder & string orchestra in G major. Op.21, no.3. Konzert für Altblockflöte mit Violinen oder Querflöten und Generalbass, G-Dur. *Schott. £0.90* VSSPK/LF (B72-50755)
Sonata for cello & basso continuo in D major, Op.26, no.1. Sonata for cello and piano. *British and Continental. Unpriced* SRPE (B72-51136)
Bolton, Cecil.
The Red Arrows march. (Banks, Eric). *Robbins Music. £0.20* QPK/AGM (B72-50610)
Themes from T.V. and film classics. *Francis, Hunter and Day. £0.75* QPK/JR/AY (B72-50616)
Bonner, Stephen. The classic image: European history and manufacture of lyre guitar, 850-1840. *128 Bishopsfield, Harlow, Essex: Bois de Boulogne. £10.00* ATJR/B (B72-50002) ISBN 0 900998 09 1
Bononcini, Giovanni Battista. Sinfonie da chiesa. Op. 5. - *Excerpts.* Sinfonia 1 und 9, for strings and basso continuo. *Schott. £1.40* RXME (B72-51087)
Book of ballet: arranged and compiled for recorder by Richard Sadleir. (Sadleir, Richard). *British & Continental. Unpriced* VSPMK/AHM/AY (B72-50747)
Book of birthdays. (Ager, Laurence). *Forsyth. Unpriced* QPJ (B72-50183)
Borodin, Alexander. Prince Igor. - Overture. Price Igor overture. *Boosey and Hawkes. £3.90* WMK (B72-51218)
Borst, Rudolf. Cornet (trumpet) music for beginners. *£0.85* WRPK/AAY (B72-50784)
Bottesini, Giovanni. Grande méthode complète de contre basse, pt.2; and, Etudes mélodiques - Excerpts. Arias for double bass and piano. *8 Cecil Rd, W.3: Yorke. Unpriced* SSPK/DW/AY (B72-50703)
Boulez, Pierre. Structures: 2 pianos à 4 mains
Livre 2: Chapitre 1 - Première pièce - Deuxième pièce - Textes 1,2,3 - Textes 4, 5, 6- Encart 1-4. *Universal. Unpriced* QNU (B72-51018)
Bowden, George. Guitar care: a manual to enable the guitar owner to service his instrument. *193 Wollaton St., Nottingham: G. Bowden. Unpriced* ATS/BT (B72-03317) ISBN 0 9502139 0 x
Bowman, J.H. Grannie's songs. *Sagittar Books. Unpriced* KEZDW (B72-50125)
Box, Sidney. Good-night Vienna: an operetta in three acts. (Posford, George). *Keith Prowse. £1.25* CF (B72-50797)
Boy friend: a play in three acts. (Wilson, Sandy). *Penguin. £0.25* BWNTMACM (B72-06766) ISBN 0 14 001350 4
Boy friend: song album. (Wilson, Sandy). *Chappell. £0.60* KDW (B72-50120)
Boyce, June B. New orbit: songs and hymns for under elevens. (Smith, Peter). *Galliard. Unpriced* JFE/LPDM/AY (B72-50908) ISBN 0 85249 134 4
Boyce, William. Ten voluntaries: for the organ or harpsichord. *Oxford University Press. £1.00* PWPJ (B72-50557) ISBN 0 19 375302 2
Boyd, Jack. Prologue for an unwritten play: for SATB chorus with B flat clarinet, orchestra chimes (or hand bells) and piano. *Warner: Blossom. Unpriced* ENYFVDW (B72-50839)
Boyd, Malcolm. La Solitudine: cantata for alto solo and basso continuo. (Handel, George Frideric). *Bärenreiter. £1.00* KFQDX (B72-50480)
Brace, Geoffrey. 35 songs from 35 counties. *Cambridge University Press. £1.60* JFDW/G/AY (B72-50907)
Brady, Nicholas. The psalm singer's amusement. - *Excerpts.* The bird: SATBB. (Billings, William). *Peters: Hinrichsen. £0.40* DM (B72-50363)
Brahms - a critical study. (James, Burnett). *Dent. £3.00* BBT (B72-16139) ISBN 0 460 03953 9
Brahms, Johannes.
Ausgewählte Lieder: für Gesang und Klavier. *Peters. £1.40* KFTDW (B72-50481)
Complete shorter works for solo piano. *Dover Publications: Constable. £2.00* QP/AZ (B72-51023)
Complete sonatas and variations for solo piano. *Dover Publications: Constable. £2.00* QP/AZ (B72-51024)
Complete transcriptions, cadenzas and exercises for solo piano. *Dover Publications: Constable. £2.00* QP/AZ (B72-51025)
Intermezzo for piano in E flat major. Op.117, no.1. Sleep soft, my babe. *Ashdown. £0.09* FDW (B72-50421)
Brahms songs. (Sams, Eric). *British Broadcasting Corporation. £0.45* BBTAKDW (B72-15425) ISBN 0 563 10431 7
Branson, David.
La Danse des ours. Bears' dances: piano solo. (Field, John). *Bosworth. £0.15* QPH (B72-51032)
John Field and Chopin. *Barrie and Jenkins. £3.00* BCE(ZF) (B72-08531) ISBN 0 214 65343 9
Braun, Gerhard.
5 Miniaturen: für Sopranblockflöte, Klavier und Schlagzeug. *Bosse: Bärenreiter. £1.85* NYFSRNQ (B72-50538)
Portrait 1: für 4 Querflöten. *Bosse: Bärenreiter. £1.50* VRNS (B72-50727)
Portrait 3: für Violoncello und kleiner Schlagzeug. *Bosse Bärenreiter. £1.25* SRPLX (B72-50701)
Bream, Julian.
Fantasy. Op.107: for solo guitar. (Arnold, Malcolm). *Faber Music. Unpriced* TSPMJ (B72-50248)
Impromptus. (Bennett, Richard Rodney). *Universal. Unpriced* TSPMJ (B72-50249)
Paseo: for solo guitar. (Fricker, Peter Racine). *Faber Music. Unpriced* TSPMJ (B72-50250)
Breathnach, Breandán. Folk music & dances of Ireland. *Talbot Press. £1.50* A/G(YDM) (B72-07358) ISBN 0 85452 014 7
Brecht, Bertold. Children's crusade = Kinderkreuzzug. Op.82: a ballad for children's voices and orchestra. (Britten, Benjamin). *Faber Music. Unpriced* FE/NYLDX (B72-50426)
Breig, Werner. Orgelwerke
Band 3: Praeambulen, Fugen, Fantasien, Canzonen und Toccaten. (Scheidemann, Heinrich). *Bärenreiter. £2.25* R/AZ (B72-50629)
Brent, Burt. Earl Scruggs and the five-string banjo. (Scruggs, Earl). *Music Sales. £1.75* TT/AC (B72-51154)
Bresgen, Cesar.
Europäische Volks-und Kinderlieder: in leichten Chorsätzen (3 Oberstimmen und 1 Unterstimme) mit Instrumenten (Blockflöten, Gitarre, Violine, Klarinette, Trompete, Violoncello ad 1 lib., Stabspiele, Schlagwerk
Band 1. *Schott. £1.40* ENYEXSDW/G/AYB (B72-50385)
Band 2. *Schott. £1.20* ENYEXSDW/G/AYB (B72-50386)
Bricusse, Leslie. Willy Wonka and the chocolate factory: vocal selections. *Taradam Music. £0.75* KDW/JR (B72-50122)
Brimhall, John. Tales of Beatrix Potter - Excerpts. Peter Rabbit and the tales of Beatrix Potter: music from the film. (Lanchbery, John). *EMI Film Music. Unpriced* QPK/JR (B72-50197)
Brinckmann, Johannes. Concerto for descant recorder & string orchestra in F major. Concerto in F: for descant recorder, strings and harpischord (piano). (Sammartini, Giuseppe). *Schott. Unpriced* RXMPVSRF (B72-50224)
Brindle, Reginald Smith.
Apocalypse: for orchestra. *Hinrichsen. £7.50* MMJ (B72-50142)
The death of Antigone: opera. *Peters. £2.20* CQC (B72-50347)
British Academy. The sources of English church music, 1549-1660. (Daniel, Ralph T). *82 High Rd, N2 9BZ: Stainer and Bell for the British Academy. £8.00* AD/LD(TE/XDXJ112) (B72-22016) ISBN 0 903000 10 5
British Broadcasting Corporation. Music guides. *(British Broadcasting Corporation)*
Chissell, Joan. Schumann piano music. *British Broadcasting Corporation. £0.45* BSGAQ (B72-22495) ISBN 0 563 12241 2
Desmond, Astra. Schumann songs. *British Broadcasting Corporation. £0.45* BSGAKDW (B72-14737) ISBN 0 563 12140 8
Horton, John. Mendelssohn chamber music. *British Broadcasting Corporation. £0.45* BMJAN (B72-15426) ISBN 0 563 12205 6
Ottaway, Hugh. Vaughan Williams symphonies. *British Broadcasting Corporation. £0.45* BVDAMME (B72-28682) ISBN 0 563 12242 0
Sadie, Stanley. Handel concertos. *British Broadcasting Corporation. £0.45* BHCAMF (B72-28683) ISBN 0 563 10349 3
Sams, Eric. Brahms songs. *British Broadcasting Corporation. £0.45* BBTAKDW (B72-15425) ISBN 0 563 10431 7
Whittall, Arnold. Schoenberg chamber music. *British Broadcasting Corporation. £0.45* BSETAN (B72-22494) ISBN 0 563 10489 9
Williams, Peter, *b.1937.* Bach organ music. *British Broadcasting Corporation. £0.45* BBCAR (B72-15429) ISBN 0 563 10348 5
British Empire: echoes of Britannia's rule: title music from the BBC TV series. (Josephs, Wilfred). *Essex Music. £0.20* QPK/JS (B72-50198)
British Federation of Music Festivals. Year book 1972. *106 Gloucester Place, W1H 3DB: British Federation of Music Festivals. £0.60* A(YC/WE/Q) (B72-13440) ISBN 0 901532 03 7
British Film Institute. Jazz in the movies: a tentative index to the work of jazz musicians for the cinema. (Meeker, David). *British Film Institute. £0.50* AMT/JR (B72-15718) ISBN 0 85170 030 6
British Museum. Ralph Vaughan Williams, 1872-1958: a guide to the centenary exhibition at the British Museum, 29 September to 15 December 1972. (Willetts, Pamela Joan). *British Museum. £0.10* BVD(WJ) (B72-28008) ISBN 0 7141 0337 3
British primary schools today. *(Macmillan for the Anglo-American Primary Education Project)* Horton, John. Music. *Macmillan for the Anglo-American Primary Education Project. £0.60* A(VG) (B72-13853) ISBN 0 333 13332 3
Britten, Benjamin.
Children's crusade = Kinderkreuzzug. Op.82: a ballad for children's voices and orchestra. *Faber Music. Unpriced* FE/NYLDX (B72-50426)
Friday afternoons. Op.7 - Excerpts. A new year carol Op.7, no.5. *Boosey and Hawkes. £0.05* FDP/LFM (B72-50072)
The prodigal son = Der verlorene Sohn. Op.81: third parable for church performance. *Faber music. Unpriced* CC (B72-50011)
Simple symphony. Op.4. *Excerpts.* Playful pizzicato. *Oxford University Press. £0.50* QNVK (B72-50173) ISBN 0 19 372375 1
Simple symphony. Op.4. *Excerpts.* Sentimental sarabande. *Oxford University Press. £0.50* QNVK/AHVL (B72-50175) ISBN 0 19 372374 3
Who are these children? Op. 84: lyrics, rhymes and riddles, for tenor and piano. *Faber Music. Unpriced* KGHDW (B72-50942)
Brocklebank, Joan. A Dorset book of folk songs. *English Folk Dance and Song Society. £0.20* JEZDW/G/AYDFK (B72-50448) ISBN 0 85418 042 7
Bronson, Bertrand Harris.
The traditional tunes of the Child ballads: with their texts, according to the extant records of Great Britain and America
Vol. 4 Ballads 245 to 299, with addenda to volumes 1-4. *Princeton University Press: Oxford University Press. Unpriced* KEZDW/K/G/AY (B72-50939)
Vol.2: Ballads 54 to 113. *Princeton University Press Oxford University Press. Unpriced* KEZDW/K/G/AY (B72-50940)
The traditional tunes of the Child ballads: with their texts, according to the extent records of Great Britain and America
Vol.3: Ballads 114 to 243. *Princeton University Press Oxford University Press. £10.00* KEZDW/K/G/AY (B72-50941)
Brooks, Keith. Ten trios for developing clarinet technique: for 3 clarinets. *Boosey and Hawkes. £0.60* VVNT (B72-51188)
Brouwer, Leo.
Canticum para guitarra. *Schott. £0.80* TSPMJ (B72-51149)
Danza caracteristica para el "Quítate de la Acera": gitarre solo. *Schott. £0.08* TSPMH (B72-51148)
Elogio de la danza: para guitarra. *Schott. £0.90* TSPMJ (B72-51150)
Tres apuntes = Three sketches. *Schott. £0.90* TSPMJ (B72-51151)
Brown, Earle.
Event - Synergy 2: for 19 wind and string instruments. *Universal. Unpriced* MRJ (B72-50980)
Music for violin, cello & piano. *Universal. Unpriced* NXNT (B72-50996)
Times five: for flute, trombone, harp, violin, cello and 4 channels of tape sound. *Universal. Unpriced* NVXPNR (B72-50990)
Brown, Frank E.
Ave Maria. Op.52, no.6. (Schubert, Franz). *Gould & Bolttler. £0.89* FDW (B72-50422)
Skye boat song: air (founded on an old 'chanty'). (MacLeod, Anne Campbell). *Cramer. £0.18* RK/DW (B72-50220)
Brown, Frank Edwin. Come shepherds. (Coleman, Henry). *Leonard, Gould and Bolttler. £0.06* DP/LF (B72-50824)
Brown, Sebastian. Tunes for my viola: fourteen pieces for viola and piano. (Murray, Eleanor). *Boosey and Hawkes. £0.75* SQPJ (B72-50236)
Brown, Earle. From here. *Universal. Unpriced* MMJ (B72-50966)
Browne, Earle. Nine rarebits: for 1 or 2 harpsichords. *Universal. Unpriced* QRPJ (B72-51051)
'Browning' fantasy: for five instruments, SATTB. (Woodcock, Clement). *Pro musica. Unpriced* LNR (B72-50949)
Bruch, Max.
Kol Nidrei. Opus 47. *Peters. Unpriced* SQPK (B72-51129)
Kol Nidrei. Opus 47. *Peters. Unpriced* VVPK (B72-51190)
Bruckner, Anton. Overture in G minor. *Eulenburg. £0.75* MMJ (B72-50513)
Brückner-Rüggeberg, Wilhelm. Serenate auf die erste hundertjährige Jubelfeyer der Hamburgische Löbliche Handlungs-Deputation - Excerpts. Symphonie: für Kammerorchester und Basso continuo. (Telemann, Georg Philipp). *Simrock. Unpriced* MRE (B72-50153)
Brüggen, Frans. Suite for tenor oboe, two violins & basso continuo, with Chaconne for two flutes, tenor oboe, two violins & basso continuo in F minor. *Excerpts.* Chaconne. (Telemann, Georg Philipp). *Schott. £1.60* NUPNQHJN (B72-50158)
Bruxner, Mervyn. Mastering the piano: a guide for the amateur. *Faber. £2.25* AQ/E (B72-28012) ISBN 0 571 09629 8
Bryan, Rosamond. Ten violin trios. *Oxford University Press. £0.50* SNTK/DW/G/AY (B72-50671) ISBN 0 19 355736 3
Bryce, Frank. Ground bass. *Paxton Music. Unpriced* WMGM (B72-50763)
Brydson, John. Five note excursions. *Freeman. £0.25* QPJ (B72-50580)
Buddy Holly. (Laing, Dave). *Studio Vista. £1.40* AKGDW/GB/E(D) (B72-07981) ISBN 0 289 70129 5
Budge, Donald. Sar-Orain le Catriona Dhughlas. (Douglas, Katherine). *Domhnall Budge. £0.30* KEZDW (B72-50126)
Bugle call blues. (New, Derek). *Studio Music. Unpriced* WMGM (B72-50302)
Bülow, Hans von. Sonatas for piano. Sechs Klavier-Sonaten. (Bach, Carl Philipp Emanuel). Neu revidierte Ausgabe. *Peters. £1.25* QPE (B72-50176)
Bunty: musette waltz, for accordion solo. (Bishop, Chiz). *Charnwood Music. Unpriced* RSPMHW (B72-51073)
Buonamente, Giovanni Battista. Sonate & canzone. Lib. 6. - *Excerpts.* Canzon à 5: for 2 cornetti and 3 trombones (2 trumpets/oboes and 3 trombones). *Musica rara. Unpriced* WNR (B72-51223)
Burden, John. Horn playing: a new approach. *Paterson. Unpriced* WT/AC (B72-51246)
Burgon, Geoffrey.
This endris night: a Christmas cantata for tenor solo, women's or boy's voices and brass. *Stainer and Bell. £0.75* DE/LF (B72-50811)
Toccata: for trumpet and piano. *Stainer and Bell. £0.40* WSPJ (B72-51235)
Burkhard, Willy.

Chor-Duette. Opus 22, 2: für gemischten Stimmen teilweise mit Violine oder Flöte. *Bärenreiter. £0.40* ESDW (B72-50388)
Drei Präludien und Fugen. Op.16: für Klavier. *Bärenreiter. £1.50* QP/Y (B72-50572)
Frage, Op.9: ein Liederzyklus für tiefe Stimme. *Bärenreiter. £1.50* KFXDW (B72-50491)
Variationen über ein Menuett von Joseph Haydn. Op.29: für Klavier. *Bärenreiter. £1.00* QPHR/T (B72-50576)
Variationen über ein Volkslied. Op.8: für Klavier. *Bärenreiter. £1.00* QP/T (B72-50568)

Burley, Rosa. Edward Elgar: the record of a friendship. *Barrie and Jenkins. £2.80* BEP(N) (B72-13441) ISBN 0 214 65410 9
Burnett, Michael. Three medieval carols: for SATB and organ (no.2 unaccompanied. *Elkin. £0.21* DP/LF (B72-50372)
Burnier, Victor. Sonata para os três tempos: piano. *Arthur Napoleão: Essex Music. Unpriced* QPE (B72-51028)
Burnley Public Libraries. *Massey Music and Gramophone Record Library. See* Massey Music and Gramophone Record Library.
Burns, Wilfred. A common prayer. *Bosworth. £0.07* FDH (B72-50070)
Burt, James.
Amazing grace: traditional melody arranged with piano or organ accompaniment. *Chappell. £0.20* KDW (B72-50459)
Noel Coward for all organs. (Coward, *Sir* Noël). *Chappell. £0.60* RK/DW (B72-51060)
Burtch, Mervyn. Babe of Bethlehem: a nativity, for unison voices, piano, recorders, tuned and untuned percussion. *Chappell. £0.50* JFE/NYFSDP/LF (B72-50911)
Burton, A J. Symphony no.9 in E minor. Op.95. - Largo. A New World prayer. (Dvorák, Antonin). *Lengnick. £0.20* KDW (B72-50924)
Bush, Geoffrey.
5 mediaeval lyrics: for baritone and piano. *Elkin. £0.75* KGNDW (B72-50134)
A menagerie: three part-songs for SATB (unaccompanied). *Elkin. £0.40* EZDW (B72-50062)
A nice derangement of epitaphs: for unaccompanied voices. *Elkin. £1.25* EZDX (B72-50068)
Bussotti, Sylvano. Sette gogli: una collezione occulta. *Universal. Unpriced* LJ (B72-50947)
Butterworth, Arthur. Processional prelude. *Novello. £1.00* WMJ (B72-51197)
Buttkewitz, Jürgen. Sonata for bassoon & piano. Sonate für Fagott und Klavier. *Peters: Hinrichsen. £1.60* VWPE (B72-50759)
Bydlo and two promenades. (Mussorgsky, Modest). *Oxford University Press. Unpriced* MK (B72-50506) ISBN 0 19 366175 6
Bye, Peter. Pat Boone rapture theme songs. (Mickelson, Paul). *Marshall, Morgan and Scott. £0.40* KDW/L/AY (B72-50123) ISBN 0 551 05159 0
Byrd, William. The carman's whistle. *Fenette Music: Breitkopf and Härtel. Unpriced* TSNTK (B72-50247)
Byrd. (Holst, Imogen). *3 Queen Sq., WC1N 3AU: Faber. £2.00* BBX(N) (B72-16876) ISBN 0 571 09813 4
Byrt, John. Dives and Lazarus: a folk ballad, for soloists, choir two-part), descant recorders, percussion, piano, guitar (optional) and double bass (optional). *Oxford University Press. £1.10* FE/NYFSRDX (B72-50425) ISBN 0 19 335490 x
Cabaret: souvenir music album. (Kander, John). *Valando Music. £0.75* KDW/JR (B72-50472)
Cader Idris: landscape for brass quintet. (Polin, Claire). *Schirmer: Chappell. Unpriced* WNR (B72-50315)
Cameos for clarinets. (Verrall, Pamela). *Feldman. £0.40* VVNT (B72-50289)
Cammarano, Salvatore. Lucia di Lammermoor. *Dover Publications: Constable. £1.00* BDRAC (B72-22490) ISBN 0 486 22110 5
Can I not syng but hoy? Op. 40, no.2: a Christmas carol, SATB unacc. (Jackson, Francis). *Banks. £0.08* EZDP/LF (B72-50850)
Canticum para guitarra. (Brouwer, Leo). *Schott. £0.80* TSPMJ (B72-51149)
Cantio: für Bariton und 2 Violoncello, Kontrabass und Orgel. (Kröll, Georg). *Bosse: Bärenreiter. £2.25* KGNE/NXNSDH (B72-50495)
Canzoni alla francese a quatro voci, nos.10, 11. Two canzonas: for 2 trumpets and 2 trombones, (2 trumpets, horn and trombone). (Banchieri, Adriano). *Musica rara. £0.90* WNS (B72-51226)
Canzoni alla francese a quattro voci, nos.6, 8. Two canzonas: for 2 trumpets and 2 trombones, (2 trumpets, horn and trombone). (Banchieri, Adriano). *Musica rara. £0.90* WNS (B72-51227)
Capriccio. Op.8. (Wood, Hugh). *Novello. £0.45* RJ (B72-50216)
Cardew, Cornelius.
The great learning: the first chapter of the Confucian classic with music in 7 paragraphs. *26 Avondale Park Gardens, W.11: Experimental Music Catalogue. Unpriced* JE/NYLDX (B72-50093)
Scratch music. *4 Alwyne Villas, N1 2HQ: Latimer New Dimensions Ltd. £3.00* AY (B72-24248) ISBN 0 901539 18 x
Careers with music. (Incorporated Society of Musicians). 2nd ed. *48 Gloucester Place, W1H 3HJ: Incorporated Society of Musicians. £0.70* A(MN) (B72-19609) ISBN 0 902900 03 x
Carlson, Betty. A singing heart: from Venice to the alps of L'Abri. *Hodder and Stoughton. £0.45* AKF/E(P) (B72-23640) ISBN 0 340 15866 2
Carman's whistle. (Byrd, William). *Fenette Music: Breitkopf and Härtel. Unpriced* TSNTK (B72-50247)
Carmen. - Avec la garde montante. Street boys' song = Choeur des gamins. (Bizet, Georges). *Schott. £0.60* JFE/NYFSRDW (B72-50913)
Carmichael, Alexander. Four prayers from the Gaelic. (Thomas, Mansel). *University of Wales Press. Unpriced* KDH (B72-50108)
Carney, James. Celtic requiem: for soprano, children's choir, chorus and orchestra. (Tavener, John). *Chester. Unpriced* EMDGKAV (B72-50383)
Carol for to-day. (Johns, Sybil Marian). *41 Padua Rd, Llandaff, Cardiff: S.M. Johns. Unpriced* JDP/LFP (B72-50089)
Carols of King David: for unison choir, congregation and organ
No.2: O Jerusalem: Psalm 122. (Williamson, Malcolm). *Weinberger. £0.05* JDR (B72-50090)
No.4: Who is the king of glory?: Psalm 24. (Williamson, Malcolm). *Weinberger. £0.05* JDR (B72-50091)
No.5: The King of love: Psalm 23. (Williamson, Malcolm). *Weinberger. £0.05* JDR (B72-50092)
Carpani, Giuseppe. Haydine, Le. *Adaptations.* Lives of Haydn, Mozart and Metastasio. (Stendhal). *Calder and Boyars. £5.50* BHE(N) (B72-14734) ISBN 0 7145 0349 5
Carr, Edwin. Aubade: for clarinet and piano. *Ricordi. £1.00* VVPJ (B72-50291)
Carr, John. The gay Delavals: portrait in music, for brass band. *Paxton. £2.50* WMJ (B72-50305)
Carruthers, Frank C. Edward Elgar: the record of a friendship. (Burley, Rosa). *Barrie and Jenkins. £2.80* BEP(N) (B72-13441) ISBN 0 214 65410 9
Carter, Sydney. Nine carols or ballads. - *Excerpts.* Every star shall sing a carol. *Chappell. Unpriced* DP/LF (B72-50823)
Caruso. (Jackson, Stanley, *b.1910*). *W.H. Allen. £3.50* AKGH/E(P) (B72-27439) ISBN 0 491 00664 0
Casey, Peter. One Friday in eternity. (Banyard, Edmund). *82 High Rd, N.2: Galliard Ltd. £0.17* BBDNACM/LK (B72-10328) ISBN 0 85249 121 2
Cassirer, Fritz. A mass of life. Eine Messe des Lebens = A mass of life: für Sopran, Alt, Tenor, Bariton, gemischten Chor und grosses Orchester. (Delius, Frederick). *Boosey and Hawkes. £6.00* EMDX (B72-50384)
Catalogue of 'Red Label' gramophone records 1904. (Gramophone and Typewriter Limited). 1st ed. reprinted with September to November supplements. *19 Glendale Rd, Bournemouth BH6 4JA: E. Bayly. £0.85* A/FD(WM) (B72-30321) ISBN 0 902338 14 5
Catalogue of twelve-inch Monarch records ... March 1904. (Gramophone and Typewriter Limited). 1st ed. reprinted with supplements. *19 Glendale Rd, Bournemouth BH6 4JA: E. Bayly. £0.85* A/FD(WM) (B72-30322) ISBN 0 902338 15 3
Catch-up: for four pianos or tape recorder and two pianos. (Hampton, Calvin). *Peters. £1.25* QNS (B72-50561)
Cathedral music. - *Excerpts.* Lord, how long wilt thou be angry?: anthem for SAATB (unaccompanied). (Hayes, William). *£0.10* EZDK (B72-50847)
Cavaccio, Giovanni. Musica a quattro voci. - *Excerpts.* Two canzonas: for 2 trumpets and 2 trombones (2 trumpets, horn and trombone). *Musica rara. £0.80* WNS (B72-51230)
Cavendish, Michael. 14 ayres in tabletorie, 1598/ by Michael Cavendish; and, Ayres, 1609/ by Alfonso Ferrabosco and, Musicke of sundrie kindes, 1607/ by Thomas Ford and, Songes of sundrie kindes, 1604/ by Thomas Greaves; and, Ayres to be sung to the lute, ca.1609/ by George Handford. *Scolar Press. £12.00* ADW(YD/XDZT12) (B72-05572) ISBN 0 85417 561 x
Cazzati, Mauritio.
Sonata for trumpet & string orchestra. Op. 35, no.10, 'La Cappara'. Sonata à 5, 'La Cappara': for trumpet and strings. *Musica rara. £1.00* WSPK/LE (B72-51239)
Sonata for trumpet & string orchestra. Op.35, no.10, 'La Cappara'. Sonata à 5, 'La Cappara': for trumpet and strings. *Musica rara. £2.50* RXMPWSE (B72-51100)
Sonata for trumpet & string orchestra. Op.35, no.11, 'La Bianchina'. Sonata à 5, 'La Bianchina': for trumpet and strings. *Musica rara.* RXMPWSE (B72-51101)
Sonata for trumpet & string orchestra. Op.35, no.12, 'La Zambecari. Sonata à 5, 'La Zambecari': for trumpet and strings. *Musica rara. £2.50* RXMPWSE (B72-51102)
Sonata for trumpet & string orchestra. Op.35, no.12, 'La Zambecari'. Sonata à 5, 'La Zambecari': for trumpet and strings. *Musica rara. £1.00* WSPK/LE (B72-51240)
Sonata for trumpet & string orchestra. Op.35, no.11, 'La Bianchina'. Sonata à 5, 'La Bianchina': for trumpet and strings. *Musica rara. £1.00* WSPK/LE (B72-51241)
Celan, Paul. Zyklus: cycle for baritone and orchestra. (Reimann, Aribert). *Schott. £3.00* KGNE/MDW (B72-50494)
Celtic requiem: for soprano, children's choir, chorus and orchestra. (Tavener, John). *Chester. Unpriced* EMDGKAV (B72-50383)
Ceol beag agus ceol mor = Little music and big music. (MacLellan, John A). *Paterson. Unpriced* VY/AY (B72-50297)
Cerha, Friedrich. Orchestra pieces, (1913). (Webern, Anton von). *Boosey and Hawkes. £2.40* MMJ (B72-50520)
Chagrin, Francis.
Preludes for four: for treble recorder (or flute), violin, cello and harpsichord (or piano). *Novello. £1.50* NUSRNS (B72-50534)
Two fanfares: for four equal instruments with optional percussion. *Novello. £1.30* LNSGN (B72-50951)
Two fanfares: for three equal instruments with optional percussion in no.2. *Novello. £1.10* LNTGN (B72-50502)
Chance, John Barnes. Elegy. *Boosey and Hawkes. £4.50* UMMJ (B72-51155)
Chanson de matin. Op.15, no.2. (Elgar, *Sir* Edward, *bart*). *Novello. Unpriced* VSNRK (B72-50270)
Chant for Spike Milligan: for voices and instruments. (Dennis, Brian). *Universal. Unpriced* XDW (B72-51250)
Chapple, Brian. Trees revisited: for piano. *Chester. Unpriced* QPJ (B72-50581)
Charles, E. Spartak-Adagio. The Adagio from Spartacus. (For my love). (Khachaturian, Aram). *Feldman. Unpriced* WMK (B72-50309)
Charles, Sydney Robinson. A handbook of music and music literature in sets and series. *Free Press: Collier-Macmillan. £5.40* A(T) (B72-12964) ISBN 0 02 905400 1
Charlie girl. (Heneker, David). *Chappell. £1.75* CM (B72-50799)
Charlie girl: a comedy musical in two acts. (Williams, Hugh). *Chappell. £0.75* BHJJACM (B72-23641) ISBN 0 85360 040 6
Chatfield, Allen W. Lord Jesus, think on me: for mixed chorus and organ. (Talmadge, Charles L). *Galaxy: Galliard. Unpriced* DM (B72-50820)
Chatschaturjan, Aram. *See* Khachaturian, Aram.
Chatshaturjan, Aram. *See* Khatchaturian, Aram.
Chemins 2 su sequenza 6: per viola & 9 strumenti. (Berio, Luciano). *Universal. Unpriced* MPSQ (B72-50974)
Cherepnin, Alexander. The nymph and the farmer. La Fée et le cultivateur = The nymph and the farmer, Op.72: a lyric legend. *Boosey and Hawkes. £4.50* CC (B72-50337)
Cherubini, Luigi. Contredanses: für Orchester. *Peters. £3.00* MRH (B72-50530)
Cheshire soul-caking song: two-part. (Pitfield, Thomas Baron). *Oxford University Press. Unpriced* FDW (B72-50075)
Chester: SATB a cappella. (Billings, William). *Peters Hinrichsen. £0.40* EZDM (B72-50400)
Chiaroscuro: for piano. (Le Fanu, Nicola). *Novello. £1.00* QPJ (B72-50190)
Children's corner - Excerpts. Golliwog's cake-walk. (Debussy, Claude). *Peters. Unpriced* QNV (B72-51022)
Children's crusade = Kinderkreuzzug. Op.82: a ballad for children's voices and orchestra. (Britten, Benjamin). *Faber Music. Unpriced* FE/NYLDX (B72-50426)
Chilese, Bastian. Canzon 22: for 3 trumpets and 2 trombones (2 trumpets, horn and 2 trombones). *Musica rara. Unpriced* WMJ (B72-50306)
Chissell, Joan. Schumann piano music. *British Broadcasting Corporation. £0.45* BSGAQ (B72-22495) ISBN 0 563 12241 2
Choice lessons for the harpsichord or spinnet. - Allmand in D major. Prelude in D. (Greene, Maurice). *Leonard, Gould & Bolttler. £0.18* RK/AHJ (B72-51059)
Chor-Duette. Opus 22, 2: für gemischten Stimmen teilweise mit Violine oder Flöte. (Burkhard, Willy). *Bärenreiter. £0.40* ESDW (B72-50388)
Choralbuch zum Evangelischen Kirchengesangbuch: mit den Begleitsätzen des Württembergischen Choralbuches bearbeitet von Karl Gerok und Hans-Arnold Metzger und mit Begleitsätzen zu den Liedern des Anhangs zum Rheinisch-Westfälisch-Lippischen Gesangbuch. (Rödding, Gerhard). *Bärenreiter. Unpriced* DM/LSET/AY (B72-50371)
Choralvorspiele für den gottesdienstlichen Gebrauch
Band 3. (Graf, Adolf). *Bärenreiter. £1.75* R/AY (B72-50624)
Choralvorspiele in tiefer Lage zum Auswahlchoralbuch. (Timme, Traugott). *Bärenreiter. £3.15* R/AY (B72-50625)
Chorische Bläserschule. Method for brass. (Schneider, Willy). *Schott. £0.50* WM/AC (B72-51194)
Chorus of Hebrew slaves. (Verdi, Giuseppe). *Norman Richardson Band Arrangements. Unpriced* WMK/DW (B72-50310)
Christ is the world's light: anthem for SATB and organ. (Thiman, Eric Harding). *Novello. £0.10* DH (B72-50026)
Christmas alleluya: S.A.T.B. (Bayco, Fredric). *Oxford University Press. Unpriced* DH/LF (B72-50027) ISBN 0 19 351111 8
Christmas day is comin': for unison, two-part or three part chorus. (Rocherolle, Eugénie R). *Warner: Blosso Music. Unpriced* FDW/LF (B72-50423)
Christmas in Spain: six traditional Spanish carols, for unison and two-part voices, recorders, tuned and untuned percussion, and piano. (Pfaff, Philip). *Chappell. £0.50* FE/NYFSDP/LF/AYK (B72-50882)
Christmas journey: S.A. (Verrall, Pamela Motley). *British and Continental. Unpriced* FE/NYFSDP/LF (B72-50881)
Chromatic fantasy in E major: violoncello. (Finney, Ross Lee). *Peters. £1.10* SRPMJ (B72-50702)
Chronological catalogue of Handel's works. *See* Bell, Arnold Craig.
Church cantatas of J.S. Bach. (Robertson, Alec). *Cassell. £5.00* BBCADE (B72-26660) ISBN 0 304 93822 x
Ciampa, Christine M. Harper's dictionary of music. (Ammer, Christine). *Hale. £4.00* A(C) (B72-10997) ISBN 0 7091 3064 3
Cimarosa, Domenico. Symphony in D major. Sinfonia D-dur: für Kammerorchester. *Peters. £2.00* MRE (B72-50526)
Cimarrón-Biography of the runaway slave Esteban Montejo: recital for four musicians. (Henze, Hans Werner). *Schott. £2.40* KE/NYERNSDX (B72-50933)
Cirandinhas, no.7. Todo o mundo passo. (Villa-Lobos, Heitor). *Arthur Napoleão: Essex Music. Unpriced* QPJ (B72-50605)

Clapham, John, *b.1908*. Smetana. *Dent. £2.10* BSIM (B72-15423) ISBN 0 460 03133 3

Clarinet and saxophone experience. (Richmond, Stanley). *Darton, Longman and Todd. £3.25* AVV(B) (B72-50004) ISBN 0 232 51148 9

Clark, Keith. Folk song and dance: a list of books. *National Book League: English Folk Dance and Song Society. £0.30* A/G(T) (B72-16428) ISBN 0 85353 138 2

Clark, Rogie. Six Afro-American carols for Christmas. *Piedmont: Distributed by Weinberger. £0.15* DP/LF/AYTLD (B72-50828)

Clarke, Jeremiah.
Suite for trumpet & orchestra in D major. Suite in D major: for trumpet, 2 oboes, bassoon, strings and continuo. *Musica rara. Unpriced* MPWSG (B72-50152)
Suite for trumpet & orchestra in D major. Suite in D major: for trumpet, 2 oboes, bassoon, strings and continuo. *Musica rara. Unpriced* WSPK/AG (B72-50325)

Classic and Romantic music: a comprehensive survey. (Blume, Friedrich). *3 Queen Sq., WC1N 3AU: Faber. £3.00* A(YB/XFY190) (B72-24250) ISBN 0 571 08215 7

Classic image: European history and manufacture of lyre guitar, 850-1840. (Bonner, Stephen). *128 Bishopsfield, Harlow, Essex: Bois de Boulogne. £10.00* ATJR/B (B72-50002) ISBN 0 900998 09 1

Classical overture. (Grundman, Clare). *Boosey and Hawkes. £1.50* UMMJ (B72-51156)

Classisches Spielbuch: für Sopran-Blockflöte, Alt-Blockflöte und Klavier. (Wohlgemuth, Gerhard). *Peters: Hinrichsen. Unpriced* VSNTPWK/AAY (B72-51172)

Claude Debussy: the story of his life and work. (Myers, Rollo Hugh). *Boosey and hawkes. Unpriced* BDJ(N) (B72-50005) ISBN 0 85162 003 5

Clavierübung. Tl.3. - *Excerpts.* Duets. S.802-805. (Bach, Johann Sebastian). *Bärenreiter. £0.50* RJ (B72-50634)

Clelland, Lamont. Hymns arranged for B flat instruments. *Feldman. Unpriced* VVNSQK/DM/AY (B72-50288)

Clements, John. A suite: for recorder trio, one descant and two trebles. *Ashdown. Unpriced* VSNTG (B72-50271)

Clemenza di Scipione. - Infelice! in van m'affano. Arsinda: Rezitativ und Arie, für Sopran und Orchester. (Bach, Johann Christian). *Peters. £3.50* KFLE/MDW (B72-50475)

Clemenza di Scipione. Op. 14. (Bach, Johann Christian). *Gregg. £9.60* CQC (B72-50802)

Clemenza di Tito. K.621: opera seria in due atti. (Mozart, Wolfgang Amadeus). *Bärenreiter. £3.75* CC (B72-50341)

Clifton, Geoffrey. In every corner sing. *Nelson. Unpriced* DM/AY (B72-50367) ISBN 0 17 437012 1

Clochemerle. (Roper, Alan). *Francis, Day and Hunter. £0.20* QPK/JS (B72-50619)

Clockshop. (Ford, Les). *Feldman. Unpriced* NYDSRNM (B72-50167)

Cloud canticles: for double chorus. (Mellers, Wilfrid). *Galliard. £0.83* EZDW (B72-50063)

Coates, Eric. Selections. The music of Eric Coates. *Chappell. Unpriced* UMK (B72-50256)

Coates, William.
Jacobean consort music: for recorders or viols
Book 1: Five fantasias and two dances of three parts. *Stainer and Bell. £0.44* C/AYD (B72-50009)
Book 2: Seven fantasias of four parts. *Stainer and Bell. £0.49* C/AYD (B72-50010)

Cod-pieces. Liber 1. - *Excerpts.* Two cod-pieces. Nos.3.4. (Warlock, Peter). *Thames. Unpriced* QNVK (B72-50174)

Coe, Richard Nelson. Lives of Haydn, Mozart and Metastasio. (Stendhal). *Calder and Boyars. £5.50* BHE(N) (B72-14734) ISBN 0 7145 0349 5

Coelius Sedulius. From east to west: SATB unacc. (Rutter, John). *Oxford University Press. Unpriced* EZDM (B72-50061) ISBN 0 19 343026 6

Coke, Roger Sacheverell. Sonata for cello & piano, no.2, in C major. Op.29. Sonata no.2 (in C major). Opus 29: for violoncello and piano. *Chappell. Unpriced* SRPE (B72-50240)

Colditz march. (Farnon, Robert J). *Leeds Music. £0.25* QPK/AGM/JS (B72-51044)

Cole, Maria. Nat King Cole: an intimate biography. *W.H. Allen. £2.10* AKG/E(P) (B72-23643) ISBN 0 491 00782 5

Cole, Tony. Beg, steal or borrow: Britain's Eurovision song 1972. *Valley Music. Unpriced* UMMK/DW/JS (B72-50259)

Cole: a biographical essay. (Gill, Brendan). *Joseph. £7.50* BPNN (B72-24253) ISBN 0 7181 1021 8

Coleman, Emmet G. The temperance songbook: a peerless collection of temperance songs and hymns for the Women's Christian Temperance Union, Loyal Temperance Union, Prohibitionists, Temperance Praise Meetings, Medal contests, etc. *Wolfe. £1.25* DM/LRT/AY (B72-50037) ISBN 0 7234 0486 0

Coleman, Henry. Come shepherds. *Leonard, Gould and Bolttler. £0.06* DP/LF (B72-50824)

Coles, Richard. Sinfonia 'Al santo sepulcro'. Rinaldi Op.50. (Vivaldi, Antonio). *c/o Stanley Glasser, Goldsmiths' College, S.E.14: Piers Press. Unpriced* VSNSK/AE (B72-50744)

Colin Davis. (Blyth, Alan). *Allan. £1.50* A/EC(P) (B72-50792) ISBN 0 7110 0319 x

Collis, James. Tom Sawyer suite: for B flat clarinet and piano. *Boosey and Hawkes. £1.25* VVPG (B72-50757)

Come, dearest Lord: anthem for SATB and organ. (Naylor, Peter). *Novello. £0.10* DH (B72-50358)

Come, let us all this day/ melody and bass by J.S. Bach words by J. Troutbeck interludes and inner parts by Gerald H. Knight; and, Prepare thyself, Zion, from the Christmas Oratorio. (Bach, Johann Sebastian). *Royal School of Church Music. Unpriced* JDH (B72-50439)

Come, let us drink: compleat, pleasant and divertive. (Purcell, Henry). *Galliard. £0.93* GEZDW/XD/AZ (B72-50893)

Come live your life with me. (Rota, Nino). *Famous Chappell. £0.20* QPK/DW/JR (B72-50613)

Come, my way, my truth, my life: anthem for SATB and organ. (Graves, Richard). *Novello. Unpriced* DH (B72-50025)

Come shepherds. (Coleman, Henry). *Leonard, Gould and Bolttler. £0.06* DP/LF (B72-50824)

Come ye sons of art. (Purcell, Henry). *Schott. £0.75* DX (B72-50048)

Come you not from Newcastle?: a collection of North Country songs. (Polworth, Gwen). *6 Queen's Terrace, Newcastle upon Tyne 2: Frank Graham. £0.60* JEZDW/G/AYDJJ (B72-50903)

Common prayer. (Burns, Wilfred). *Bosworth. £0.07* FDH (B72-50070)

Communion service, series 3. (Hurford, Peter). *Novello. £0.14* DGS (B72-50815)

Company: song book. (Sondheim, Stephen). *Valando Music. £0.60* KDW (B72-50117)

Comparison between the French and Italian musick and operas. (Raguenet, François). 1st English ed., reprinted. *Gregg. £11.40* AC(YJ/XF/ZB) (B72-09123) ISBN 0 576 28446 7

Complete catalogue of contemporary Welsh music No.5. (Guild for the Promotion of Welsh Music). *c/o G. Williams, 10 Llanerch Path, Fairwater, Cwmbran, Mon. NP4 4QN: Guild for the Promotion of Welsh Music. Unpriced* A(YDK/TC) (B72-19872) ISBN 0 901248 01 0

Complete method for the harp. (Watkins, David). *Boosey and Hawkes. Unpriced* TQ/AC (B72-50704)

Complexi sonori: für Streicher. (Kasandiev, Vasil). *Peters. £2.00* RXMJ (B72-50654)

Concerte, Componisten und Virtuosen der letzten fünfzehn Jahre, 1870-1885: Kritiken. (Hanslick, Eduard). 2.Aufl. reprinted. *Gregg. £7.80* A(YEMB/XKK16) (B72-09122) ISBN 0 576 28226 x

Concertgoer's companions. *(Bingley)* Cudworth, Charles. Handel: a biography, with a survey of books, editions and recording. *Bingley. £1.75* BHC (B72-07357) ISBN 0 85157 137 9

Concerti with orchestra for young players. (Pehkonen, Elis). *Universal. Unpriced* MF (B72-50138)

Concerto espressivo: für Viola und Orchester. (Jentzsch, Wilfried). *Peters: Hinrichsen. £4.00* MPSQF (B72-50523)

Concerto-rhapsody for cello. Konzert-Rhapsodie: für Violoncello und Orchester,. (Khachaturian, Aram). *Peters: Hinrichsen. £2.00* SRPK (B72-50697)

Concise history of opera. (Orrey, Leslie). *Thames and Hudson. £2.50* AC(X) (B72-28009) ISBN 0 500 18130 6

Cone, Edward T. Episode de la vie d'un artiste. Fantastic symphony. (Berlioz, Hector). *Chappell. Unpriced* MME (B72-50507) ISBN 0 900277 02 5

Constant lovers: more English folk songs from the Hammond & Gardiner Mss. (Purslow, Frank). *English Folk Dance Society Publications. £0.50* KEZDW/G/AYD (B72-50127)

Contemplazione: per flauto e pianoforte. (Sári, József). *Boosey and Hawkes. £1.00* VRPJ (B72-50736)

Contemporary British music: the twenty-five years from 1945 to 1970. (Routh, Francis). *Macdonald and Co. £6.95* A(YC/XPE26) (B72-26091) ISBN 0 356 03773 8

Contemporary 'cellist: a collection of graded pieces for violoncello and pianoforte
Book 1: Grades 1,2,3. (Associated Board of the Royal Schools of Music). *Associated Board of the Royal Schools of Music. £0.95* SRP/AY (B72-51134)
Book 2: Grades 4,5. (Associated Board of the Royal Schools of Music). *Associated Board of the Royal Schools of Music. £0.95* SRP/AY (B72-51135)

Contorni: per arpa. (Patachich, Ivan). *Boosey and Hawkes. £0.60* TQPMJ (B72-51143)

Cooney, Ray.
Charlie girl. (Heneker, David). *Chappell. £1.75* CM (B72-50799)
Charlie girl: a comedy musical in two acts. (Williams, Hugh). *Chappell. £0.75* BHJJACM (B72-23641) ISBN 0 85360 040 6

Cooper, Barry. Concerto for trumpet, oboe & string orchestra in E flat major. Concerto à 6: for trumpet, oboe, strings and continuo. (Hertel, Johann Wilhelm). *Musica rara. Unpriced* VTPLWSK/LF (B72-51185)

Cooper, Paul. Variations: violin and piano, 1967. *Chester. Unpriced* SP/T (B72-50232)

Cope, Cecil. The apple: unison song. *Boosey and Hawkes. £0.09* JFDP (B72-50904)

Copland, Aaron.
Appalachian spring. (Ballet for Martha): suite; version for 13 instruments. *Boosey and Hawkes. £6.00* MRG (B72-50527)
Appalachian spring. (Ballet for Martha): suite; version for 13 instruments. *Boosey and Hawkes. £1.25* MRG (B72-50528)
Duos for flute and piano. *Boosey and Hawkes. £1.25* VRPG (B72-50266)

Coppélia. My daughter Coppelia: a musical play adapted from the ballet. (Delibes, Léo). *Oxford University Press. £1.20* CN (B72-50014) ISBN 0 19 338227 x

Corelli, Arcangelo. Sonata for violin & basso continuo in D minor. Op.5 no.12. La Follia: for treble recorder and basso continuo. *Schott. £1.00* VSSPK/AE (B72-51177)

Cornelius, Peter. Weihnachtslieder Op.8. - Die Könige. The kings: SSATB (acc. or unacc.). *Oxford University Press. Unpriced* DP/LF (B72-50373) ISBN 0 19 343029 0

Cornish, William. Pleasure it is: unison. (Thackray, Roy). *Oxford University Press. Unpriced* JDP/LF (B72-50897) ISBN 0 19 351115 0

Cornish dialect & folk songs: a sequel to the 'Cornish song book'. (Dunstan, Ralph). *Loedenek Press: Ascherburg, Hopwood & Crewe. £1.20* KDW/G/AYDFR (B72-50470)

Corrette, Michel.
Concerto for keyboard & string orchestra in A major. Op 26, no.2. Concerto 2, A-Dur: für Cembalo oder Orgel und Streicher. *Schott. £1.20* RXMPPWF (B72-51090)
Méthodes pour apprendre à jouer de la contre-basse. *Excerpts.* Sonate für Viola und Klavier. *Schott. Unpriced* SQPE (B72-51126)
Zwei Sonaten und ein Menuett: für 2 Bratschen (Alto 1,2). *Schott. £1.00* SQPJ (B72-51127)

Cosi fan tutte: komische Oper in zwei Akten. (Mozart, Wolfgang Amadeus). *Peters: Hinrichsen. Unpriced* CQC (B72-50804)

Coulthard, Jean. Variations on Bach: for piano. *Novello. £0.50* QP/T (B72-50569)

Counting the beats: song for high voice and piano. (Berkeley, Lennox). *Thames. Unpriced* KFTDW (B72-50131)

Country
Vol.1, no.1- ; March 1972-. *61 Berners St., W1P 3AE: Hanover Books Ltd. £0.20* ADW/GCW(B) (B72-09749)

Courte, Robert.
Sonata for viola & piano no.1, in A minor. Sonata in A minor: viola and piano. (Finney, Ross Lee). *Peters. £2.50* SQPE (B72-50689)
Sonata for viola & piano no.2. Second sonata: viola and pianoby Ross Lee Finney. (Finney, Ross Lee). *Peters. £2.05* SQPE (B72-50690)

Coward, *Sir* Noël. Noel Coward for all organs. *Chappell. £0.60* RK/DW (B72-51060)

Cowley, Abraham.
Awake, awake my lyre: for soprano (or tenor), solo optional baritone, chorus, strings and continuo. (Blow, John). *Hinrichsen. Unpriced* DX (B72-50047)
Awake awake my lyre: for soprano (or tenor) solo, optional baritone, chorus, strings and continuo. (Blow, John). *Hinrichsen. Unpriced* ERXMDX (B72-50053)

Craft, Robert. Stravinsky - chronicle of a friendship, 1948-1971. *Gollancz. £4.00* BSV(N/XPH24) (B72-28680) ISBN 0 575 01503 9

Crane, Stephen. Prologue for an unwritten play: for SATB chorus with B flat clarinet, orchestra chimes (or hand bells) and piano. (Boyd, Jack). *Warner: Blossom. Unpriced* ENYFVDW (B72-50839)

Craxton, Janet. Four pieces. (Grieg, Edvard). *Chester. Unpriced* VTPK (B72-51182)

Credidi: motet for SSAA, strings & organ continuo. (Porpora, Nicolò Antonio). *Novello. £0.35* DJ (B72-50029)

Crib-side carol. (Méhul, Etienne). *Novello. £0.07* DP/LF (B72-50375)

Criswick, Mary. Elizabethan and Jacobean songs: for voice and guitar. *Stainer and Bell. £0.75* KE/TSDW/AY (B72-50935)

Crosse, Gordon. For the unfallen. Op.9: for tenor voice, solo French horn and string orchestra. *Oxford University Press. £2.50* KGNE/RXMPWTDX (B72-50135) ISBN 0 19 345267 7

Crossman, Gerald.
Fortitude: march for accordion solo. *Charnwood Music. Unpriced* RSPMGM (B72-51067)
Gavottina for accordion or piano. *Bosworth. £0.15* RSPMHM (B72-51070)
Michella: accordion solo. *Charnwood Music. Unpriced* RSPMJ (B72-51077)

Crumb, George. Ancient voices of children: a cycle of songs for soprano, boy soprano, oboe, mandolin, harp, electric piano, percussion. *Peters: Hinrichsen. £6.00* JNFLEE/NYDTNPDW (B72-50457)

Crumhorn consort anthology
Vol.1. (Thomas, Bernard). *Musica rara. Unpriced* VTWNSK/AAY (B72-51187)

Cuckston, Alan. Sonata for two flutes & basso continuo in E minor. Sonata in E minor: 2 flutes and continuo, (v'c ad libitum). (Handel, George Frideric). *Peters. £1.40* VRNTPWE (B72-50728)

Cudworth, Charles. Handel: a biography, with a survey of books, editions and recording. *Bingley. £1.75* BHC (B72-07357) ISBN 0 85157 137 9

Cum Baija: African folk song. (Smith-Masters, Stanley). *Studio Music. Unpriced* WMK/DW (B72-50779)

Cumming, Richard. Twenty-four preludes: for solo piano. *Boosey and Hawkes. £1.75* QPJ (B72-50184)

Cummings, Edward Estlin. Hist whist: for voice, flute, viola and percussion. (Jong, Conrad de). *Schirmer: Chappell. Unpriced* KE/NYERNTDW (B72-50124)

Da Palestrina, Giovanni Pierluigi. *See* Palestrina, Giovanni Pierluigi da.

'Daily Mirror' specials. *('Daily Mirror' Books)* The fantastic Osmonds! *'Daily Mirror' Books. £0.25* AB/GB/E(P) (B72-32462) ISBN 0 600 32890 2

Dalby, Martin. Missa fi-fi. *Chester. Unpriced* DG (B72-50018)

Dallas, Gloria. Singers of an empty day: last sacraments for the superstars. (Dallas, Karl). *25 Thurloe St., S.W.7: Kahn and Averill. £2.00* A/GB(XPQ17) (B72-02167) ISBN 0 900707 12 7

Dallas, Karl. Singers of an empty day: last sacraments for

the superstars. *25 Thurloe St., S.W.7: Kahn and Averill. £2.00* A/GB(XPQ17) (B72-02167) ISBN 0 900707 12 7
Dalton, David.
Janis. *Calder and Boyars: New English Library. £1.25* AKDW/HHW/E(P) (B72-26094) ISBN 0 7145 0943 4
Rolling Stones. *Amsco Music Publishing; 78 Newman St., W1E 4JZ: Music Sales Ltd. Unpriced* AB/GB/E(P) (B72-24870) ISBN 0 8256 2653 6
Dance bands. (Rust, Brian Arthur Lovell). *Allan. £3.75* ALH(QB/XMP35) (B72-27440) ISBN 0 7110 0341 6
Dance-movements: for horn, violin & piano. (McCabe, John). *Novello. £2.25* NUXTNTH (B72-50162)
Danckert, Werner. Sonata for two harpsichords in D minor. Sonata in D minor: for two pianos (harpsichords). (Pasquini, Bernardo). *Nagel. £0.75* QRNUE (B72-50621)
Daniel, Oliver.
The New England Psalm singer. - *Excerpts.* Chester: SATB a cappella. (Billings, William). *Peters: Hinrichsen. £0.40* EZDM (B72-50400)
The psalm singer's amusement. - *Excerpts.* The angel's carol: SATBB a capella. (Billings, William). *Peters Hinrichsen. £0.50* EZDP/LF (B72-50404)
The psalm singer's amusement. - *Excerpts.* The bird: SATBB. (Billings, William). *Peters: Hinrichsen. £0.40* DM (B72-50363)
The psalm-singer's amusement. - *Excerpts.* Modern music: SATB a cappella. (Billings, William). *Peters: Hinrichsen. £0.75* EZDW (B72-50410)
The singing master's assistant. - *Excerpts.* Bethlehem: SAATB a cappella. (Billings, William). *Peters Hinrichsen. £0.40* EZDP/LF (B72-50405)
The singing master's assistant. - *Excerpts.* David's lamentation: SATBB a cappella. (Billings, William). *Peters: Hinrichsen. £0.40* EZDM (B72-50401)
The singing master's assistant. - *Excerpts.* Lamentation over Boston; and, Jargon: SATB (or male chorus or mixed quartet). (Billings, William). *Peters: Hinrichsen. £0.75* EZDW (B72-50411)
The singing master's assistant. - *Excerpts.* Peace be on earth = Retrospect: an anthem from sundry Scriptures for SATB (or male chorus or mixed chorus). (Billings, William). *Peters: Hinrichsen. Unpriced* DK (B72-50360)

Daniel, Ralph T. The sources of English church music, 1549-1660. *82 High Rd, N2 9BZ: Stainer and Bell for the British Academy. £8.00* AD/LD(TE/XDXJ112) (B72-22016) ISBN 0 903000 10 5
Danse des ours. Bears' dances: piano solo. (Field, John). *Bosworth. £0.15* QPH (B72-51032)
Danvers, Charles. Till. *Chappell. Unpriced* WMK/DW (B72-50776)
Danza caracteristica para el "Quítate de la Acera": gitarre solo. (Brouwer, Leo). *Schott. £0.08* TSPMH (B72-51148)
Danzas españolas. - *Excerpts.* Villanesca. Vol.2, no.4. (Granados, Enrique). *Boosey and Hawkes. £3.65* MK/AH (B72-50960)
Danzi, Franz. Quartet for flute & strings in D major. Op.56, no.1. Quartet in D major: for flute, violin, viola and cello. *Musica rara. Unpriced* NVRNS (B72-50988)
Darke, Dennis. Band call: 76 tunes for folk dance musicians and bands. *English Folk Dance and Song Society. £0.40* LH/G/AYC (B72-50498)
Dart, Thurston.
Jacobean consort music: for recorders or viols
Book 1: Five fantasias and two dances of three parts. *Stainer and Bell. £0.44* C/AYD (B72-50009)
Book 2: Seven fantasias of four parts. *Stainer and Bell. £0.49* C/AYD (B72-50010)
Dartington College of Art. *Music for Slow Learners Project. See* Music for Slow Learners Project.
Darvas, Gábor. Missa L'homme armé: for mixed choir (SATB) à cappella. (Obrecht, Jacob). *Boosey and Hawkes. £1.00* EZDG (B72-50840)
Davey, Brian. Sonata for two treble recorders, nos.1 & 2. Two sonatas for two treble recorders. (Gorton, William). *Schott. £0.40* VSSNUE (B72-50751)
David, Ferdinand. Concerto for violin in D major. K.218. Konzert, D-dur: für Violine und Orchester. (Mozart, Wolfgang Amadeus). *Peters. Unpriced* SPK/LF (B72-51120)
David, Gyula. Quintet for wind instruments, no.4. Quintetto a fiati no.4. *Boosey and Hawkes. £1.50* UNR (B72-50262)
David's lamentation: SATBB a cappella. (Billings, William). *Peters: Hinrichsen. £0.40* EZDM (B72-50401)
Davies, Iolo. Two Welsh love songs: SATB unacc. (Thomas, Mansel). *Oxford University Press. Unpriced* EZDW (B72-50866) ISBN 0 19 343032 0
Davies, Laurence H. Slavonic dances. Op.72, no.2. Moon rainbow. (Dvořák, Antonín). *Ashdown. £0.05* JDW (B72-50443)
Davies, Laurence Hector. Thou knowest, Lord, the secrets of our hearts. Z.580. (Purcell, Henry). *Oxford University Press. Unpriced* FLDK (B72-50890) ISBN 0 19 351113 4
Davies, Peter Maxwell.
St Thomas Wake: foxtrot for orchestra on a pavan by John Bull. *Boosey and Hawkes. Unpriced* MMHKEF (B72-50511)
St Thomas Wake: foxtrot for orchestra on a pavan by John Bull. *Boosey and Hawkes. £2.50* MMHKEF (B72-50512)
Taverner: an opera in two acts. *Boosey and Hawkes. £0.50* BDEAC (B72-18917) ISBN 0 85162 005 1
Taverner: an opera in two acts. *Boosey and Hawkes. Unpriced* CC (B72-50338)
Davies, William H. Three songs. (Bliss, *Sir* Arthur). *Novello. Unpriced* KDW (B72-50923)
Davis, D H. The song of little Jesus = Cân y baban Jesu: unison. (Thomas, Mansel). *Oxford University Press. Unpriced* JDP/LF (B72-50898) ISBN 0 19 342049 x
Dawes, Frank. Sonata for cello & harpsichord in A major. Op.l, no.1. Sonata in A. Op.l, no.1: for cello and harpsichord (or piano). (Paxton, Stephen). *Schott. £0.75* SRPE (B72-50694)
Dawson, David. Songs for living and words of worship: a hymn and worship book for the young. (Knight, Sydney H). *The Lindsey Press. £1.25* JFDM/LSL/AY (B72-50100)
Day of Pentecost: for choir, or solo voice, or as an organ solo. (Edwards, D W). *67 Lang Lane, West Kirby, Wirral, Cheshire: D.W. Edwards. Unpriced* DK (B72-50819)
De Boismortier, Joseph Bodin. *See* Boismortier, Joseph Bodin de.
De Haan, Stefan. *See* Haan, Stefan de.
De Jong, Conrad. *See* Jong, Conrad de.
De Nevers, Bernard. *See* Nevers, Bernard de.
De Sancta Maria, Thomas. *See* Thomas de Sancta Maria.
De Smet, Robin.
Kol Nidrei. Opus 47. (Bruch, Max). *Peters. Unpriced* SQPK (B72-51129)
Kol Nidrei. Opus 47. (Bruch, Max). *Peters. Unpriced* VVPK (B72-51190)
Sonata for cello & basso continuo in C major. Sonata no.6. (Marcello, Benedetto). *Peters. Unpriced* VVPK/AE (B72-51191)
Dean, Stephen. Praise the Lord. (Ainslie, John). Revised ed. *Chapman. Unpriced* DM/LSB/AY (B72-50822) ISBN 0 225 65838 0
Deans, Mickey. Weep no more, my lady: an intimate biography of Judy Garland. *W.H. Allen. £2.50* AKF/E(P) (B72-08534) ISBN 0 491 00941 0
Dearmer, Percy. The Oxford book of carols. Revised ed.. *Oxford University Press. £0.90* DP/LF/AY (B72-50827) ISBN 0 19 313120 x
Dearnley, Christopher. Two anthems. *Royal School of Church Music. Unpriced* JDK (B72-50086)
Death of Antigone: opera. (Brindle, Reginald Smith). *Peters. £2.20* CQC (B72-50347)
Debussy, Claude.
Children's corner - Excerpts. Golliwog's cake-walk. *Peters. Unpriced* QNV (B72-51022)
L'Isle joyeuse: piano solo. *Peters. Unpriced* QPJ (B72-51034)
Petite suite. - *Excerpts.* En bateaux. *Oxford University Press. £0.50* VSRNTQK (B72-50276) ISBN 0 19 356150 6
Prélude à l'après-midi d'un faune. *Peters: Hinrichsen. £3.50* MMJ (B72-50143)
Prélude à l'après-midi d'un faune. *Peters: Hinrichsen. £0.75* MMJ (B72-50144)
Prélude à l'après-midi d'un faune. Prelude to 'The afternoon of a faun'. *Chappell. Unpriced* MMJ (B72-50967)
Quartet for strings. Op. 10. Streichquartett. Op. 10. *Peters: Hinrichsen. Unpriced* RXNS (B72-51108)
Selected piano works
Volume 5: Douze études. *Peters: Hinrichsen. £1.85* QPJ (B72-50582)
Sonata for flute, viola & harp. *Peters: Hinrichsen. £2.00* NVRNTE (B72-50539)
Decca Record Company. Decca Group records, musicassettes and stereo 8 cartridges, main catalogue: (alphabetical & numerical)
1972. *Decca Record Co. £5.00* A/FD(WM) (B72-04763) ISBN 0 901364 03 7
Deep river; and, Wade in the water; and, Gonna lay down my burden: a quodlibet arranged from three negro spirituals for either trebles 1 and 2, or basses 1 and 2, or treble 1 and bass 2. (Hudson, Hazel). *Ashdown. £0.09* FLDW/LC (B72-50431)
Del Mar, Norman. Richard Strauss: a critical commentary on his life and works
Vol.3. *Barrie and Jenkins. £7.00* BSU(N) (B72-20309) ISBN 0 214 65158 4
Delaware waltz. (Siebert, Edrich). *Studio Music. Unpriced* WMHW (B72-50767)
Delibes, Clément Philibert Léo. My daughter Coppelia: a musical play (adapted from Delibes' ballet 'Coppelia'). (Griffiths, Philip). *Oxford University Press. £0.40* BDKACN (B72-03927) ISBN 0 19 338228 8
Delibes, Léo. Coppélia. My daughter Coppelia: a musical play adapted from the ballet. *Oxford University Press. £1.20* CN (B72-50014) ISBN 0 19 338227 x
Delius, Frederick. A mass of life. Eine Messe des Lebens = A mass of life: für Sopran, Alt, Tenor, Bariton, gemischten Chor und grosses Orchester. *Boosey and Hawkes. £6.00* EMDX (B72-50384)
Delius, Nikolaus. L'Art de préluder sur la flûte. Op.7. - *Excerpts.* 48 Préludes in 24 keys: for treble recorder, (flute oboe). (Hotteterre Le Romain, Jacques). *Schott. £0.90* VSSPMJ (B72-51178)
Delius. (Jefferson, Alan). *Dent. £2.25* BDL(N) (B72-05571) ISBN 0 460 03131 7
Dello Joio, Norman. Lyric pieces for the young: for piano. *Boosey and Hawkes. £0.50* QPJ (B72-50583)
Delroy, Albert.
Bluette: continental accordion solo. (Staquet, Willy). *Charnwood Music. £0.19* RSPMHW (B72-51075)
Three advanced studies: accordion solo. *Charnwood Music. Unpriced* RSPM/AF (B72-51064)
Denisoff, R. Serge. Great day coming: folk music and the American left. *University of Illinois Press. £3.60* A/GB(ZC) (B72-30745) ISBN 0 252 00179 6
Denisov, Edisson. Bagatelles for piano. Bagatellen: für Klavier. *Peters: Hinrichsen. £0.65* QPJ (B72-50584)
Dennis, Brian. Chant for Spike Milligan: for voices and instruments. *Universal. Unpriced* XDW (B72-51250)
Dennison, Peter. Musica Britannica: a national collection of music
Vol.35: Pelham Humfrey: Complete church music, II. *Stainer and Bell. Unpriced* C/AYD (B72-50794)
Department of Education and Science. *See* Great Britain. *Department of Education and Science.*
Descants' delight: three pieces for descant recorder(s) and piano. (Enfield, Patrick). *Elkin. £0.50* VSRPJ (B72-51176)
Desmond, Astra. Schumann songs. *British Broadcasting Corporation. £0.45* BSGAKDW (B72-14737) ISBN 0 563 12140 8
Deutsche Sprüche von Leben und Tod: four-part mixed chorus. (Lechner, Leonard). *Bärenreiter. £0.70* EZDU (B72-50408)
Dexter, Harry.
Give us, O Lord. *Ashdown. £0.09* FDH (B72-50868)
Intermezzo for piano in E flat major. Op.117, no.1. Sleep soft, my babe. (Brahms, Johannes). *Ashdown. £0.09* FDW (B72-50421)
A midsummer night's dream. Excerpts. Wedding march. (Mendelssohn, Felix). *Ashdown. Unpriced* RK/KDD (B72-50221)
Peer Gynt -. *Excerpts.* Morning. (Grieg, Edvard). *Keith Prowse Music. £0.15* QPK/JM (B72-50614)
Pizzicato for a poodle: for string orchestra. *Ashdown. Unpriced* RXMJ (B72-50651)
Scottish street dance: descant recorders and/or melody instruments and piano. *Ashdown. Unpriced* NWSRH (B72-50543)
Scottish street dance for string orchestra with ad lib. melody instruments. *Ashdown. £1.05* MH (B72-50504)
What is the meaning of it all?: two-part song with piano accompaniment. *Novello. £0.10* FDW (B72-50875)
The wild horseman: arranged for two-part singing, with piano accompaniment. *Ashdown. £0.09* FDW (B72-50074)
Dialoge: für Klavier. (Genzmer, Harald). *Peters. £1.80* QPJ (B72-50586)
Dialogue. Op. 16: for violin and orchestra. (Routh, Francis). *Lengnick. £1.00* SPK (B72-51119)
Diamond jubilee songbook. (Smith, Hettie). *Girl Guides Association. £0.10* JFEZDW/AY (B72-50916)
Dichterliebe. (Schumann, Robert). *Chappell. Unpriced* KDW (B72-50469) ISBN 0 900277 04 1
Dickinson, Peter. Outcry: a cycle of nature poems for contralto solo, SATB and orchestra. *Novello. £1.10* DW (B72-50043)
Dickson, Joan. Sonata for cello & basso continuo in A minor. Op.3, no.6. Sonata in A minor: for cello (or bassoon) and continuo (harpsichord or piano). (Mercy, Louis). *Schott. Unpriced* SRPE (B72-50241)
Diletti pastorali, nos.1, 5, 6, 13, 15. Hirten last: fünf weltliche Madrigale, für fünf stimmen und Basso Continuo. (Schein, Johann Hermann). *Bärenreiter. £0.95* DU (B72-50377)
Dinham, K J. Four carols of other nations: SATB (unacc.). (Dinham, Kenneth J). *Banks. £0.08* EZDP/LF/AY (B72-50856)
Dinham, Kenneth J. Four carols of other nations: SATB (unacc.). *Banks. £0.08* EZDP/LF/AY (B72-50856)
Dinn, Freda.
Eight English songs: for voice and two treble recorders. *Schott. £0.70* KE/VSSNUDW/G/AYD (B72-50473)
Eighteen short studies: for treble recorder. *Schott. £0.35* VSS/AF (B72-50278)
More tunes for my recorder: for the descant recorder. Revised ed. *Schott. £0.15* VSRPMK/DW/G/AY (B72-50277)
Orchésographie. - *Excerpts.* Twelve dances. (Arbeau, Thoinot). *Schott. Unpriced* VSNUK/AH (B72-50273)
Sing a son, play a song: a recorder book for sixes and sevens. *Schott. £0.95* VSK/DW/AY (B72-50740)
Disappointed fairy. (Gompers, Montague). *48 Addison Gdns, W.14: Montague Gompers. Unpriced* QPJ (B72-51035)
Discourse. Op.27: for harp & cello. (Rubbra, Edmund). *Lengnick. £0.25* SRPLTS (B72-50243)
Dives and Lazarus: a folk ballad, for soloists, choi two-part), descant recorders, percussion, piano, guitar (optional) and double bass (optional). (Byrt, John). *Oxford University Press. £1.10* FE/NYFSRDX (B72-50425) ISBN 0 19 335490 x
Do you hear what I hear?: Stadium dimension for marching bands. (Regney, Noel). *Jewel Music. Unpriced* UMMK/DW (B72-50258)
Dobrée, Georgina. Quartet for clarinet, viola & cello in F major. Quartet in F: for clarinet, violin and cello. (Vanhal, Jan). *Musica rara. Unpriced* NVVNS (B72-50163)
Doe, Paul.
Hear the voice and prayer: anthem for S (or A) ATB. (Tallis, Thomas). *Novello. £0.10* EZDK (B72-50849)
O sacrum convivium. I call and cry to thee: anthem for SAATB. (Tallis, Thomas). *Novello. £0.17* EZDJ (B72-50845)
Doflein, Elma. Music for violin and piano: a collection in 4 books in progressive order
4: Duos for piano and violin. *Schott. £1.50* SP/AY (B72-50672)
Doflein, Erich.
L'Art de préluder sur la flûte. Op.7. - *Excerpts.* 48 Préludes in 24 keys: for treble recorder, (flute oboe). (Hotteterre Le Romain, Jacques). *Schott. £0.90* VSSPMJ (B72-51178)

Concerto for treble recorder & string orchestra in G major. Op.21, no.3. Konzert für Altblockflöte mit Violinen oder Querflöten und Generalbass, G-Dur. (Boismortier, Joseph Bodin de). *Schott. £1.60* RXMPVSSF (B72-50660)
Concerto for treble recorder & string orchestra in G major. Op.21, no.3. Konzert für Altblockflöte mit Violinen oder Querflöten und Generalbass, G-Dur. (Boismortier, Joseph Bodin de). *Schott. £0.90* VSSPK/LF (B72-50755)
Little fugues for piano with a preparatory course in fugal playing: 27 short and easy fugues by German composers around 1700. Enlarged edition. *Bärenreiter. £0.65* PWP/Y/AYE(XF) (B72-50553)
Méthodes pour apprendre à jouer de la contre-basse. *Excerpts.* Sonate für Viola und Klavier. (Corrette, Michel). *Schott. Unpriced* SQPE (B72-51126)
Music for violin and piano: a collection in 4 books in progressive order
4: Duos for piano and violin. (Doflein, Elma). *Schott. £1.50* SP/AY (B72-50672)
Zwei Sonaten und ein Menuett: für 2 Bratschen (Alto 1,2). (Corrette, Michel). *Schott. £1.00* SQPJ (B72-51127)
Donahue, John. Postcard from Morocco: an opera. (Argento, Dominick). *London: Boosey and Hawkes. £10.00* CC (B72-50336)
Donald, Mike. North by north-east. *Galliard. £0.44* KE/TSDW (B72-50934) ISBN 0 85249 154 9
Donizetti, Gaetano.
Allegro in F: für Klavier. *Litolff: Peters. £0.80* QPJ (B72-50185)
Lucia di Lammermoor. (Cammarano, Salvatore). *Dover Publications: Constable. £1.00* BDRAC (B72-22490) ISBN 0 486 22110 5
Trio for flute, bassoon & piano in F major. Trio: für Flöte, Fagott und Klavier. *Peters. Unpriced* NWPNT (B72-50991)
Trio for strings & piano in E flat major. Trio: für Violine, Violoncello und Klavier. *Peters. Unpriced* NXNT (B72-50997)
Donlon, Kenneth L. Harper's dictionary of music. (Ammer, Christine). *Hale. £4.00* A(C) (B72-10997) ISBN 0 7091 3064 3
Doon valley: a suite for brass. (Street, Allan). *Boosey and Hawkes. £3.30* WMG (B72-51195)
Dorset book of folk songs. (Brocklebank, Joan). *English Folk Dance and Song Society. £0.20* JEZDW/G/AYDFK (B72-50448) ISBN 0 85418 042 7
Douglas, Katherine. Sar-Orain le Catriona Dhughlas. *Domhnall Budge. £0.30* KEZDW (B72-50126)
Douglas, Roy. Working with R.V.W. *Oxford University Press. £0.80* BVD(N/XPDI5) (B72-21776) ISBN 0 19 315427 7
Dove. (Verrall, Pamela Motley). *Bosworth. Unpriced* FDW (B72-50876)
Dover opera guide and libretto series. *(Dover Publications)* Cammarano, Salvatore. Lucia di Lammermoor. *Dover Publications: Constable. £1.00* BDRAC (B72-22490) ISBN 0 486 22110 5
Dowland, John.
First booke of songes. - If my complaints. The Galliard carol: SSA and piano. *Boosey and Hawkes. Unpriced* FDP/LF (B72-50870)
Der Fluyten Lust-Hof. Deel 1. - *Excerpts.* Pavane lachrymae: two settings with variations for solo decant recorder. (Eyk, Jacob van). *Schott. £0.45* VSRPMHVG/T (B72-50750)
Drakeford, Richard. Hors d'oeuvres: eight pieces for piano. *Elkin. £0.30* QPJ (B72-50186)
Draths, Willi. Aus fremden Ländern: Lieder und Tänze für drei Sopranblockflöten der andere Melodie - Instrumente, Gitarre und Schlagwerk ad lib
Band 2. *Schott. £0.70* VSRNTK/DW/AY (B72-50748)
Drayton, Paul.
Ecce ancilla Domini: anthem for the Annunciation. *Oxford University Press. Unpriced* DK (B72-50030) ISBN 0 19 350330 1
How like an Angel came I down: anthem for SATB and organ. *Novello. £0.14* DH (B72 50357)
The spacious firmament: SSATTBB. *Oxford University Press. Unpriced* DH (B72-50024)
Dream of Olwen: piano solo. (Williams, Charles). *Lawrence Wright Music. £0.25* QPK/JR (B72-51048)
Dreimäderlhaus. Lilac time: operetta in three acts. (Schubert, Franz). *Chappell: Weinberger. Unpriced* CF (B72-50012)
Dryden, John. King Arthur. The music in King Arthur: a dramatic opera (1691),. (Purcell, Henry). *Novello. £1.50* CC (B72-50342)
Du Bois, Rob. Muziek voor altblokfluit = Music for alto recorder. *Schott. Unpriced* VSSPMJ (B72-50280)
Du Tertre, Etienne. Septème livre de danceries: for four instruments, SATB. *Pro musica. Unpriced* LNSH (B72-50952)
Dunn, F Vivian. Supreme command: for fanfare trumpets and brass band. *Boosey and Hawkes. £0.45* WMPWSVN (B72-50780)
Dunstan, Ralph. Cornish dialect & folk songs: a sequel to the 'Cornish song book'. *Loedenek Press: Ascherburg, Hopwood & Crewe. £1.20* KDW/G/AYDFR (B72-50470)
Dürenmatt, Friedrich. Der Besuch der alten Dame= The visit of the old lady. Op.35: opera in three acts after Friedrich Dürrenmatt's tragi-comedy. (Einem, Gottfried von). *Boosey and Hawkes. £10.00* CQC (B72-50803)
Durkó, Zsolt.
Altamira: for chamber choir and orchestra. *Boosey and Hawkes. £1.50* EMDX (B72-50051)
Fire music: sextet for flute (doubling piccolo and alto flute in G), clarinet in B flat (doubling bass clarinet-B flat), piano, violin, viola and violoncello. *Boosey and Hawkes. £2.50* NUPNQ (B72-50984)
Iconography no. 1: for two bass viols and harpsichord or two violoncellos and piano (or harpsichord). *Boosey and Hawkes. £1.00* STUNTPW (B72-51141)
Durkó Zsolt. Iconography no.2: for horn solo and chamber ensemble. *Boosey and Hawkes. £1.50* NYENN (B72-51001)
Durr, Alfred. Er rufet seinen Schafen mit Namen = He calleth his own sheep each by name: cantata for Whit Tuesday. (Bach, Johann Sebastian). *Bärenreiter. £0.65* DE/LN (B72-50353)
Dürr, Alfred. Sechs Kantaten
für Bass, zwei Violinen und Basso continuo. (Schelle, Johann). *Bärenreiter. £3.65* KGXE/SNTPWDE (B72-50496)
Durr, Alfred. Wachet auf ruft uns die Stimme = Wake ye maids! hark, strikes the hour. S.140: cantata for 27. Sunday after Trinity. (Bach, Johann Sebastian). *Bärenreiter. £1.00* DE (B72-50350)
Dürr, Walther. Goethe songs: original pitch (high). (Schubert, Franz). *Bärenreiter. £1.15* KFTDW (B72-50483)
Durr, Walther. La Solitudine: cantata for alto solo and basso continuo. (Handel, George Frideric). *Bärenreiter. £1.00* KFQDX (B72-50480)
Dürrenmatt, Friedrich.
Der Besuch der alten Dame = The visit of the old lady. Op.35: Oper in drei Akten. (Einem, Gottfried von). *Boosey and Hawkes. £8.00* CC (B72-50339)
The visit of the old lady. *Boosey and Hawkes. £0.55* BELAC (B72-19611) ISBN 0 85162 006 x
Duthoit, W J. American patrol. (Gray, Jerry). *Chappell. Unpriced* UMMK (B72-50719)
Dvořák, Antonín. Slavonic dances. Op.72, no.2. Moon rainbow. *Ashdown. £0.05* JDW (B72-50443)
Dvorák, Antonin. Symphony no.9 in E minor. Op.95. - Largo. A New World prayer. *Lengnick. £0.20* KDW (B72-50924)
Earl Scruggs and the five-string banjo. (Scruggs, Earl). *Music Sales. £1.75* TT/AC (B72-51154)
'Early English church music' supplementary volumes. *(Stainer and Bell for the British Academy)* Daniel, Ralph T. The sources of English church music, 1549-1660. *82 High Rd, N2 9BZ: Stainer and Bell for the British Academy. £8.00* AD/LD(TE/XDXJ112) (B72-22016) ISBN 0 903000 10 5
Ebb, Fred. Cabaret: souvenir music album. (Kander, John). *Valando Music. £0.75* KDW/JR (B72-50472)
Eben, Peter. Liturgische Gesänge. *Bärenreiter. £1.25* FDGK (B72-50416)
Ecce ancilla Domini: anthem for the Annunciation. (Drayton, Paul). *Oxford University Press. Unpriced* DK (B72-50030) ISBN 0 19 350330 1
'Echanges. Symphony, (Les Echanges): for percussion-ensemble (7 players). (Liebermann, Rolf). *Simrock. Unpriced* XNPK (B72-50330)
Edenbrow, John. North by north-east. (Donald, Mike). *Galliard. £0.44* KE/TSDW (B72-50934) ISBN 0 85249 154 9
Edison-Bell Consolidated Phonograph Company.
Catalogue. Bell 'popular' phonograph records, new catalogue no.9. *19 Glendale Rd, Bournemouth, Hants. BH6 4JA: 'Talking Machine Review'. Unpriced* A/FE(WM) (B72-05227) ISBN 0 902338 13 7
Catalogue. List of records (no.3) possessing great volume, perfect reproduction and superb quality of tone. *19 Glendale Rd, Bournemouth, Hants. BH6 4JA: 'Talking Machine Review'. £0.45* A/FE(WM) (B72-04764) ISBN 0 902338 12 9
Edward Elgar: the record of a friendship. (Burley, Rosa). *Barrie and Jenkins. £2.80* BEP(N) (B72-13441) ISBN 0 214 65410 9
Edwards, D W.
The day of Pentecost: for choir, or solo voice, or as an organ solo. *67 Lang Lane, West Kirby, Wirral, Cheshire: D.W. Edwards. Unpriced* DK (B72-50819)
Hymns and choruses
Book 1. *159 Station Rd. Kingswood, Bristol: D.W. Edwards. Unpriced* DM (B72-50364)
Book 2. *159 Station Rd. Kingswood, Bristol: D.W. Edwards. Unpriced* DM (B72-50365)
Edwards, Owain Tudor. Beethoven. *Walton Hall, Bletchley, Bucks.: Open University Press. Unpriced* BBJ (B72-22483) ISBN 0 335 00572 1
Edwards, Ron. The Overlander song book. *Hale. £3.00* ADW/G(YX) (B72-12721) ISBN 0 7091 3070 8
Ehmann, Wilhelm.
Junktim-Sätze: Doppelchörige Choralsätze, für bläser oder Sänger und Bläser. *Bärenveiter. £1.50* EWNDM/AY (B72-50390)
Lobe den Herren, den mächtigen König der Ehren: Choralkantate für vierstimmigen gemischten Chor, Gemeindegesang (ad lib.), sechsstimmigen Bläserchor und Orgel. (Zipp, Friedrich). *Bärenreiter. y1.75* EWNPRDE (B72-50391)
Eight, four, five. *See* Pointon, Malcolm.
Einem, Gottfried von.
Der Besuch der alten Dame = The visit of the old lady. Op.35: Oper in drei Akten. *Boosey and Hawkes. £8.00* CC (B72-50339)
Der Besuch der alten Dame= The visit of the old lady. Op.35: opera in three acts after Friedrich Dürrenmatt's tragi-comedy. *Boosey and Hawkes. £10.00* CQC (B72-50803)
Hexameron. Op.37. *Boosey and Hawkes. £1.75* MMJ (B72-50145)
Hexameron. Op.37. *Boosey and Hawkes. £5.25* MMJ (B72-50514)
The visit of the old lady. (Dürrenmatt, Friedrich). *Boosey and Hawkes. £0.55* BELAC (B72-19611) ISBN 0 85162 006 x
Einsingen in Chor: methodische Anleitung und Ubungen zur chorischen Stimmbildung. (Schneider, Walther). *Litolff: Peters. Unpriced* D/AC (B72-50809)
Einstein, Alfred.
Divertimento, E flat major. KV App, 182: 2 oboes, 2 clarinets in B flat, 2 bassoons, 2 horns in E flat. (Mozart, Wolfgang Amadeus). *Peters. £1.80* UNN (B72-50721)
Divertimento for wind octet in B flat major. K. Anh. 227. Divertimento, B flat major, KV app. 227: 2 oboes, 2 clarinets in B flat, 2 bassoons, 2 horns in E flat. (Mozart, Wolfgang Amadeus). *Peters. £1.50* UNN (B72-50722)
Divertimento for wind octet in E flat major. K. Anh, 226. Divertimento, E flat major. KV App, 226: 2 oboes, 2 clarinets in B flat, 2 bassoons, 2 horns in E flat,. (Mozart, Wolfgang Amadeus). *Peters. £1.80* UNN (B72-50723)
Electric and Musical Industries. *Record Division.*
Alphabetical catalogue of EMI records
1970-71: available and issued up to and including 30 May 1970. *20 Manchester Sq., W1A 1ES: EMI Records. Unpriced* A/FD(WM) (B72-30323) ISBN 0 901401 03 x
1971-72: available and issued up to and including 30 June 1971. *20 Manchester Sq., W1A 1ES: EMI Records. Unpriced* A/FD(WM) (B72-30324) ISBN 0 901401 04 8
1972-73: available and issued up to and including 30 June 1972. *20 Manchester Sq., W1A 1ES: EMI Records. Unpriced* A/FD(WM) (B72-30325) ISBN 0 901401 05 6
Electronic organ: a course for beginners. (Rothenberg, Peter). *Schott. Unpriced* RPV/AC (B72-50646)
Elegy. (Chance, John Barnes). *Boosey and Hawkes. £4.50* UMMJ (B72-51155)
Elegy for strings. Op.13. (Josephs, Wilfred). *Weinberger. Unpriced* RXMJ (B72-50223)
Elegy: for viola and cello. (Musgrave, Thea). *Chester. Unpriced* SQPLSR (B72-50238)
Elegy in memory of Karol Rathaus. Op. 23: for 3 trumpets, 2 horns, 3 trombones and baritone and tuba. (Turok, Paul). *Musica rara. Unpriced* WMJ (B72-51217)
Elementary method for oboe. (Hinke, Gustav Adolf). *Peters. £0.70* VT/AC (B72-50281)
Elgar - a life in photographs. (Moore, Jerrold Northrop). *Oxford University Press. £3.00* BEP/N(EM) (B72-28697) ISBN 0 19 315425 0
Elgar, *Sir* Edward, *bart.* Chanson de matin. Op.15, no.2. *Novello. Unpriced* VSNRK (B72-50270)
Elgar, Raymond. Introduction to the double bass. 3rd ed., revised and reprinted. *31 Charles Rd West, St Leonards-on-Sea, Sussex: R. Elgar. £1.26* ASS/B (B72-32463) ISBN 0 9502431 1 6
Elias, Brian. Five piano pieces for right hand. *Chester. Unpriced* QPPR (B72-50620)
Eliot, Thomas Stearns. Landscapes: a choral suite for mixed voices (with optional oboe). (Paynter, John). *Oxford University Press. Unpriced* EZDW (B72-50064)
Elizabethan and Jacobean songs: for voice and guitar. (Criswick, Mary). *Stainer and Bell. £0.75* KE/TSDW/AY (B72-50935)
Ellerton, J. From east to west: SATB unacc. (Rutter, John). *Oxford University Press. Unpriced* EZDM (B72-50061) ISBN 0 19 343026 6
Ellis, Olive Senior-. *See* Senior-Ellis, Olive.
Elms, Albert.
Wembley way: quick march. *Boosey and Hawkes. £0.55* UMMGM (B72-50717)
Wembley way: quick march. *Boosey and Hawkes. £0.45* WMJ (B72-50770)
Elogio de la danza: para guitarra. (Brouwer, Leo). *Schott. £0.90* TSPMJ (B72-51150)
Elvis: a biography. (Hopkins, Jerry). *4 Little Essex St., W.C.2: Open Gate Books. £1.95* AKGDW/HK/E(P) (B72-21779) ISBN 0 333 13617 9
EM: for 24 voices. (Hoyland, Victor). *Universal. Unpriced* EZDW (B72-50864)
E.M.I. *See* Electric and Musical Industries.
En bateaus. (Debussy, Claude). *Oxford University Press. £0.50* VSRNTQK (B72-50276) ISBN 0 19 356150 6
Encounters with Stravinsky: a personal record. (Horgan, Paul). Abridged ed.. *Bodley Head. £3.00* BSV(N/XPS15) (B72-27437) ISBN 0 370 10299 1
Enfield, Patrick. Descants' delight: three pieces for descant recorder(s) and piano. *Elkin. £0.50* VSRPJ (B72-51176)
Engel, Sid. Nicholas and Alexandra: theme. (Bennett, Richard Rodney). *Columbia Music, Chappell. £0.20* QPK/JR (B72-50196)
Englert, Giuseppe. Palaestra 64: pro organo. *Peters. £1.25* RJ (B72-50635)
English church music: a collection of essays
1972. *Addington Palace, Croydon, CR9 5AD: Royal School of Church Music. £0.76* A/LD(YC/D) (B72-18918) ISBN 0 85402 048 9
English Folk Dance and Song Society.
Folk directory
1972. *English Folk Dance and Song Society. £1.00 (£0.75 to members of the EFDSS)* A/G(BC) (B72-06764) ISBN 0 85418 034 6
Folk song and dance: a list of books. (Clark, Keith). *National Book League: English Folk Dance and Song Society. £0.30* A/G(T) (B72-16428) ISBN 0 85353 138 2
English lute songs, 1597-1632. *(Scolar Press)*
Cavendish, Michael. 14 ayres in tabletorie, 1598/ by Michael Cavendish; and, Ayres, 1609/ by Alfonso Ferrabosco; and, Musicke of sundrie kindes, 1607/ by Thomas Ford; and, Songes of sundrie kindes, 1604/ by

Thomas Greaves; and, Ayres to be sung to the lute, ca.1609/ by George Handford. *Scolar Press. £12.00* ADW(YD/XDZT12) (B72-05572) ISBN 0 85417 561 x

Jones, Robert, *fl.1597-1614*. The first booke of songes and ayres, 1600; and, The second booke of songs and ayres, 1601; and, Ultimum vale, 1605; and, A musicall dreame, 1609; and, The muses gardin, 1610. *Scolar Press. £12.00* ADW(YD/XE11) (B72-05573) ISBN 0 85417 559 8

English madrigals, 1558-1630. *(Scolar Press)* Wilbye, John. The second set of madrigals, 1609. *Scolar Press. £7.75* BWNRBADU (B72-10330) ISBN 0 85417 572 5

English solos for flute (violin) and harpsichord, (v'c/va. da gamba ad lib.). Opus 1. (Stanley, John). *Peters. Unpriced* VRPE (B72-51165)

Enzensberger, Hans Magnus. El Cimarrón-Biography of the runaway slave Esteban Montejo: recital for four musicians. (Henze, Hans Werner). *Schott. £2.40* KE/NYERNSDX (B72-50933)

'Episode de la vie d'un artiste. Fantastic symphony. (Berlioz, Hector). *Chappell. Unpriced* MME (B72-50507) ISBN 0 900277 02 5

Epps, David. Spare time for music. *British Broadcasting Corporation. £1.20* C/AY (B72-50793) ISBN 0 563 10689 1

Er rufet seinen Schafen mit Namen = He calleth his own sheep each by name: cantata for Whit Tuesday. (Bach, Johann Sebastian). *Bärenreiter. £0.65* DE/LN (B72-50353)

Erbse, Heimo.
Fünf Orchestergesänge nach Georg Trakl. Op.27: für Bariton und Orchester. *Peters. £3.20* KGNE/MDW (B72-50492)

Das Hohelied Salomo's. Opus 26a: Sopran, Bariton und Klavier. *Peters. £4.50* JNEDE (B72-50455)

Erickson, Frank. Symphony no.2. Op.132. - Andante con moto. Mysterious mountain. (Hovhaness, Alan). *Associated Music. Unpriced* UMK (B72-50257)

Ernte des Lebens/ by Paul Ernst Ruppel; Worte from 2. Korinther and Gerhard Valentin, with Osterlied/ by Paul Ernst Ruppel; Worte: Alter Osterruf and Gerhard Valentin. (Ruppel, Paul Ernst). *Bärenreiter. Unpriced* EZDH (B72-50397)

Eroica: for piano solo. (Liszt, Franz). *Bärenreiter. £0.50* QPJ (B72-50593)

Espalhafatoso: chôro (tango brejeiro) for piano,. *Arthur Napoleão: Essex Music. Unpriced* QPHVR (B72-50578)

Essays in musical analysis
Supplementary volume: Chamber music. (Tovey, *Sir* Donald Francis). *Oxford University Press. £0.80* A/CB (B72-26081) ISBN 0 19 315136 7

Vol.1: Symphonies. (Tovey, *Sir* Donald Francis). *Oxford University Press. £0.80* A/CB (B72-26082) ISBN 0 19 315137 5

Vol.2: Symphonies (2), variations and orchestral polyphony. (Tovey, *Sir* Donald Francis). *Oxford University Press. £0.80* A/CB (B72-26083) ISBN 0 19 315138 3

Vol.3: Concertos. (Tovey, *Sir* Donald Francis). *Oxford University Press. £0.80* A/CB (B72-26084) ISBN 0 19 315139 1

Vol.3: Concertos. (Tovey, *Sir* Donald Francis). *Oxford University Press. £0.80* 780.15 (B72-26084) ISBN 0 19 315139 1

Vol.4: Illustrative music. (Tovey, *Sir* Donald Francis). *Oxford University Press. £0.80* A/CB (B72-26085) ISBN 0 19 315140 5

Vol.5: Vocal music. (Tovey, *Sir* Donald Francis). *Oxford University Press. £0.80* A/CB (B72-26086) ISBN 0 19 315141 3

Vol.6: Supplementary essays, glossary and index. (Tovey, *Sir* Donald Francis). *Oxford University Press. £0.80* A/CB (B72-26087) ISBN 0 19 315142 1

'Etrangété. Op.63, no.2: piano solo. (Skriabin, Alexander). *Peters. £0.25* QPJ (B72-50604)

'Etudes d'execation transcendante, no.4. Mazeppa for piano solo. (Liszt, Franz). *Bärenreiter. £0.65* QPJ (B72-50591)

'Etudes d'exécution transcendante, no.5. Feux follets: for piano solo. (Liszt, Franz). *Bärenreiter. £0.65* QPJ (B72-50592)

'Etudes d'exécution transcendante, no.7. Eroica: for piano solo. (Liszt, Franz). *Bärenreiter. £0.50* QPJ (B72-50593)

'Etudes d'exécution transcendante, no.8. Wilde Jagd: for piano solo. (Liszt,, Franz). *Bärenreiter. £0.65* QPJ (B72-50594)

'Etudes d'exécution transcendante, no.9. Ricordanza: for piano solo. (Liszt, Franz). *Bärenreiter. £0.65* QPJ (B72-50595)

'Etudes d'exécution transcendante, no.10. Study in F minor for piano solo. (Liszt, Franz). *Bärenreiter. £0.65* QPJ (B72-50596)

'Etudes d'exécution transcendante, no.11. Harmonies du Soir: for piano solo. (Liszt, Franz). *Bärenreiter. £0.50* QPJ (B72-50597)

Euripides. The death of Antigone: opera. (Brindle, Reginald Smith). *Peters. £2.20* CQC (B72-50347)

Eve, my sweet: S.fl unaccompanied. (Kodály, Zoltán). *Boosey and Hawkes. £0.05* FEZDW (B72-50428)

Evening. (Bennett, F Roy). *Ashdown. £0.05* FDW (B72-50420)

Evening song: for clarinet (B flat) and piano. (Foster, Ivor Reginald). *Schott. Unpriced* VVPJ (B72-50293)

Event - Synergy 2: for 19 wind and string instruments. (Brown, Earle). *Universal. Unpriced* MRJ (B72-50980)

Everlasting Mary: carol. (Rose, Gregory). *Boosey and Hawkes. £0.05* EZDW/LF (B72-50854)

Every star shall sing a carol. (Carter, Sydney). *Chappell. Unpriced* DP/LF (B72-50823)

Ew'ge Quelle, milder Strom: Kantate auf den Sonntag Cantate, für mittlere Stimme, Querflöte (Violine) und Basso continuo. (Telemann, Georg Philipp). *Bärenreiter. £1.00* KFTE/SPLRDE (B72-50486)

Ewing, Montague.
Purple heather. *Norman Richardson Band Arrangements. Unpriced* UMMHW (B72-50718)
Purple heather. *Norman Richardson Band Arrangements. Unpriced* WMHW (B72-50766)

Examinations in pianoforte playing and singing sight reading tests, as set throughout 1971: Grades I-VIII and diplomas. (London College of Music). *Ashdown. £0.30* Q/EG/AL (B72-50170)

Exodus. - Excerpts. Main theme. (Gold, Ernest). *Chappell. Unpriced* UMMK/JR (B72-50720)

Experimental research in music. (Madsen, Clifford K). *Prentice-Hall. Unpriced* A/B (B72-21770) ISBN 0 13 295097 9

Explore and discover music: creative approaches to music education in elementary, middle, and junior high schools. (Marsh, Mary Val). *Macmillan (N.Y.): Collier-Macmillan. £2.25* A(VF) (B72-00905) ISBN 0 02 376270 5

Explosions - Polka. Op.43. (Strauss, Johann, *b.1825*). *Studio Music. Unpriced* WMK/AHVH (B72-50773)

Exton, John. Three pieces for solo oboe. *Chester. Unpriced* VTPMJ (B72-50756)

Eyk, Jacob van. Der Fluyten Lust-Hof. Deel 1. - Excerpts. Pavane lachrymae: two settings with variations for solo decant recorder. *Schott. £0.45* VSRPMHVG/T (B72-50750)

Faber book of French folk songs. *Faber Music. £3.00* JDW/G/AYH (B72-50899) ISBN 0 571 09944 0

Façade: an entertainment. (Walton, *Sir* William). *Oxford University Press. £12.00* HYE/NYENQ (B72-50084) ISBN 0 19 359402 1

Faith, Richard. Sonatinas for piano, nos 1-3. Three sonatinas: for piano. *Schirmer: Chappell. Unpriced* QPEM (B72-50177)

False spring: SSA unaccompanied. (Kodály, Zoltán). *Boosey and Hawkes. £0.05* FEZDW (B72-50429)

Fantasia on British airs. (Barsotti, Roger). *Boosey and Hawkes. Unpriced* WMJ (B72-50769)

Fantasie und Lobpreisung. Op.58: für Orgel. (Klebe, Giselher). *Bärenreiter. £1.25* RJ (B72-50641)

Fantastic Osmonds! *'Daily Mirror' Books. £0.25* AB/GB/E(P) (B72-32462) ISBN 0 600 32890 2

Fantastic symphony. (Berlioz, Hector). *Chappell. Unpriced* MME (B72-50507) ISBN 0 900277 02 5

Fantasy for harp. Opus 68, no.2. (Hoddinott, Alun). *Oxford University Press. £0.70* TQPMJ (B72-51142) ISBN 0 19 357154 4

Fantasy. Op.107: for solo guitar. (Arnold, Malcolm). *Faber Music. Unpriced* TSPMJ (B72-50248)

Fantasy trio. Op.26: for clarinet, cello and piano. (Muczynski, Robert). *Schirmer: Chappell. Unpriced* NUVNT (B72-50160)

Fantini, Girolamo.
Eight sonatas: for trumpet and organ. *Musica rara. Unpriced* WSPLRE (B72-51245)
Modo per imparare a sonare di tromba. - Excerpts. Eight sonatas: for trumpet & organ. *Musica rara. Unpriced* WSLRE (B72-50318)

Farkas, Ferenc. Festive overture = Commemoratio agriae: for orchestra. *Boosey and Hawkes. £1.25* MMJ (B72-50968)

Farnon, Robert. Symphonic marches for concert band. (Rodgers, Richard). *Williamson. Unpriced* UMGM (B72-50254)

Farnon, Robert J. Colditz march. *Leeds Music. £0.25* QPK/AGM/JS (B72-51044)

Fasch, Johann Friedrich. Sonata for flute, violin, bassoon & basso continuo in D major. Sonata in D major for flute, violin, bassoon and basso continuo. *Bärenreiter. £1.40* NUPNSE (B72-50532)

Favourites for recorder
No.1. (Sansom, Clive A). *Feldman. £0.25* VSPMK/DW/G/AY (B72-50274)

Fedtke, Traugott. Orgelwerke
Band 1: Choralfugen und Choräle aus dem Weimarer Tabulaturbuch, 1704. (Pachelbel, Johann). *Peters. Unpriced* R/AZ (B72-51053)

Fée et le cultivateur = The nymph and the farmer, Op.72: a lyric legend. (Cherepnin, Alexander). *Boosey and Hawkes. £4.50* CC (B72-50337)

Fegers, Karl. Suite nach französischen Volksliedern: für 3 Blockflöten (2 Sopran - und 1 Altflöte), 1-3 andere Instrumente (Violine, Klarinette, Akkordeon o.a.) Gitarre oder Bass, Stabspiele (Xylophone, Glockenspiel) oder Klavier. *Schott. £0.90* MG (B72-50503)

Fekete Györ, István. Three duos for flute and piano. *Boosey and Hawkes. £0.55* VRPJ (B72-51166)

Feldman, Morton.
The viola in my life
1: Flute, violin, viola (solo), cello, piano, percussion. *Universal. Unpriced* NYDRNQ (B72-51000)
2: Flute, clarinet, violin, viola (solo), cello, piano, percussion. *Universal. Unpriced* NYDPNP (B72-50998)
3: Viola and piano. *Universal. Unpriced* SQPJ (B72-51128)

Felix Mendelssohn Bartholdy. (Bodleian Library). *Bodleian Library. £1.00* BMJ(EM) (B72-19610) ISBN 0 900177 15 2

Ferdinand, *III, Emperor*. Musikalische Werke der Kaiser Ferdinand III, Leopold I und Joseph I im Auftrage des K.K. Ministeriums für Cultur und Unterricht. *Gregg. £18.00* C/AZ (B72-50335)

Ferguson, Barry. Two carols: for SATB unaccompanied. *Novello. £0.07* EZDP/LF (B72-50406)

Ferguson, Howard.
Simple symphony. Op.4. *Excerpts.* Playful pizzicato. (Britten, Benjamin). *Oxford University Press. £0.50* QNVK (B72-50173) ISBN 0 19 372375 1
Simple symphony. Op.4. *Excerpts.* Sentimental sarabande. (Britten, Benjamin). *Oxford University Press. £0.50* QNVK/AHVL (B72-50175) ISBN 0 19 372374 3

Ferlinghetti, Lawrence. The vision: full chorus and seven soloists. (Jergenson, Dale). *Schirmer: Chappell. Unpriced* HY (B72-50083)

Festival service books
6. (Royal School of Church Music). *Royal School of Church Music. Unpriced* DGM (B72-50022) ISBN 0 85402 047 0

Festive piece. (Grundman, Clare). *Boosey and Hawkes. £2.00* UMMJ (B72-51157)

Feux follets: for piano solo. (Liszt, Franz). *Bärenreiter. £0.65* QPJ (B72-50592)

Fiddler on the roof: selection for all organs. (Bock, Jerry). *Valando. £0.60* RK/DW (B72-50643)

Field, John. La Danse des ours. Bears' dances: piano solo. *Bosworth. £0.15* QPH (B72-51032)

Fiesta: ein Anti-Lehrstück mit Musik. (Vogt, Paul G). *Schott. £3.20* DX (B72-50381)

Fight the good fight. (Long, Kenneth Roy). *Royal School of Church Music. Unpriced* JDM (B72-50087)

Fink, Siegfried.
Beat the beat: solo for beat percussion. *Schott. £0.80* XQ/AF (B72-51252)
Les Echanges. Symphony, (Les Echanges): for percussion-ensemble (7 players). (Liebermann, Rolf). *Simrock. Unpriced* XNPK (B72-50330)
Mini Musik: for two percussionists. *Schott. £1.00* XNU (B72-51251)
Studies for snare drum
Vol.6: Studies for 2-3-4 snare drums. *Simrock. Unpriced* XQ/AF (B72-50790)

Finney, Ross Lee.
24 piano inventions. *Peters. £1.50* QPJ (B72-50585)
Chromatic fantasy in E major: violoncello. *Peters. £1.10* SRPMJ (B72-50702)
Five fantasies: for organ
No.1: So long as the mind keeps silent. *Peters. £1.00* RJ (B72-50636)
No.2: There are no summits without abysses. *Peters. £1.00* RJ (B72-50637)
No.3: Advice which the hours of darkness give. *Peters. £1.00* RJ (B72-50638)
No.4: The leaves on the trees spoke. *Peters. £1.00* RJ (B72-50639)
No.5: Each answer hides future questions. *Peters. £1.00* RJ (B72-50640)
Sonata for viola & piano no.1, in A minor. Sonata in A minor: viola and piano. *Peters. £2.50* SQPE (B72-50689)

Sonata for viola & piano no.2. Second sonata: viola and pianoby Ross Lee Finney. *Peters. £2.05* SQPE (B72-50690)

Fire music: sextet for flute (doubling piccolo and alto flute in G), clarinet in B flat (doubling bass clarinet-B flat), piano, violin, viola and violoncello. (Durkó, Zsolt). *Boosey and Hawkes. £2.50* NUPNQ (B72-50984)

First book of solos for the classical guitar. (Pearse, John). *Scatchwood Music. Unpriced* TSPMK/AAY (B72-50251)

First booke of songes and ayres, 1600; and, The second booke of songs and ayres, 1601; and, Ultimum vale, 1605; and, A musicall dreame, 1609; and, The muses gardin, 1610. (Jones, Robert, *fl.1597-1614*). *Scolar Press. £12.00* ADW(YD/XE11) (B72-05573) ISBN 0 85417 559 8

First star: for voices and instruments. (Paynter, John). *Universal. Unpriced* JFTE/XTPRDW (B72-50918)

Fischer, Johann Caspar Ferdinand. Le Journal de printemps. - Suites 5, 6. Suites for four strings or wind instruments and basso continuo, nos.5 in G major, 6 in F major. *Bärenreiter. £1.50* NXNRG (B72-50545)

Fischer, Kurt von.
Twelve variations in C major, 'Ah, vous dirai - je maman', K.265: for piano. (Mozart, Wolfgang Amadeus). *Nagel. £0.35* QP/T (B72-50570)
Variations for piano in G major, Unser dummer Pöbel meint. K. 455. Ten variations in G major, 'Unser dummer Pöbel meint. K. 455: for piano. (Mozart, Wolfgang Amadeus). *Nagel. £0.40* QP/T (B72-50571)
Variations for piano. K. 24 & 25. Eight variations in G.K. 24; with, Seven variations in D. K 25 for piano. (Mozart, Wolfgang Amadeus). *Nage. £0.50* PWP/T (B72-50552)

Fischer, Wilfried.
Concerto for harpsichord in A major. S.1055. Concerto in A major for oboe d'amore, strings and basso continuo. (Bach, Johann Sebastian). *Bärenreiter. £1.50* RXMPVTQK/LF (B72-50661)
Concerto for harpsichord in F minor. S.1056. Concerto in G minor for violin, strings and basso continuo. (Bach, Johann Sebastian). *Bärenreiter. £1.25* RXMPSK/LF (B72-50658)
Concerto for three harpsichords in D major. S.1064. Concerto in D major for three violins, strings and basso continuo. (Bach, Johann Sebastian). *Bärenreiter. £1.85* RXMPSNTK/LF (B72-50659)

Five Finnish Christmas songs: for mixed chorus and orchestra (or piano)
1: Christmas = No, onkos tullut kesä. (Head, Michael). *Boosey and Hawkes. £0.14* DW/LF (B72-50830)
2: When it is Christmas = Kun joulu on. (Head, Michael). *Boosey and Hawkes. £0.14* DW/LF (B72-50831)
3: A sparrow on Christmas morning = Varpunen

jouluaamuna. (Head, Michael). *Boosey and Hawkes.* *£0.09* DW/LF (B72-50832)
4: Christmas bells = Joulun kellot. (Head, Michael). *Boosey and Hawkes. £0.14* DW/LF (B72-50833)
5: Uncle Frost = Halla. (Head, Michael). *Boosey and Hawkes. £0.14* DW/LF (B72-50834)
Five note excursions. (Brydson, John). *Freeman. £0.25* QPJ (B72-50580)
Five piano pieces for right hand. (Elias, Brian). *Chester. Unpriced* QPPR (B72-50620)
Five thousand nights at the opera. 5,000 nights at the opera. (Bing, *Sir* Rudolf). *Hamilton. £4.00* AC(WB/P) (B72-26658) ISBN 0 241 02201 0
Fleming, Christopher le. *See* Le Fleming, Christopher.
Flesch, Siegfried.
Sonatas for two violins & basso continuo. Op.5 nos.7,1. Two triosonatas for two violins and basso continuo. (Handel, Georg Frideric). *Nagel. £1.25* NXNT (B72-50547)
Trio sonata for treble recorder, violin & basso continuo in C minor. Op.2, no.1. Trio sonata in C minor: for treble recorder, violin (two violins) AND BASSO CONTINUO. (Handel, George Frideric). *Nagel. £1.15* NUSSNTE (B72-50535)
Trio sonata for treble recorder, violin & basso continuo in F major. Op.2, no.4. Trio sonata in F major: for treble recorder, violin (two violins) and basso continuo. (Handel, George Frideric). *Nagel. £1.00* NUSSNTE (B72-50536)
Fletcher, Stanley.
New tunes for strings
Book 1. *Boosey and Hawkes. £4.90* RXM/AF (B72-51085)
Book 2. *Boosey and Hawkes. £4.90* RXM/AF (B72-51086)
Floreal: für Orchester. (Kelemen, Milko). *Peters. £2.40* MMJ (B72-50516)
Florence, *Sister.* Come shepherds. (Coleman, Henry). *Leonard, Gould and Bolttler. £0.06* DP/LF (B72-50824)

Flourish of fanfares: for 4 flat trumpets. (Roe, Betty). *Thames. Unpriced* WSNSGN (B72-50322)
Flower, *Sir* Newman. George Frideric Handel: his personality and his times. Revised ed. *Panther. £0.75* BHC(N) (B72-21775) ISBN 0 586 03778 0
Flute music for beginners. (Kovács, Imre). *Boosey and Hawkes. £0.85* VRPK/AAY (B72-50737)
Fluyten Lust-Hof. Deel 1. - *Excerpts.* Pavane lachrymae: two settings with variations for solo decant recorder. (Eyk, Jacob van). *Schott. £0.45* VSRPMHVG/T (B72-50750)
Fly, Leslie. Sea tang: 3 pieces for clarinet and piano. *Forsyth. Unpriced* VVPJ (B72-50292)
Fock, Gustav.
Harmonischer Gottes-Dienst - Excerpts. Ew'ge Quelle, milder Strom: Kantate auf den Sonntag Cantate, für mittlere Stimme, Querflöte (Violine) und Basso continuo. (Telemann, Georg Philipp). *Bärenreiter. £1.00* KFTE/SPLRDE (B72-50486)
Harmonischer Gottes-Dienst. - *Excerpts.* Gott will Mensch und sterblich werden: Kantate zum Fest der Verkündigung Mariä, für hohe Stimme, Violine und Basso continuo. (Telemann, Georg Philipp). *Bärenreiter. £1.00* KFTE/SPLRDE (B72-50487)
Harmonischer Gottes-Dienst - Excerpts. Jauchzt, ihr Christen, seid vergnügt: Kantate am dritten Osterfreitag, für hohe Stimme, Violine and Basso Continuo. (Telemann, Georg Philipp). *Bärenreiter. £1.00* KFTE/SPLRDE (B72-50488)
Harmonischer Gottes-Dienst. *Excerpts.* Ihr Völker, hört: Kantate am Fest der Heiligen drei Könige, für mittlere Stimme, Querflöte und Basso continuo. (Telemann, Georg Philipp). *Bärenreiter. £1.00* KFVE/VRPLRDE/LFP (B72-50489)
Orgelwerke
Band 1: Magnificat - Bearbeitungen. (Scheidemann, Heinrich). *Barenreiter. £2.75* R/AZ (B72-50628)
Ruft es aus in alle Welt. (In Festo Nativatatis): Weihnachts Kantate, für Sopran, Alt, Tenor, Bass, Vierstimmigen gemischten Chor, drei Trompeten, Pauken, Streicher und Basso continuo. (Telemann, Georg Philipp). *Bärenreiter. £1.25* EMDE/LF (B72-50382)
Folia: neue Variationen nach Farinelli - Corelli, für 4 Soloviolinen. (Sigmund, Oskar). *Bosse: Bärenreiter. £1.20* RXNS/T (B72-50669)
Folk directory
1972. *English Folk Dance and Song Society. £1.00 (£0.75 to members of the EFDSS)* A/G(BC) (B72-06764) ISBN 0 85418 034 6
Folk music & dances of Ireland. (Breathnach, Breandán). *Talbot Press. £1.50* A/G(YDM) (B72-07358) ISBN 0 85452 014 7
Folk music of Hungary. (Kodály, Zoltán). 2nd ed. *Barrie and Jenkins. £2.25* A/G(YG/XA1914 (B72-13442) ISBN 0 214 65327 7
Folk song and dance: a list of books. (Clark, Keith). *National Book League: English Folk Dance and Song Society. £0.30* A/G(T) (B72-16428) ISBN 0 85353 138 2
Follia: for treble recorder and basso continuo. (Corelli, Arcangelo). *Schott. £1.00* VSSPK/AE (B72-51177)
For my love. (Khachaturian, Aram). *Plantagenet music. £0.20* KDW (B72-50112)
For the unfallen. Op.9: for tenor voice, solo French horn and string orchestra. (Crosse, Gordon). *Oxford University Press. £2.50* KGNE/RXMPWTDX (B72-50135) ISBN 0 19 345267 7
Forbes, Elliot. Symphony no.5 in C minor. Op. 67. (Beethoven, Ludwig van). *Chappell. £1.75* MME (B72-50962) ISBN 0 900277 08 4
Forbes, Sebastian. Haec dies. *Oxford University Press. £0.75* RJ (B72-50210) ISBN 0 19 375381 2
Ford, Les.
The clockshop. *Feldman. Unpriced* NYDSRNM (B72-50167)
Frisky. *Feldman. Unpriced* MSHVKK (B72-50156)
Ford Foundation. Music. (Horton, John). *Macmillan for the Anglo-American Primary Education Project. £0.60* A(VG) (B72-13853) ISBN 0 333 13332 3
Fortitude: march for accordion solo. (Crossman, Gerald). *Charnwood Music. Unpriced* RSPMGM (B72-51067)
Foster, George Murphy. *See* Foster, Pops.
Foster, Ivor Reginald. An evening song: for clarinet (B flat) and piano. *Schott. Unpriced* VVPJ (B72-50293)
Foster, Pops. The autobiography of a New Orleans Jazzman. *2 Brook St., W1Y 1AA: University of California Press. £4.25* AMT/E(P) (B72-02170) ISBN 0 520 01826 5
Four carols of other nations: SATB (unacc.). (Dinham, Kenneth J). *Banks. £0.08* EZDP/LF/AY (B72-50856)
Four Christmas carols. *Lengnick. £0.15* DP/LF/AY (B72-50826)
Four corners of the world. (Hanmer, Ronald). *Studio Music. Unpriced* WMG (B72-50300)
Four prayers from the Gaelic. (Thomas, Mansel). *University of Wales Press. Unpriced* KDH (B72-50108)
Fourteen ayres in tabletorie, 1598. *See* Cavendish, Michael.
Foust, Alan. Put your hand in the hand: for mixed chorus SATB. (MacLellan, Gene). *Ardmore and Beechwood. Unpriced* ENYGNTDH (B72-50387)
Fox, Charles. The jazz scene. *Hamlyn. £1.75* AMT(X) (B72-24869) ISBN 0 600 02119 x
Fox, Lilla Margaret. A history of musical instruments. *(Lutterworth Press)* Fox, Lilla Margaret. Instruments of the orchestra. *Lutterworth Press. £1.25* AM/B (B72-03315) ISBN 0 7188 1710 9
Fox, Lilla Margaret. Instruments of the orchestra. *Lutterworth Press. £1.25* AM/B (B72-03315) ISBN 0 7188 1710 9
Frage, Op.9: ein Liederzyklus für tiefe Stimme. (Burkhard, Willy). *Bärenreiter. £1.50* KFXDW (B72-50491)
Françaix, Jean. Concerto for violin. Concerto: violin et orchestre. *Schott. £5.00* SPK/LF (B72-50685)
Franklin, Erik. Music education: psychology and method. *Harrap. £1.40* A/CS(VC) (B72-13438) ISBN 0 245 50659 4
Franklin Pike, Eleanor. *See* Pike, Eleanor Franklin.
Frazier, Kathleen. My story. *12 Forde Park, Newton Abbot, Devon: K. Frazier. £0.50* AQ/E(P) (B72-26661) ISBN 0 9502464 0 9
Freedland, Michael. Al Jolson. *W.H. Allen. £3.00* AKG/E(P) (B72-28010) ISBN 0 491 00633 0
Freie Orgelstücke alter Meister
Band 2. (Graf, Adolf). *Bärenreiter. £3.00* R/AYE (B72-50627)
Fricker, Peter Racine. Paseo: for solo guitar. *Faber Music. Unpriced* TSPMJ (B72-50250)
Frickert, Walter. Six diverses pièces. Op.1, nos.2-3, 5-6. Vier Stücke: fur Klavier oder Cembalo. (Schulz, Johann Abraham Peter). *Peters: Hinrichsen. £1.75* PWPJ (B72-50558)
Friday afternoons. Op.7 - Excerpts. A new year carol. Op.7, no.5. (Britten, Benjamin). *Boosey and Hawkes. £0.05* FDP/LFM (B72-50072)
Friedlaender, Max.
Ausgewählte Lieder: für Gesang und Klavier. (Brahms, Johannes). *Peters. £1.40* KFTDW (B72-50481)
Ausgewählte Lieder: für Gesang und Klavier. (Schubert, Franz). *Peters. £1.40* KFTDW (B72-50482)
Ausgewählte Lieder: für Gesang und Klavier. (Schumann, Robert). *Peters. £1.40* KFTDW (B72-50485)
Friml, Rudolf. The vagabond king. - Come all you beggars. Song of the brigands. *Feldman. £0.20* KDW (B72-50460)
Frisky. (Ford, Les). *Feldman. Unpriced* MSHVKK (B72-50156)
From east to west: SATB unacc. (Rutter, John). *Oxford University Press. Unpriced* EZDM (B72-50061) ISBN 0 19 343026 6
From here. (Brown, Earle). *Universal. Unpriced* MMJ (B72-50966)
Frost, H V. A history of ringing in Hertfordshire. (Goodman, Lilian Gordon). *3 Lea Rd, Harpenden, Herts.: Hertford County Association of Change Ringers. £0.15* AXSR/E(YDED) (B72-16879) ISBN 0 9502366 0 8
Frost, Tony. Divertimento for wind sextet in B flat major. K. 240. - Excerpts. Allegro: for descant, 2 treble and tenor recorders. (Mozart, Wolfgang Amadeus). *Chester. Unpriced* VSNSK (B72-50743)
Frühlingsbotschaft: Konzertwalzer. (Fucik, Julius). *Bosworth. £0.50* MSHW (B72-50982)
Fucik, Julius. Frühlingsbotschaft: Konzertwalzer. *Bosworth. £0.50* MSHW (B72-50982)
Full swell. (Reynolds, Gordon). *Borough Green, Sevenoaks, Kent: Novello. £0.40* AR/E (B72-22496) ISBN 0 85360 039 2
Funeral march on the death of a parrot: for four-part chorus of mixed voices with organ, or piano, or woodwind accompaniment. (Alkan, Charles Henri Valentin). *Schirmer: Chappell. Unpriced* D (B72-50015)
Fünf Jahre Musik, 1891-1895: Kritiken. (Hanslick, Eduard). 3. Aufl. reprinted. *Gregg. £7.20* A (B72-07354) ISBN 0 576 28187 5
Fünf Orchestergesänge nach Georg Trakl. Op.27: für Bariton und Orchester. (Erbse, Heimo). *Peters. £3.20* KGNE/MDW (B72-50492)
Funk, Heinrich. Service music for the organ: preludes, interludes and postludes grouped according to keys Vol.3. *Hinrichsen. £2.70* R/AY (B72-50623)
Fürchte dich nicht, ich bin bei dir. S.228: motet for two four - part mixed choirs. (Bach, Johann Sebastian). *Bärenreiter. £0.35* EZDH (B72-50392)
Füssl, Karlheinz.
Concerto for cello, no.1, in G major. Concerto 1, G major, violoncello - small orchestra. (Stamitz, Carl). *Bärenreiter. £1.00* SRPK/LF (B72-50699)
Concerto for cello, no.3, in C major. Concerto 3, C major, violoncello - small orchestra. (Stamitz, Carl). *Bärenreiter. £1.05* SRPK/LF (B72-50700)
Gabrieli, Andrea. Madrigali et ricercari a quattro voci. - *Excerpts.* Ricercari a quattro, nos.6 & 7: for four recorders (descant, treble, tenor and bass). *Schott. £1.20* VSNS (B72-51170)
Gabrieli, Giovanni.
Canzoni 1 & 2: for 2 trumpets and 2 trombones (2 trumpets, horn & trombone). *Musica rara. £0.90* WMJ (B72-50307)
Canzoni 3 and 4: for 2 trumpets and 2 trombones (2 trumpets, horn & trombone). *Musica rara. £0.90* WMJ (B72-50308)
Sacrae symphoniae. Bk. 1. Symphoniae sacrae
Vol.1: Canzon primi toni à 8: for 4 trumpets and 4 trombones. *Musica rara. Unpriced* WMJ (B72-51198)
Sacrae symphoniae. Bk. 1. Symphoniae sacrae
Vol.2: Canzon septimi toni à 8 (no.1): for 4 trumpets and 4 trombones. *Musica rara. Unpriced* WMJ (B72-51199)
Sacrae symphoniae. Bk. 1. Symphoniae sacrae
Vol.3: Canzon septimi toni à 8 (no.2): for 4 trumpets and 4 trombones. *Musica rara. Unpriced* WMJ (B72-51200)
Sacrae symphoniae. Bk. 1. Symphoniae sacrae
Vol.4: Canzon noni toni à 8: for 4 trumpets and 4 trombones. *Musica rara. Unpriced* WMJ (B72-51201)
Sacrae symphoniae. Bk. 1. Symphoniae sacrae
Vol.5: Canzon duo decimi toni à 8: for 4 trumpets and 4 trombones. *Musica rara. £2.00* WMJ (B72-51202)
Sacrae symphoniae. Bk. 1. Symphoniae sacrae
Vol.6: Sonata pian e forte à 8: for 2 trumpets and 6 trombones. *Musica rara. £1.80* WMJ (B72-51203)
Sacrae symphoniae. Bk. 1. Symphoniae sacrae
Vol.7: Canzon primi toni à 10: for 7 trumpets and 3 trombones, (5 trumpets and 5 trombones). *Musica rara. £2.50* WMJ (B72-51204)
Sacrae symphoniae. Bk. 1. Symphoniae sacrae
Vol.8: Canzon duo decimi toni à 10 (no.1): for 6 trumpets and 4 trombones. *Musica rara. £2.85* WMJ (B72-51205)
Sacrae symphoniae. Bk. 1. Symphoniae sacrae
Vol.9: Canzon duo decimi toni à 10 (no.2): for 6 trumpets and 4 trombones. *Musica rara. £3.00* WMJ (B72-51206)
Sacrae symphoniae. Bk. 1. Symphoniae sacrae
Vol.10: Canzon duo decimi toni à 10 (no.3): for 5 trumpets and 5 trombones. *Musica rara. £2.50* WMJ (B72-51207)
Sacrae symphoniae. Bk. 1. Symphoniae sacrae
Vol.11: Canzon duo decimi toni à 10 (no.4): for 6 trumpets and 4 trombones. *Musica rara. £3.50* WMJ (B72-51208)
Sacrae symphoniae. Bk. 1. Symphoniae sacrae
Vol.12: Canzon in echo duo decima toni à 10: for 6 trumpets, 4 trombones and 2 organs (4 trumpets, 2 horns, 4 trombones and 2 organs). *Musica rara. £3.00* WMJ (B72-51209)
Sacrae symphoniae. Bk. 1. Symphoniae sacrae
Vol.13: Canzon septimi octavi toni à 12: for 6 trumpets and 6 trombones. *Musica rara. Unpriced* WMJ (B72-51210)
Sacrae symphoniae. Bk. 1. Symphoniae sacrae
Vol.14: Canzon noni toni à 12: for 6 trumpets and 6 trombones. *Musica rara. Unpriced* WMJ (B72-51211)
Sacrae symphoniae. Bk. 1. Symphoniae sacrae
Vol.15: Sonata octavi toni à 12: for 2 trumpets and 10 trombones (2 trumpets, 2 horns and 8 trombones). *Musica rara. Unpriced* WMJ (B72-51212)
Sacrae symphoniae. Bk. 1. Symphoniae sacrae
Vol.16: Canzon quarti toni à 15: for 3 trumpets and 12 trombones. *Musica rara. Unpriced* WMJ (B72-51213)
Gabrielli, Domenico.
Sonata for trumpet, cello & string orchestra in D major. Sonata no.4 in D: for trumpet, strings and basso continuo. *Musica rara. £1.00* NUXSNTK/LE (B72-50985)
Sonata for trumpet, cello & string orchestra in D major. Sonata no.4 in D: for trumpet, strings and basso continuo. *Musica rara. y2.50* RXMPWSPLSRE (B72-51106)
Gál, Hans. Divertimento. Op.98: for 3 recorders (descant, treble, tenor). *Schott. £0.80* VSNT (B72-50745)
Gal, Hans. Quartet for strings , no.4. String quartet 4. *Simrock. Unpriced* RXNS (B72-50228)
Galliard, Johann Ernst. Paralèle des Italiens et des François, en ce qui regard la musique et les opéras. A comparison between the French and Italian musick and operas. (Raguenet, François). 1st English ed., reprinted. *Gregg. £11.40* AC(YJ/XF/ZB) (B72-09123) ISBN 0 576 28446 7
Galliard carol: SSA and piano. (Dowland, John). *Boosey and Hawkes. Unpriced* FDP/LF (B72-50870)
Gallico, Claudio. Contredanses: für Orchester. (Cherubini, Luigi). *Peters. £3.00* MRH (B72-50530)
Gammond, Peter.
Best music hall and variety songs. *Wolfe. £5.00* ADW/GM(YD) (B72-30743) ISBN 0 7234 0451 8
One man's music. *Wolfe. £3.00* A (B72-02714) ISBN 0 7234 0424 0
Garcia Lorca, Federico. Ancient voices of children: a cycle of songs for soprano, boy soprano, oboe, mandolin, harp, electric piano, percussion. (Crumb, George). *Peters Hinrichsen. £6.00* JNFLEE/NYDTNPDW (B72-50457)
Gardner, Ward. Two fantasias. (Gibbons, Orlando). *Schott. £0.75* VSNSK (B72-51171)

Gárdonyi, Zoltán. Ab irato; and, Two concert studies for piano solo. (Liszt, Franz). *Bärenreiter. £0.90* QPJ (B72-50590)
Gardonyi, Zoltan. Etudes d'execution transcendante, no.4. Mazeppa for piano solo. (Liszt, Franz). *Bärenreiter. £0.65* QPJ (B72-50591)
Gárdonyi, Zoltán.
Etudes d'exécution transcendante, no.5. Feux follets: for piano solo. (Liszt, Franz). *Bärenreiter. £0.65* QPJ (B72-50592)
Etudes d'exécution transcendante, no.7. Eroica: for piano solo. (Liszt, Franz). *Bärenreiter. £0.50* QPJ (B72-50593)
Etudes d'exécution transcendante, no.8. Wilde Jagd: for piano solo. (Liszt,, Franz). *Bärenreiter. £0.65* QPJ (B72-50594)
Etudes d'exécution transcendante, no.9. Ricordanza: for piano solo. (Liszt, Franz). *Bärenreiter. £0.65* QPJ (B72-50595)
Etudes d'exécution transcendante, no.10. Study in F minor for piano solo. (Liszt, Franz). *Bärenreiter. £0.65* QPJ (B72-50596)
Etudes d'exécution transcendante, no.11. Harmonies du Soir: for piano solo. (Liszt, Franz). *Bärenreiter. £0.50* QPJ (B72-50597)
Grand duo concertant. R.462; based on the romance 'Le Marin' by Philippe Lafont; with, Epithalam. (Wedding Music). R.466: for piano and violin. (Liszt, Franz). *Bärenreiter. £2.00* SPK (B72-50684)
Grandes études de Paganini: for piano solo. (Liszt, Franz). *Bärenreiter. £1.25* QPJ (B72-50598)
Gardonyi, Zoltàn.
Piano works
Vol.1: Studies 1. (Liszt, Franz). *Bärenreiter. £2.00* QP/AZ (B72-50566)
Vol.2: Studies 2. (Liszt, Franz). *Bärenreiter. £2.00* QP/AZ (B72-50567)
Gárdonyi, Zoltàn. Trois études de concert: trois caprices poetiques, for piano solo. (Liszt, Franz). *Bärenreiter. £0.90* QPJ (B72-50599)
Garrick, Michael.
Judas kiss: for SATB choir, instrumentalists and soloists
Part 1. *Robbins Music. Unpriced* CM/L (B72-50344)
Part 2. *Robbins Music. Unpriced* CM/L (B72-50345)
Part 3. *Robbins Music. Unpriced* CM/L (B72-50346)
Gaslini, Giorgio. Magnificat: per voce di soprano, saxofone contralto, contrabasso, pianoforte. *Universal. Unpriced* KFLE/NUUNTDGKK (B72-50476)
Gatt, Martin. Suites for cello, nos.1-3. S.1007-9. - *Excerpts.* Three movements from the solo cello suites. (Bach, Johann Sebastian). *Associated Board of the Royal Schools of Music. £0.15* VWPK/AH (B72-51192)
Gavottina for accordion or piano. (Crossman, Gerald). *Bosworth. £0.15* RSPMHM (B72-51070)
Gay, Brian. 12 kleine Stücke. Twelve little pieces for brass quintet
Book 1. (Maurer, Ludwig). *Novello. £2.70* WNR (B72-51224)
Gay Delavals: portrait in music, for brass band. (Carr, John). *Paxton. £2.50* WMJ (B72-50305)
Gay puppet: accordion solo. (Pasby, Cyril). *Charnwood Music. Unpriced* RSPMJ (B72-51078)
Geary, Ron. Musical instruments. (Hindley, Geoffrey). *Hamlyn. £0.40* AL/B (B72-06765) ISBN 0 600 00294 2
Gebauer, François René. Quintet for wind instruments in E flat major. Quintet in E flat major: for flute, oboe, clarinet, horn and bassoon. *Universal. Unpriced* UNR (B72-51160)
Geissler, Fritz. Sonata for viola & piano. Sonate für Viola und Klavier. *Peters: Hinrichsen. £1.80* SQPE (B72-50691)
Geistlicher Harmonien, erster Teil. *Excerpts.* Jauchzet dem Herrn, alle Welt: für zwei Soprane, zwei Violinen und Basso continuo. (Bernhard, Christoph). *Bärenreiter. £1.00* JNFLEE/SNTRDE (B72-50458)
Gelalian, Boghos. Sept sequences pour orchestre. *Peters Hinrichsen. £3.00* MMJ (B72-50515)
Gelineau, Joseph. An order for Holy Communion, (Series 3). *Ascherberg, Hopwood & Crew. Unpriced* JDGS (B72-50895)
Gelobet seist du, Jesu Christ: Choralmotette für vier-bis sechsstimmigen Chor a cappella. (Micheelsen, Hans Friedrich). *Bärenreiter. £0.60* EZDH (B72-50395)
Genesis: for voices, instruments and tapes. (Pehkonen, Elis). *Universal. Unpriced* FE/LDW (B72-50880)
Genzmer, Harald.
Concerto for cello and wind band. Konzert für Violoncello und Bläser. *Litolff: Hinrichsen. £3.50* UMPSRF (B72-50261)
Concerto for organ. Konzert für Orgel und Orchester. *Peters. £3.00* MPRF (B72-50522)
Dialoge: für Klavier. *Peters. £1.80* QPJ (B72-50586)
Introduzione, aria e finale: für Violine und Orgel. *Litolff: Peters. £1.80* SPLR (B72-50235)
George Frideric Handel: his personality and his times. (Flower, *Sir* Newman). Revised ed. *Panther. £0.75* BHC(N) (B72-21775) ISBN 0 586 03778 0
Gerhard, Roberto.
Quartet for strings, no.2. String quartet, no.2. *Oxford University Press. £2.00* RXNS (B72-50229) ISBN 0 19 356754 7
Symphony 3 (Collages). *Oxford University Press. £5.00* MME (B72-50508) ISBN 0 19 363618 2
Gerlach, Reinhard. Sonata for flute, violin, bassoon & basso continuo in D major. Sonata in D major for flute, violin, bassoon and basso continuo. (Fasch, Johann Friedrich). *Bärenreiter. £1.40* NUPNSE (B72-50532)
Gerok, Karl. Choralbuch zum Evangelischen Kirchengesangbuch: mit den Begleitsätzen des Württembergischen Choralbuches bearbeitet von Karl Gerok und Hans-Arnold Metzger und mit Begleitsätzen zu den Liedern des Anhangs zum Rheinisch-Westfälisch-Lippischen Gesangbuch. (Rödding, Gerhard). *Bärenreiter. Unpriced* DM/LSET/AY (B72-50371)
Gervaise, Claude.
Sixième livre de danceries: for four instruments, SATB. *Pro musica. Unpriced* LNSH (B72-50953)
Troisième livre de danceries: for four instruments, SATB. *Pro Musica. Unpriced* LNSH (B72-50954)
Gervinus, Georg Gottfried. Joshua. Josua: oratorio for four solo-voices, choir and orchestra by Georg Friedrich Händel. (Handel, George Frideric). *Peters. Unpriced* DD (B72-50810)
Gesänge zu Georg Christian Schmellis 'Musicalischen Gesang-Buch' S.439-507 sowie sechs Lieder aus dem 'Klavierbüchlein für Anne Magdalena Bach'. S.511-14, 516, 517. (Bach, Johann Sebastian). *Bärenreiter. Unpriced* KFXDH/AY (B72-50490)
Geschichte des Concertwesens in Wien. (Hanslick, Eduard). *Gregg. £14.40* A(W/YEMB/XFK119) (B72-07361) ISBN 0 576 28227 8
Gibbons, Orlando.
I am the resurrection and the life: SAATB (unacc.). *Oxford University Press. Unpriced* EZDK (B72-50058) ISBN 0 19 350323 9
Two fantasias. *Schott. £0.75* VSNSK (B72-51171)
Giegling, Franz.
Concerto for oboe & string orchestra in G minor. Op. 9 no.8. Concerto á 5: for oboe and strings. (Albinoni, Tommaso). *Musica rara. Unpriced* VTPK/LF (B72-51183)
Concerto for oboe & string orchestra in G minor. Op.9, no.8. Concerto a 5: for oboe and strings. (Albinoni, Tommaso). *Musica rara. Unpriced* RXMPVTF (B72-51091)
Gift of madrigals and motets
Vol. 1: Description and analysis. (Slim, H Colin). *Chicago University Press. Unpriced* EZDU/AY (B72-50858) ISBN 0 226 76271 8
Vol.2: Transcriptions. Description and analysis. (Slim, H Colin). *Chicago University Press. Unpriced* EZDU/AY (B72-50859) ISBN 0 226 76272 6
Gilbert, Bryan. Songs for one step forward. *Marshall, Morgan and Sc tt. £0.30* JE/TSDM/AY (B72-50096)
Gilbert, Norman.
Praise to the Lord, the Almighty: SATB. *Oxford University Press. Unpriced* DH (B72-50817) ISBN 0 19 351112 6
Praise to the Lord, the Almighty: two-part. *Oxford University Press. Unpriced* FDH (B72-50869) ISBN 0 19 341506 2
Gilbert and Sullivan companion. (Ayre, Leslie). *W.H. Allen. £4.50* BSWACF(C) (B72-26093) ISBN 0 491 00832 5
Gilbert and Sullivan song book: for all-organs. (Sullivan, *Sir* Arthur). *Francis, Day & Hunter. £0.75* RK/DW (B72-50644)
Gill, Brendan. Cole: a biographical essay. *Joseph. £7.50* BPNN (B72-24253) ISBN 0 7181 1021 8
Gillett, Charlie. The sound of the city. *Sphere. £0.60* A/GB(YT/XPE25) (B72-07349) ISBN 0 7221 3860 1
Gishford, Anthony. Grand opera: the story of the world's leading opera houses and personalities. *Weidenfeld and Nicolson. £4.25* AC/E(XA1971) (B72-29419) ISBN 0 297 99472 7
Give almes of thy goods. (Tye, Christopher). *Oxford University Press. Unpriced* DK (B72-50361) ISBN 0 19 352113 x
Give us, O Lord. (Dexter, Harry). *Ashdown. £0.09* FDH (B72-50868)
Glasser, Stanley.
Four inventions: for violin and viola. *Piers Press. Unpriced* SPLSQ (B72-50686)
Three pieces, Op. 2.: for piano. *Essex Music. Unpriced* QPJ (B72-50587)
Glazer, Tom. A new treasury of folk songs. *Corgi Books. £0.30* JE/TSDW/G/AYT (B72-50901)
Glazounov, Alexander. Prince Igor. - Overture. Price Igor overture. (Borodin, Alexander). *Boosey and Hawkes. £3.90* WMK (B72-51218)
Gleich wie der Regen und Schnee von Himmel fällt = Like as the raindrops and snow from heaven fall, S.18: cantata for Sunday, sexagesimae. (Bach, Johann Sebastian). *Bärenreiter. £0.65* DE/LG (B72-50352)
Glenn, Neal Edwin. Secondary school music: philosophy, theory and practice. *Prentice-Hall. £4.00* A(VK) (B72-50333) ISBN 0 13 797522 8
Globokar, Vinko. La Ronde: experiment in collective work by an indefinite number of performers. *Litolff: Peters. Unpriced* CB (B72-50795)
Glory of Scotland. (Jackson, Roy Garrick). *Chappell-Solomon. £0.20* KDW (B72-50462)
Godfather. - *Excerpts.* The godfather waltz. (Rota, Nino). *Famous Chappell. £0.20* QPK/AHW/JR (B72-50611)
Godfather - love theme. (Rota, Nino). *Famous Chappell. £0.20* QPK/JR (B72-50615)
Godfather. - Love theme. Speak softly, love. (Rota, Nina). *Chappell. £0.25* KDW (B72-50468)
Godfather. - Waltz. Come live your life with me. (Rota, Nino). *Famous Chappell. £0.20* QPK/DW/JR (B72-50613)
Godfather: selection of themes from the film. (Rota, Nina). *Chappell. Unpriced* WMK/JR (B72-51219)
Godfather: souvenir song album. (Rota, Nino). *Chappell. £1.25* KDW/JR (B72-50932)
Godfather waltz. (Rota, Nino). *Famous Chappell. £0.20* QPK/AHW/JR (B72-50611)
God's mercy: T. Bar. B. unaccompanied. (Kodály, Zoltán). *Boosey and Hawkes. £0.09* GEZDH (B72-50435)
Goethe, Johann Wolfgang von. Goethe-Briefe: Kantate für Bariton, gemischten Chor und Orchester nach Texten von Johann Wolfgang von Goethe und Charlotte von Stein in einer Auswahl des Komponisten. (Baird, Tadensz). *Peters. £2.20* DX (B72-50379)
Goethe-Briefe: Kantate für Bariton, gemischten Chor und Orchester nach Texten von Johann Wolfgang von Goethe und Charlotte von Stein in einer Auswahl des Komponisten. (Baird, Tadensz). *Peters. £2.20* DX (B72-50379)
Goethe songs: original pitch (high). (Schubert, Franz). *Bärenreiter. £1.15* KFTDW (B72-50483)
Gold, Ernest. Exodus. - *Excerpts.* Main theme. *Chappell. Unpriced* UMMK/JR (B72-50720)
Golden classics: a selection of the world's best loved classics for piano. (Wickham, E H ). *Keith Prowse. Unpriced* QP/AY (B72-50565)
Golden legend. (Arch, Gwyn). *British and Continental. Unpriced* CQN/L (B72-50808)
Goldene Brücke: Volkskinderlieder für Hans und Kindergarten, Spielplatz und Schule. (Wenz, Josef). *Bärenreiter. £1.00* JFDW/GJ/AYE (B72-50453)
Golle, Jürgen. Vier leichte Stücke: für Flote und Klavier. *Peters: Hinrichsen. £0.80* VRPJ (B72-50734)
Golliwog's cake-walk. (Debussy, Claude). *Peters. Unpriced* QNV (B72-51022)
Gompers, Montague. The disappointed fairy. *48 Addison Gdns, W.14: Montague Gompers. Unpriced* QPJ (B72-51035)
Gone with the wind: souvenir music album. (Rome, Harold). *Chappell. £0.75* KDW (B72-50467)
Good housewife: folk-song, S.S. unaccompanied. (Kodály, Zoltán). *Boosey and Hawkes. £0.05* FLEZDW (B72-50434)
Good-night Vienna: an operetta in three acts. (Posford, George). *Keith Prowse. £1.25* CF (B72-50797)
Goodman, Lilian Gordon. A history of ringing in Hertfordshire. *3 Lea Rd, Harpenden, Herts.: Hertford County Association of Change Ringers. £0.15* AXSR/E(YDED) (B72-16879) ISBN 0 9502366 0 8
Gorton, William. Sonata for two treble recorders, nos.1 & 2. Two sonatas for two treble recorders. *Schott. £0.40* VSSNUE (B72-50751)
Gossett, Philip. Treatise on harmony. (Rameau, Jean Philippe). *Dover Publications: Constable. £8.75* A/R (B72-01562) ISBN 0 486 22461 9
Gott will Mensch und sterblich werden: Kantate zum Fest der Verkündigung Mariä, für hohe Stimme, Violine und Basso continuo. (Telemann, Georg Philipp). *Bärenreiter. £1.00* KFTE/SPLRDE (B72-50487)
Gow, David. Music: for chorus (SATB). *Chester. Unpriced* EZDW (B72-50863)
Gowers, Patrick. Toccata. *Oxford University Press. £1.00* RJ (B72-50211)
Graf, Adolf.
Choralvorspiele für den gottesdienstlichen Gebrauch
Band 3. *Bärenreiter. £1.75* R/AY (B72-50624)
Freie Orgelstücke alter Meister
Band 2. *Bärenreiter. £3.00* R/AYE (B72-50627)
Grainger, Percy Aldridge. Lisbon: for wind five-some (flute, oboe, clarinet, horn and bassoon). *Schott. £0.65* UNRK/DW (B72-50724)
Gramophone and Typewriter Limited.
Catalogue of 'Red Label' gramophone records 1904. 1st ed. reprinted with September to November supplements. *19 Glendale Rd, Bournemouth BH6 4JA: E. Bayly. £0.85* A/FD(WM) (B72-30321) ISBN 0 902338 14 5
Catalogue of twelve-inch Monarch records ... March 1904 1st ed. reprinted with supplements. *19 Glendale Rd, Bournemouth BH6 4JA: E. Bayly. £0.85* A/FD(WM) (B72-30322) ISBN 0 902338 15 3
Gramophone Company Limited. *For earlier works of this Company see* Gramophone and Typewriter Limited.
Granados, Enrique.
Danzas españolas. - *Excerpts.* Villanesca. Vol.2, no.4. *Boosey and Hawkes. £3.65* MK/AH (B72-50960)
Valses poéticas. *British and Continental. Unpriced* TSPMK/AHW (B72-51153)
Grand opera: the story of the world's leading opera houses and personalities. (Gishford, Anthony). *Weidenfeld and Nicolson. £4.25* AC/E(XA1971) (B72-29419) ISBN 0 297 99472 7
Grand traité d'instrumentation et d'orchestration: opus 10. Traité d'instrumentation et d'orchestration: suivie de 'L'Art du chef d'orchestre'. (Berlioz, Hector). Nouvelle éd., reprinted. *Gregg. £21.00* AM/DF (B72-06769) ISBN 0 576 28418 1
Grande méthode complète de contre basse, pt.2; and, Etudes mélodiques - Excerpts. Arias for double bass and piano. (Bottesini, Giovanni). *8 Cecil Rd, W.3: Yorke. Unpriced* SSPK/DW/AY (B72-50703)
Grandes études de Paganini: for piano solo. (Liszt, Franz). *Bärenreiter. £1.25* QPJ (B72-50598)
Grannie's songs. (Bowman, J.H.). *Sagittar Books. Unpriced* KEZDW (B72-50125)
Granville Bantock: a personal portrait. (Bantock, Myrrha). *Dent. £3.50* BBE(N) (B72-11534) ISBN 0 460 03971 7
Graves, Richard.
Come, my way, my truth, my life: anthem for SATB and organ. *Novello. Unpriced* DH (B72-50025)
Joseph. - Ah, lorsque la mort trop cruelle. A crib-side carol. (Méhul, Etienne). *Novello. £0.07* DP/LF (B72-50375)
Graves, Robert. Counting the beats: song for high voice and piano. (Berkeley, Lennox). *Thames. Unpriced* KFTDW (B72-50131)
Gray, Jerry. American patrol. *Chappell. Unpriced* UMMK

(B72-50719)

Gray, Michael. Song & dance man: the art of Bob Dylan. *3 Upper James St., W1R 4BP: Hart-Davis, MacGibbon. £2.50* AKG/E(P) (B72-30744) ISBN 0 261 10000 9

Great Britain. *Department of Education and Science. Schools Council. See* Schools Council.

Great Britain. *Department of Education and Science. Welsh Education Office. See* Great Britain. *Welsh Education Office.*

Great Britain. *Schools Council. See* Schools Council.

Great Britain. *Welsh Education Office.* Welsh education surveys. *See* Welsh education surveys.

Great Britain. *Welsh Office.* Music. *31 Cathedral Rd, Cardiff CF1 9UJ: Welsh Education Office. £0.20* A(V/YDK) (B72-31877) ISBN 0 903702 00 2

Great composers. *(Faber)* Holst, Imogen. Byrd. *3 Queen Sq., WC1N 3AU: Faber. £2.00* BBX(N) (B72-16876) ISBN 0 571 09813 4

Great composers. *(Faber and Faber Ltd)* Landon, Howard Chandler Robbins. Haydn. *3 Queen Sq., WC1N 3AU: Faber and Faber Ltd. £1.75* BHE(N) (B72-09750) ISBN 0 571 08361 7

Great day coming: folk music and the American left. (Denisoff, R. Serge). *University of Illinois Press. £3.60* A/GB(ZC) (B72-30745) ISBN 0 252 00179 6

Great learning: the first chapter of the Confucian classic with music in 7 paragraphs. (Cardew, Cornelius). *26 Avondale Park Gardens, W.11: Experimental Music Catalogue. Unpriced* JE/NYLDX (B72-50093)

Great piano virtuosos of our time. (Lenz, Wilhelm von). *Regency Press. £1.20* AQ/E(M/XHH45) (B72-13443) ISBN 0 7212 0138 5

Green, F Pratt.

26 hymns. *Epworth Press. £0.40* DM/AY (B72-50036) ISBN 0 7162 0181 x

Christ is the world's light: anthem for SATB and organ. (Thiman, Eric Harding). *Novello. £0.10* DH (B72-50026)

Greene, Maurice.

Acquaint thyself with God: anthem for alto (or tenor) solo, chorus, and organ. *Novello. £0.17* DK (B72-50031)

Choice lessons for the harpsichord or spinnet. - Allmand in D major. Prelude in D. *Leonard, Gould & Bolttler. £0.18* RK/AHJ (B72-51059)

Greenfield, Edward.

Joan Sutherland. *Allan. £1.50* AKFL/E(P) (B72-15424) ISBN 0 7110 0318 1

The stereo record guide

Vol.7: Composer index A-Ma. *Squires Gate, Station Approach, Blackpool, Lancs. FY82 SP: Long Playing Record Library Ltd. £1.95* A/FF(WT) (B72-08760) ISBN 0 901143 02 2

The third Penguin guide to bargain records. *Penguin. £0.60* A/FD(WT) (B72-21267) ISBN 0 14 003454 4

Greening, Anthony. Give almes of thy goods. (Tye, Christopher). *Oxford University Press. Unpriced* DK (B72-50361) ISBN 0 19 352113 x

Greer, David.

14 ayres in tabletorie, 1598/ by Michael Cavendish; and, Ayres, 1609/ by Alfonso Ferrabosco; and, Musicke of sundrie kindes, 1607/ by Thomas Ford; and, Songes of sundrie kindes, 1604/ by Thomas Greaves; and, Ayres to be sung to the lute, ca.1609/ by George Handford. (Cavendish, Michael). *Scolar Press. £12.00* ADW(YD/XDZT12) (B72-05572) ISBN 0 85417 561 x

The first booke of songes and ayres, 1600; and, The second booke of songs and ayres, 1601; and, Ultimum vale, 1605; and, A musicall dreame, 1609; and, The muses gardin, 1610. (Jones, Robert, *fl.1597-1614*). *Scolar Press. £12.00* ADW(YD/XE11) (B72-05573) ISBN 0 85417 559 8

Greeting on St John's day: SAB unaccompanied. (Kodály, Zoltán). *Boosey and Hawkes. £0.05* EZDW (B72-50413)

Grieg, Edvard.

Four pieces. *Chester. Unpriced* VTPK (B72-51182)

Lyric pieces. Op. 12. Lyrical pieces. Opus 12: for piano. *Chappell. £0.45* QPJ (B72-51036)

Peer Gynt -. *Excerpts.* Morning. *Keith Prowse Music. £0.15* QPK/JM (B72-50614)

Symphonic dance. Op.64, no.2. *Oxford University Press. Unpriced* MH (B72-50505) ISBN 0 19 363819 3

Griffin, K. Exodus. - *Excerpts.* Main theme. (Gold, Ernest). *Chappell. Unpriced* UMMK/JR (B72-50720)

Griffiths, Philip.

Coppélia. My daughter Coppelia: a musical play adapted from the ballet. (Delibes, Léo). *Oxford University Press. £1.20* CN (B72-50014) ISBN 0 19 338227 x

My daughter Coppelia: a musical play (adapted from Delibes' ballet 'Coppelia'). *Oxford University Press. £0.40* BDKACN (B72-03927) ISBN 0 19 338228 8

Grillo, Giovanni Battista. Sacrae concentus ac symphoniae. - *Excerpts.* Canzona quarta: for 4 trumpets and 4 trombones (4 trumpets, 2 horns and 2 trombones). *Musica rara. £1.50* WNN (B72-51220)

Gritton, Eric. Sonata for violin & basso continuo, no.4, in D minor. Liv. 4. - Allegro spiritusoso. Allegro. (Senaillé, Jean Baptiste). *Associated Board of the Royal Schools of Music. £0.25* SRPK (B72-51139)

Grossi, Andrea.

Sonata for trumpet & string orchestra in D major. Op.3, no.10. Sonata decima: for trumpet and strings. *Musica rara. £2.00* RXMPWSE (B72-51103)

Sonata for trumpet & string orchestra in D major. Op.3, no.10. Sonata decima: for trumpet and strings. *Musica rara. £1.00* WSPK/LE (B72-51242)

Grossman, Stefan. Ragtime blues guitarists. *Oak Publications; 78 Newman St., W.1: Music Sales Ltd. £1.60* ATS/HHW/E(M) (B72-50003) ISBN 0 8256 0118 5

Grotesques de la musique. (Berlioz, Hector). *Gregg. £8.40* A(D) (B72-06099) ISBN 0 576 28421 1

Ground bass. (Bryce, Frank). *Paxton Music. Unpriced* WMGM (B72-50763)

Grow, tresses = Hajinšvesztö: SSA unaccompanied. (Kodály, Zoltán). *Boosey and Hawkes. £0.05* FEZDW (B72-50888)

Grundman, Clare.

A classical overture. *Boosey and Hawkes. £1.50* UMMJ (B72-51156)

Festive piece. *Boosey and Hawkes. £2.00* UMMJ (B72-51157)

Grusnick, Bruno. Geistlicher Harmonien, erster Teil. *Excerpts.* Jauchzet dem Herrn, alle Welt: für zwei Soprane, zwei Violinen und Basso continuo. (Bernhard, Christoph). *Bärenreiter. £1.00* JNFLEE/SNTRDE (B72-50458)

Guami, Gioseffo. La Guamina: for 2 trumpets and 2 trombones, (2 trumpets, horn and trombone). *Musica rara. £0.70* WNS (B72-51231)

Guamina: for 2 trumpets and 2 trombones, (2 trumpets, horn and trombone). (Guami, Gioseffo). *Musica rara. £0.70* WNS (B72-51231)

Gubby, Roy. Suite for three recorders: treble (tenor 1), tenor 2 and bass (or cello). *Boosey and Hawkes. £0.50* VSNTG (B72-50746)

Guide my head: spiritual arranged for four-part chorus of men's voices a cappella. (Heath, Fenno). *Schirmer Chappell. Unpriced* GEZDW/LC (B72-50082)

Guild for the Promotion of Welsh Music. A complete catalogue of contemporary Welsh music

No.5. *c/o G. Williams, 10 Llanerch Path, Fairwater, Cwmbran, Mon. NP4 4QN: Guild for the Promotion of Welsh Music. Unpriced* A(YDK/TC) (B72-19872) ISBN 0 901248 01 0

Guitar care: a manual to enable the guitar owner to service his instrument. (Bowden, George). *193 Wollaton St., Nottingham: G. Bowden. Unpriced* ATS/BT (B72-03317) ISBN 0 9502139 0 x

Gurgel, Gaó. Symphony no.5 in E minor. Op.64. - Andante cantabile. Andante da 5a sinfonia. (Tchaikovsky, Peter). *MCA: Leeds Music. Unpriced* QPK (B72-50608)

Guttler, Ludwig.

Complete trumpet repertoire

Vol.1. (Bach, Johann Sebastian). *Musica rara. £2.75* WSN/AZ (B72-50319)

Vol.2. (Bach, Johann Sebastian). *Musica rara. £2.75* WSN/AZ (B72-50320)

Vol.3. (Bach, Johann Sebastian). *Musicara rara. £2.75* WSN/AZ (B72-50321)

Guy, Barry. 4 miniatures: for flute and piano. *Novello. £1.50* VRPJ (B72-50735)

Gyodai. Autumn: for voices and instruments. (Paynter, John). *Universal. Unpriced* JFE/XPQDW (B72-50915)

Györ, István Fekete. *See* Fekete Györ, István.

Haan, Stefan de. Jazz songs for soprano & double bass. (Roe, Betty). *Yorke. Unpriced* KFLE/SSDW (B72-50478)

Hader, Widmar. Duet for trumpet and trombone (1960). Duett für Trompete in C und Posaune. *Bosse Bärenreiter. £0.85* WSPLWU (B72-50786)

Haec dies. (Forbes, Sebastian). *Oxford University Press. £0.75* RJ (B72-50210) ISBN 0 19 375381 2

Haidmayer, Karl. Sonata for viola and piano, no.1. Sonate 1 for viola and piano. *Bärenreiter. £1.25* SQPE (B72-50692)

Hajinövesztö. Grow, tresses = Hajinšvesztö: SSA unaccompanied. (Kodály, Zoltán). *Boosey and Hawkes. £0.05* FEZDW (B72-50888)

Halévy, L. Carmen. - Avec la garde montante. Street boys' song = Choeur des gamins. (Bizet, Georges). *Schott. £0.60* JFE/NYFSRDW (B72-50913)

Halffter, Cristóbal. Planto por las victimas de la violencia: para conjunto instrumental y transformacion electronica del sonido. *Universal. Unpriced* MMJ (B72-50146)

Hall, Alan. The first book of solos for the classical guitar. (Pearse, John). *Scatchwood Music. Unpriced* TSPMK/AAY (B72-50251)

Hall, Graeme. Beg, steal or borrow: Britain's Eurovision song 1972. (Cole, Tony). *Valley Music. Unpriced* UMMK/DW/JS (B72-50259)

Hallé, *Sir* Charles. The autobiography of Charles Hallé, with correspondence and diaries. *Elek. £3.25* A(P) (B72-31293) ISBN 0 236 15448 6

Hamlyn all-colour paperbacks: arts. *(Hamlyn)* Hindley, Geoffrey. Musical instruments. *Hamlyn. £0.40* AL/B (B72-06765) ISBN 0 600 00294 2

Hammerstein, Oscar, *b.1895.*

Rodgers & Hammerstein revisited

Vol.1. (Rodgers, Richard). *Williamson Music. £0.75* KDW (B72-50114)

Vol.2. (Rodgers, Richard). *Williamson Music. £0.75* KDW (B72-50115)

Hammond, Tom. Hansel and Gretel: a fairy opera in three acts. (Humperdinck, Engelbert). *Schott. £1.05* CC (B72-50340)

Hampton, Calvin. Catch-up: for four pianos or tape recorder and two pianos. *Peters. £1.25* QNS (B72-50561)

Handbook of music and music literature in sets and series. (Charles, Sydney Robinson). *Free Press: Collier-Macmillan. £5.40* A(T) (B72-12964) ISBN 0 02 905400 1

Handel - chronological thematic catalogue. (Bell, Arnold Craig). 2nd ed.. *Darley, Harrogate, Yorkshire: Grian-aig Press. £12.00* BHC(TD) (B72-32113) ISBN 0 9500714 4 7

Handel, Georg Frideric. Sonatas for two violins & basso continuo. Op.5 nos.7,1. Two triosonatas for two violins and basso continuo. *Nagel. £1.25* NXNT (B72-50547)

Handel, George Frideric.

Ariodante. - Overture, 3rd section. Rigaudon. *Bosworth. £1.80* MJ (B72-50958)

Handel - chronological thematic catalogue. (Bell, Arnold Craig). 2nd ed.. *Darley, Harrogate, Yorkshire: Grian-aig Press. £12.00* BHC(TD) (B72-32113) ISBN 0 9500714 4 7

Joshua. Josua: oratorio for four solo-voices, choir and orchestra

by Georg Friedrich Händel. *Peters. Unpriced* DD (B72-50810)

Keyboard works

Vol.2: Second set of 1733. *Bärenreiter. £1.85* QRP/AZ (B72-50622)

La Solitudine: cantata for alto solo and basso continuo. *Bärenreiter. £1.00* KFQDX (B72-50480)

Sonata for two flutes & basso continuo in E minor. Sonata in E minor: 2 flutes and continuo, (v'c ad libitum). *Peters. £1.40* VRNTPWE (B72-50728)

Trio sonata for treble recorder, violin & basso continuo in C minor. Op.2, no.1. Trio sonata in C minor: for treble recorder, violin (two violins) AND BASSO CONTINUO. *Nagel. £1.15* NUSSNTE (B72-50535)

Trio sonata for treble recorder, violin & basso continuo in F major. Op.2, no.4. Trio sonata in F major: for treble recorder, violin (two violins) and basso continuo. *Nagel. £1.00* NUSSNTE (B72-50536)

Triosonata for two violins & basso continuo in G minor. Op.2, no. 8. Trio sonata in G minor: for two violins and basso continuo. *Nagel. £1.00* NXNTE (B72-50549)

Handel: a biography, with a survey of books, editions and recording. (Cudworth, Charles). *Bingley. £1.75* BHC (B72-07357) ISBN 0 85157 137 9

Handel concertos. (Sadie, Stanley). *British Broadcasting Corporation. £0.45* BHCAMF (B72-28683) ISBN 0 563 10349 3

Handle, Johnny. The High Level Ranters song and tune book. *Galliard. £0.55* JEZDW/G/AYC (B72-50447) ISBN 0 85249 151 4

Handy, William Christopher. Blues: an anthology, complete words and music of 53 great songs. *Macmillan: Collier-Macmillan. Unpriced* KDW/HHW/AY (B72-50471)

Hanmer, Ronald.

Das Dreimäderlhaus. Lilac time: operetta in three acts. (Schubert, Franz). *Chappell: Weinberger. Unpriced* CF (B72-50012)

The four corners of the world. *Studio Music. Unpriced* WMG (B72-50300)

Hänsel and Gretel. (Humperdinck, Engelbert). *Studio Music. Unpriced* WMK/CC (B72-50774)

Hänsel and Gretel. - *Excerpts.* Hänsel and Gretel song book by Engelbert Humperdinck. (Humperdinck, Engelbert). *Francis, Day and Hunter. £0.35* KDW (B72-50461)

Hänsel and Gretel. (Humperdinck, Engelbert). *Studio Music. Unpriced* WMK/CC (B72-50774)

Hansel and Gretel: a fairy opera in three acts. (Humperdinck, Engelbert). *Schott. £1.05* CC (B72-50340)

Hänsel and Gretel song book

by Engelbert Humperdinck. (Humperdinck, Engelbert). *Francis, Day and Hunter. £0.35* KDW (B72-50461)

Hansel and Gretel. - *Excerpts.* Prelude. (Humperdinck, Engelbert). *Weinberger. Unpriced* WMJ (B72-51214)

Hanslick, Eduard.

Am Ende des Jahrhunderts, 1895-1899: musikalische Kritiken und Schilderungen. 2. Aufl. reprinted. *Gregg. £7.20* A (B72-07355) ISBN 0 576 28188 3

Aus dem Opernleben der Gegenwart: neue Kritiken und Studien. *Gregg. £6.00* AC (B72-07360) ISBN 0 576 28183 2

Aus dem Tagebuche eines Musikers: Kritiken und Schilderungen. *Gregg. £6.00* A (B72-07353) ISBN 0 576 28186 7

Aus meinem Leben. *Gregg. £10.20* A/CC(P) (B72-07348) ISBN 0 576 28225 1

Aus neuer und neuester Zeit: musikalische Kritiken und Schilderungen. 3. Aufl. reprinted. *Gregg. £7.20* A (B72-07356) ISBN 0 576 28189 1

Concerte, Componisten und Virtuosen der letzten fünfzehn Jahre, 1870-1885: Kritiken. 2.Aufl., reprinted. *Gregg. £7.80* A(YEMB/XKK16) (B72-09122) ISBN 0 576 28226 x

Fünf Jahre Musik, 1891-1895: Kritiken. 3. Aufl. reprinted. *Gregg. £7.20* A (B72-07354) ISBN 0 576 28187 5

Geschichte des Concertwesens in Wien. *Gregg. £14.40* A(W/YEMB/XFK119) (B72-07361) ISBN 0 576 28227 8

Die moderne Oper: Kritiken und Studien. *Gregg. £6.00* AC (B72-07359) ISBN 0 576 28181 6

Musikalische Stationem. *Gregg. £6.00* A (B72-07350) ISBN 0 576 28182 4

Musikalisches Skizzenbuch: neue Kritiken und Schildenrungen. *Gregg. £6.00* A (B72-07351) ISBN 0 576 28184 0

Musikalisches und Litterarisches: Kritiken und Schilderungen. 2. Aufl. reprinted. *Gregg. £6.00* A (B72-07352) ISBN 0 576 28185 9

Harding, James. The ox on the roof: scenes from musical life in Paris in the twenties. *Macdonald and Co. £3.00* A/D(YH/XMS13/P) (B72-14735) ISBN 0 356 03967 6

Harding, Rosamond Evelyn Mary. A thematic catalogue of the works of Matthew Locke: with a calendar of the main events of his life. *R.E.M. Harding: Distributed by Blackwell. £7.00* BLOC(TD) (B72-02957) ISBN 0 9502117 0 2

Hardwick, Michael. The Osprey guide to Gilbert and Sullivan. *Osprey.* *£2.50* BSWACF (B72-26659) ISBN 0 85045 100 0

Harley, E Daker. Blessed art thou Mary: Advent carol for soprano solo SA and piano or organ. *Novello. £0.07* FDP/LEZ (B72-50418)

Harlow, Frank. Colditz march. (Farnon, Robert J). *Leeds Music. £0.25* QPK/AGM/JS (B72-51044)

Harmonies du Soir: for piano solo. (Liszt, Franz). *Bärenreiter. £0.50* QPJ (B72-50597)

Harmonischer Gottes-Dienst - Excerpts. Ew'ge Quelle, milder Strom: Kantate auf den Sonntag Cantate, für mittlere Stimme, Querflöte (Violine) und Basso continuo. (Telemann, Georg Philipp). *Bärenreiter. £1.00* KFTE/SPLRDE (B72-50486)

Harmonischer Gottes-Dienst. - *Excerpts.* Gott will Mensch und sterblich werden: Kantate zum Fest der Verkündigung Mariä, für hohe Stimme, Violine und Basso continuo. (Telemann, Georg Philipp). *Bärenreiter. £1.00* KFTE/SPLRDE (B72-50487)

Harmonischer Gottes-Dienst - Excerpts. Jauchzt, ihr Christen, seid vergnügt: Kantate am dritten Osterfreitag, für hohe Stimme, Violine and Basso Continuo. (Telemann, Georg Philipp). *Bärenreiter. £1.00* KFTE/SPLRDE (B72-50488)

Harmonischer Gottes-Dienst. *Excerpts.* Ihr Völker, hört: Kantate am Fest der Heiligen drei Könige, für mittlere Stimme, Querflöte und Basso continuo. (Telemann, Georg Philipp). *Bärenreiter. £1.00* KFVE/VRPLRDE/LFP (B72-50489)

Harnoncourt, Nikolaus. Sinfonie da chiesa. Op. 5. - *Excerpts.* Sinfonia 1 und 9, for strings and basso continuo. (Bononcini, Giovanni Battista). *Schott. £1.40* RXME (B72-51087)

Harper's dictionary of music. (Ammer, Christine). *Hale. £4.00* A(C) (B72-10997) ISBN 0 7091 3064 3

Harris, A D. Sonata for cello & basso continuo in D major, Op.26, no.1. Sonata for cello and piano. (Boismortier, Joseph Bodin de). *British and Continental. Unpriced* SRPE (B72-51136)

Harrison, Max. The lieder of Brahms. *Cassell. £1.75* BBTAKDW (B72-16878) ISBN 0 304 93876 9

Hartig, Heinz Friedrich. Solo for guitar (1951). *Novello. £0.25* TSPMJ (B72-50708)

Hartmann, Karl Amadeus. Dance suite: for wind quintet, clarinet, bassoon, horn, trumpet and trombone. *Schott. £4.40* WNRHG (B72-51225)

Harverson, Alan. Spare time for music. (Epps, David). *British Broadcasting Corporation. £1.20* C/AY (B72-50793) ISBN 0 563 10689 1

Hashagen, Klaus. 'Septalie': Studie für 7 Spieler - 6 beliebige Instrumente und Klavier. *Bosse: Bärenreiter. £0.95* LNPQ (B72-50501)

Hathaway, W G. Selected Christian songs
Album 12. *Gospel Music. Unpriced* DM/AY (B72-50368)

Hauser, Karlheinz Schultz-. *See* Schultz-Hauser, Karlheinz.

Hautus, Loek. Salve regina, A-moll: für Sopran, Alt und Basso continuo. (Scarlatti, Domenico). *Bärenreiter. £1.00* JNFEDJ (B72-50456)

Havergal Brian: perspective on the music. (MacDonald, Malcolm). *5 Mayfield Rd, W.3: Triad Press. £1.25* BBTN (B72-04569) ISBN 0 902070 03 7

Haydine, Le. *See* Carpani, Giuseppe.

Haydn, Joseph.
Die drei- und vierstimmigen Gesänge. *Bärenreiter. £2.00* DW (B72-50378)
Mass no.16 in B flat major, 'Theresienmesse'. - Kyrie. Kyrie: for four-part chorus of mixed voices with organ or piano accompaniment. *Schirmer: Chappell. Unpriced* DGB (B72-50020)
Mass no.16, 'Theresa mass'. Missa, Theresa mass. *Bärenreiter. £3.15* DG (B72-50354)

Haydn, Michael.
Concerto for trumpet, no.2, in C major. Trumpet concerto no.2 in C major: for trumpet, 2 flutes, strings and continuo. *Musica rara. Unpriced* WSPK/LF (B72-50326)
Concerto for trumpet, strings & basso continuo no.1 in C major. Concerto no.1 in C major: for solo trumpet, strings and continuo (bassoon ad lib.). *Musica rara. Unpriced* MPWSF (B72-50151)

Haydn. (Landon, Howard Chandler Robbins). *3 Queen Sq., WC1N 3AU: Faber and Faber Ltd. £1.75* BHE(N) (B72-09750) ISBN 0 571 08361 7

Hayes, William. Cathedral music. - *Excerpts.* Lord, how long wilt thou be angry?: anthem for SAATB (unaccompanied). *£0.10* EZDK (B72-50847)

Hazell, Chris. Holy Moses: pop cantata for unison voices and piano. *Novello. £0.50* JDE (B72-50894)

Hazell, Christopher. Monsieur de la plume: fragments from the life of Robert Louis Stevenson: music for children's voices and piano. (Rowley, Alec). *Ashdown. Unpriced* CN (B72-50800)

He delivered the poor. (Parry, *Sir* Charles Hubert Hastings). *Royal School of Church Music. Unpriced* KFLDH (B72-50129)

Head, Michael.
Five Finnish Christmas songs: for mixed chorus and orchestra (or piano)
1: Christmas = No, onkos tullut kesä. *Boosey and Hawkes. £0.14* DW/LF (B72-50830)
2: When it is Christmas = Kun joulu on. *Boosey and Hawkes. £0.14* DW/LF (B72-50831)
3: A snowing on Christmas morning = Varpunen jouluaamuna. *Boosey and Hawkes. £0.09* DW/LF (B72-50832)
4: Christmas bells = Joulun kellot. *Boosey and Hawkes. £0.14* DW/LF (B72-50833)
5: Uncle Frost = Halla. *Boosey and Hawkes. £0.14* DW/LF (B72-50834)

Hear my words, ye people. *Excerpts.* He delivered the poor. (Parry, *Sir* Charles Hubert Hastings). *Royal School of Church Music. Unpriced* KFLDH (B72-50129)

Hear the voice and prayer: anthem for S (or A) ATB. (Tallis, Thomas). *Novello. £0.10* EZDK (B72-50849)

Heart's awakening: a song cycle. (Larbalestier, Philip George). *Regina Music. £0.35* KDW (B72-50463)

Heath, Fenno. Guide my head: spiritual arranged for four-part chorus of men's voices a cappella. *Schirmer Chappell. Unpriced* GEZDW/LC (B72-50082)

Heath-Stubbs, John. The history of the Flood: for narrator, chorus, percussion, and piano duet. (Lord, David). *Oxford University Press. £1.50* ENYLDE (B72-50052) ISBN 0 19 337380 7

Hebrew University. *Jewish Music Research Centre. See* Jewish Music Research Centre.

Hedges, Anthony. A British folk song suite. *British and Continental Music. Unpriced* RXMK/DW/G/AYC (B72-50656)

Heider, Werner. Bezirk: für Klavier und Orchester. *Peters. £3.50* MPQ (B72-50521)

Heliogabalus imperator: allegoria per musica. (Henze, Hans Werner). *Schott. £4.80* MMJ (B72-50969)

Henderson, Harold G. Autumn: for voices and instruments. (Paynter, John). *Universal. Unpriced* JFE/XPQDW (B72-50915)

Hendrie, Gerald. Renaissance music. *Walton Hall, Bletchley, Bucks.: Open University Press. £1.10* A(XRE201) (B72-50334) ISBN 0 335 00657 4

Heneker, David.
Charlie girl. *Chappell. £1.75* CM (B72-50799)
Charlie girl: a comedy musical in two acts. (Williams, Hugh). *Chappell. £0.75* BHJJACM (B72-23641) ISBN 0 85360 040 6

Henze, Hans Werner.
El Cimarrón-Biography of the runaway slave Esteban Montejo: recital for four musicians. *Schott. £2.40* KE/NYERNSDX (B72-50933)
Heliogabalus imperator: allegoria per musica. *Schott. £4.80* MMJ (B72-50969)

Herbert, George. Come, my way, my truth, my life: anthem for SATB and organ. (Graves, Richard). *Novello. Unpriced* DH (B72-50025)

Hermann-Hesse-Gesänge, 'Gesänge des Abschieds': für Bariton und Orchester. (Wagner-Régeny, Rudolf). *Peters: Hinrichsen. £2.80* KGNE/MDW (B72-50493)

Heroic overture. (Panufnik, Andrzej). *Boosey and Hawkes. UNpriced* MMJ (B72-50518)

Heroic overture. (Panufnik, Andrzej). *Boosey and Hawkes. Unpriced* MMJ (B72-50519)

Herrick, Robert. First booke of songes. - If my complaints. The Galliard carol: SSA and piano. (Dowland, John). *Boosey and Hawkes. Unpriced* FDP/LF (B72-50870)

Herrmann, William.
Intende voci orationis mea: offertory for tenor solo and four-part chorus of mixed voices with organ or piano accompaniment. (Schubert, Franz). *Schirmer: Chappell. Unpriced* DGKAF (B72-50021)
Mass no.16 in B flat major, 'Theresienmesse'. - Kyrie. Kyrie: for four-part chorus of mixed voices with organ or piano accompaniment. (Haydn, Joseph). *Schirmer Chappell. Unpriced* DGB (B72-50020)

Hertel, Johann Wilhelm.
Concerto for trumpet & string orchestra in E flat. Concerto no.2 in E flat: for trumpet, strings and major continuo. *Musica rara. Unpriced* RXMPWSF (B72-51104)
Concerto for trumpet & string orchestra in E flat major. Concerto no.2 in E flat: for trumpet, strings and continuo. *Musica rara. Unpriced* WSPK/LF (B72-51243)
Concerto for trumpet, oboe & string orchestra in E flat major. Concerto à 6: for trumpet, oboe, strings and continuo. *Musica rara. Unpriced* RXMPWSPLVTF (B72-51107)
Concerto for trumpet, oboe & string orchestra in E flat major. Concerto à 6: for trumpet, oboe, strings and continuo. *Musica rara. Unpriced* VTPLWSK/LF (B72-51185)
Concerto for trumpet, oboe & string orchestra in E flat major. Doppel Konzert, Es-dur: für Trompete, Oboe, Streicher und Basso continuo. *Schott. £2.00* RXMPVTPLWSF (B72-51093)

Hertel, Klaus. Concertino: für Violine (1.Lage) und Klavier. *Peters: Hinrichsen. £0.75* SPFL (B72-50678)

Hertford County Association of Change Ringers. A history of ringing in Hertfordshire. (Goodman, Lilian Gordon). *3 Lea Rd, Harpenden, Herts.: Hertford County Association of Change Ringers. £0.15* AXSR/E(YDED) (B72-16879) ISBN 0 9502366 0 8

Herzogenberg, Heinrich von. Quintet for oboe, clarinet, horn, bassoon & piano in E flat major. Op.43. Quintet. Op.43: for oboe, clarinet, horn, bassoon & pianoforte. *Musica rara. Unpriced* NWNR (B72-50164)

Hessenberg, Kurt. Quartet for strings, no.5. Streichquartett No.5 (in einem Satz). *Bosse: Bärenreiter. £1.05* RXNS (B72-50667)

Hexameron. Op.37. (Einem, Gottfried von). *Boosey and Hawkes. £1.75* MMJ (B72-50145)

Hexameron. Op.37. (Einem, Gottfried von). *Boosey and Hawkes. £5.25* MMJ (B72-50514)

Heyworth, Peter. Berlioz, romantic and classic: writings by Ernest Newman. (Newman, Ernest). *Gollancz. £3.00* BBM(D) (B72-03314) ISBN 0 575 01365 6

H.H.: a tribute to Herbert Howells on his eightieth birthday. (Spearing, Robert). *10e Prior Bolton St., Canonbury, N.1: Triad Press. £0.90* BHS(N) (B72-30070) ISBN 0 902070 05 3

High Level Ranters song and tune book. *Galliard. £0.55* JEZDW/G/AYC (B72-50447) ISBN 0 85249 151 4

Hill, Geoffrey. For the unfallen. Op.9: for tenor voice, solo French horn and string orchestra. (Crosse, Gordon). *Oxford University Press. £2.50* KGNE/RXMPWTDX (B72-50135) ISBN 0 19 345267 7

Hill, John D.
Sonata for two violins, trombone & organ continuo, no.1, in D minor. Sonata á 3, no.1 in D minor: for 2 violins, trombone and organ continuo. (Bertali, Antonio). *Musica rara. £1.50* NUXUNSE (B72-50986)
Sonata for two violins, trombone & organ continuo, no.2 in D minor. Sonata á 3, no.2 in D minor: for 2 violins, trombone and organ continuo. (Bertali, Antonio). *Musica rara. £1.50* NUXUNSE (B72-50987)
Sonatas for brass quintet & basso continuo, nos.1-6. Six sonatas: for 2 trumpets, 3 trombones and continuo (2 trumpets, horn, 2 trombones and continuo). (Bertali, Antonio). *Musica rara. Unpriced* NWXPNRE (B72-50993)

Hindemith, Paul. Konzertmusik. Op.41: für Bläsorchester. *Schott. £1.60* UMJ (B72-50713)

Hindley, Geoffrey. Musical instruments. *Hamlyn. £0.40* AL/B (B72-06765) ISBN 0 600 00294 2

Hinke, Gustav Adolf.
Neue Oboenschule. (Sous, Alfred). *Litolff: Peters. £3.80* VT/AC (B72-50282)
Praktische Elementar-Schule für die Oboe. Elementary method for oboe. *Peters. £0.70* VT/AC (B72-50281)

Hirten last: fünf weltliche Madrigale, für fünf stimmen und Basso Continuo. (Schein, Johann Hermann). *Bärenreiter. £0.95* DU (B72-50377)

Hist whist: for voice, flute, viola and percussion. (Jong, Conrad de). *Schirmer: Chappell. Unpriced* KE/NYERNTDW (B72-50124)

Historische Bläsermusiken: 25 Militärmärsche des 18, Jahrhunderts; erste Urtextausgabe nach den Originalhandschriften für den praktischen Gebrauch
Heft 1. (Pätzig, Gerhard). *Bärenreiter. £2.50* UMM/AY (B72-50714)
Heft 2. (Pätzig, Gerhard). *Bärenreiter. £3.00* UMM/AY (B72-50715)
Heft 3. (Pätzig, Gerhard). *Bärenreiter. £2.00* UMM/AY (B72-50716)

History of musical instruments. *See* Fox, Lilla Margaret.

History of ringing in Hertfordshire. (Goodman, Lilian Gordon). *3 Lea Rd, Harpenden, Herts.: Hertford County Association of Change Ringers. £0.15* AXSR/E(YDED) (B72-16879) ISBN 0 9502366 0 8

History of the Flood: for narrator, chorus, percussion, and piano duet. (Lord, David). *Oxford University Press. £1.50* ENYLDE (B72-50052) ISBN 0 19 337380 7

Hochkofler, Max. Concerto for cello in A minor. Op.129. Cello concerto, A minor. Op.129. (Schumann, Robert). *Eulenburg. £0.80* MPSRF (B72-50149)

Hodder Christian paperbacks. *(Hodder and Stoughton)*
Carlson, Betty. A singing heart: from Venice to the alps of L'Abri. *Hodder and Stoughton. £0.45* AKF/E(P) (B72-23640) ISBN 0 340 15866 2
Swann, Donald. The space between the bars: a book of reflections. *Hodder and Stoughton. £0.45* BSWN(N) (B72-16877) ISBN 0 340 16001 2

Hoddinott, Alun.
Fantasy for harp. Opus 68, no.2. *Oxford University Press. £0.70* TQPMJ (B72-51142) ISBN 0 19 357154 4
Puer natus: SSAATTBB (or SSAA or TTBB). *Oxford University Press. Unpriced* DP/LF (B72-50374) ISBN 0 19 343030 4
Sinfonietta 4. Opus 72, no.3. *Oxford University Press. £2.00* MMEM (B72-50965) ISBN 0 19 364652 8
Sonata for violin & piano, no.2. Op.73, no.1. Sonata no.2, Op.73, no.1: for violin and piano. *Oxford University Press. £2.00* SPE (B72-50673) ISBN 0 19 357152 8

Hodgson, Martyn. Die Zauberflöte. - *Excerpts.* Six airs. (Mozart, Wolfgang Amadeus). *Regina Music. Unpriced* TSPMK/DW (B72-50712)

Hoffmann, Adolf. Tanzbüchlein für zwei Bratschen: Tanzlieder und Volkstänze. *Schott. £0.80* SQNUH (B72-50688)

Hoffstetter, Roman. Concerto for viola in C major. Konzert, C-Dur: für Viola, Streicher, 2 Oboen und 2 Hörner. *Schott. £1.80* MPSQF (B72-50975)

Hofmann, Klaus. Sonata for two violins, two violas, cello & harpsichord in F minor. Sonata in F minor for two violins, two violas, violoncello and harpsichord (double bass ad lib). (Telemann, Georg Philipp). *Bärenreiter. £1.50* NXNQE (B72-50544)

Hofstatter, Peter R. Psylex (1968): für Mezzosopran, Flöte und Tonband. (Karkoschka, Erhard). *Bosse: Bärenreiter. £2.25* KFNE/VRDX (B72-50479)

Hohelied Salomonis: for four part mixed chorus. (Lechner, Leonhard). *Bärenreiter. £0.70* EZDU (B72-50409)

Hohelied Salomo's. Opus 26a: Sopran, Bariton und Klavier. (Erbse, Heimo). *Peters. £4.50* JNEDE (B72-50455)

Holloway, Stanley. The world of Stanley Holloway: songs and musical monologues by various composers and writers. *Francis, Day and Hunter. £0.75* KHY (B72-50497)

Hollowood, Bernard. Full swell. (Reynolds, Gordon). *Borough Green, Sevenoaks, Kent: Novello. £0.40* AR/E (B72-22496) ISBN 0 85360 039 2

Holman, Derek.
Jesus Christ the apple tree. *Royal School of Church Music. Unpriced* JDK (B72-50440)
Thee we adore. *Royal School of Church Music. Unpriced* FLDH (B72-50081)

Holroyde, Peggy. Indian music: a vast ocean of promise. *Allen and Unwin. £5.25* BZF (B72-17505)

ISBN 0 04 780020 8
Holst, Gustav.
Lyric movement: for viola and small orchestra. *Oxford University Press. £0.75* SQPK (B72-50237)
ISBN 0 19 357254 0
Margrete's cradle-song. Op.4, no.2. *Bosworth. £0.20* KDW (B72-50925)
St Paul's suite: for string orchestra. *Curwen Edition. Unpriced* RXMG (B72-50649)
Holst, Imogen.
Byrd. *3 Queen Sq., WC1N 3AU: Faber. £2.00* BBX(N) (B72-16876) ISBN 0 571 09813 4
Holst. *Novello. £0.15* BHP(N) (B72-15422)
ISBN 0 85360 010 4
Lyric movement: for viola and small orchestra. (Holst, Gustav). *Oxford University Press. £0.75* SQPK (B72-50237) ISBN 0 19 357254 0
Holst. (Holst, Imogen). *Novello. £0.15* BHP(N) (B72-15422) ISBN 0 85360 010 4
Holy Moses: pop cantata for unison voices and piano. (Hazell, Chris). *Novello. £0.50* JDE (B72-50894)
Homage to Beatrix Potter: six short pieces for wind ensemble (flute, oboe, 2 clarinets and bassoon). (Le Fleming, Christopher). *Chester. Unpriced* VNRG (B72-50263)
Homage to Tchaikovsky: for piano solo. (Pitfield, Thomas Baron). *Freeman. £0.20* QPJ (B72-51041)
Home from the range: for full chorus of mixed voices a cappella. (Wilson, Richard). *Schirmer: Chappell. Unpriced* EZDW (B72-50067)
Honulka, Kurt. La Clemenza di Tito. K.621: opera seria in due atti. (Mozart, Wolfgang Amadeus). *Bärenreiter. £3.75* CC (B72-50341)
Hooker, Brian. The vagabond king. - Come all you beggars. Song of the brigands. (Friml, Rudolf). *Feldman. £0.20* KDW (B72-50460)
Hop-a-long Jenny. (Judd, Margaret). *Bosworth. Unpriced* QPJ (B72-51037)
Hopkins, Antony. Sonatine for piano. *Oxford University Press. £0.45* QPEM (B72-50178) ISBN 0 19 372902 4
Hopkins, Gerard Manley.
Resurrection canticle: for sixteen solo voices. (Mellers, Wilfrid). *Galliard. £0.83* EZDH/LL (B72-50056)
The windhover: SATB unacc. (Paynter, John). *Oxford University Press. Unpriced* EZDW (B72-50414)
ISBN 0 19 343006 1
Hopkins, Jerry. Elvis: a biography. *4 Little Essex St., W.C.2: Open Gate Books. £1.95* AKGDW/HK/E(P) (B72-21779) ISBN 0 333 13617 9
Hopson, Hal H. O brother man, fold to thy heart thy brother: SATB. *Warner: Blossom Music. Unpriced* EZDH (B72-50054)
Horgan, Paul. Encounters with Stravinsky: a personal record. Abridged ed.. *Bodley Head. £3.00* BSV(N/XPS15) (B72-27437) ISBN 0 370 10299 1
Horn playing: a new approach. (Burden, John). *Paterson. Unpriced* WT/AC (B72-51246)
Horovitz, Joseph.
Concerto for euphonium. Euphonium concerto. *Novello. £1.25* WWPK/LF (B72-51249)
Quartet for strings no.5. String quartet no.5. *Novello. Unpriced* RXNS (B72-50230)
The search for the Nile. *Francis, Day and Hunter. £0.20* QPK/JS (B72-50617)
Sing unto the Lord a new song: motet for SATB with divisions, unaccompanied. *Novello. £0.35* EZDH (B72-50842)
Hors d'oeuvres: eight pieces for piano. (Drakeford, Richard). *Elkin. £0.30* QPJ (B72-50186)
Horton, John.
Carmen. - Avec la garde montante. Street boys' song = Choeur des gamins. (Bizet, Georges). *Schott. £0.60* JFE/NYFSRDW (B72-50913)
Mendelssohn chamber music. *British Broadcasting Corporation. £0.45* BMJAN (B72-15426)
ISBN 0 563 12205 6
Music. *Macmillan for the Anglo-American Primary Education Project. £0.60* A(VG) (B72-13853)
ISBN 0 333 13332 3
Hotteterre Le Romain, Jacques. L'Art de préluder sur la flûte. Op.7. - *Excerpts.* 48 Préludes in 24 keys: for treble recorder, (flute oboe). *Schott. £0.90* VSSPMJ (B72-51178)
Hovhaness, Alan.
Armenian rhapsody, no.3. Op.189: for string orchestra,. *Peters. £1.50* RXMJ (B72-50652)
Symphony no.2. Op.132. - Andante con moto. Mysterious mountain. *Associated Music. Unpriced* UMK (B72-50257)
Varak. Opus 47: violin and piano. *Peters. £1.00* SPJ (B72-50681)
How like an Angel came I down: anthem for SATB and organ. (Drayton, Paul). *Novello. £0.14* DH (B72-50357)
How to produce concert versions of Gilbert & Sullivan. (Taylor, Ian). *Hale. £3.50* BSWACF/E (B72-31878)
ISBN 0 7091 2973 4
Howells, Herbert.
Magnificat and Nunc dimittis 'Collegium magdalenae oxoniense': for SATB and organ. *Novello. £0.28* DGPP (B72-50814)
Magnificat and Nunc dimittis in B flat (for the Cathedral Church of Hereford): for SATB and organ,. *Novello. £0.21* DGPP (B72-50355)
Partita: for organ. *Novello. £1.00* RG (B72-51054)
Hoyland, Victor. EM: for 24 voices. *Universal. Unpriced* EZDW (B72-50864)
Hudson, Hazel.
Deep river; and, Wade in the water; and, Gonna lay down my burden: a quodlibet arranged from three negro spirituals for either trebles 1 and 2, or basses 1 and 2, or treble 1 and bass 2. *Ashdown. £0.09* FLDW/LC (B72-50431)
Nobody knows; and, Balm in Gilead: a quodlibet based on two negro spirituals, for either trebles 1 and 2, or basses 1 and 2, or treble 1 and bass 2. *Ashdown. £0.09* FLDW/LC (B72-50432)
Nursery rhymes with a new look. *Edwin Ashdown. Unpriced* JFDW/GK/AY (B72-50102)
Steal away - Were you there?: a quodlibet based on two negro spirituals, (for either trebles 1 and 2, or basses 1 and 2, or treble 1 and bass 2). *Ashdown. £0.10* FLDW/LC (B72-50430)
Steal away - Were you there?: a quodlibet based on two negro spirituals, (for either trebles 1 and 2, or basses 1 and 2, or treble 1 and bass 2). (Hudson, Hazel). *Ashdown. £0.10* FLDW/LC (B72-50430)
Hughes-Jones, Llifon. Ariodante. - Overture, 3rd section. Rigaudon. (Handel, George Frideric). *Bosworth. £1.80* MJ (B72-50958)
Hummel, Bertold.
Invocation 52: piano solo. *Simrock. Unpriced* QPJ (B72-50588)
Sonatina for violin & piano (1969). Sonatina for viola and piano. *Simrock. Unpriced* SQPK/AEM (B72-50693)
Sonatina for violin & piano (1969). Sonatina for violoncello and piano. *Simrock. Unpriced* SRPK/AEM (B72-50698)
Hummel, Johann Nepomuck. Concerto for bassoon in F major. Grand concerto: for bassoon and orchestra. *Musica rara. £2.50* VWPK/LF (B72-51193)
Humperdinck, Engelbert.
Hänsel and Gretel. *Studio Music. Unpriced* WMK/CC (B72-50774)
Hänsel and Gretel. - *Excerpts.* Hänsel and Gretel song book
by Engelbert Humperdinck. *Francis, Day and Hunter. £0.35* KDW (B72-50461)
Hansel and Gretel: a fairy opera in three acts. *Schott. £1.05* CC (B72-50340)
Hansel und Gretel. - *Excerpts.* Prelude. *Weinberger. Unpriced* WMJ (B72-51214)
Humphrey, Pelham. Musica Britannica: a national collection of music
Vol.35: Pelham Humfrey: Complete church music, II. *Stainer and Bell. Unpriced* C/AYD (B72-50794)
Humphreys, D L. I am the resurrection and the life: SAATB (unacc.). (Gibbons, Orlando). *Oxford University Press. Unpriced* EZDK (B72-50058)
ISBN 0 19 350323 9
Humphreys, Garry Paul. Singers: a directory of freelance amateur singers in London and the Home Counties '72. *14 Barlby Rd, W10 6AR: Autolycus Publications. £0.30* AB/E(YDC/BC) (B72-14106)
ISBN 0 903413 00 0
Humphries, Mary. A world that sings: an account of the 26 years of the International Musical Eisteddfod. *21 Duffryn Close, Cardiff CF2 6HT: John Jones Cardiff Ltd. £0.50* AD(YDKRL/WB/XPG26) (B72-22481)
ISBN 0 902375 24 5
Hungar, Paul. Sonata for violin & piano, no.2, in C major. Sonate Nr.2, C-Dur: für Violine und Klavier. *Peters Hinrichsen. £1.50* SPE (B72-50674)
Hunt, Edgar.
Chorische Bläserchule. Method for brass. (Schneider, Willy). *Schott. £0.50* WM/AC (B72-51194)
Der Fluyten Lust-Hof. Deel 1. - *Excerpts.* Pavane lachrymae: two settings with variations for solo decant recorder. (Eyk, Jacob van). *Schott. £0.45* VSRPMHVG/T (B72-50750)
Suite for treble recorder & string orchestra in A minor. Suite in A minor: for treble recorder and string orchestra. (Telemann, Georg Philipp). *Schott. £1.25* VSSPK/LG (B72-50279)
Hunt, Reginald.
More fun with tunes: couplings of national songs. *Boosey and Hawkes. £0.60* FDW/G/AYC (B72-50080)
Welcome Yule: carol for voices, violins or flutes, descant recorders, guitars, percussion and piano. *Ashdown. £0.09* FE/NYDSRDP/LF (B72-50424)
Huray, Peter le. *See* Le Huray, Peter.
Hurd, Michael. O come, let us sing unto the Lord: anthem for SATB and organ. *Novello. £0.10* DK (B72-50032)
Hurford, Peter.
Communion service, series 3. *Novello. £0.14* DGS (B72-50815)
Two sentences: for SATB with divisions and organ. *Novello. £0.10* DGSKAD (B72-50816)
Hurley, Bernard. The Romano Drum song book
Vol.1. *Romanestan Publications. £0.25* JFEZDW/GJ/AYCG (B72-50105)
Hyde, D E. Credidi: motet for SSAA, strings & organ continuo. (Porpora, Nicolò Antonio). *Novello. £0.35* DJ (B72-50029)
Hyfrydol. Hymn for our time: for three-part chorus of mixed voices with piano (or organ) accompaniment. (Prichard, Rowland H). *Schirmer: Chappell. Unpriced* DM (B72-50033)
Hymn for our time: for three-part chorus of mixed voices with piano (or organ) accompaniment. (Prichard, Rowland H). *Schirmer: Chappell. Unpriced* DM (B72-50033)
Hymns for the new generation. (Illsley, Derrick). *Rainbow Music. Unpriced* JFDM/GJ/AY (B72-50099)
Hymns for today: a selection of hymns from the television series 'A hymn for today'. *High-Fye Music. Unpriced* RK/DM/JS/AY (B72-50219)
Hymns of eternal truth: with music. *Sherborne Road Church Trust. Unpriced* DM/AY (B72-50369)
I am the resurrection and the life: SAATB (unacc.). (Gibbons, Orlando). *Oxford University Press. Unpriced* EZDK (B72-50058) ISBN 0 19 350323 9
I beheld her, beautiful as a dove: SATB unacc. (Willan, Healey). *Oxford University Press. Unpriced* EZDW (B72-50415) ISBN 0 19 343027 4
I call and cry to thee: anthem for SAATB. (Tallis, Thomas). *Novello. £0.17* EZDJ (B72-50845)
'I turned and saw all the injustices that are committed under the sun': ecclesiastical action for two speakers, bass soloist and orchestra. (Zimmerman, Bernd Alois). *Schott. £3.20* KGXE/MDE (B72-50945)
Ibsen, Henrik. Margrete's cradle-song. Op.4, no.2. (Holst, Gustav). *Bosworth. £0.20* KDW (B72-50925)
Ich spiele vom Blatt. Introduction to sight reading: at the piano or other keyboard instrument. (Keilmann, Wilhelm). *Litolff: Peters. Unpriced* Q/EG (B72-51017)
Ich weiss ein lieblich Engelspiel: Choralkonzert für Orgel. (Reda, Siegfried). *Bärenreiter. £1.50* RF (B72-50633)
Iconography no. 1: for two bass viols and harpsichord or two violoncellos and piano (or harpsichord). (Durkó, Zsolt). *Boosey and Hawkes. £1.00* STUNTPW (B72-51141)
Iconography no.2: for horn solo and chamber ensemble. (Durkó Zsolt). *Boosey and Hawkes. £1.50* NYENN (B72-51001)
If ye love me: SATB. (Tallis, Thomas). *Oxford University Press. Unpriced* EZDK (B72-50060)
ISBN 0 19 352138 5
Ihr Völker, hört: Kantate am Fest der Heiligen drei Könige, für mittlere Stimme, Querflöte und Basso continuo. (Telemann, Georg Philipp). *Bärenreiter. £1.00* KFVE/VRPLRDE/LFP (B72-50489)
I.L.E.A. *See* Inner London Education Authority.
Illsley, Derrick. Hymns for the new generation. *Rainbow Music. Unpriced* JFDM/GJ/AY (B72-50099)
Illy, Hedda. Concerto for organ in A Major. Op.9 No.1. Concerto 1, A major: for harpsichord (organ), two violins and basso continuo. (Sammartini, Giuseppe). *Bärenreiter. £2.15* RXMPRF (B72-50657)
Imagine. (Lennon, John). *Wise Publications, Music Sales. £0.95* KDW (B72-50464)
Imagine. (Lennon, John). *Wise Publications, Music Sales. £0.95* KDW (B72-50465)
Immortals of mankind series. *(F. Watts)* Reingold, Carmel Berman. Johann Sebastian Bach. *32 Palmer St., S.W.1: F. Watts. £1.50* BBC(N) (B72-22482)
ISBN 0 85166 320 6
Impromptus. (Bennett, Richard Rodney). *Universal. Unpriced* TSPMJ (B72-50249)
Improvisation: 'In memoriam Maurice de Sausmarez',. (Leighton, Kenneth). *Novello. £0.33* RJ (B72-51055)
Improvisation über ein mittelalterliches Lied 'Es sass ein edly maget schön'. Op 46: fur Gitarre. (Stingl, Anton). *Schott. Unpriced* TSPMJ (B72-50709)
In every corner sing. (Clifton, Geoffrey). *Nelson. Unpriced* DM/AY (B72-50367) ISBN 0 17 437012 1
In freezing winter night: carol for unison voices and piano. (Morris, Peter). *Elkin. Unpriced* JDP/LF (B72-50088)
In midst of woods: part-song for SSA and piano. (Blower, Maurice). *Elkin. £0.10* FDW (B72-50073)
In praise of Essex. (Stapleton, Eric). *Feldman. Unpriced* FDW (B72-50076)
In quires and places. (Mason, Phil). *1 Whitney Rd, Burton Latimer, Northants.: Phil Mason. £0.20* AD/LD/E (B72-07980) ISBN 0 9500388 1 4
Incorporated Society of Musicians. Careers with music. 2nd ed. *48 Gloucester Place, W1H 3HJ: Incorporated Society of Musicians. £0.70* A(MN) (B72-19609)
ISBN 0 902900 03 x
Index of musical wind-instrument makers. (Langwill, Lyndesay Graham). 3rd ed. revised, enlarged and illustrated. *7 Dick Place, Edinburgh EH9 2JS: L.G. Langwill. £5.00* AV/BC(M) (B72-12676)
ISBN 0 902153 01 3
Indian music: a vast ocean of promise. (Holroyde, Peggy). *Allen and Unwin. £5.25* BZF (B72-17505)
ISBN 0 04 780020 8
Individual note: of music, sound and electronics. (Oram, Daphne). *Queen Anne's Rd, Great Yarmouth, Norfolk: Galliard. £0.99* APV/D (B72-50001)
ISBN 0 85249 109 3
Inner London Education Authority. *Music Centre.* Instrumental teaching. *Ebury Bridge, S.W.1.: I.L.E.A. Music Centre. Free* AL/E(VC) (B72-26657)
ISBN 0 7168 0428 x
Instrumental teaching. (Inner London Education Authority. *Music Centre*). *Ebury Bridge, S.W.1.: I.L.E.A. Music Centre. Free* AL/E(VC) (B72-26657)
ISBN 0 7168 0428 x
Instruments of the orchestra. *(Benn)* Nelson, Sheila M. The violin and viola. *Benn. £3.00* AS/B(X) (B72-15430)
ISBN 0 510 36651 1
Instruments of the orchestra. (Fox, Lilla Margaret). *Lutterworth Press. £1.25* AM/B (B72-03315)
ISBN 0 7188 1710 9
Intende voci orationis mea: offertory for tenor solo and four-part chorus of mixed voices with organ or piano accompaniment. (Schubert, Franz). *Schirmer: Chappell. Unpriced* DGKAF (B72-50021)
International Association of Music Libraries. *United Kingdom Branch.* Directory of United Kingdom Branch members
1972. *c/o Michael Short, Haldane Library, Imperial College of Science and Technology, SW7 2AZ: International Association of Music Libraries, United Kingdom Branch. Free to members only* A(U/YC/BC) (B72-12968) ISBN 0 9502339 0 0

Introduction and allegro: for double bass and piano. (Berkeley, Lennox). *Yorke. Unpriced* SSPJ (B72-50244)
Introduction to sight reading: at the piano or other keyboard instrument. (Keilmann, Wilhelm). *Litolff: Peters. Unpriced* Q/EG (B72-51017)
Introduction to the double bass. (Elgar, Raymond). 3rd ed., revised and reprinted. *31 Charles Rd West, St Leonards-on-Sea, Sussex: R. Elgar. £1.26* ASS/B (B72-32463) ISBN 0 9502431 1 6
Introduction to the guitar. (Quine, Hector). *Oxford University Press. £0.80* TS/AC (B72-50245) ISBN 0 19 322325 2
Introduzione, aria e finale: für Violine und Orgel. (Genzmer, Harald). *Litolff: Peters. £1.80* SPLR (B72-50235)
Invocation 52: piano solo. (Hummel, Bertold). *Simrock. Unpriced* QPJ (B72-50588)
Inwood, Paul. Praise the Lord. (Ainslie, John). Revised ed. *Chapman. Unpriced* DM/LSB/AY (B72-50822) ISBN 0 225 65838 0
Isaac, Anthony. Spartak - Excerpts. The 'Onedin Line'. (Khachaturian, Aram). *Palace Music. £0.20* QPK (B72-50194)
Isaac, Heinrich. A la bataglia: for four instruments, ATTB, by Heinrich Isaac. *Pro musica. Unpriced* LNS (B72-50950)
Island love: duet for soprano and tenor. (McKellar, Kenneth). *Boosey and Hawkes. £0.35* JNEDW (B72-50920)
Isle joyeuse: piano solo. (Debussy, Claude). *Peters. Unpriced* QPJ (B72-51034)
Jackson, Francis.
  Can I not syng but hoy? Op. 40, no.2: a Christmas carol, SATB unacc. *Banks. £0.08* EZDP/LF (B72-50850)
  Soneta for organ in G minor. Op.35. Sonata in G minor. Op.35. *Oxford University Press. £1.50* RE (B72-50632) ISBN 0 19 375484 3
Jackson, Roy Garrick. Glory of Scotland. *Chappell-Solomon. £0.20* KDW (B72-50462)
Jackson, Stanley, *b.1910.* Caruso. *W.H. Allen. £3.50* AKGH/E(P) (B72-27439) ISBN 0 491 00664 0
Jacob, Gordon.
  Partita: for solo bassoon. *Oxford University Press. £0.35* VWPMG (B72-50296) ISBN 0 19 357364 4
  Quartet for piano and strings. *Novello. £2.75* NXNS (B72-50546)
  Seven bagatelles: for solo oboe. *Oxford University Press. £0.35* VTPMJ (B72-50286) ISBN 0 19 357366 0
  Sospan fach = The little saucepan: march: a prelude to a Welsh football match, for brass band. *Novello. £1.75* WMGM (B72-51196)
  A Swedish rhapsody: for brass band. *Novello. £3.40* WMJ (B72-51215)
Jacobean consort music: for recorders or viols
  Book 1: Five fantasias and two dances of three parts. *Stainer and Bell. £0.44* C/AYD (B72-50009)
  Book 2: Seven fantasias of four parts. *Stainer and Bell. £0.49* C/AYD (B72-50010)
Jacobi, Wolfgang. Jota: Spanish dance: accordion solo. *Charnwood Music. £0.30* RSPMHPD (B72-51071)
Jacobs, Arthur.
  The music yearbook: a survey and directory with statistics and reference articles
  1972/3. *Macmillan. £4.95* A(BC) (B72-21777) ISBN 0 333 13355 2
  A short history of Western music. *Penguin. £0.60* A(X) (B72-21774) ISBN 0 14 021421 6
  A short history of Western music: a listener's guide. *David and Charles. £3.75* A(X) (B72-30740) ISBN 0 7153 5743 3
Jacques, Michael. Divertimento for recorder quartet, no.3. Divertimento no.3: for recorder quartet (2 descant, treble & tenor). *Schott. £1.00* VSNS (B72-50742)
Jahresanfang in Japan: Trio für Flöte, Violoncello und Klavier (1969). (Okumara, Hajime). *Bosse: Eulenburg. £2.25* NURNT (B72-50533)
James, Burnett. Brahms - a critical study. *Dent. £3.00* BBT (B72-16139) ISBN 0 460 03953 9
Janis. (Dalton, David). *Calder and Boyars: New English Library. £1.25* AKDW/HHW/E(P) (B72-26094) ISBN 0 7145 0943 4
Járdányi, Pál. Sinfonietta for string orchestra. Sinfonietta per archi. *Boosey and Hawkes. Unpriced* RXMEM (B72-51088)
Jasper, Tony. Understanding pop. *S.C.M. Press. £1.95* A/GB(XPQ17) (B72-10327) ISBN 0 334 01728 9
Jauchzet dem Herrn, alle Welt: für zwei Soprane, zwei Violinen und Basso continuo. (Bernhard, Christoph). *Bärenreiter. £1.00* JNFLEE/SNTRDE (B72-50458)
Jauchzt, ihr Christen, seid vergnügt: Kantate am dritten Osterfreitag, für hohe Stimme, Violine und Basso Continuo. (Telemann, Georg Philipp). *Bärenreiter. £1.00* KFTE/SPLRDE (B72-50488)
Jazz: an introduction. (Lee, Edward). *25 Thurloe St., S.W.7: Kahn and Averill. £2.50* AMT(X) (B72-23639) ISBN 0 900707 11 9
Jazz in the movies: a tentative index to the work of jazz musicians for the cinema. (Meeker, David). *British Film Institute. £0.50* AMT/JR (B72-15718) ISBN 0 85170 030 6
Jazz master: a collection of famous piano solos from the golden age of jazz. (Mayerl, William). *Keith Prowse. £1.00* QPJ (B72-51040)
Jazz scene. (Fox, Charles). *Hamlyn. £1.75* AMT(X) (B72-24869) ISBN 0 600 02119 x
Jazz style in Kansas City and the Southwest. (Russell, Ross). *2 Brook St., W1Y 1AA: University of California Press. £5.95* AMT/E(M/YTSWK/XNF15) (B72-02169) ISBN 0 520 01853 2
Jefferson, Alan.
  Delius. *Dent. £2.25* BDL(N) (B72-05571) ISBN 0 460 03131 7
  The lieder of Richard Strauss. *Cassell. £1.75* BSUAKDW (B72-01564) ISBN 0 304 93735 5
Jelinek, Jerome. Chromatic fantasy in E major: violoncello. (Finney, Ross Lee). *Peters. £1.10* SRPMJ (B72-50702)
Jenkyns, Peter. Snakes: song for unison voices and piano. *Elkin. £0.07* JFDW (B72-50906)
Jennie's theme: from the film. (Ralston, Alfred). *Chappell. £0.25* QPK/JR (B72-51047)
Jentzsch, Wilfried. Concerto espressivo: für Viola und Orchester. *Peters: Hinrichsen. £4.00* MPSQF (B72-50523)
Jeremiah, Dorothy Adams. *See* Adams-Jeremiah, Dorothy.
Jergenson, Dale. The vision: full chorus and seven soloists. *Schirmer: Chappell. Unpriced* HY (B72-50083)
Jesu, der du meine Seele = Jesus, by thy Cross and Passion, S.78: cantata for 14. Sunday after Trinity. (Bach, Johann Sebastian). *Bärenreiter. £0.90* DE (B72-50349)
Jesus Christ superstar: a rock opera. (Webber, Andrew Lloyd). *Leeds Music. £1.25* KDW (B72-50119)
Jesus Christ the apple tree. (Holman, Derek). *Royal School of Church Music. Unpriced* JDK (B72-50440)
Jeux: pour (1 à 4) hautbois. (Amy, Gilbert). *Universal. Unpriced* VTN (B72-51181)
Jewish Music Research Centre. Yuval: studies of the Jewish Music Research Centre
  Vol.2. *Magnes Press: Distributed by Oxford University Press. £6.15* A(YBU) (B72-12719) ISBN 0 19 647627 5
Joachim, Joseph. Concerto for violin in D major. K.218. Konzert, D-dur: für Violine und Orchester. (Mozart, Wolfgang Amadeus). *Peters. Unpriced* SPK/LF (B72-51120)
Joan Sutherland. (Greenfield, Edward). *Allan. £1.50* AKFL/E(P) (B72-15424) ISBN 0 7110 0318 1
Johann Sebastian Bach. (Reingold, Carmel Berman). *32 Palmer St., S.W.1: F. Watts. £1.50* BBC(N) (B72-22482) ISBN 0 85166 320 6
John Dowland. (Poulton, Diana). *3 Queen Sq., WC1N 3AU: Faber and Faber Ltd. £12.00* BDT (B72-10999) ISBN 0 571 08711 6
John Field and Chopin. (Branson, David). *Barrie and Jenkins. £3.00* BCE(ZF) (B72-08531) ISBN 0 214 65343 9
John McCormack discography. (Roe, Leonard McDermott). *Oakwood Press. £1.20* AKGH/FD(P/WT) (B72-27620) ISBN 0 85361 106 8
Johns, Sybil Marian. A carol for to-day. *41 Padua Rd, Llandaff, Cardiff: S.M. Johns. Unpriced* JDP/LFP (B72-50089)
Johnson, David, *b.1942.* Music and society in lowland Scotland in the eighteenth century. *Oxford University Press. £3.30* A(YDLG/XF101) (B72-26090) ISBN 0 19 316401 9
Johnson, Reginald. Sinfonie musicali. Op.18. - *Excerpts.* Canzona - La Padovana: 8 recorders. (Viadana, Lodovico). *Universal. Unpriced* VSNN (B72-51169)
Johnson, Ronald. The book of the green man. Cloud canticles: for double chorus. (Mellers, Wilfrid). *Galliard. £0.83* EZDW (B72-50063)
Johnson, Thomas A.
  Children's corner - Excerpts. Golliwog's cake-walk. (Debussy, Claude). *Peters. Unpriced* QNV (B72-51022)
  Concerto for piano, no.17, in G major. K.453. Piano concerto, G major, no.17. K.453. (Mozart, Wolfgang Amadeus). *Peters. Unpriced* QNUK/LF (B72-51019)
  Toccata and fugue in D minor. D.565. (Bach, Johann Sebastian). *Peters. £0.40* QPK (B72-50606)
Johnson, Thomss Arnold. The vicar of Bray: piano duet. *Bosworth. Unpriced* QNV (B72-51021)
Johnstone, H Diack. Acquaint thyself with God: anthem for alto (or tenor) solo, chorus, and organ. (Greene, Maurice). *Novello. £0.17* DK (B72-50031)
Joio, Norman Dello. *See* Dello Joio, Norman.
Jolly, Cynthia. Folk music of Hungary. (Kodály, Zoltán). 2nd ed. *Barrie and Jenkins. £2.25* A/G(YG/XA1914 (B72-13442) ISBN 0 214 65327 7
Joly shepard: cantata no.5, for SATB and small orchestra or two pianos. (Kellam, Ian). *Novello. £0.60* DE/LF (B72-50351)
Jomelli, Nicolò. Il Parataio. - Overture. Sinfonia D-Dur: für Streichorchester und zwei Horner ad lib. *Peters Hinrichsen. £1.20* RXMJ (B72-50653)
Jones, Kelsey. Sonata da camera: for flute, oboe and harpsichord. *Peters. Unpriced* NWPNTE (B72-50992)
Jones, Llifon Hughes-. *See* Hughes-Jones, Llifon.
Jones, Robert, *fl.1597-1614.* The first booke of songes and ayres, 1600; and, The second booke of songs and ayres, 1601; and, Ultimum vale, 1605; and, A musicall dreame, 1609; and, The muses gardin, 1610. *Scolar Press. £12.00* ADW(YD/XE11) (B72-05573) ISBN 0 85417 559 8
Jong, Conrad de. Hist whist: for voice, flute, viola and percussion. *Schirmer: Chappell. Unpriced* KE/NYERNTDW (B72-50124)
Jonson, Ben. The noble nature: two part songs for SATB a cappella,. (Stoker, Richard). *Leeds Music. Unpriced* EZDW (B72-50065)
Joseph. - Ah, lorsque la mort trop cruelle. A crib-side carol. (Méhul, Etienne). *Novello. £0.07* DP/LF (B72-50375)
Joseph I, *Emperor.* Musikalische Werke der Kaiser Ferdinand III, Leopold I und Joseph I im Aufrage des K.K. Ministeriums für Cultur und Unterricht. (Ferdinand, *III, Emperor*). *Gregg. £18.00* C/AZ (B72-50335)
Josephs, Wilfred.
  The British Empire: echoes of Britannia's rule: title music from the BBC TV series. *Essex Music. £0.20* QPK/JS (B72-50198)
  Elegy for strings. Op.13. *Weinberger. Unpriced* RXMJ (B72-50223)
  Rail. Op.57: symphonic picture for orchestra. *Galaxy: Galliard. Unpriced* MM/JR (B72-50140)
  Requiem. Op.39: for solo bass-baritone, chorus, string quintet and orchestra. *Weinberger. Unpriced* EMDE/KDN (B72-50049)
Joshua. Josua: oratorio for four solo-voices, choir and orchestra
  by Georg Friedrich Händel. (Handel, George Frideric). *Peters. Unpriced* DD (B72-50810)
Jota: Spanish dance: accordion solo. (Jacobi, Wolfgang). *Charnwood Music. £0.30* RSPMHPD (B72-51071)
Joubert, John. Duo for violin and cello. Op.65. *Novello. £2.00* SPLSR (B72-50687)
Journal de printemps. - Suites 5, 6. Suites for four strings or wind instruments and basso continuo, nos.5 in G major, 6 in F major. (Fischer, Johann Caspar Ferdinand). *Bärenreiter. £1.50* NXNRG (B72-50545)
Judas kiss: for SATB choir, instrumentalists and soloists
  Part 1. (Garrick, Michael). *Robbins Music. Unpriced* CM/L (B72-50344)
  Part 2. (Garrick, Michael). *Robbins Music. Unpriced* CM/L (B72-50345)
  Part 3. (Garrick, Michael). *Robbins Music. Unpriced* CM/L (B72-50346)
Judd, Margaret. Hop-a-long Jenny. *Bosworth. Unpriced* QPJ (B72-51037)
Jugendalbum: für Klavier. (Nikolovski, Vlastimir). *Peters Hinrichsen. Unpriced* QPJ (B72-50602)
Junktim-Sätze: Doppelchörige Choralsätze, für bläser oder Sänger und Bläser. (Ehmann, Wilhelm). *Bärenveiter. £1.50* EWNDM/AY (B72-50390)
Kaan, Fred. Pilgrim praise: hymns. *Galliard. £1.54* DM/AY (B72-50034) ISBN 0 85249 108 5
Kadosa, Pál.
  Sonata for violin & piano, no.1. Op.5. Sonata no.1. Op.5: for violin and piano. *Boosey and Hawkes. £1.00* SPE (B72-50233)
  Suite for piano no.1. Op.1. *Boosey and Hawkes. £0.75* QPG (B72-50180)
  Suite for piano, no.3, Op.1, no.3. *Boosey and Hawkes. £0.50* QPG (B72-51030)
  Suite for violin and piano. Op.6. *Boosey and Hawkes. £1.00* SPG (B72-50679)
Kagel, Mauricio.
  Metapiece (Mimetics): für Klavier. *Universal. Unpriced* QPJ (B72-50187)
  Prima vista: für Diapositivbilder und unbestimmte Schallquellen. *Universal. Unpriced* LN (B72-50136)
Kalabis, Viktor. Sonata for trombone & piano. Op.32. Sonate für Posaune und Klavier. Opus 32. *Schott. £2.00* WUPE (B72-51248)
Kalinka: traditional Russian folksong. (Pitfield, Thomas Baron). *Charnwood Music. £0.22* RSPMJ (B72-51079)
Kallaway, Bill. London Philharmonic: music makers since 1932. *K. Mason. £2.50* AMM/E(QB/X) (B72-30072) ISBN 0 900534 75 3
Kalmár, László. Sonata for flute & piano. Sonate per flauto e pianoforte. *Boosey and Hawkes. £0.60* VRPE (B72-51162)
Kander, John. Cabaret: souvenir music album. *Valando Music. £0.75* KDW/JR (B72-50472)
Karkoschka, Erhard. Psylex (1968): für Mezzosopran, Flöte und Tonband. *Bosse: Bärenreiter. £2.25* KFNE/VRDX (B72-50479)
Kasandiev, Vasil. Complexi sonori: für Streicher. *Peters. £2.00* RXMJ (B72-50654)
Kasandjiev, Wassil. *See* Kasandiev, Vasil.
Kátyn epitaph. (Panufnik, Andrzej). *Boosey and Hawkes. £1.00* MMJ (B72-50517)
Keating, John. Spartak - Excerpts. The 'Onedin Line' theme. (Khachaturian, Aram). *Essex Music International. £0.20* QPK (B72-50195)
Keene, Christopher. El Cimarrón-Biography of the runaway slave Esteban Montejo: recital for four musicians. (Henze, Hans Werner). *Schott. £2.40* KE/NYERNSDX (B72-50933)
Keilmann, Wilhelm. Ich spiele vom Blatt. Introduction to sight reading: at the piano or other keyboard instrument. *Litolff: Peters. Unpriced* Q/EG (B72-51017)
Keith, Billy. Earl Scruggs and the five-string banjo. (Scruggs, Earl). *Music Sales. £1.75* TT/AC (B72-51154)
Kelemen, Milko. Floreal: für Orchester. *Peters. £2.40* MMJ (B72-50516)
Kellam, Ian. The joly shepard: cantata no.5, for SATB and small orchestra or two pianos. *Novello. £0.60* DE/LF (B72-50351)
Keller, Hans.
  Children's crusade = Kinderkreuzzug. Op.82: a ballad for children's voices and orchestra. (Britten, Benjamin). *Faber Music. Unpriced* FE/NYLDX (B72-50426)
  The prodigal son = Der verlorene Sohn. Op.81: third parable for church performance. (Britten, Benjamin). *Faber music. Unpriced* CC (B72-50011)
Kelly, Brian. Sancho Panza: orchestral overture. *Chappell. £4.25* MMJ (B72-50147)
Kelly, Bryan. Divertimento. *Novello. £3.80* WMJ (B72-50771)
Kelterborn, Rudolf.
  Quartet for strings, no.4. String quartet no.4. *Bärenreiter. £1.15* RXNS (B72-50668)
  Symphony no.2. Sinfonie 2: in two movements for large orchestra. *Bärenreiter. £3.15* MME (B72-50509)
Kendall, Alan. The world of musical instruments. *Hamlyn. £1.75* AL/B (B72-08532) ISBN 0 600 35957 3
Kennedy, Michael, *b.1926.* The autobiography of Charles Hallé, with correspondence and diaries. (Hallé, *Sir* Charles). *Elek. £3.25* A(P) (B72-31293)

ISBN 0 236 15448 6
Kensington concerto for brass band. (Ball, Eric). *Boosey and Hawkes. £3.75* WMJ (B72-50768)
Kereki, Gabor. Songs for living and words of worship: a hymn and worship book for the young. (Knight, Sydney H). *The Lindsey Press. £1.25* JFDM/LSL/AY (B72-50100)
Kerridge, William Henry. Arnold Schoenberg. (Wellesz, Egon). 1st ed. reprinted. *Queen Anne's Rd, Great Yarmouth, Norfolk: Galliard Ltd. Unpriced* BSET (B72-01561) ISBN 0 85249 104 2
Kershaw, Doug. Lou'siana man: the Doug Kershaw songbook. *Collier Books: Collier-Macmillan. £0.90* KDW (B72-50111) ISBN 0 02 061050 5
Keyboard instruments: studies in keyboard organology. (Ripin, Edwin M). *Edinburgh University Press. £3.00* APW/B (B72-15427) ISBN 0 85224 202 6
Keyboard music. (Matthews, Denis). *Penguin. £0.75* APW/ED(X) (B72-10332) ISBN 0 14 021250 7
Keyboard music. (Matthews, Denis). *David and Charles. £3.50* APW/ED(X) (B72-15428) ISBN 0 7153 5612 7
Khachaturian, Aram.
Children's album: for piano solo. *Peters. £0.60* QPJ (B72-50589)
Concerto-rhapsody for cello. Konzert-Rhapsodie: für Violoncello und Orchester,. *Peters: Hinrichsen. £2.00* SRPK (B72-50697)
Spartak. - Adagio. For my love. *Plantagenet music. £0.20* KDW (B72-50112)
Spartak - Excerpts. The 'Onedin Line'. *Palace Music. £0.20* QPK (B72-50194)
Spartak - Excerpts. The 'Onedin Line' theme. *Essex Music International. £0.20* QPK (B72-50195)
Spartak-Adagio. The Adagio from Spartacus. (For my love). *Feldman. Unpriced* WMK (B72-50309)
Trio for clarinet, violin & piano (1932). Trio für Klarinette, Violine und Klavier (1932). *Peters Hinrichsen. £2.00* NUVNT (B72-50537)
Kiesewetter, Peter. Szenen: für Flöte, Oboe und Klavier. *Bosse: Bärenreiter. £4.75* NWPNT (B72-50542)
Killmayer, Wilhelm. Sinfonia 1: Fogli per orchestra; and, Sinfonia 2: Ricordanze. *Schott. £1.90* MMJ (B72-50970)

Kimball, Robert. Cole: a biographical essay. (Gill, Brendan). *Joseph. £7.50* BPNN (B72-24253) ISBN 0 7181 1021 8
Kindermann, Jurgen. Twelve easy pieces for piano duet. Op.3 and Op.10. (Weber, Carl Maria von, *Freiherr*). *Barenreiter. £1.25* QNV (B72-50564)
Kindersley, Biddie. A Dorset book of folk songs. (Brocklebank, Joan). *English Folk Dance and Song Society. £0.20* JEZDW/G/AYDFK (B72-50448) ISBN 0 85418 042 7
King Arthur. The music in King Arthur: a dramatic opera (1691),. (Purcell, Henry). *Novello. £1.50* CC (B72-50342)
Kings: SSATB (acc. or unacc.). (Cornelius, Peter). *Oxford University Press. Unpriced* DP/LF (B72-50373) ISBN 0 19 343029 0
Kirk, E Vickers. Give us, O Lord. (Dexter, Harry). *Ashdown. £0.09* FDH (B72-50868)
Kitchin, Therese. Monsieur de la plume: fragments from the life of Robert Louis Stevenson: music for children's voices and piano. (Rowley, Alec). *Ashdown. Unpriced* CN (B72-50800)
Klangspiel 1: für Streicher. (Wangenheim, Volker). *Peters. £2.20* RXMJ (B72-50655)
Klebe, Giselher. Fantasie und Lobpreisung. Op.58: für Orgel. *Bärenreiter. £1.25* RJ (B72-50641)
Klemm, Eberhardt. Selected piano works
Volume 5: Douze études. (Debussy, Claude). *Peters Hinrichsen. £1.85* QPJ (B72-50578)
Klepper, Jochen. Neujahrslied 'Der du die Zeit in Handen hast'. (Reda, Siegfried). *Bärenreiter. £0.05* EZDP/LGM (B72-50407)
Kluvetasch, Margarete. Sonata for flute, viola & harp. (Debussy, Claude). *Peters: Hinrichsen. £2.00* NVRNTE (B72-50539)
Knight, Gerald. Come, let us all this day/ melody and bass by J.S. Bach, words by J. Troutbeck interludes and inner parts by Gerald H. Knight; and, Prepare thyself, Zion, from the Christmas Oratorio. (Bach, Johann Sebastian). *Royal School of Church Music. Unpriced* JDH (B72-50439)
Knight, Sydney H. Songs for living and words of worship: a hymn and worship book for the young. *The Lindsey Press. £1.25* JFDM/LSL/AY (B72-50100)
Kocsár, Miklos. Repliche: per flauto e zimbalo ungherese (o clavicembalo) by Miklos Kocsár. *Boosey and Hawkes. £0.85* VRPLTWT (B72-50738)
Kodály, Zoltán.
The arms of Hungary: SATB unaccompanied. *Boosey and Hawkes. £0.05* EZDW (B72-50412)
Eve, my sweet: S.fl unaccompanied. *Boosey and Hawkes. £0.05* FEZDW (B72-50428)
False spring: SSA unaccompanied. *Boosey and Hawkes. £0.05* FEZDW (B72-50429)
Folk music of Hungary. 2nd ed. *Barrie and Jenkins. £2.25* A/G(YG/XA1914 (B72-13442) ISBN 0 214 65327 7
God's mercy: T. Bar. B. unaccompanied. *Boosey and Hawkes. £0.09* GEZDH (B72-50435)
The good housewife: folk-song, S.S. unaccompanied. *Boosey and Hawkes. £0.05* FLEZDW (B72-50434)
Greeting on St John's day: SAB unaccompanied. *Boosey and Hawkes. £0.05* EZDW (B72-50413)
Grow, tresses = Hajinšvesztö: SSA unaccompanied. *Boosey and Hawkes. £0.05* FEZDW (B72-50888)
Mid the oak trees: folk song SSA unaccompanied. *Boosey and Hawkes. y0.05* FEZDW (B72-50427)
Pentatonic music
Vol.3: 100 Cheremissian melodies. *Boosey and Hawkes. £0.30* JFEZDW/PP (B72-50917)
Wine, sweet wine = Méz, méz: SSSAAA unaccompanied. *Boosey and Hawkes. Unpriced* FEZDW (B72-50889)
Kol Nidrei. Opus 47. (Bruch, Max). *Peters. Unpriced* SQPK (B72-51129)
Kol Nidrei. Opus 47. (Bruch, Max). *Peters. Unpriced* VVPK (B72-51190)
Kolneder, Walter.
Sonatas for violin & harpsichord. Op.2. Sonata accademiche. Op.2: für Violine und bezifferten Bass, Violine und Klavier (Cembalo, Orgel) mit Violoncello ad libitum
Sonata 10, F-Dur. (Veracini, Francesco Maria). *Peters Hinrichsen. £0.90* SPE (B72-50676)
Sonatas for violin & harpsichord. Op.2. Sonata accademiche. Op.2: für Violine und bezifferten Bass, Violine und Klavier (Cembalo, Orgel) mit Violoncello ad libitum
Sonata 11, E-Dur. (Veracini, Francesco Maria). *Peters Hinrichsen. £0.90* SPE (B72-50677)
Komar, Arthur. Dichterliebe. (Schumann, Robert). *Chappell. Unpriced* KDW (B72-50469) ISBN 0 900277 04 1
Komm, Jesu, komm. S.229: motet for two four-part mixed choirs. (Bach, Johann Sebastian). *Bärenreiter. £0.40* EZDH (B72-50393)
Komorous, Rudolf. York: per flauto, oboe (ossia tromba), fagotto, mandolina, pianoforte, triangolo e contrabasso. *Universal. Unpriced* NYDPNP (B72-50999)
Konietzny, Heinrich. Toccatina for two pianos. *London: Simrock. Unpriced* QNU (B72-50562)
Konzertmusik. Op.41: für Bläsorchester. (Hindemith, Paul). *Schott. £1.60* UMJ (B72-50713)
Kosmogonia: für Soli, Chor und Orchester. (Penderecki, Krysztof). *Schott. Unpriced* EMDX (B72-50837)
Kovács, Imre. Flute music for beginners. *Boosey and Hawkes. £0.85* VRPK/AAY (B72-50737)
Kozeluch, Leopold. La Ritrovata figlia. Op. 39. - *Excerpts.* Andantino. *Charnwood Music. Unpriced* RSPMK (B72-51082)
Krentz, Alfred.
Das wohltemperierte Klavier. S.846-893
Band 1. (Bach, Johann Sebastian). *Peters: Hinrichsen. Unpriced* PWP/Y (B72-51003)
Band 2. (Bach, Johann Sebastian). *Peters: Hinrichsen. Unpriced* PWP/Y (B72-51004)
Kriegslieder = Tears of battle: for solo tenor, mixed chorus, trumpet and percussion. (Victory, Gerard). *Fairfield Music. £1.00* KGHE/NYHXSDX (B72-50133)
Krol, Bernhard. Vier Gesänge auf den Heiligen Geist. Op.45: für gemischten Chor und Orgel. *Simrock. Unpriced* DH (B72-50818)
Kröll, Georg. Cantio: für Bariton und 2 Violoncello, Kontrabass und Orgel. *Bosse: Bärenreiter. £2.25* KGNE/NXNSDH (B72-50495)
Krupp, Karlheinz. London - Bridge: Lieder und Tänze aus Grossbritannien, für Akkordeon mit 2. Stimme ad lib. *Schott. £0.80* RSPMK/DW/AYC (B72-51084)
Kuhlau, Friedrich.
Introduction and variations on a theme from Carl Maria von Weber's 'Euryanthe' Op.63. *Bärenreiter. £1.50* VRP/T (B72-50730)
Quartet for four flutes in E major. Op.103. Quartett, E-dur: für vier Flöten. *Litolff: Peters. £3.00* VRNS (B72-50265)
Kümmerling, Harald. Biblische Motetten: für das Kirchen jahr
Band 1: Erster Advent bis letzter Sonntag nach Epiphanias. (Ameln, Konrad). *Bärenreiter. £2.00* EZDH/AYE (B72-50398)
Kupferberg, Herbert. The Mendelssohns: three generations of genius. *W.H. Allen. £3.50* BMJB(N) (B72-17503) ISBN 0 491 00732 9
Kusik, Larry.
The godfather. - Love theme. Speak softly, love. (Rota, Nina). *Chappell. £0.25* KDW (B72-50468)
The godfather. - Waltz. Come live your life with me. (Rota, Nino). *Famous Chappell. £0.20* QPK/DW/JR (B72-50613)
Kyrie: for choir and piano. (Patterson, Paul). *Weinberger. Unpriced* DGB (B72-50813)
L.A. *See* Library Association.
Laing, Dave. Buddy Holly. *Studio Vista. £1.40* AKGDW/GB/E(D) (B72-07981) ISBN 0 289 70129 5
Lamentation over Boston; and, Jargon: SATB (or male chorus or mixed quartet). (Billings, William). *Peters Hinrichsen. £0.75* EZDW (B72-50411)
Lanchbery, John. Tales of Beatrix Potter - Excerpts. Peter Rabbit and the tales of Beatrix Potter: music from the film. *EMI Film Music. Unpriced* QPK/JR (B72-50197)
Landon, Christa. Six minuets for wind instruments
Vol.1: Nos.1 - 3. (Schubert, Franz). *Bärenreiter. £1.20* WMHR (B72-50764)
Landon, Howard Chandler Robbins. Haydn. *3 Queen Sq., WC1N 3AU: Faber and Faber Ltd. £1.75* BHE(N) (B72-09750) ISBN 0 571 08361 7
Landscapes: a choral suite for mixed voices (with optional oboe). (Paynter, John). *Oxford University Press. Unpriced* EZDW (B72-50064)
Landshoff, Ludwig.
Fifteen 2-part inventions. S.772-786. (Bach, Johann Sabastian). *Peters. £0.45* PWPJ (B72-50554)
Fifteen 3-part inventions (sinfonias). S.787-801. (Bach, Johann Sebastian). *Peters. £0.45* PWPJ (B72-50555)
Lane, Philip. Three carols. *Galliard. £0.50* FDP/LF/AY (B72-50874)
Langwill, Lyndesay Graham. An index of musical wind-instrument makers. 3rd ed. revised, enlarged and illustrated. *7 Dick Place, Edinburgh EH9 2JS: L.G. Langwill. £5.00* AV/BC(M) (B72-12676) ISBN 0 902153 01 3
Larbalestier, Philip George.
The heart's awakening: a song cycle. *Regina Music. £0.35* KDW (B72-50463)
Life's olympics: a demonstration service of song and praise for young people. *John Blackburn. Unpriced* JFDM (B72-50097)
Largo al factotum. (Rossini, Gioacchino Antonio). *Charnwood Music. Unpriced* RSPMK/DW (B72-51083)

Lasocki, David.
Concerto for oboe & string orchestra in G major. Concerto in G major: for oboe, strings and basso continuo. (Besozzi, Alessandro). *Musica rara. Unpriced* RXMPVTF (B72-51092)
Concerto for oboe & string orchestra in G major. Concerto in G major: for oboe, strings and basso continuo. (Besozzi, Alessandro). *Musica rara. £1.00* VTPK/LF (B72-51184)
Concerto for treble recorder in G minor. P.402. Concerto in G minor: for flute, (clarinet), oboe and bassoon or treble recorder, oboe and basso continuo ad lib. (Vivaldi, Antonio). *Musica rara. Unpriced* NWNSF (B72-50165)
Quartet for flute & strings in D major. Op.56, no.1. Quartet in D major: for flute, violin, viola and cello. (Danzi, Franz). *Musica rara. Unpriced* NVRNS (B72-50988)
Quartet for flute & strings in F major. Op.17, no. 2. Quartet in F major. Op.17, no.2: for flute, violin, viola and cello. (Pleyel, Ignaz). *Musica rara. Unpriced* NVRNS (B72-50989)
Lassus & Palestrina. (Sharp, Geoffrey B). *Novello. £0.15* BLC(N) (B72-18916) ISBN 0 85360 038 4
Last, Joan.
Tom Tiddler's tunes: little piano pieces
Book 1. *Bosworth. Unpriced* QPJ (B72-50188)
Book 2. *Bosworth. Unpriced* QPJ (B72-50189)
The young pianist: a new approach for teachers and students. 2nd ed. *Oxford University Press. £1.40* AQ/E(VC) (B72-10331) ISBN 0 19 318420 6
Latin American album: for B flat trumpet(s) and piano. (Siebert, Edrich). *Boosey and Hawkes. £0.95* WSPK/AAY (B72-50324)
Laudate Dominum. K.339, no.5. (Mozart, Wolfgang Amadeus). *Novello. £0.10* FDGKJ (B72-50867)
Laurents, Arthur. West Side story: a musical. *Heinemann Educational. £0.50* BBMMACM (B72-08533) ISBN 0 435 23529 x
Laurie, Margaret. King Arthur. The music in King Arthur: a dramatic opera (1691),. (Purcell, Henry). *Novello. £1.50* CC (B72-50342)
Lawes, William. Fantasia and air. *Faber. Unpriced* VSNRK (B72-50741)
Lawrence, Ian. Fantasia and air. (Lawes, William). *Faber. Unpriced* VSNRK (B72-50741)
Lawrence, Roy. Sing life, sing love. (Lewis, Peter). *Holmes McDougall. Unpriced* DM/AY (B72-50370) ISBN 0 7157 1005 2
Lawson, Peter. Valentia extramaterial: flute, piano, 2 or 4 percussion. *Peters. £1.50* NYFR (B72-50551)
Lawton, Sidney Maurice. Old English trumpet tunes: for trumpet in B flat. *Oxford University Press. £0.80* WSPK/AAY (B72-50323)
Layton, Robert.
The stereo record guide
Vol.7: Composer index A-Ma. *Squires Gate, Station Approach, Blackpool, Lancs. FY82 SP: Long Playing Record Library Ltd. £1.95* A/FF(WT) (B72-08760) ISBN 0 901143 02 2
Twentieth century composers
Vol.3: Britain, Scandinavia and the Netherlands. *Weidenfeld and Nicolson. £3.50* A(XM71) (B72-28679) ISBN 0 297 99377 1
Le Fanu, Nicola. Chiaroscuro: for piano. *Novello. £1.00* QPJ (B72-50190)
Le Fleming, Christopher. Homage to Beatrix Potter: six short pieces for wind ensemble (flute, oboe, 2 clarinets and bassoon). *Chester. Unpriced* VNRG (B72-50263)
Le Huray, Peter.
If ye love me: SATB. (Tallis, Thomas). *Oxford University Press. Unpriced* EZDK (B72-50060) ISBN 0 19 352138 5
The sources of English church music, 1549-1660. (Daniel, Ralph T). *82 High Rd, N2 9BZ: Stainer and Bell for the British Academy. £8.00* AD/LD(TE/XDXJ112) (B72-22016) ISBN 0 903000 10 5
'Lead us, heavenly Father ...': chorale improvisation. (Macer, Aubrey William John). *Cramer. £0.24* RJ (B72-51056)
Lear, Edward. Three limericks: for voices, instruments and piano. (Pehkonen, Elis). *Lengnick. £0.25* HYE/LDW (B72-50437)
Learning the recorder. (Martin, Nancy). *F. Warne. £1.00* AVS/E (B72-14738) ISBN 0 7232 1280 5
Lebermann, Walter.
Concerto for clarinet & string orchestra, no.1, in F major. Konzert No.1, F - Dur: für Klarinette (C oder B). (Stamitz, Carl). *Schott. £3.00* RXMPVVF (B72-51094)
Concerto for viola in C major. Konzert, C-Dur: für Viola, Streicher, 2 Oboen und 2 Hörner. (Hoffstetter, Roman). *Schott. £1.80* MPSQF (B72-50975)
Madrigali et ricercari a quattro voci. - *Excerpts.* Ricercari a quattro, nos.6 & 7: for four recorders (descant, treble, tenor and bass). (Gabrieli, Andrea). *Schott. £1.20* VSNS (B72-51170)
Lechner, Leonard. Deutsche Sprüche von Leben und Tod: four-part mixed chorus. *Bärenreiter. £0.70* EZDU (B72-50408)

Lechner, Leonhard. Das Hohelied Salomonis: for four part mixed chorus. *Bärenreiter. £0.70* EZDU (B72-50409)
Lee, Edward. Jazz: an introduction. *25 Thurloe St., S.W.7: Kahn and Averill. £2.50* AMT(X) (B72-23639) ISBN 0 900707 11 9
Lee, Noël. Sonatine for piano solo. *Oxford University Press. £0.50* QPEM (B72-50179) ISBN 0 19 373205 x
Lees, Benjamin. Odyssey: piano solo. *Boosey and Hawkes. £0.65* QPJ (B72-51038)
Leeson, Jane E. Loving shepherd of thy sheep: unison anthem for children's voices with organ (or piano). (Pasfield, William Reginald). *Ashdown. £0.05* JFDM (B72-50450)
Legrenzi, Giovanni.
Sonata for two trumpets, bassoon & string orchestra, in A minor. Lib.3. Op.8, 'La Buscha'. Sonata, 'La Buscha': for 2 trumpets (cornetti), bassoon, and strings. *Musica rara. £1.00* NWXPNSE (B72-50994)
Sonata for two trumpets, bassoon & string orchestra, in A minor. Lib.3, Op.8, 'La Buscha'. Sonata, 'La Buscha': for 2 trumpets (cornetti), bassoon, and strings. *Musica rara. £1.00* RXMPWNTE (B72-51096)
Leighton, Kenneth.
Improvisation: 'In memoriam Maurice de Sausmarez',. *Novello. £0.33* RJ (B72-51055)
Six studies: study-variations. Op.56: for piano. *Novello. £0.90* QP/T (B72-51026)
Veris gratia. Opus 9: suite for oboe, cello & strings. *Novello. £1.60* MRG (B72-50529)
Leinert, Friedrich. Six German songs. Op.103: for voices, clarinet and piano. (Spohr, Louis). *Bärenreiter. £0.90* KE/VVPDW (B72-50474)
Lekberg, Sven.
The spring and the fall: for voice and piano. *Schirmer Chappell. Unpriced* KDW (B72-50113)
The truth of the Lord endureth forever: for four-part chorus of mixed voices a cappella. *Schirmer: Chappell. Unpriced* EZDK (B72-50059)
Lendvay, Kamilló. Quartet for strings. String quartet. *Boosey and Hawkes. £2.00* RXNS (B72-50231)
Lennon, John.
The Beatles year: piano vocal or easy organ. *Northern Songs. Unpriced* QPK/DW (B72-50612)
Imagine. *Wise Publications, Music Sales. £0.95* KDW (B72-50464)
Imagine. *Wise Publications, Music Sales. £0.95* KDW (B72-50465)
Lenz, Wilhelm von. The great piano virtuosos of our time. *Regency Press. £1.20* AQ/E(M/XHH45) (B72-13443) ISBN 0 7212 0138 5
Leopold I, *Emperor.* Musikalische Werke der Kaiser Ferdinand III, Leopold I und Joseph I im Aufrage des K.K. Ministeriums für Cultur und Unterricht. (Ferdinand, *III, Emperor*). *Gregg. £18.00* C/AZ (B72-50335)
Lerche, Juliane. New compendium of piano technique Book 3: Alternation of the hands. *Peters: Hinrichsen. £1.25* Q/AF (B72-50560)
Lerich, Rudolf. Sonatina for descant recorder & piano. Sonatine in F major: for descant recorder or oboe and piano. *Barenreiter. £0.60* VSRPEM (B72-50749)
Let us with a gladsome mind: anthem for harvest or other festivals. (Nicholson, *Sir* Sydney Hugo). *Royal School of Church Music. Unpriced* DH/LP (B72-50028)
Let's play recorders: a simple recorder tutor for very young children, including 28 folk songs to play. (Blackburn, Marie). *Feldman. £0.20* VS/AC (B72-50269)
Levas, Santeri. Sibelius, a personal portrait. *Dent. £2.95* BSH(N) (B72-11000) ISBN 0 460 03978 4
Levin, Robert D. Allegro for clarinet, two violins, viola & cello in B flat major.K.Anh.91. Allegro in B flat.K.Anh.91: fragment of a quintet for clarinet, two violins, viola and violoncello. (Mozart, Wölfgang Amadeus). *Nagel. £2.00* NVVNR (B72-50541)
Lewenthal, Raymond. Marcia funèbre d'un Pappagallo. Funeral march on the death of a parrot: for four-part chorus of mixed voices with organ, or piano, or woodwind accompaniment. (Alkan, Charles Henri Valentin). *Schirmer: Chappell. Unpriced* D X (B72-50015)
Lewis, Peter. Sing life, sing love. *Holmes McDougall. Unpriced* DM/AY (B72-50370) ISBN 0 7157 1005 2
Lewitskaja, W. Symphony no.7. Opus 131. Sinfonie Nr.7. Opus 131. (Prokofiev, Sergei). *Peters: Hinrichsen. Unpriced* MME (B72-50963)
Liberated woman's songbook: seventy-seven singable folk songs about women and their battles with husbands, lovers, the devil, the system ... and themselves with lyrics, guitar arrangements, and entertaining photographs. (Silverman, Jerry). *Collier Books: Collier-Macmillan. £1.25* KFE/TSDW/G/AY (B72-50128) ISBN 0 02 082040 2
Libman, Lillian. And music at the close: Stravinsky's last years: a personal memoir. *Macmillan. £3.50* BSV(N/XPU13) (B72-30741) ISBN 0 333 14304 3
Library Association. Research publications. *(Library Association)* Long, Maureen W. Musicians and libraries in the United Kingdom. *Library Association. £2.25(£1.80 to members of the Library Association)* A(U/YC) (B72-08765) ISBN 0 85365 355 0
Libro llamado arte de tañer fantasia. (Thomas de Sancta Maria). *Gregg. £14.40* AQT/E (B72-30746) ISBN 0 576 28229 4
Lidholm, Ingvar. Quattro pezzi per violoncello & pianoforte. *Universal. Unpriced* SRPJ (B72-51137)
Liebermann, Rolf. Les Echanges. Symphony, (Les Echanges): for percussion-ensemble (7 players). *Simrock. Unpriced* XNPK (B72-50330)
Liebner, János. Mozart on the stage. *Calder and Boyars. £3.25* BMSAC (B72-14736) ISBN 0 7145 0758 x
Lieder of Brahms. (Harrison, Max). *Cassell. £1.75* BBTAKDW (B72-16878) ISBN 0 304 93876 9
Lieder of Richard Strauss. (Jefferson, Alan). *Cassell. £1.75* BSUAKDW (B72-01564) ISBN 0 304 93735 5
Lieder of Schumann. (Walsh, Stephen). *Cassell. £1.75* BSGAKDW (B72-01563) ISBN 0 304 93736 3
Lieutenant Kije. Op.60. - Wedding of Kije, Troika. Two pieces. (Prokofiev, Sergei). *Boosey and Hawkes. £3.00* WMK/JR (B72-50312)
Life's olympics: a demonstration service of song and praise for young people. (Larbalestier, Philip George). *John Blackburn. Unpriced* JFDM (B72-50097)
Like a mad animal ...: for double bass, piano, violin, viola, alto flute and clarinet. (Bland, William). *Yorke. Unpriced* NUPNQ (B72-50983)
Lilac time: operetta in three acts. (Schubert, Franz). *Chappell: Weinberger. Unpriced* CF (B72-50012)
Linde, Hans Martin.
Sonata for violin & basso continuo in D minor. Op.5 no.12. La Follia: for treble recorder and basso continuo. (Corelli, Arcangelo). *Schott. £1.00* VSSPK/AE (B72-51177)
Venezianische Musik um 1600: Stücke von Frescobaldi, Castello und Fontana, für Sopran - oder Tenorblockflöte oder andere Melodieinstrumente und Basso continuo. *Schott. £1.10* VSRP/AYJV(XE) (B72-51175)
Lindum suite. (Stephens, Denzil). *Novello. £3.50* WMG (B72-50762)
Lines: for string quartet, or quartet of stringed instruments. (Wolff, Christian). *Peters. Unpriced* RXNS (B72-51109)
Lipphardt, Walther.
Deutsche Sprüche von Leben und Tod: four-part mixed chorus. (Lechner, Leonard). *Bärenreiter. £0.70* EZDU (B72-50408)
Das Hohelied Salomonis: for four part mixed chorus. (Lechner, Leonhard). *Bärenreiter. £0.70* EZDU (B72-50409)
Lisbon: for wind five-some (flute, oboe, clarinet, horn and bassoon). (Grainger, Percy Aldridge). *Schott. £0.65* UNRK/DW (B72-50724)
List, Erich.
Concerto for flute, no.2, in D major. K.314. Konzert Nr.2, D dur, für Flöte und Orchester. K.314. (Mozart, Wolfgang Amadeus). *Peters. Unpriced* VRPK/LF (B72-51168)
Sonata for flute, viola & harp. (Debussy, Claude). *Peters Hinrichsen. £2.00* NVRNTE (B72-50539)
Liszt, Franz.
Ab irato; and, Two concert studies for piano solo. *Bärenreiter. £0.90* QPJ (B72-50590)
Complete organ works. *Boosey and Hawkes. £2.50* R/AZ (B72-50630)
Etudes d'execation transcendante, no.4. Mazeppa for piano solo. *Bärenreiter. £0.65* QPJ (B72-50591)
Etudes d'exécution transcendante, no.5. Feux follets: for piano solo. *Bärenreiter. £0.65* QPJ (B72-50592)
Etudes d'exécution transcendante, no.7. Eroica: for piano solo. *Bärenreiter. £0.50* QPJ (B72-50593)
Liszt,, Franz. Etudes d'exécution transcendante, no.8. Wilde Jagd: for piano solo. *Bärenreiter. £0.65* QPJ (B72-50594)

Liszt, Franz.
Etudes d'exécution transcendante, no.9. Ricordanza: for piano solo. *Bärenreiter. £0.65* QPJ (B72-50595)
Etudes d'exécution transcendante, no.10. Study in F minor for piano solo. *Bärenreiter. £0.65* QPJ (B72-50596)
Etudes d'exécution transcendante, no.11. Harmonies du Soir: for piano solo. *Bärenreiter. £0.50* QPJ (B72-50597)

Grand duo concertant. R.462; based on the romance 'Le Marin' by Philippe Lafont; with, Epithalam. (Wedding Music). R.466: for piano and violin. *Bärenreiter. £2.00* SPK (B72-50684)
Grandes études de Paganini: for piano solo. *Bärenreiter. £1.25* QPJ (B72-50598)
Missa solennis: S.A.T.B. solos, chorus and orchestra. *Gregg. Unpriced* EMDG (B72-50050)
Piano works
Vol.1: Studies 1. *Bärenreiter. £2.00* QP/AZ (B72-50566)
Vol.2: Studies 2. *Bärenreiter. £2.00* QP/AZ (B72-50567)

Trois études de concert: trois caprices poetiques, for piano solo. *Bárenreiter. £0.90* QPJ (B72-50599)
Two episodes from Lenau's Faust, no.2. - First Mephisto waltz. Mephisto waltz no.1. *Peters. £0.50* QPHW (B72-50182)
Liszt. (Rostand, Claude). *Calder and Boyars. £2.50* BLJ(N) (B72-27438) ISBN 0 7145 0342 8
Little dance suite. Op.45: for piano. (Pike, Eleanor Franklin). *Ashdown. Unpriced* QPHG (B72-50181)
Little king's carol: calypso. (Verrall, Pamela). *British and Continental. Unpriced* FE/XDP/LF (B72-50883)
Little music and big music. *See* MacLellan, John A.
Little saucepan. *See* Jacob, Gordon.
Little shepherd: SATB. (Marriott, Michael J). *Cramer. £0.09* DP/LF (B72-50038)
Little suite: for two descant recorders & treble recorders. (Simpson, John). *Feldman. Unpriced* VSNTG (B72-50272)
Liturgische Gesänge. (Eben, Peter). *Bärenreiter. £1.25* FDGK (B72-50416)
Livermore, Ann. A short history of Spanish music. *43 Gloucester Cres., N.W.1: Duckworth. £4.45* A(YK/X) (B72-24251) ISBN 0 7156 0634 4
Lives of Haydn, Mozart and Metastasio. (Stendhal). *Calder and Boyars. £5.50* BHE(N) (B72-14734) ISBN 0 7145 0349 5
Lloyd Webber, Andrew. *See* Webber, Andrew Lloyd.
Lobb, John. Three short solos: for piano. *Bosworth. £0.15* QPJ (B72-51039)
Lobe den Herren, den mächtigen König der Ehren: Choralkantate für vierstimmigen gemischten Chor, Gemeindegesang (ad lib.), sechstimmigen Bläserchor und Orgel. (Zipp, Friedrich). *Bärenreiter. y1.75* EWNPRDE (B72-50391)
Lobos, Heitor Villa-. *See* Villa-Lobos, Heitor.
Lockyer, Malcolm. Pathfinders march: theme in the TV series. *Berry Music, Campbell, Connelly. £0.20* QPK/JS (B72-50618)
Lollipop tree: two-part song (with optional recorders, glockenspiel, xylophone and timps). (Verrall, Pamela Motley). *Bosworth. £0.175* FDW (B72-50877)
London - Bridge: Lieder und Tänze aus Grossbritannien, für Akkordeon mit 2. Stimme ad lib. (Krupp, Karlheinz). *Schott. £0.80* RSPMK/DW/AYC (B72-51084)
London, Christa. Two songs: original pitch (high). (Schubert, Franz). First edition. *Bärenreiter. £0.50* KFTDW (B72-50484)
London. *Inner London Education Authority. See* Inner London Education Authority.
London College of Music. Examinations in pianoforte playing and singing sight reading tests, as set throughout 1971: Grades I-VIII and diplomas. *Ashdown. £0.30* Q/EG/AL (B72-50170)
London Philharmonic: music makers since 1932. (Kallaway, Bill). *K. Mason. £2.50* AMM/E(QB/X) (B72-30072) ISBN 0 900534 75 3
London sparrow: unison song for children. (Ager, Laurence). *Cramer. £0.06* JFDW/GJ (B72-50451)
London Symphony. (Vaughan Williams, Ralph). Centenary ed. *Stainer & Bell. £2.50* MME (B72-50510)
Long, Kenneth R. The music of the English church. *Hodder and Stoughton. £7.00* AD/LD(YD/X) (B72-06767) ISBN 0 340 14962 0
Long, Kenneth Roy. Fight the good fight. *Royal School of Church Music. Unpriced* JDM (B72-50087)
Long, Marguerite. At the piano with Debussy. *Dent. £2.75* BDJAQ (B72-03316) ISBN 0 460 03821 4
Long, Maureen W. Musicians and libraries in the United Kingdom. *Library Association. £2.25(£1.80 to members of the Library Association)* A(U/YC) (B72-08765) ISBN 0 85365 355 0
Longmire, John. Nautical suite. - *Excerpts.* Ship ahoy: for piano. *Bosworth. Unpriced* QPGM (B72-51031)
Looking glass: for organ. (Raxach, Enrique). *Hinrichsen. £1.25* RJ (B72-50213)
Looking-glass: for organ. (Raxach, Enrique). *Peters. Unpriced* RJ (B72-51057)
Lorca, Federico García. *See* García Lorca, Federico.
Lord, David. The history of the Flood: for narrator, chorus, percussion, and piano duet. *Oxford University Press. £1.50* ENYLDE (B72-50052) ISBN 0 19 337380 7
Lord, how long wilt thou be angry?: anthem for SAATB (unaccompanied). (Hayes, William). *£0.10* EZDK (B72-50847)
Lord Jesus, think on me: for mixed chorus and organ. (Talmadge, Charles L). *Galaxy: Galliard. Unpriced* DM (B72-50820)
Louisiana polka. (Siebert, Edrich). *Studio Music. Unpriced* WMHVH (B72-50765)
Lou'siana man: the Doug Kershaw songbook. (Kershaw, Doug). *Collier Books: Collier-Macmillan. £0.90* KDW (B72-50111) ISBN 0 02 061050 5
Love came down at Christmas: SATB. (Rutter, John). *Oxford University Press. Unpriced* DP/LF (B72-50040) ISBN 0 19 343025 8
Love one another/ by S.S. Wesley; words from I St Peter and, O worship the Lord/ by John Travers; words from Psalm 96. (Wesley, Samuel Sebastian). *Royal School of Church Music. Unpriced* JDK (B72-50441)
Love, the sentinel: for chorus a capella sic. (Williamson, Malcolm). *Weinberger. £0.15* EZDW (B72-50066)
Love will find out the way: for S.A. and piano. (Thiman, Eric Harding). *Novello. £0.10* FDW (B72-50077)
Lovers. Op.43: for baritone, mixed chorus and orchestra. (Barber, Samuel). *Schirmer. Unpriced* DX (B72-50045)
Loving shepherd of thy sheep: unison anthem for children's voices with organ (or piano). (Pasfield, William Reginald). *Ashdown. £0.05* JFDM (B72-50450)
Lowe, Augustus. Perpetuity: a church solo. *Edgar Newgass Distributed by Paterson. £0.20* KDH (B72-50922)
Luboff, Norman. Yellow bird. *Frank Music. Unpriced* WMK/DW (B72-50777)
Lucia di Lammermoor. (Cammarano, Salvatore). *Dover Publications: Constable. £1.00* BDRAC (B72-22490) ISBN 0 486 22110 5
Lumen Christi. Op. 15: a meditation on the festival of Easter: organ solo. (Routh, Francis). *Boosey and Hawkes. £1.30* R/LL (B72-50631)
Lumsden, Alan.
Canzoni 1 & 2: for 2 trumpets and 2 trombones (2 trumpets, horn & trombone). (Gabrieli, Giovanni). *Musica rara. £0.90* WMJ (B72-50307)
Canzoni 3 and 4: for 2 trumpets and 2 trombones (2 trumpets, horn & trombone). (Gabrieli, Giovanni). *Musica rara. £0.90* WMJ (B72-50308)
Lute-book lullaby: for treble voices and organ. (Pehkonen, Elis). *Chappell. Unpriced* FLDP/LF (B72-50891)
Lyons, Lyn. My story. (Frazier, Kathleen). *12 Forde Park, Newton Abbot, Devon: K. Frazier. £0.50* AQ/E(P) (B72-26661) ISBN 0 9502464 0 9
Lyric movement: for viola and small orchestra. (Holst, Gustav). *Oxford University Press. £0.75* SQPK (B72-50237) ISBN 0 19 357254 0
Lyric pieces for the young: for piano. (Dello Joio, Norman). *Boosey and Hawkes. £0.50* QPJ (B72-50583)
Lyric pieces. Op. 12. Lyrical pieces. Opus 12: for piano.

(Grieg, Edvard). *Chappell. £0.45* QPJ (B72-51036)
McBride, William B. Secondary school music: philosophy, theory and practice. (Glenn, Neal Edwin). *Prentice-Hall. £4.00* A(VK) (B72-50333) ISBN 0 13 797522 8
McCabe, John.
Aspects of whiteness: cantata for SSAATTBB and piano, by John McCabe. *Novello. £1.75* DX (B72-50380)
Aubade. (Study no.4): for piano. *Novello. £0.45* QPJ (B72-50600)
Dance-movements: for horn, violin & piano. *Novello. £2.25* NUXTNTH (B72-50162)
Intermezzi for piano. *Novello. Unpriced* QPJ (B72-50191)
Norwich canticles: Magnificat; and, Nunc dimittis: for SATB unaccompanied. *Novello. £0.17* EZDGPP (B72-50841)
Sonata for clarinet, cello & piano (1969). *Novello. £1.50* NUVNTE (B72-50161)
Sostenuto: study no.2 (1969), for piano. *Novello. £0.50* QPJ (B72-50601)
McCaldin, Denis. Stravinsky. *Novello. £0.15* BSV(N) (B72-12718) ISBN 0 85360 009 0
McCarthy, Tony. Bawdy British folk songs. *Wolfe. £0.60* KE/TSDW/K/G/KDX/AYC (B72-50938) ISBN 0 7234 0492 5
MacDonald, Malcolm. Havergal Brian: perspective on the music. *5 Mayfield Rd, W.3: Triad Press. £1.25* BBTN (B72-04569) ISBN 0 902070 03 7
Macer, Aubrey William John. 'Lead us, heavenly Father ...': chorale improvisation. *Cramer. £0.24* RJ (B72-51056)
Machlis, Joseph. The nymph and the farmer. La Fée et le cultivateur = The nymph and the farmer, Op.72: a lyric legend. (Cherepnin, Alexander). *Boosey and Hawkes. £4.50* CC (B72-50337)
McIntyre, William. Sing life, sing love. (Lewis, Peter). *Holmes McDougall. Unpriced* DM/AY (B72-50370) ISBN 0 7157 1005 2
McKellar, Kenneth. Island love: duet for soprano and tenor. *Boosey and Hawkes. £0.35* JNEDW (B72-50920)
Mackerras, Colin P. The rise of the Peking Opera, 1770-1870: social aspects of the theatre in Manchu China. *Clarendon Press. £6.00* BZHKAC(XFYK101) (B72-31290) ISBN 0 19 815137 3
MacLellan, Gene. Put your hand in the hand: for mixed chorus SATB. *Ardmore and Beechwood. Unpriced* ENYGNTDH (B72-50387)
MacLellan, John A. Ceol beag agus ceol mor = Little music and big music. *Paterson. Unpriced* VY/AY (B72-50297)
MacLeod, Anne Campbell. Skye boat song: air (founded on an old 'chanty'). *Cramer. £0.18* RK/DW (B72-50220)
Maconchy, Elizabeth.
3 easy duets: for two cellos. *Faber Music. Unpriced* SRNU (B72-51133)
3 easy duets: for two violas. *Faber Music. Unpriced* SQNU (B72-51122)
3 easy pieces: for violin and viola. *Faber Music. Unpriced* SPLSQ (B72-51121)
4 easy trios: for two violins and viola, or violin and two violas. *Faber Music. Unpriced* RXNT (B72-51110)
Sonatina for harpsichord. *Lengnick. £0.50* QRPEM (B72-51050)
Maddox, Hugh.
Alive! *Queen Anne's Rd, Southtown, Great Yarmouth, Norfolk: Distributed by Publishing Services Partnership for Galliard Ltd. £0.17* BMDACM/LGZ (B72-10329) ISBN 0 85249 122 0
Alive!. - *Excerpts.* Five new songs. *Galliard. £0.27* JE/TSDW (B72-50445) ISBN 0 85249 141 7
Madsen, Charles H. Experimental research in music. (Madsen, Clifford K). *Prentice-Hall. Unpriced* A/B (B72-21770) ISBN 0 13 295097 9
Madsen, Clifford K. Experimental research in music. *Prentice-Hall. Unpriced* A/B (B72-21770) ISBN 0 13 295097 9
Magnificat and Nunc dimittis 'Collegium magdalenae oxoniense': for SATB and organ. (Howells, Herbert). *Novello. £0.28* DGPP (B72-50814)
Magnificat and Nunc dimittis: for SATB. (Blow, John). *Novello. £0.17* DGPP (B72-50023)
Mahler, Gustav.
Complete horn parts to 1st & 2nd symphonies and Lieder eines fahrenden Gesellen. *Paxman. £1.50* WT (B72-50787)
Symphony no.5 in C minor. - *Excerpts.* Adagietto. *Ashdown. Unpriced* RK (B72-50217)
Mairants, Ivor.
The carman's whistle. (Byrd, William). *Fenette Music: Breitkopf and Härtel. Unpriced* TSNTK (B72-50247)
Six part suite: for solo guitar. *Fenette Music, Breitkopf and Härtel. Unpriced* TSPMG (B72-51147)
Valses poéticas. (Granados, Enrique). *British and Continental. Unpriced* TSPMK/AHW (B72-51153)
Mandyczewski, Eusebius.
Complete shorter works for solo piano. (Brahms, Johannes). *Dover Publications: Constable. £2.00* QP/AZ (B72-51023)
Complete sonatas and variations for solo piano. (Brahms, Johannes). *Dover Publications: Constable. £2.00* QP/AZ (B72-51024)
Complete transcriptions, cadenzas and exercises for solo piano. (Brahms, Johannes). *Dover Publications: Constable. £2.00* QP/AZ (B72-51025)
Mantilla: Spanish serenade: accordion solo. (Blair, Jimmy). *Charnwood Music. Unpriced* RSPMJ (B72-51076)
Mar, Norman Del. *See* Del Mar, Norman.
Mar la mar: per soprano, mezzo-soprano e 7 strumenti. (Berio, Luciano). *Universal. Unpriced* JNEE/NVPNPDW (B72-50106)
Marcello, Benedetto. Sonata for cello & basso continuo in C major. Sonata no.6. *Peters. Unpriced* VVPK/AE (B72-51191)
March, Ivan.
The stereo record guide
Vol.7: Composer index A-Ma. *Squires Gate, Station Approach, Blackpool, Lancs. FY82 SP: Long Playing Record Library Ltd. £1.95* A/FF(WT) (B72-08760) ISBN 0 901143 02 2
The third Penguin guide to bargain records. (Greenfield, Edward). *Penguin. £0.60* A/FD(WT) (B72-21267) ISBN 0 14 003454 4
Marcia funèbre d'un Pappagallo. Funeral march on the death of a parrot: for four-part chorus of mixed voices with organ, or piano, or woodwind accompaniment. (Alkan, Charles Henri Valentin). *Schirmer: Chappell. Unpriced* D (B72-50015)
Margetts; (hymn). (Spencer, Sheila R). *Flying Dragon Publications. £0.04* DM (B72-50366)
Margrete's cradle-song. Op.4, no.2. (Holst, Gustav). *Bosworth. £0.20* KDW (B72-50925)
Mark: für Klavier. (Bahk, Junsang). *Peters. £2.80* QPJ (B72-50579)
Marlow, Richard. O Lord God: anthem for SATB unaccompanied). *Novello. £0.07* EZDK (B72-50848)
Marriott, Michael J. Little shepherd: SATB. *Cramer. £0.09* DP/LF (B72-50038)
Marsh, Mary Val. Explore and discover music: creative approaches to music education in elementary, middle, and junior high schools. *Macmillan (N.Y.): Collier-Macmillan. £2.25* A(VF) (B72-00905) ISBN 0 02 376270 5
Marshall, Nicholas. Arion and the dolphins: for unison choir and instruments. *Chester. Unpriced* CQN (B72-50348)
Marshall, Philip. Three short improvisations: for organ. *Ashdown. Unpriced* RJ (B72-50212)
Martin, Nancy. Learning the recorder. *F. Warne. £1.00* AVS/E (B72-14738) ISBN 0 7232 1280 5
Marx, Karl. Neujahrslied 'Der du die Zeit in Handen hast'. (Reda, Siegfried). *Bärenreiter. £0.05* EZDP/LGM (B72-50407)
Maschera, Florentino. Libro primo de canzoni da sonare, nos.5, 7. Two canzonas: for 2 trumpets and 2 trombones (2 trumpets, horn and trombone). *Musica rara. £0.70* WNS (B72-51232)
Maschera, Florentio. Libro primo de canzoni da sonare, nos.13, 12. Two canzonas: for 2 trumpets and 2 trombones (2 trumpets, horn and trombone). *Musica rara. £0.80* WNS (B72-51233)
Maschwitz, Eric. Good-night Vienna: an operetta in three acts. (Posford, George). *Keith Prowse. £1.25* CF (B72-50797)
Mason, Marilyn.
Five fantasies: for organ
No.3: Advice which the hours of darkness give. (Finney, Ross Lee). *Peters. £1.00* RJ (B72-50638)
No.5: Each answer hides future questions. (Finney, Ross Lee). *Peters. £1.00* RJ (B72-50640)
Mason, Phil. In quires and places. *1 Whitney Rd, Burton Latimer, Northants.: Phil Mason. £0.20* AD/LD/E (B72-07980) ISBN 0 9500388 1 4
Mass: a theatre piece for singers, players and dancers. (Bernstein, Leonard). *Amberson: Chappell. Unpriced* CM (B72-50013)
Mass for all ages and Offertory hymn. (Rock, Gordon F). *Gordon F. Rock. Unpriced* JE/TSDG (B72-50094)
Mass of life. Eine Messe des Lebens = A mass of life: für Sopran, Alt, Tenor, Bariton, gemischten Chor und grosses Orchester. (Delius, Frederick). *Boosey and Hawkes. £6.00* EMDX (B72-50384)
Massey Music and Gramophone Record Library.
List of brass and military band works available for loan. *Central Library, Burnley, Lancs.: Burnley Public Libraries. £0.15* AWM(TC) (B72-03562) ISBN 0 9501268 4 5
A list of multiple copies of vocal music available for loan. 2nd ed. *Central Library, Burnley, Lancs.: Burnley Public Libraries. £0.125* AD(TC) (B72-03560) ISBN 0 9501268 5 3
List of orchestral works available for loan. 2nd ed. *Central Library, Burnley, Lancs.: Burnley Public Libraries. £0.125* AM(TC) (B72-03561) ISBN 0 9501268 6 1
Master musician series. *(Dent)* Clapham, John, *b.1908.* Smetana. *Dent. £2.10* BSIM (B72-15423) ISBN 0 460 03133 3
Master musicians series. *(Dent)* Jefferson, Alan. Delius. *Dent. £2.25* BDL(N) (B72-05571) ISBN 0 460 03131 7
Mastering the piano: a guide for the amateur. (Bruxner, Mervyn). *Faber. £2.25* AQ/E (B72-28012) ISBN 0 571 09629 8
Masters, Stanley Smith-. *See* Smith-Masters, Stanley.
Mathias, William. A Babe is born. Op.55: S.A.T.B. *Oxford University Press. Unpriced* DP/LF (B72-50039) ISBN 0 19 343023 1
Mattfield, Julius. Tom Sawyer suite: for B flat clarinet and piano. (Collis, James). *Boosey and Hawkes. £1.25* VVPG (B72-50757)
Matthews, Betty. The organs and organists of Wimborne Minster, 1408-1972. *9 St Winifred's Rd, Bournemouth BH2 6NY: Kenneth Mummery Ltd. £0.30* AR/B(YDFKWB) (B72-20310) ISBN 0 9502449 0 2
Matthews, David. The prodigal son = Der verlorene Sohn. Op.81: third parable for church performance. (Britten, Benjamin). *Faber music. Unpriced* CC (B72-50011)
Matthews, Denis.
Keyboard music. *Penguin. £0.75* APW/ED(X) (B72-10332) ISBN 0 14 021250 7
Keyboard music. *David and Charles. £3.50* APW/ED(X) (B72-15428) ISBN 0 7153 5612 7
Maurer, Ludwig. 12 kleine Stücke. Twelve little pieces for brass quintet
Book 1. *Novello. £2.70* WNR (B72-51224)
Maw, Nicholas. Scenes and arias: for soprano, mezzo-soprano, contralto and orchestra. *Boosey and Hawkes. £7.50* JNFDE/MDW (B72-50107)
Max, Wenzel. Deutsche Volksweisen aus Südmähren: im Auftrag des deutschen Volksliederarchivs. *Bärenreiter. £1.00* JEZDW/G/AYFSM (B72-50449)
Maxwell Davies, Peter. *See* Davies, Peter Maxwell.
May, Helmut. Sinfonie da chiesa. Op. 5. - *Excerpts.* Sinfonia 1 und 9, for strings and basso continuo. (Bononcini, Giovanni Battista). *Schott. £1.40* RXME (B72-51087)
Mayerl, William. The jazz master: a collection of famous piano solos from the golden age of jazz. *Keith Prowse. £1.00* QPJ (B72-51040)
Maynard, John. So much to sing: over 50 songs for young people. *Vanguard Music. Unpriced* JFDM/AY (B72-50098)
Mazeppa for piano solo. (Liszt, Franz). *Bärenreiter. £0.65* QPJ (B72-50591)
Mazzola, Caterino. La Clemenza di Tito. K.621: opera seria in due atti. (Mozart, Wolfgang Amadeus). *Bärenreiter. £3.75* CC (B72-50341)
Meditation on 'Austria' by Haydn: for brass band. (Bevan, Clifford). *Feldman. Unpriced* WMJ (B72-50304)
Medley of folk-songs. (Stuart, Forbes). *Longman. Unpriced* JDW/G/AY (B72-50444) ISBN 0 582 15331 x
Meeker, David. Jazz in the movies: a tentative index to the work of jazz musicians for the cinema. *British Film Institute. £0.50* AMT/JR (B72-15718) ISBN 0 85170 030 6
Méhul, Etienne. Joseph. - Ah, lorsque la mort trop cruelle. A crib-side carol. *Novello. £0.07* DP/LF (B72-50375)
Meilhac, H. Carmen. - Avec la garde montante. Street boys' song = Choeur des gamins. (Bizet, Georges). *Schott. £0.60* JFE/NYFSRDW (B72-50913)
Mellers, Wilfrid.
Cloud canticles: for double chorus. *Galliard. £0.83* EZDW (B72-50063)
Resurrection canticle: for sixteen solo voices. *Galliard. £0.83* EZDH/LL (B72-50056)
Melville, Herman. Aspects of whiteness: cantata for SSAATTBB and piano, by John McCabe. (McCabe, John). *Novello. £1.75* DX (B72-50380)
Menagerie: three part-songs for SATB (unaccompanied). (Bush, Geoffrey). *Elkin. £0.40* EZDW (B72-50062)
Mendelssohn, Felix. A midsummer night's dream. Excerpts. Wedding march. *Ashdown. Unpriced* RK/KDD (B72-50221)
Mendelssohn chamber music. (Horton, John). *British Broadcasting Corporation. £0.45* BMJAN (B72-15426) ISBN 0 563 12205 6
Mendelssohns: three generations of genius. (Kupferberg, Herbert). *W.H. Allen. £3.50* BMJB(N) (B72-17503) ISBN 0 491 00732 9
Menotti, Gian Carlo. Triplo concerto a tre. *Schirmer. Unpriced* MMF (B72-50141)
Menuhin, Yehudi.
Partita for viola on themes of Walton. (Williamson, Malcolm). *Weinberger. Unpriced* SQPMG (B72-51130)
Violin: six lessons with Yehudi Menuhin. *38 Russell Sq., W.C.1: Faber Music Ltd. £2.50* AS/CY (B72-11002) ISBN 0 571 10000 7
Mephisto waltz no.1. (Liszt, Franz). *Peters. £0.50* QPHW (B72-50182)
Merchant, W Moelwyn. Puer natus: SSAATTBB (or SSAA or TTBB). (Hoddinott, Alun). *Oxford University Press. Unpriced* DP/LF (B72-50374) ISBN 0 19 343030 4
Merci, Luidgi. *See* Mercy, Louis.
Mercy, Louis. Sonata for cello & basso continuo in A minor. Op.3, no.6. Sonata in A minor: for cello (or bassoon) and continuo (harpsichord or piano). *Schott. Unpriced* SRPE (B72-50241)
Merewether, Richard. Complete horn parts to 1st & 2nd symphonies and Lieder eines fahrenden Gesellen. (Mahler, Gustav). *Paxman. £1.50* WT (B72-50787)
Merrill, William P. Hyfrydol. Hymn for our time: for three-part chorus of mixed voices with piano (or organ) accompaniment. (Prichard, Rowland H). *Schirmer Chappell. Unpriced* DM (B72-50033)
Merwein, Georg. Trio for piano, flute and cello. Op.29. Grand trio: for piano, flute and cello. (Pleyel, Ignaz Joseph). *Musica rara. Unpriced* NURNT (B72-50159)
Messe des Lebens = A mass of life: für Sopran, Alt, Tenor, Bariton, gemischten Chor und grosses Orchester. (Delius, Frederick). *Boosey and Hawkes. £6.00* EMDX (B72-50384)
Mestrel, Billy. The godfather. - Waltz. Come live your life with me. (Rota, Nino). *Famous Chappell. £0.20* QPK/DW/JR (B72-50613)
Metamorphosis. (Standford, Patric). *Novello. £0.33* RJ (B72-51058)
Metapiece (Mimetics): für Klavier. (Kagel, Mauricio). *Universal. Unpriced* QPJ (B72-50187)
Metastasio, Pietro. La Clemenza di Tito. K.621: opera seria in due atti. (Mozart, Wolfgang Amadeus). *Bärenreiter. £3.75* CC (B72-50341)
Method for brass. (Schneider, Willy). *Schott. £0.50* WM/AC (B72-51194)
Methode der Musikgeschichte. (Adler, Guido). *Gregg. £6.60* A(VX) (B72-03925) ISBN 0 576 28180 8
Méthodes pour apprendre à jouer de la contre-basse. *Excerpts.* Sonate für Viola und Klavier. (Corrette, Michel). *Schott. Unpriced* SQPE (B72-51126)
Metzger, Hans-Arnold. Choralbuch zum Evangelischen Kirchengesangbuch: mit den Begleitsätzen des Württembergischen Choralbuches bearbeitet von Karl

Gerok und Hans-Arnold Metzger und mit Begleitsätzen zu den Liedern des Anhangs zum Rheinisch-Westfälisch-Lippischen Gesangbuch. (Rödding, Gerhard). *Bärenreiter. Unpriced* DM/LSET/AY (B72-50371)

Mexican shuffle. (Stone, Pol). *Peter Maurice. Unpriced* WMK (B72-50772)

Meyer, C F. Chor-Duette. Opus 22, 2: für gemischten Stimmen teilweise mit Violine oder Flöte. (Burkhard, Willy). *Bärenreiter. £0.40* ESDW (B72-50388)

Meylan, Raymond.

Allegro in F: für Klavier. (Donizetti, Gaetano). *Litolff: Peters. £0.80* QPJ (B72-50185)

Arianna: Kantate für Sopran, zwei Violinen und Basso continuo. (Scarlatti, Alessandro). *Peters. £2.00* KFLE/SNTPWDX (B72-50477)

La Clemenza di Scipione. - Infelice! in van m'affano. Arsinda: Rezitativ und Arie, für Sopran und Orchester. (Bach, Johann Christian). *Peters. £3.50* KFLE/MDW (B72-50475)

Miall, Antony. The parlour song book: a casquet of vocal gems. (Turner, Michael R). *Joseph. £5.00* KDW/GB/AY(XHS64) (B72-50931) ISBN 0 7181 0381 5

Michaels, Jost. Concertino for clarinet in F minor. Concertino in F minor for clarinet and orchestra. (Molique, Bernhard). *Bärenreiter. £1.50* VVPK/LF (B72-50758)

Micheelsen, Hans Friedrich. Gelobet seist du, Jesu Christ: Choralmotette für vier-bis sechsstimmigen Chor a cappella. *Bärenreiter. £0.60* EZDH (B72-50395)

Michella: accordion solo. (Crossman, Gerald). *Charnwood Music. Unpriced* RSPMJ (B72-51077)

Mickelson, Paul. Pat Boone rapture theme songs. *Marshall, Morgan and Scott. £0.40* KDW/L/AY (B72-50123) ISBN 0 551 05159 0

Mid the oak trees: folk song SSA unaccompanied. (Kodály, Zoltán). *Boosey and Hawkes. y0.05* FEZDW (B72-50427)

Middleton, James Roland. Sanctify, O Lord: a chorister's prayer. *Royal School of Church Music. Unpriced* FDH (B72-50417)

Middleton, Richard. Pop music and the blues: a study of the relationship and its significance. *Gollancz. £4.00* A/GB(ZF) (B72-29416) ISBN 0 575 01442 3

Midsummer night's dream. Excerpts. Wedding march. (Mendelssohn, Felix). *Ashdown. Unpriced* RK/KDD (B72-50221)

Mies, Paul.

Quartet for strings in C major. Op.59, no.3. String quartet in C major. Op.59/3. (Beethoven, Ludwig van). *Bärenreiter. £0.45* RXNS (B72-50662)

Quartet for strings in E flat major. Op.74. String quartet in E flat major. Op.74. (Beethoven, Ludwig van). *Bärenreiter. £0.45* RXNS (B72-50663)

Quartet for strings in F major. Op.59, no.1. String quartet in F major. Op.59/1. (Beethoven, Ludwig van). *Bärenreiter. £0.60* RXNS (B72-50665)

Quartet for strings in F minor. Op.95. String quartet in F minor. Op.74. (Beethoven, Ludwig van). *Bärenreiter. £0.45* RXNS (B72-50666)

Millay, Edna St Vincent. The spring and the fall: for voice and piano. (Lekberg, Sven). *Schirmer: Chappell. Unpriced* KDW (B72-50113)

Miller, Peter. Two carols for children. Op216: for unison voices, piano, recorder and percussion. *Keith Prowse. £0.25* JFE/NYFSDP/LF (B72-50912)

Milligan, Spike. Chant for Spike Milligan: for voices and instruments. (Dennis, Brian). *Universal. Unpriced* XDW (B72-51250)

Milton, John. Let us with a gladsome mind: anthem for harvest or other festivals. (Nicholson, *Sir* Sydney Hugo). *Royal School of Church Music. Unpriced* DH/LP (B72-50028)

Mini Musik: for two percussionists. (Fink, Siegfried). *Schott. £1.00* XNU (B72-51251)

Miniature scores:.

Bach, Johann Christian. Symphony in B flat major. (Overture, Lucio Silla). Op.18, no.2. *Eulenburg. £0.40* MRE (B72-50525)

Bach, Johann Sebastian. Das wohltemperierte Klavier. S.846-893

Band 1. *Peters: Hinrichsen. Unpriced* PWP/Y (B72-51003)

Bach, Johann Sebastian. Das wohltemperierte Klavier. S.846-893

Band 2. *Peters: Hinrichsen. Unpriced* PWP/Y (B72-51004)

Beethoven, Ludwig van. Quartet for strings in C major. Op.59, no.3. String quartet in C major. Op.59/3. *Bärenreiter. £0.45* RXNS (B72-50662)

Beethoven, Ludwig van. Quartet for strings in E flat major. Op.74. String quartet in E flat major. Op.74. *Bärenreiter. £0.45* RXNS (B72-50663)

Beethoven, Ludwig van. Quartet for strings in E minor. Op.59, no.2. String quartet in E minor. Op.59/2. *Bärenreiter. £0.45* RXNS (B72-50664)

Beethoven, Ludwig van. Quartet for strings in F major. Op.59, no.1. String quartet in F major. Op.59/1. *Bärenreiter. £0.60* RXNS (B72-50665)

Beethoven, Ludwig van. Quartet for strings in F minor. Op.95. String quartet in F minor. Op.74. *Bärenreiter. £0.45* RXNS (B72-50666)

Beethoven, Ludwig van. Symphony no.5 in C minor. Op. 67. *Chappell. £1.75* MME (B72-50962) ISBN 0 900277 08 4

Beethoven, Ludwig van. Trio for piano, flute & bassoon in G major. K-H37. *Eulenburg. £0.60* NWPNT (B72-50166)

Berkeley, Lennox. Windsor variations: for chamber orchestra. *Chester. Unpriced* MR/T (B72-50976)

Berlioz, Hector. Episode de la vie d'un artiste. Fantastic symphony. *Chappell. Unpriced* MME (B72-50507) ISBN 0 900277 02 5

Bruckner, Anton. Overture in G minor. *Eulenburg. £0.75* MMJ (B72-50513)

Copland, Aaron. Appalachian spring. (Ballet for Martha): suite; version for 13 instruments. *Boosey and Hawkes. £1.25* MRG (B72-50528)

Davies, Peter Maxwell. St Thomas Wake: foxtrot for orchestra on a pavan by John Bull. *Boosey and Hawkes. £2.50* MMHKEF (B72-50512)

Debussy, Claude. Prélude à l'après-midi d'un faune. *Peters: Hinrichsen. £0.75* MMJ (B72-50144)

Debussy, Claude. Prélude à l'après-midi d'un faune. Prelude to 'The afternoon of a faun'. *Chappell. Unpriced* MMJ (B72-50967)

Debussy, Claude. Quartet for strings. Op. 10. Streichquartett. Op. 10. *Peters: Hinrichsen. Unpriced* RXNS (B72-51108)

Delius, Frederick. A mass of life. Eine Messe des Lebens = A mass of life: für Sopran, Alt, Tenor, Bariton, gemischten Chor und grosses Orchester. *Boosey and Hawkes. £6.00* EMDX (B72-50384)

Durkó, Zsolt. Altamira: for chamber choir and orchestra. *Boosey and Hawkes. £1.50* EMDX (B72-50051)

Einem, Gottfried von. Der Besuch der alten Dame= The visit of the old lady. Op.35: opera in three acts after Friedrich Dürrenmatt's tragi-comedy. *Boosey and Hawkes. £10.00* CQC (B72-50803)

Einem, Gottfried von. Hexameron. Op.37. *Boosey and Hawkes. £1.75* MMJ (B72-50145)

Erbse, Heimo. Fünf Orchestergesänge nach Georg Trakl. Op.27: für Bariton und Orchester. *Peters. £3.20* KGNE/MDW (B72-50492)

Farkas, Ferenc. Festive overture = Commemoratio agriae: for orchestra. *Boosey and Hawkes. £1.25* MMJ (B72-50968)

Genzmer, Harald. Concerto for cello and wind band. Konzert für Violoncello und Bläser. *Litolff: Hinrichsen. £3.50* UMPSRF (B72-50261)

Genzmer, Harald. Concerto for organ. Konzert für Orgel und Orchester. *Peters. £3.00* MPRF (B72-50522)

Hessenberg, Kurt. Quartet for strings, no.5. Streichquartett No.5 (in einem Satz). *Bosse: Bärenreiter. £1.05* RXNS (B72-50667)

Kelemen, Milko. Floreal: für Orchester. *Peters. £2.40* MMJ (B72-50516)

Kelterborn, Rudolf. Quartet for strings, no.4. String quartet no.4. *Bärenreiter. £1.15* RXNS (B72-50668)

Kelterborn, Rudolf. Symphony no.2. Sinfonie 2: in two movements for large orchestra. *Bärenreiter. £3.15* MME (B72-50509)

Mozart, Wolfgang Amadeus. Così fan tutte: komische Oper in zwei Akten. *Peters: Hinrichsen. Unpriced* CQC (B72-50804)

Panufnik, Andrzej. Old Polish music. *Boosey and Hawkes. £2.50* RXM/AYLC (B72-50222)

Panufnik, Andrzej. Uwertura bohaterska. Heroic overture. *Boosey and Hawkes. Unpriced* MMJ (B72-50519)

Papastavrou, Krinió. 'St Nicholas': suite for flute, viola & harp. *Stackwood Cottage, Monks Eleigh, Ipswich: Krinió Papastavrou. Unpriced* NVRNTG (B72-50540)

Prokofiev, Sergei. Concerto for piano, no.5, in G major. Op.55. Piano concerto 5. Opus 55. *Boosey and Hawkes. £1.75* MPQF (B72-50971)

Prokofiev, Sergei. London: Boosey and Hawkes. *Boosey and Hawkes. Unpriced* MPQF (B72-50972)

Prokofiev, Sergei. Symphony no.7. Opus 131. Sinfonie Nr.7. Opus 131. *Peters: Hinrichsen. Unpriced* MME (B72-50963)

Schumann, Robert. Concerto for cello in A minor. Op.129. Cello concerto, A minor. Op.129. *Eulenburg. £0.80* MPSRF (B72-50149)

Schumann, Robert. Dichterliebe. *Chappell. Unpriced* KDW (B72-50469) ISBN 0 900277 04 1

Shostakovich, Dmitri. Symphony no.7. Opus 60. *Peters Hinrichsen. Unpriced* MME (B72-50964)

Sigmund, Oskar. La Folia: neue Variationen nach Farinelli - Corelli, für 4 Soloviolinen. *Bosse: Bärenreiter. £1.20* RXNS/T (B72-50669)

Stadlmair, Hans. Concerto for trumpet & string orchestra. Konzert für Trompete in D und Streicher. *Litolff Hinrichsen. Unpriced* RXMPWSF (B72-51105)

Vaughan Williams, Ralph. Riders to the sea: an opera in one act. *Oxford University Press. £5.00* CQC (B72-50805) ISBN 0 19 339335 2

Veerhoff, Carlos. Textur: fur Streicher. *Litolff: Hinrichsen. Unpriced* RXMJ (B72-51089)

Miniature suite: for two B flat trumpets or cornets and piano. (Benger, Richard). *Chester. Unpriced* WSNTQG (B72-51234)

Minter, R.L.

Suite for trumpet & orchestra in D major. Suite in D major: for trumpet, 2 oboes, bassoon, strings and continuo. (Clarke, Jeremiah). *Musica rara. Unpriced* MPWSG (B72-50152)

Suite for trumpet & orchestra in D major. Suite in D major: for trumpet, 2 oboes, bassoon, strings and continuo. (Clarke, Jeremiah). *Musica rara. Unpriced* WSPK/AG (B72-50325)

Minter, Robert L.

Concerto for trumpet, oboe & string orchestra in E flat major. Concerto à 6: for trumpet, oboe, strings and continuo. (Hertel, Johann Wilhelm). *Musica rara. Unpriced* RXMPWSPLVTF (B72-51107)

Concerto for trumpet, oboe & string orchestra in E flat major. Concerto à 6: for trumpet, oboe, strings and continuo. (Hertel, Johann Wilhelm). *Musica rara. Unpriced* VTPLWSK/LF (B72-51185)

Missa de saeculis. (Rock, Gordon F). *Gordon F. Rock. Unpriced* JE/TSDG (B72-50095)

Missa fi-fi. (Dalby, Martin). *Chester. Unpriced* DG (B72-50018)

Missa L'homme armé': for mixed choir (SATB) à cappella. (Obrecht, Jacob). *Boosey and Hawkes. £1.00* EZDG (B72-50840)

Modern music: SATB a cappella. (Billings, William). *Peters Hinrichsen. £0.75* EZDW (B72-50410)

Moderne Oper: Kritiken und Studien. (Hanslick, Eduard). *Gregg. £6.00* AC (B72-07359) ISBN 0 576 28181 6

Modo per imparare a sonare di tromba. - *Excerpts.* Eight sonatas: for trumpet & organ. (Fantini, Girolamo). *Musica rara. Unpriced* WSLRE (B72-50318)

Modo per imparare a sonare di tromba. - *Excerpts.* Eight sonatas: for trumpet and organ. (Fantini, Girolamo). *Musica rara. Unpriced* WSPLRE (B72-51245)

Moehn, Heinz.

La Clemenza di Tito. K.621: opera seria in due atti. (Mozart, Wolfgang Amadeus). *Bärenreiter. £3.75* CC (B72-50341)

Mass no.16, 'Theresa mass'. Missa, Theresa mass. (Haydn, Joseph). *Bärenreiter. £3.15* DG (B72-50354)

Mohr, Wilhelm. Concerto for descant recorder & string orchestra in F major. Concerto in F: for descant recorder, strings and harpischord (piano). (Sammartini, Giuseppe). *Schott. Unpriced* RXMPVSRF (B72-50224)

Mölich, Theo. Mass in C major. K.317, 'Coronation'. Missa, C-dur, 'Krönungs-Messe': für vier Solostimme, Chor und Orchester. (Mozart, Wolfgang Amadeus). *Litolff: Peters. £1.25* DG (B72-50019)

Molique, Bernhard. Concertino for clarinet in F minor. Concertino in F minor for clarinet and orchestra. *Bärenreiter. £1.50* VVPK/LF (B72-50758)

Molter, Johann Melchior.

Concerto for trumpet, strings & basso continuo, no.1 in D major. MWV IV/12. Concerto no.1: for solo trumpet, strings and continuo (bassoon ad lib.). *Musica rara. Unpriced* WSPK/LF (B72-50327)

Concerto for trumpet, strings & basso continuo no.1 in D major. MWV IV/14. Concerto no.1 in D major: for solo trumpet, strings and continuo (bassoon ad lib.). *Musica rara. Unpriced* RXMPWSF (B72-50225)

Concerto for trumpet, strings & basso continuo, no.2 in D major. MWV IV/13. Concerto no.2: for solo trumpet, strings and continuo (bassoon ad lib). *Musica rara. Unpriced* RXMPWSF (B72-50226)

Concerto for trumpet, strings & basso continuo, no.2 in D major. MWV IV/13. Concerto no.2: for solo trumpet, strings and continuo (bassoon ad lib.). *Musica rara. Unpriced* WSPK/LF (B72-50328)

Concerto for trumpet, strings & basso continuo, no.3 in D major. MWV IV/14. Concerto no.3: for solo trumpet, strings and continuo (bassoon ad lib.). *Musica rara. Unpriced* RXMPWSF (B72-50227)

Concerto for trumpet, strings & basso continuo, no.3 in D major. MWV IV/14. Concerto no.3: for solo trumpet, strings and continuo (bassoon ad lib.). *Musica rara. Unpriced* WSPK/LF (B72-50329)

Monelle, Raymond.

First booke of songes. - If my complaints. The Galliard carol: SSA and piano. (Dowland, John). *Boosey and Hawkes. Unpriced* FDP/LF (B72-50870)

Nowell sing we, both all and some: Christmas carol, SSA and piano. *Boosey and Hawkes. Unpriced* FDP/LF (B72-50871)

Monolog: für Oboe solo. (Barkauskas, Vytantas). *Peters. Unpriced* VTPMJ (B72-51186)

Monsell, J S B. Fight the good fight. (Long, Kenneth Roy). *Royal School of Church Music. Unpriced* JDM (B72-50087)

Monsieur de la plume: fragments from the life of Robert Louis Stevenson: music for children's voices and piano. (Rowley, Alec). *Ashdown. Unpriced* CN (B72-50800)

Monteverdi: creator of modern music. (Schrade, Leo). *Gollancz. £2.50* BMN(N) (B72-17504) ISBN 0 575 01472 5

Moon canticle: large mixed chorus a cappella and violoncello obbligato. (Bassett, Leslie). *Peters. £1.20* ESRDX (B72-50389)

Moon rainbow. (Dvořák, Antonín). *Ashdown. £0.05* JDW (B72-50443)

Moore, Elizabeth. Ballet music from the French operas. *Cramer. Unpriced* QPK/HM/AYH (B72-51046)

Moore, Jerrold Northrop. Elgar - a life in photographs. *Oxford University Press. £3.00* BEP/N(EM) (B72-28697) ISBN 0 19 315425 0

More fun with tunes: couplings of national songs. (Hunt, Reginald). *Boosey and Hawkes. £0.60* FDW/G/AYC (B72-50080)

More tunes for my recorder: for the descant recorder. (Dinn, Freda). Revised ed. *Schott. £0.15* VSRPMK/DW/G/AY (B72-50277)

Morell, Thomas. Joshua. Josua: oratorio for four solo-voices, choir and orchestra by Georg Friedrich Händel. (Handel, George Frideric). *Peters. Unpriced* DD (B72-50810)

Morgan, Robert. L'Après - midi du Dracoula for sound - producing instruments; and, Elegant journey with stopping points of interest: for chamber orchestra or percussion ensemble. *Ars viva: Schott. £2.00* LJ (B72-50499)

Morning. (Grieg, Edvard). *Keith Prowse Music. £0.15* QPK/JM (B72-50614)

Morris, Peter. In freezing winter night: carol for unison voices and piano. *Elkin. Unpriced* JDP/LF (B72-50088)

Morse, David. Motown & the arrival of black music. *Studio*

*Vista. £1.40* A/GB (B72-30069) ISBN 0 289 70131 7

Morsicat(h)y: per la mano destra. (Berberian, Cathy). *Universal. Unpriced* PWPR (B72-50168)

Morton, Garth. The zoo: a musical folly. (Sullivan, *Sir* Arthur). *William Reeves. Unpriced* CF (B72-50798)

Motown & the arrival of black music. (Morse, David). *Studio Vista. £1.40* A/GB (B72-30069) ISBN 0 289 70131 7

Mozart, Wölfgang Amadeus. Allegro for clarinet, two violins, viola & cello in B flat major.K.Anh.91. Allegro in B flat.K.Anh.91: fragment of a quintet for clarinet, two violins, viola and violoncello. *Nagel. £2.00* NVVNR (B72-50541)

Mozart, Wolfgang Amadeus.

La Clemenza di Tito. K.621: opera seria in due atti. *Bärenreiter. £3.75* CC (B72-50341)

Concerto for flute, no.2, in D major. K.314. Konzert Nr.2, D dur, für Flöte and Orchester. K.314. *Peters. Unpriced* VRPK/LF (B72-51168)

Concerto for piano, no.17, in G major. K.453. Piano concerto, G major, no.17. K.453. *Peters. Unpriced* QNUK/LF (B72-51019)

Concerto for violin in D major. K.218. Konzert, D-dur: für Violine und Orchester. *Peters. Unpriced* SPK/LF (B72-51120)

Così fan tutte: komische Oper in zwei Akten. *Peters Hinrichsen. Unpriced* CQC (B72-50804)

Divertimento, E flat major. KV App, 182: 2 oboes, 2 clarinets in B flat, 2 bassoons, 2 horns in E flat. *Peters. £1.80* UNN (B72-50721)

Divertimento for wind octet in B flat major. K. Anh. 227. Divertimento, B flat major, KV app. 227: 2 oboes, 2 clarinets in B flat, 2 bassoons, 2 horns in E flat. *Peters. £1.50* UNN (B72-50722)

Divertimento for wind octet in E flat major. K. Anh, 226. Divertimento, E flat major. KV App, 226: 2 oboes, 2 clarinets in B flat, 2 bassoons, 2 horns in E flat,. *Peters. £1.80* UNN (B72-50723)

Divertimento for wind sextet in B flat major. K. 240. - Excerpts. Allegro: for descant, 2 treble and tenor recorders. *Chester. Unpriced* VSNSK (B72-50743)

Mass in C major. K.317, 'Coronation'. Missa, C-dur, 'Krönungs-Messe': für vier Solostimme, Chor und Orchester. *Litolff: Peters. £1.25* DG (B72-50019)

Sympony no.40 in G minor. K.550. - Allegro molto. Exposition of Mozart's Symphony no.40 (1st movement). *Bosworth. £2.30* MJ (B72-50959)

Twelve variations in C major, 'Ah, vous dirai - je maman', K.265: for piano. *Nagel. £0.35* QP/T (B72-50570)

Variations for piano in G major, Unser dummer Pöbel meint. K. 455. Ten variations in G major, 'Unser dummer Pöbel meint. K. 455: for piano. *Nagel. £0.40* QP/T (B72-50571)

Variations for piano. K. 24 & 25. Eight variations in G.K. 24; with, Seven variations in D. K 25 for piano. *Nage. £0.50* PWP/T (B72-50552)

Vesperae solemnes de confessore. K.339. - *Excerpts.* Laudate Dominum. K.339, no.5. *Novello. £0.10* FDGKJ (B72-50867)

Die Zauberflöte. - *Excerpts.* Six airs. *Regina Music. Unpriced* TSPMK/DW (B72-50712)

Mozart on the stage. (Liebner, János). *Calder and Boyars. £3.25* BMSAC (B72-14736) ISBN 0 7145 0758 x

Muczynski, Robert.

Fantasy trio. Op.26: for clarinet, cello and piano. *Schirmer: Chappell. Unpriced* NUVNT (B72-50160)

Voyage. Op.27: seven pieces for brass trio (B flat trumpet, F horn, trombone). *Schirmer: Chappell. Unpriced* WNT (B72-50316)

Munich melody: original theme of BBC TV Olympic Grandstand. (Zacharias, Helmut). *Ardmore and Beechwood. Unpriced* QPK/AGM/JS (B72-51045)

Munro, Blanche. Shepherds in fields: SATB. (Nops, Marjory). *British and Continental. Unpriced* EZDP/LF (B72-50851)

Murray, Eleanor. Tunes for my viola: fourteen pieces for viola and piano. *Boosey and Hawkes. £0.75* SQPJ (B72-50236)

Murray, Gregory. Chanson de matin. Op.15, no.2. (Elgar, *Sir* Edward, *bart*). *Novello. Unpriced* VSNRK (B72-50270)

Musae Sioniae. - *Excerpts.* 'Allein Gott in der Hör sei Ehr' T.3, no.11, T1.9, no.54, T1.5, no.21: chorale arrangements for three, four and eight voices. (Praetorius, Michael). *Bärenreiter. £0.60* EZDM (B72-50402)

Musgrave, Thea.

Elegy: for viola and cello. *Chester. Unpriced* SQPLSR (B72-50238)

Night music: for chamber orchestra. *Chester. Unpriced* MRJ (B72-50531)

Music. (Great Britain. *Welsh Office*). *31 Cathedral Rd, Cardiff CF1 9UJ: Welsh Education Office. £0.20* A(V/YDK) (B72-31877) ISBN 0 903702 00 2

Music. (Horton, John). *Macmillan for the Anglo-American Primary Education Project. £0.60* A(VG) (B72-13853) ISBN 0 333 13332 3

Music and musical life in Soviet Russia, 1917-1970. (Schwarz, Boris). *Barrie and Jenkins. £6.00* A(YM/XMS58) (B72-04570) ISBN 0 214 65264 5

Music and society in lowland Scotland in the eighteenth century. (Johnson, David, *b.1942*). *Oxford University Press. £3.30* A(YDLG/XF101) (B72-26090) ISBN 0 19 316401 9

Music-box polka: accordion solo. (Wright, Rosemary). *Charnwood Music. Unpriced* RSPMHVH (B72-51072)

Music education: psychology and method. (Franklin, Erik). *Harrap. £1.40* A/CS(VC) (B72-13438) ISBN 0 245 50659 4

Music: for chorus (SATB). (Gow, David). *Chester. Unpriced* EZDW (B72-50863)

Music for Slow Learners Project. Sound approaches for slow learners: a report on experimental work in schools being part of the Music for Slow Learners Project at Dartington College of Arts. (Ward, David). *Bedford Square Press for the Standing Conference for Amateur Music. £0.35* A(VMWR) (B72-16605) ISBN 0 7199 0829 9

Music in American education: past and present. (Tellstrom, A Theodore). *Holt, Rinehart and Winston. £4.40* A(VF/YT/X) (B72-07977) ISBN 0 03 083579 8

Music in American life series. *(University of Illinois Press)* Denisoff, R. Serge. Great day coming: folk music and the American left. *University of Illinois Press. £3.60* A/GB(ZC) (B72-30745) ISBN 0 252 00179 6

Music in the classroom. (Rainbow, Bernarr). 2nd ed. *Heinemann Educational. £1.25* A(VC) (B72-26088) ISBN 0 435 81746 9

Music of St Paul's Cathedral. (Scott, David, *b.1943*). *Stainer and Bell; 82 High Rd, East Finchley, N2 9PW Distributed by Publishing Services Partnership. £0.60* AD/LE(YDBB) (B72-30071) ISBN 0 903000 08 3

Music of the English church. (Long, Kenneth R). *Hodder and Stoughton. £7.00* AD/LD(YD/X) (B72-06767) ISBN 0 340 14962 0

Music of York Minster. (Aston, Peter). *29 Newman St., W.1: Stainer and Bell. £0.50* AD/LE(YDJGYB) (B72-22491) ISBN 0 903000 07 5

Music on stamps

Part 1: A-B. (Peat, Sylvester). *63 St Mary St., Chippenham, Wilts: Picton Publishing. £0.44* A(ZE) (B72-03311) ISBN 0 902633 08 2

Music since 1900. (Slonimsky, Nicolas). 4th ed. *Cassell. £21.00* A(XM73) (B72-17502) ISBN 0 304 29069 6

Music workshop books

Book 1. (Pont, Kenneth). *Oxford University Press. £1.45* JFE/NYDSRDW/G/AY (B72-50909) ISBN 0 19 344905 6

Book 2. (Pont, Kenneth). *Oxford University Press. £1.45* JFE/NYDSRDW/G/AY (B72-50910) ISBN 0 19 344912 9

Music yearbook: a survey and directory with statistics and reference articles

1972/3. *Macmillan. £4.95* A(BC) (B72-21772) ISBN 0 333 13355 2

Musica a quattro voci. - *Excerpts.* Two canzonas: for 2 trumpets and 2 trombones (2 trumpets, horn and trombone). (Cavaccio, Giovanni). *Musica rara. £0.80* WNS (B72-51230)

Musica Britannica: a national collection of music

Vol.31: Matthew Locke: Chamber music 1. *Published for the Royal Music Association by Stainer and Bell. £10.00* C/AYD (B72-50007)

Vol.32: Matthew Locke: Chamber music 2. *Published for the Royal Music Association by Stainer and Bell. £10.00* C/AYD (B72-50008)

Vol.35: Pelham Humfrey: Complete church music, II. *Stainer and Bell. Unpriced* C/AYD (B72-50794)

Musica Transalpina

Vol.1. (Yonge, Nicolas). 1st ed. reprinted. *Gregg. £12.00* AEZDU (B72-26095) ISBN 0 576 28178 6

Musical instruments. (Hindley, Geoffrey). *Hamlyn. £0.40* AL/B (B72-06765) ISBN 0 600 00294 2

Musicians and libraries in the United Kingdom. (Long, Maureen W). *Library Association. £2.25(£1.80 to members of the Library Association)* A(U/YC) (B72-08765) ISBN 0 85365 355 0

Musiciens et la musique. (Berlioz, Hector). *Gregg. £9.60* A(D/XFZ84) (B72-06101) ISBN 0 576 28424 6

Musikalische Stationem. (Hanslick, Eduard). *Gregg. £6.00* A (B72-07350) ISBN 0 576 28182 4

Musikalisches Skizzenbuch: neue Kritiken und Schildenrungen. (Hanslick, Eduard). *Gregg. £6.00* A (B72-07351) ISBN 0 576 28184 0

Musikalisches und Litterarisches: Kritiken und Schilderungen. (Hanslick, Eduard). 2. Aufl. reprinted. *Gregg. £6.00* A (B72-07352) ISBN 0 576 28185 9

Mussorgsky, Modest. Pictures at an exhibition. - *Excerpts.* Bydlo and two promenades. *Oxford University Press. Unpriced* MK (B72-50506) ISBN 0 19 366175 6

My daughter Coppelia: a musical play (adapted from Delibes' ballet 'Coppelia'). (Griffiths, Philip). *Oxford University Press. £0.40* BDKACN (B72-03927) ISBN 0 19 338228 8

My daughter Coppelia: a musical play adapted from the ballet. (Delibes, Léo). *Oxford University Press. £1.20* CN (B72-50014) ISBN 0 19 338227 x

My land. (Tindle, Anna). *Ashdown. £0.09* GEZDW (B72-50436)

My story. (Frazier, Kathleen). *12 Forde Park, Newton Abbot, Devon: K. Frazier. £0.50* AQ/E(P) (B72-26661) ISBN 0 9502464 0 9

Myers, Rollo Hugh. Claude Debussy: the story of his life and work. *Boosey and hawkes. Unpriced* BDJ(N) (B72-50005) ISBN 0 85162 003 5

Mysterious mountain. (Hovhaness, Alan). *Associated Music. Unpriced* UMK (B72-50257)

Nabucodonosor. - Va pensiero. The chorus of Hebrew slaves. (Verdi, Giuseppe). *Norman Richardson Band Arrangements. Unpriced* WMK/DW (B72-50310)

Nagel, Frank. Quartet for four flutes in E major. Op.103. Quartett, E-dur: für vier Flöten. (Kuhlau, Friedrich). *Litolff: Peters. £3.00* VRNS (B72-50265)

Naples and Neapolitan opera. (Robinson, Michael Finlay). *Clarendon Press. £8.00* AC(YJN/XF101) (B72-30742) ISBN 0 19 816124 7

Nat King Cole: an intimate biography. (Cole, Maria). *W.H. Allen. £2.10* AKG/E(P) (B72-23643) ISBN 0 491 00782 5

National Association of Youth Clubs. *Politics Working Party.* Night assembly? *N.A.Y.C. £0.03* A/GB(WE) (B72-16874) ISBN 0 901528 56 0

National Book League. Folk song and dance: a list of books. (Clark, Keith). *National Book League: English Folk Dance and Song Society. £0.30* A/G(T) (B72-16428) ISBN 0 85353 138 2

National music, and other essays. (Vaughan Williams, Ralph). *Oxford University Press. £2.50* A(D) (B72-15421) ISBN 0 19 311207 8

Nautical suite. - *Excerpts.* Ship ahoy: for piano. (Longmire, John). *Bosworth. Unpriced* QPGM (B72-51031)

N.A.Y.C. *See* National Association of Youth Clubs.

Naylor, Peter. Come, dearest Lord: anthem for SATB and organ. *Novello. £0.10* DH (B72-50358)

Nazareth, Ernestò. A meno vesedá: polca. *Arthur Napoleão: Essex Music. Unpriced* QPHVH (B72-50577)

Neander, J.

Praise to the Lord, the Almighty: SATB. (Gilbert, Norman). *Oxford University Press. Unpriced* DH (B72-50817) ISBN 0 19 351112 6

Praise to the Lord, the Almighty: two-part. (Gilbert, Norman). *Oxford University Press. Unpriced* FDH (B72-50869) ISBN 0 19 341506 2

Nelson, Havelock.

Plenty good room: negro spiritual. *Boosey and Hawkes. Unpriced* DW/LC (B72-50044)

Sister Mary had - a but one child: negro spiritual, SSA and piano. *Boosey and Hawkes. Unpriced* FDW/LC (B72-50878)

Weary travellers: negro spiritual, SATB and piano. *Boosey and Hawkes. Unpriced* DW/LC (B72-50829)

Nelson, Sheila M. The violin and viola. *Benn. £3.00* AS/B(X) (B72-15430) ISBN 0 510 36651 1

Neubert, Günter. Musik für Flöte solo. *Peters: Hinrichsen. £0.50* VRPMJ (B72-50739)

Neue Bläserstücke. Partitur in C: für 4 Blechbläser (Trompeten Posaunen). (Zehm, Friedrich). *Schott. £0.80* WNSG (B72-50783)

Neue Duettstudien: für Querflöten. (Zehm, Friedrich). *Schott. Unpriced* VRNU (B72-51161)

Neue Oboenschule. (Sous, Alfred). *Litolff: Peters. £3.80* VT/AC (B72-50282)

Neujahrslied 'Der du die Zeit in Handen hast'. (Reda, Siegfried). *Bärenreiter. £0.05* EZDP/LGM (B72-50407)

Nevers, Bernard de. Sinfonia sacra: 'The resurrection'. Op.140: for soprano, contralto, baritone, chorus and orchestra. (Rubbra, Edmund). *Lengnick. £1.00* DE/LL (B72-50812)

New, Derek. Bugle call blues. *Studio Music. Unpriced* WMGM (B72-50302)

New climax albums: for piano

No.1. *Paxton. £0.47* QPK/AAY (B72-51043)

New compendium of piano technique

Book 3: Alternation of the hands. (Lerche, Juliane). *Peters: Hinrichsen. £1.25* Q/AF (B72-50560)

New England Psalm singer. - *Excerpts.* Chester: SATB a cappella. (Billings, William). *Peters: Hinrichsen. £0.40* EZDM (B72-50400)

New orbit: songs and hymns for under elevens. (Smith, Peter). *Galliard. Unpriced* JFE/LPDM/AY (B72-50908) ISBN 0 85249 134 4

New treasury of folk songs. (Glazer, Tom). *Corgi Books. £0.30* JE/TSDW/G/AYT (B72-50901)

New tunes for strings

Book 1. (Fletcher, Stanley). *Boosey and Hawkes. £4.90* RXM/AF (B72-51085)

Book 2. (Fletcher, Stanley). *Boosey and Hawkes. £4.90* RXM/AF (B72-51086)

New World prayer. (Dvorák, Antonin). *Lengnick. £0.20* KDW (B72-50924)

New year carol. Op.7, no.5. (Britten, Benjamin). *Boosey and Hawkes. £0.05* FDP/LFM (B72-50072)

Newell, N. Spartak-Adagio. The Adagio from Spartacus. (For my love). (Khachaturian, Aram). *Feldman. Unpriced* WMK (B72-50309)

Newell, Norman. Spartak - Adagio. For my love. (Khachaturian, Aram). *Plantagenet music. £0.20* KDW (B72-50112)

Newgass, Edgar. Perpetuity: a church solo. (Lowe, Augustus). *Edgar Newgass: Distributed by Paterson. £0.20* KDH (B72-50922)

Newley, Anthony. Willy Wonka and the chocolate factory: vocal selections. (Bricusse, Leslie). *Taradam Music. £0.75* KDW/JR (B72-50122)

Newman, Ernest. Berlioz, romantic and classic: writings by Ernest Newman. *Gollancz. £3.00* BBM(D) (B72-03314) ISBN 0 575 01365 6

Newman, William Stein. Performance practices in Beethoven's piano sonatas: an introduction. *Dent. £2.50* BBJAQPE/E (B72-17506) ISBN 0 460 07868 2

Newman, John Henry. Celtic requiem: for soprano, children's choir, chorus and orchestra. (Tavener, John). *Chester. Unpriced* EMDGKAV (B72-50383)

Newsome, R. Two London sketches. *Feldman. Unpriced* WNR (B72-50314)

Newsome, Roy. Explosions - Polka. Op.43. (Strauss, Johann, *b.1825*). *Studio Music. Unpriced* WMK/AHVH (B72-50773)

Newton, John. Amazing grace: early American melody, SATB and piano; words by John Newton. *Keith Prowse. Unpriced* DM (B72-50362)

Nice derangement of epitaphs: for unaccompanied voices. (Bush, Geoffrey). *Elkin. £1.25* EZDX (B72-50068)

Nicholas and Alexandra: theme. (Bennett, Richard Rodney). *Columbia Music, Chappell. £0.20* QPK/JR (B72-50196)

Nicholson, Roger. Nonesuch for dulcimer. *Scratchwood Music: Feldman. Unpriced* TWTPMJ (B72-50252)

Nicholson, *Sir* Sydney Hugo. Let us with a gladsome mind:

anthem for harvest or other festivals. *Royal School of Church Music. Unpriced* DH/LP (B72-50028)
Nielsen, Carl. Music: for chorus (SATB). (Gow, David). *Chester. Unpriced* EZDW (B72-50863)
Nietzsche, Friedrich. A mass of life. Eine Messe des Lebens = A mass of life: für Sopran, Alt, Tenor, Bariton, gemischten Chor und grosses Orchester. (Delius, Frederick). *Boosey and Hawkes. £6.00* EMDX (B72-50384)
Night assembly? (National Association of Youth Clubs. *Politics Working Party*). *N.A.Y.C. £0.03* A/GB(WE) (B72-16874) ISBN 0 901528 56 0
Night music: for chamber orchestra. (Musgrave, Thea). *Chester. Unpriced* MRJ (B72-50531)
Nikolovski, Vlastimir. Omladinski album. Jugendalbum: für Klavier. *Peters: Hinrichsen. Unpriced* QPJ (B72-50602)
Nine rarebits: for 1 or 2 harpsichords. (Browne, Earle). *Universal. Unpriced* QRPJ (B72-51051)
Noble, Robert. Folk tunes to accompany: a guide to simple accompaniment for beginners of all ages
Book 4: Music for Christmas: 30 folk carols. *Novello. £0.45* LN/ED (B72-50500)
Noble nature: two part songs for SATB a cappella,. (Stoker, Richard). *Leeds Music. Unpriced* EZDW (B72-50065)
Nobody knows; and, Balm in Gilead: a quodlibet based on two negro spirituals, for either trebles 1 and 2, or basses 1 and 2, or treble 1 and bass 2. (Hudson, Hazel). *Ashdown. £0.09* FLDW/LC (B72-50432)
Nocturne: for small orchestra. (Standford, Patric). *Novello. £0.60* MRJ (B72-50155)
Noehren, Robert.
Five fantasies: for organ
No.1: So long as the mind keeps silent. (Finney, Ross Lee). *Peters. £1.00* RJ (B72-50636)
No.2: There are no summits without abysses. (Finney, Ross Lee). *Peters. £1.00* RJ (B72-50637)
No.4: The leaves on the trees spoke. (Finney, Ross Lee). *Peters. £1.00* RJ (B72-50639)
Noel Coward for all organs. (Coward, *Sir* Noël). *Chappell. £0.60* RK/DW (B72-51060)
Nonesuch for dulcimer. (Nicholson, Roger). *Scratchwood Music: Feldman. Unpriced* TWTPMJ (B72-50252)
Nops, Marjory.
Oh hurry, hurry to Bethlehem: a carol for SATB, organ or guitar. *British and Continental. Unpriced* DP/LF (B72-50825)
Shepherds in fields: SATB. *British and Continental. Unpriced* EZDP/LF (B72-50851)
There was a Maid: a carol for SATB, organ, piano or unaccompanied. *British and Continental. Unpriced* EZDP/LF (B72-50852)
North by north-east. (Donald, Mike). *Galliard. £0.44* KE/TSDW (B72-50934) ISBN 0 85249 154 9
Northern accent: the life story of the Northern School of Music. (Robert-Blunn, John). *Sherratt. £2.00* A(VP/YDJE(X) (B72-18915) ISBN 0 85427 029 9
Northway, Peter. Keyboard works
Vol.2: Second set of 1733. (Handel, George Frideric). *Bärenreiter. £1.85* QRP/AZ (B72-50622)
Norton, Mary Dows Herter. Classic and Romantic music: a comprehensive survey. (Blume, Friedrich). *3 Queen Sq., WC1N 3AU: Faber. £3.00* A(YB/XFY190) (B72-24250) ISBN 0 571 08215 7
Norwich canticles: Magnificat; and, Nunc dimittis: for SATB unaccompanied. (McCabe, John). *Novello. £0.17* EZDGPP (B72-50841)
Notte: for chamber orchestra. (Standford, Patric). *Novello. £1.25* MRJ (B72-50981)
Nott'num town: suite for symphonic band. (Street, Allan). *Boosey and Hawkes. £5.25* UMG (B72-50253)
Nourse, John. A short Communion service: for unison voices and organ. *Novello. £0.14* JDGS (B72-50896)
Novello short biographies. *(Novello)*
Holst, Imogen. Holst. *Novello. £0.15* BHP(N) (B72-15422) ISBN 0 85360 010 4
McCaldin, Denis. Stravinsky. *Novello. £0.15* BSV(N) (B72-12718) ISBN 0 85360 009 0
Sharp, Geoffrey B. Lassus & Palestrina. *Novello. £0.15* BLC(N) (B72-18916) ISBN 0 85360 038 4
Nowell sing we, both all and some: Christmas carol, SSA and piano. (Monelle, Raymond). *Boosey and Hawkes. Unpriced* FDP/LF (B72-50871)
Nursery rhymes with a new look. (Hudson, Hazel). *Edwin Ashdown. Unpriced* JFDW/GK/AY (B72-50102)
Nursery songs and carols. (Waters, Frank). *Franklin Watts. £0.25* JFDW/GK/AY (B72-50103) ISBN 0 85166 258 7
Nursery songs from Humberside. (Reaks, Brian). *British and Continental. £0.25* JFDW/GJ/AYDJGX (B72-50101)
Nyman, Michael. Come, let us drink: compleat, pleasant and divertive. (Purcell, Henry). *Galliard. £0.93* GEZDW/XD/AZ (B72-50893)
Nymph and the farmer. La Fée et le cultivateur = The nymph and the farmer, Op.72: a lyric legend. (Cherepnin, Alexander). *Boosey and Hawkes. £4.50* CC (B72-50337)
O brother man, fold to thy heart thy brother: SATB. (Hopson, Hal H). *Warner: Blossom Music. Unpriced* EZDH (B72-50054)
O come, let us sing unto the Lord: anthem for SATB and organ. (Hurd, Michael). *Novello. £0.10* DK (B72-50032)
O Lord God: anthem for SATB unaccompanied). (Marlow, Richard). *Novello. £0.07* EZDK (B72-50848)
O sacrum convivium. I call and cry to thee: anthem for SAATB. (Tallis, Thomas). *Novello. £0.17* EZDJ (B72-50845)
Obrecht, Jacob. Missa L'homme armé: for mixed choir (SATB) à cappella. *Boosey and Hawkes. £1.00* EZDG (B72-50840)
Odam, George. Tutankhamun. *Chester. Unpriced* CQN (B72-50806)
Ode for Queen Mary's birthday, 1694. Come ye sons of art. (Purcell, Henry). *Schott. £0.75* DX (B72-50048)
Odyssey: piano solo. (Lees, Benjamin). *Boosey and Hawkes. £0.65* QPJ (B72-51038)
Oh how great is thy goodness: two-part (S.A.) anthem with piano accompaniment. (Palmer, Florence Margaret Spencer). *Cramer. £0.09* FDK (B72-50071)
Oh hurry, hurry to Bethlehem: a carol for SATB, organ or guitar. (Nops, Marjory). *British and Continental. Unpriced* DP/LF (B72-50825)
Oistrach, David.
Concerto for violin in D major. K.218. Konzert, D-dur: für Violine und Orchester. (Mozart, Wolfgang Amadeus). *Peters. Unpriced* SPK/LF (B72-51120)
Sonata for violin & piano. Op.134. Sonate für Violine und Klavier. Opus 134. (Shostakovich, Dmitri). *Peters. Unpriced* SPE (B72-51118)
Oklahoma!. - *Excerpts.* Four songs. (Rodgers, Richard). *Williamson. Unpriced* LNSK/DW (B72-50137)
Okumara, Hajime. Jahresanfang in Japan: Trio für Flöte, Violoncello und Klavier (1969). *Bosse: Eulenburg. £2.25* NURNT (B72-50533)
Old English organ music for manuals
Book 5. (Trevor, Caleb Henry). *Oxford University Press. £0.50* R/AYD (B72-50208) ISBN 0 19 375828 8
Old English trumpet tunes: for trumpet in B flat. (Lawton, Sidney Maurice). *Oxford University Press. £0.80* WSPK/AAY (B72-50323)
Old Hundredth psalm tune: All people that on earth do dwell, for mixed or unison voices and orchestra. (Vaughan Williams, Ralph). *Oxford University Press. Unpriced* EMDM (B72-50836) ISBN 0 19 369530 8
Old Polish music. (Panufnik, Andrzej). *Boosey and Hawkes. £2.50* RXM/AYLC (B72-50222)
Olon, John. The shoemakers' holiday: a ballad-opera based on the play by Thomas Dekker. (Argento, Dominick). *Boosey and Hawkes. £6.00* CLM (B72-50343)
Omladinski album. Jugendalbum: für Klavier. (Nikolovski, Vlastimir). *Peters: Hinrichsen. Unpriced* QPJ (B72-50602)
One Friday in eternity. (Banyard, Edmund). *82 High Rd, N.2: Galliard Ltd. £0.17* BBDNACM/LK (B72-10328) ISBN 0 85249 121 2
One hand alone: album of 17 well-known pieces arranged for either left hand or right hand solo. (Schultze-Biesantz, Clemens). *Peters. Unpriced* QPPR (B72-51049)
One man's music. (Gammond, Peter). *Wolfe. £3.00* A (B72-02714) ISBN 0 7234 0424 0
'Onedin Line'. (Khachaturian, Aram). *Palace Music. £0.20* QPK (B72-50194)
'Onedin Line' theme. (Khachaturian, Aram). *Essex Music International. £0.20* QPK (B72-50195)
Open University. *Age of Revolutions Course Team.* Beethoven. (Edwards, Owain Tudor). *Walton Hall, Bletchley, Bucks.: Open University Press. Unpriced* BBJ (B72-22483) ISBN 0 335 00572 1
Open University. *Renaissance and Reformation Course Team.* Renaissance music. (Hendrie, Gerald). *Walton Hall, Bletchley, Bucks.: Open University Press. £1.10* A(XRE201) (B72-50334) ISBN 0 335 00657 4
Opera - origins and side lights. *See* Berges, Ruth.
Opera. (Wechsberg, Joseph). *Weidenfeld and Nicolson. £4.95* AC (B72-24252) ISBN 0 297 99508 1
Opera library. *(Calder and Boyars)*
Liebner, János. Mozart on the stage. *Calder and Boyars. £3.25* BMSAC (B72-14736) ISBN 0 7145 0758 x
Stendhal. Lives of Haydn, Mozart and Metastasio. *Calder and Boyars. £5.50* BHE(N) (B72-14734) ISBN 0 7145 0349 5
Oram, Daphne. An individual note: of music, sound and electronics. *Queen Anne's Rd, Great Yarmouth, Norfolk: Galliard. £0.99* APV/D (B72-50001) ISBN 0 85249 109 3
Orchésographie. - *Excerpts.* Twelve dances. (Arbeau, Thoinot). *Schott. Unpriced* VSNUK/AH (B72-50273)
Organs and organists of Wimborne Minster, 1408-1972. (Matthews, Betty). *9 St Winifred's Rd, Bournemouth BH2 6NY: Kenneth Mummery Ltd. £0.30* AR/B(YDFKWB) (B72-20310) ISBN 0 9502449 0 2
Orr, Buxton. Divertimento for brass quintet (1969). *Novello. Unpriced* WNR (B72-50782)
Orrey, Leslie. A concise history of opera. *Thames and Hudson. £2.50* AC(X) (B72-28009) ISBN 0 500 18130 6
Osprey guide to Gilbert and Sullivan. (Hardwick, Michael). *Osprey. £2.50* BSWACF (B72-26659) ISBN 0 85045 100 0
Ottaway, Hugh. Vaughan Williams symphonies. *British Broadcasting Corporation. £0.45* BVDAMME (B72-28682) ISBN 0 563 12242 0
Outcry: a cycle of nature poems for contralto solo, SATB and orchestra. (Dickinson, Peter). *Novello. £1.10* DW (B72-50043)
Overlander song book. (Edwards, Ron). *Hale. £3.00* ADW/G(YX) (B72-12721) ISBN 0 7091 3070 8
Ox on the roof: scenes from musical life in Paris in the twenties. (Harding, James). *Macdonald and Co. £3.00* A/D(YH/XMS13/P) (B72-14735) ISBN 0 356 03967 6
Oxford book of carols. Revised ed.. *Oxford University Press. £0.90* DP/LF/AY (B72-50827) ISBN 0 19 313120 x
Oxford monographs on music. *(Clarendon Press)* Robinson, Michael Finlay. Naples and Neapolitan opera. *Clarendon Press. £8.00* AC(YJN/XF101) (B72-30742) ISBN 0 19 816124 7
Oxford University. *See* University of Oxford.
Pachelbel, Johann. Orgelwerke
Band 1: Choralfugen und Choräle aus dem Weimarer Tabulaturbuch, 1704. *Peters. Unpriced* R/AZ (B72-51053)
Paisiello, Giovanni. Symphony in D major. Sinfonia, D-dur: für Kammerorchester. *Litolff: Peters. Unpriced* MRE (B72-50978)
Palaestra 64: pro organo. (Englert, Giuseppe). *Peters. £1.25* RJ (B72-50635)
Palmer, Florence Margaret Spencer. Oh how great is thy goodness: two-part (S.A.) anthem with piano accompaniment. *Cramer. £0.09* FDK (B72-50071)
Palmer, Peggy Spencer. *See* Palmer, Florence Margaret Spencer.
Panufnik, Andrzej.
Kátyń epitaph. *Boosey and Hawkes. £1.00* MMJ (B72-50517)
Old Polish music. *Boosey and Hawkes. £2.50* RXM/AYLC (B72-50222)
Reflections: piano solo. *Boosey and Hawkes. £0.75* QPJ (B72-50192)
Uwertura bohaterska. Heroic overture. *Boosey and Hawkes. UNpriced* MMJ (B72-50518)
Uwertura bohaterska. Heroic overture. *Boosey and Hawkes. Unpriced* MMJ (B72-50519)
Papastavrou, Krinió. 'St Nicholas': suite for flute, viola & harp. *Stackwood Cottage, Monks Eleigh, Ipswich: Krinió Papastavrou. Unpriced* NVRNTG (B72-50540)
Paralèle des Italiens et des François, en ce qui regard la musique et les opéras. A comparison between the French and Italian musick and operas. (Raguenet, François). 1st English ed., reprinted. *Gregg. £11.40* AC(YJ/XF/ZB) (B72-09123) ISBN 0 576 28446 7
Paraphrase: pour voix d'alto et 11 instrumentistes. (Raxach, Enrique). *Peters, Hinrichsen. £1.80* KFQE/MRDX (B72-50130)
Parataio. - Overture. Sinfonia D-Dur: für Streichorchester und zwei Horner ad lib. (Jomelli, Nicolò). *Peters Hinrichsen. £1.20* RXMJ (B72-50653)
Park, Phil. Das Dreimäderlhaus. Lilac time: operetta in three acts. (Schubert, Franz). *Chappell: Weinberger. Unpriced* CF (B72-50012)
Parlett, Graham. Arnold Bax, a catalogue of his music. *10e Prior Bolton St., N.1: Triad Press. £1.50* BBH(WJ) (B72-24473) ISBN 0 902070 04 5
Parlour song book: a casquet of vocal gems. (Turner, Michael R). *Joseph. £5.00* KDW/GB/AY(XHS64) (B72-50931) ISBN 0 7181 0381 5
Parry, *Sir* Charles Hubert Hastings. Hear my words, ye people. *Excerpts.* He delivered the poor. *Royal School of Church Music. Unpriced* KFLDH (B72-50129)
Parry, Enid. Four prayers from the Gaelic. (Thomas, Mansel). *University of Wales Press. Unpriced* KDH (B72-50108)
Parry, Thomas. The song of little Jesus = Cân y baban Jesu: unison. (Thomas, Mansel). *Oxford University Press. Unpriced* JDP/LF (B72-50898) ISBN 0 19 342049 x
Parry, William Howard. Rise up shepherd: a hymn-sequence with readings for voices with optional baritone solo with accompaniments for piano and optional instruments. *Keith Prowse. £0.50* DPDE/LF (B72-50042)
Partita for viola on themes of Walton. (Williamson, Malcolm). *Weinberger. Unpriced* SQPMG (B72-51130)
Party piece: for piano and small orchestra. (Bennett, Richard Rodney). *Universal. Unpriced* MPQ (B72-50148)
Pasby, Cyril. The gay puppet: accordion solo. *Charnwood Music. Unpriced* RSPMJ (B72-51078)
Paseo: for solo guitar. (Fricker, Peter Racine). *Faber Music. Unpriced* TSPMJ (B72-50250)
Pasfield, W R. Symphony no.5 in C minor. - *Excerpts.* Adagietto. (Mahler, Gustav). *Ashdown. Unpriced* RK (B72-50217)
Pasfield, William Reginald.
Loving shepherd of thy sheep: unison anthem for children's voices with organ (or piano). *Ashdown. £0.05* JFDM (B72-50450)
Thou whose birth on earth: carol for Christmas. *Ashdown. £0.05* FDP/LF (B72-50419)
Pasquini, Bernardo. Sonata for two harpsichords in D minor. Sonata in D minor: for two pianos (harpsichords). *Nagel. £0.75* QRNUE (B72-50624)
Pat Boone rapture theme songs. (Mickelson, Paul). *Marshall, Morgan and Scott. £0.40* KDW/L/AY (B72-50123) ISBN 0 551 05159 0
Patachich, Ivan. Contorni: per arpa. *Boosey and Hawkes. £0.60* TQPMJ (B72-51143)
Pathfinders march: theme in the TV series. (Lockyer, Malcolm). *Berry Music, Campbell, Connelly. £0.20* QPK/JS (B72-50618)
Patterson, Paul.
Concerto for trumpet. Trumpet concerto. *Weinberger. Unpriced* WSPK/LF (B72-51244)
Kyrie: for choir and piano. *Weinberger. Unpriced* DGB (B72-50813)
Rebecca. *Weinberger. Unpriced* KHYE/MPQ (B72-50946)
Pätzig, Gerhard.
Historische Bläsermusiken: 25 Militärmärsche des 18, Jahrhunderts; erste Urtextausgabe nach den Originalhandschriften für den praktischen Gebrauch
Heft 1. *Bärenreiter. £2.50* UMM/AY (B72-50714)
Heft 2. *Bärenreiter. £3.00* UMM/AY (B72-50715)
Heft 3. *Bärenreiter. £2.00* UMM/AY (B72-50716)
Paüler, Bernhard. Symphony in D major. Sinfonia D-dur: für Kammerorchester. (Cimarosa, Domenico). *Peters. £2.00* MRE (B72-50526)
Päuler, Bernhard.
Symphony in D major. Sinfonia, D-dur: für Kammerorchester. (Paisiello, Giovanni). *Litolff: Peters. Unpriced* MRE (B72-50978)
Trio for flute, bassoon & piano in F major. Trio: für Flöte,

Fagott und Klavier. (Donizetti, Gaetano). *Peters. Unpriced* NWPNT (B72-50991)

Trio for strings & piano in E flat major. Trio: für Violine, Violoncello und Klavier. (Donizetti, Gaetano). *Peters. Unpriced* NXNT (B72-50997)

Paumgartner, Bernhard. Die drei- und vierstimmigen Gesänge. (Haydn, Joseph). *Bärenreiter. £2.00* DW (B72-50378)

Paxton, Stephen. Sonata for cello & harpsichord in A major. Op.l, no.1. Sonata in A. Op.l, no.1: for cello and harpsichord (or piano). *Schott. £0.75* SRPE (B72-50694)

Paynter, John.
Autumn: for voices and instruments. *Universal. Unpriced* JFE/XPQDW (B72-50915)
First star: for voices and instruments. *Universal. Unpriced* JFTE/XTPRDW (B72-50918)
Landscapes: a choral suite for mixed voices (with optional oboe). *Oxford University Press. Unpriced* EZDW (B72-50064)
The space-dragon of Galatar. *Universal. Unpriced* CQN (B72-50807)
The windhover: SATB unacc. *Oxford University Press. Unpriced* EZDW (B72-50414) ISBN 0 19 343006 1

Peace be on earth = Retrospect: an anthem from sundry Scriptures, for SATB (or male chorus or mixed chorus). (Billings, William). *Peters: Hinrichsen. Unpriced* DK (B72-50360)

Peace pieces: for organ, by Malcolm Williamson
Book 1. (Williamson, Malcolm). *Weinberger. Unpriced* RJ (B72-50214)
Book 2. (Williamson, Malcolm). *Weinberger. Unpriced* RJ (B72-50215)

Pearsall, Ronald. Victorian sheet music covers. *David and Charles. £3.25* A(RC/XHS64) (B72-28659) ISBN 0 7153 5561 9

Pearse, John.
The first book of solos for the classical guitar. *Scatchwood Music. Unpriced* TSPMK/AAY (B72-50251)
Nonesuch for dulcimer. (Nicholson, Roger). *Scratchwood Music: Feldman. Unpriced* TWTPMJ (B72-50252)

Pearson, Johnny.
Sleepy shores. *Keith Prowse Music. Unpriced* MSJ (B72-50157)
Sleepy shores: theme from the BBC TV series Owen M.D. *Keith Prowse Music. Unpriced* UMMK/JS (B72-50260)
Sleepy shores: theme from the BBC TV series Owen M.D. *Keith Prowse Music. Unpriced* WMK/JS (B72-50313)

Peat, Sylvester. Music on stamps
Part 1: A-B. *63 St Mary St., Chippenham, Wilts: Picton Publishing. £0.44* A(ZE) (B72-03311) ISBN 0 902633 08 2

Peer Gynt -. *Excerpts.* Morning. (Grieg, Edvard). *Keith Prowse Music. £0.15* QPK/JM (B72-50614)

Pehkonen, Elis.
Concerti with orchestra for young players. *Universal. Unpriced* MF (B72-50138)
Genesis: for voices, instruments and tapes. *Universal. Unpriced* FE/LDW (B72-50880)
Lute-book lullaby: for treble voices and organ. *Chappell. Unpriced* FLDP/LF (B72-50891)
Three limericks: for voices, instruments and piano. *Lengnick. £0.25* HYE/LDW (B72-50437)
Torches: for treble voices and organ. *Chappell. Unpriced* FLDP/LF (B72-50892)

Pelican books. *(Penguin)* Jacobs, Arthur. A short history of Western music. *Penguin. £0.60* A(X) (B72-21774) ISBN 0 14 021421 6

Pelican originals. *(Penguin)* Matthews, Denis. Keyboard music. *Penguin. £0.75* APW/ED(X) (B72-10332) ISBN 0 14 021250 7

Penderecki, Krysztof. Kosmogonia: für Soli, Chor und Orchester. *Schott. Unpriced* EMDX (B72-50837)

Pennington, John. Apollo: aleatoric piece for band. *Schirmer: Chappell. Unpriced* UMJ (B72-50255)

Percussion-Duos. (Regner, Hermann). *Schott. Unpriced* XNU (B72-50789)

Performance of music: a study in terms of the pianoforte. (Barnett, David, *b.1907*). *Barrie and Jenkins. £4.00* AQ/E (B72-12722) ISBN 0 214 65403 6

Performance practices in Beethoven's piano sonatas: an introduction. (Newman, William Stein). *Dent. £2.50* BBJAQPE/E (B72-17506) ISBN 0 460 07868 2

Periodicals:, *New periodicals and those issued with changed titles.*
Country
Vol.1, no.1- ; March 1972-. *61 Berners St., W1P 3AE: Hanover Books Ltd. £0.20* ADW/GCW(B) (B72-09749)

Record Collector: monthly guide to your kind of music
No.1- ; Feb. 1972-. *Hanover Publications; 34 Foubert's Place, W.1: Haymarket Publishing Ltd. £0.10* A/FD(B) (B72-07362)

Perpetuity: a church solo. (Lowe, Augustus). *Edgar Newgass: Distributed by Paterson. £0.20* KDH (B72-50922)

Peter Grimes fantasy on themes from Britten's opera: piano solo. (Stevenson, Ronald). *Boosey and Hawkes. Unpriced* QPJ (B72-51042)

Peter Rabbit and the tales of Beatrix Potter: music from the film. (Lanchbery, John). *EMI Film Music. Unpriced* QPK/JR (B72-50197)

Peterson, John W. The story of Christmas: a cantata. *Marshall, Morgan and Scott. Unpriced* DE/LF (B72-50016) ISBN 0 551 05128 0

Petite suite. - *Excerpts.* En bateaus. (Debussy, Claude). *Oxford University Press. £0.50* VSRNTQK (B72-50276) ISBN 0 19 356150 6

Pfaff, Philip. Christmas in Spain: six traditional Spanish carols, for unison and two-part voices, recorders, tuned and untuned percussion, and piano. *Chappell. £0.50* FE/NYFSDP/LF/AYK (B72-50882)

Phillips, Gordon.
Anthology of organ music: works for two manuals and pedals
Vol.7: Works by Boyvin, Couperin, Reichardt, Adams, Merkel, Beechey. *Hinrichsen. £0.90* R/AY (B72-50199)
Vol.8: Works by Le Bègue, J.S. Bach, Albrechtsberger, Rembt, S.S. Wesley, Guilmant, Spooner. *Hinrichsen. £0.90* R/AY (B72-50200)
Vol.9: Works by Marchand, Guilain, Vivaldi, A.W. Bach, Karg-Elert, Eberlin, Stevens, Guilmant. *Hinrichsen. £0.90* R/AY (B72-50201)
Vol.10: Works by J.S. Bach, Russell, Merkel, Rheinberger, Sowerby. *Hinrichsen. £0.90* R/AY (B72-50202)
Vol.11: Works by Boyvin, du Mage, Raison, J.S. Bach, Martini, Rinck, Cooke. *Hinrichsen. £0.90* R/AY (B72-50203)
Vol.12: Works by de Grigny, J.S. Bach, Krebs, Vierling, Chipp, Phillips. *Hinrichsen. £0.90* R/AY (B72-50204)

Phillips, Ivan Clarence.
The beginner's repertoire for flute
Vol.1. *Oxford University Press. £0.50* VRPK/AAY (B72-50267) ISBN 0 19 358220 1
Vol.2. *Oxford University Press. £0.65* VRPK/AAY (B72-50268) ISBN 0 19 358221 x

Phillips, John C. Vesperae solemnes de confessore. K.339. - *Excerpts.* Laudate Dominum. K.339, no.5. (Mozart, Wolfgang Amadeus). *Novello. £0.10* FDGKJ (B72-50867)

Picken, Laurence. Folk music of Hungary. (Kodály, Zoltán). 2nd ed. *Barrie and Jenkins. £2.25* A/G(YG/XA1914 (B72-13442) ISBN 0 214 65327 7

Pickles, Sydney. Duets for piano. *Freeman. £0.30* QPK/AAY (B72-50609)

Pictures at an exhibition. - *Excerpts.* Bydlo and two promenades. (Mussorgsky, Modest). *Oxford University Press. Unpriced* MK (B72-50506) ISBN 0 19 366175 6

Pike, Eleanor Franklin. A little dance suite. Op.45: for piano. *Ashdown. Unpriced* QPHG (B72-50181)

Pilgrim praise: hymns. (Kaan, Fred). *Galliard. £1.54* DM/AY (B72-50034) ISBN 0 85249 108 5

Pinchot, Ann. Weep no more, my lady: an intimate biography of Judy Garland. (Deans, Mickey). *W.H. Allen. £2.50* AKF/E(P) (B72-08534) ISBN 0 491 00941 0

Pitfield, Thomas.
Bits and pieces for piano. *Forsyth. Unpriced* QPJ (B72-50603)
Planibestiary: a zoological sequence in space for speakers, soloists, SAB choir, flute, oboe, bassoon, piano & percussion. *Lengnick. £0.75* ENYFPDX (B72-50838)

Pitfield, Thomas Baron.
Cheshire soul-caking song: two-part. *Oxford University Press. Unpriced* FDW (B72-50075)
Homage to Tchaikovsky: for piano solo. *Freeman. £0.20* QPJ (B72-51041)
Kalinka: traditional Russian folksong. *Charnwood Music. £0.22* RSPMJ (B72-51079)
Song of rest: accordion solo. *Charnwood Music. Unpriced* RSPMJ (B72-51080)

Pizzicato for a poodle: for string orchestra. (Dexter, Harry). *Ashdown. Unpriced* RXMJ (B72-50651)

Planibestiary: a zoological sequence in space for speakers, soloists, SAB choir, flute, oboe, bassoon, piano & percussion. (Pitfield, Thomas). *Lengnick. £0.75* ENYFPDX (B72-50838)

Planto por las victimas de la violencia: para conjunto instrumental y transformacion electronica del sonido. (Halffter, Cristòbal). *Universal. Unpriced* MMJ (B72-50146)

Plath, Wolfgang.
6 divertimenti da camera: for harpsichord (piano) and violin
Vol.2: Nos.4 - 6. (Schubert, Franz). *Nagel. SPJ* SPJ (B72-50682)
Volume 1: Divertimenti 1 & 2. (Schuster, Joseph). *Nagel. £1.75* SPJ (B72-50683)

Platts, Kenneth. All seasons shall be sweet. Opus 6: for treble voices, percussion and piano. *Ashdown. Unpriced* FLE/NYLNSDX (B72-50433)

Play the recorder. (Salkeld, Robert). *Chappell. £1.40* VSR/AC (B72-50275)

Playa las canteras: Spanish dance: accordion solo. (Walker, Wilfred). *Charnwood Music. £0.19* RSPMH (B72-51069)

Playful pizzicato. (Britten, Benjamin). *Oxford University Press. £0.50* QNVK (B72-50173) ISBN 0 19 372375 1

Pleasure it is: unison. (Thackray, Roy). *Oxford University Press. Unpriced* JDP/LF (B72-50897) ISBN 0 19 351115 0

Pleasures of youth. Op.11: cantata for mixed chorus and orchestra. (Rose, John Luke). *Boosey and Hawkes. Unpriced* DX (B72-50835)

Plenty good room: negro spiritual. (Nelson, Havelock). *Boosey and Hawkes. Unpriced* DW/LC (B72-50044)

Pleyel, Ignaz. Quartet for flute & strings in F major. Op.17, no. 2. Quartet in F major. Op.17, no.2: for flute, violin, viola and cello. *Musica rara. Unpriced* NVRNS (B72-50989)

Pleyel, Ignaz Joseph. Trio for piano, flute and cello. Op.29. Grand trio: for piano, flute and cello. *Musica rara. Unpriced* NURNT (B72-50159)

Plomer, William. The prodigal son = Der verlorene Sohn. Op.81: third parable for church performance. (Britten, Benjamin). *Faber music. Unpriced* CC (B72-50011)

Pointon, Malcolm. 8, 4, 5: eight pieces in the five-finger position for beginner pianists of any age. *Boosey and Hawkes. £0.40* Q/AF (B72-50169)

Polin, Claire. Cader Idris: landscape for brass quintet. *Schirmer: Chappell. Unpriced* WNR (B72-50315)

Polnauer, F.F. Variations for two flutes. Op.20. (Reicha, Anton). *Peters. £1.60* VRNU/T (B72-50729)

Polworth, Gwen. Come you not from Newcastle?: a collection of North Country songs. *6 Queen's Terrace, Newcastle upon Tyne 2: Frank Graham. £0.60* JEZDW/G/AYDJJ (B72-50903)

Pommer, Max.
Prélude à l'après-midi d'un faune. (Debussy, Claude). *Peters: Hinrichsen. £3.50* MMJ (B72-50143)
Prélude à l'après-midi d'un faune. (Debussy, Claude). *Peters: Hinrichsen. £0.75* MMJ (B72-50144)

Pont, Kenneth.
Music workshop books
Book 1. *Oxford University Press. £1.45* JFE/NYDSRDW/G/AY (B72-50909) ISBN 0 19 344905 6
Book 2. *Oxford University Press. £1.45* JFE/NYDSRDW/G/AY (B72-50910) ISBN 0 19 344912 9

Pop music and the blues: a study of the relationship and its significance. (Middleton, Richard). *Gollancz. £4.00* A/GB(ZF) (B72-29416) ISBN 0 575 01442 3

Pope, Alan. Alleluia, now may we mirthës make: SATB(unacc.). *Oxford University Press. Unpriced* EZDP/LF (B72-50853) ISBN 0 19 343035 5

Porpora, Nicolò Antonio. Credidi: motet for SSAA, strings & organ continuo. *Novello. £0.35* DJ (B72-50029)

Portrait 1: für 4 Querflöten. (Braun, Gerhard). *Bosse Bärenreiter. £1.50* VRNS (B72-50727)

Portrait 3: für Violoncello und kleiner Schlagzeug. (Braun, Gerhard). *Bosse: Bärenreiter. £1.25* SRPLX (B72-50701)

Portrait of F.B. (Frances Blood): for voice and piano. (Thomson, Virgil). *Schirmer: Chappell. Unpriced* KDW (B72-50118)

Posford, George. Good-night Vienna: an operetta in three acts. *Keith Prowse. £1.25* CF (B72-50797)

Postcard from Morocco: an opera. (Argento, Dominick). *London: Boosey and Hawkes. £10.00* CC (B72-50336)

Poston, Elizabeth.
The baby's song book. *Bodley Head. £4.20* JFDW/GJ/AY (B72-50452)
The Faber book of French folk songs. *Faber Music. £3.00* JDW/G/AYH (B72-50899) ISBN 0 571 09944 0

Poulton, Diana. John Dowland. *3 Queen Sq., WC1N 3AU: Faber and Faber Ltd. £12.00* BDT (B72-10999) ISBN 0 571 08711 6

Praetorius, Michael. Musae Sioniae. - *Excerpts.* 'Allein Gott in der Hör sei Ehr'. T.3, no.11, T1.9, no.54, T1.5, no.21: chorale arrangements for three, four and eight voices. *Bärenreiter. £0.60* EZDM (B72-50402)

Praise the Lord. (Ainslie, John). Revised ed. *Chapman. Unpriced* DM/LSB/AY (B72-50822) ISBN 0 225 65838 0

Praise the Lord our King: for mixed chorus and organ with optional brass accompaniment. (Traver, James Ferris). *Galaxy: Galliard. Unpriced* DH (B72-50359)

Praise to the Lord, the Almighty: SATB. (Gilbert, Norman). *Oxford University Press. Unpriced* DH (B72-50817) ISBN 0 19 351112 6

Praise to the Lord, the Almighty: two-part. (Gilbert, Norman). *Oxford University Press. Unpriced* FDH (B72-50869) ISBN 0 19 341506 2

Praises for the nativity: for four solo voices (SATB) mixed chorus and organ. (Rorem, Ned). *Boosey and Hawkes. £0.75* DE/LF (B72-50017)

Praktische Elementar-Schule für die Oboe. Elementary method for oboe. (Hinke, Gustav Adolf). *Peters. £0.70* VT/AC (B72-50281)

Preliminary exercises for the oboe. (Beaumont, Adrian). *Schott. £0.40* VT/AF (B72-51180)

Prélude à l'après-midi d'un faune. (Debussy, Claude). *Peters: Hinrichsen. £3.50* MMJ (B72-50143)

Prélude à l'après-midi d'un faune. (Debussy, Claude). *Peters: Hinrichsen. £0.75* MMJ (B72-50144)

Prélude à l'après-midi d'un faune. Prelude to 'The afternoon of a faun'. (Debussy, Claude). *Chappell. Unpriced* MMJ (B72-50967)

Prelude and fugue on a theme by Liszt. (Stevenson, Ronald). *Oxford University Press. £0.50* R/Y (B72-50209) ISBN 0 19 375780 x

Preludes for four: for treble recorder (or flute), violin, cello and harpsichord (or piano). (Chagrin, Francis). *Novello. £1.50* NUSRNS (B72-50534)

Premru, Raymond. Tissington variations: for four trombones. *Musica rara. Unpriced* WUNS/T (B72-51247)

Prentice-Hall contemporary perspectives in music education series. *(Prentice-Hall)* Madsen, Clifford K. Experimental research in music. *Prentice-Hall. Unpriced* A/B (B72-21770) ISBN 0 13 295097 9

Preparatory exercises, Op. 16: for piano. (Schmitt, Aloys). *Chappell. £0.45* Q/AF (B72-51005)

Preset chords for guitar. (Roberts, Don). *Francis, Day and Hunter. £0.75* TS/AF (B72-50706)

Prichard, Rowland H. Hyfrydol. Hymn for our time: for three-part chorus of mixed voices with piano (or organ) accompaniment. *Schirmer: Chappell. Unpriced* DM (B72-50033)

Prima vista: für Diapositivbilder und unbestimmte Schallquellen. (Kagel, Mauricio). *Universal. Unpriced* LN (B72-50136)

Prince Igor. - Overture. Price Igor overture. (Borodin, Alexander). *Boosey and Hawkes. £3.90* WMK (B72-51218)

Processional prelude. (Butterworth, Arthur). *Novello. £1.00* WMJ (B72-51197)
Prodigal son = Der verlorene Sohn. Op.81: third parable for church performance. (Britten, Benjamin). *Faber music. Unpriced* CC (B72-50011)
Progressive organist: all grades Associated Board standard Book 8. (Trevor, C H). *Elkin. £0.55* R/AY (B72-50205)
Prokofieff, Serge. *See* Prokofiev, Sergei.
Prokofiev, Sergei.
Concerto for piano, no.5, in G major. Op.55. Piano concerto 5. Opus 55. *Boosey and Hawkes. £1.75* MPQF (B72-50971)
Lieutenant Kije. Op.60. - Wedding of Kije, Troika. Two pieces. *Boosey and Hawkes. £3.00* WMK/JR (B72-50312)
Symphony no.7. Opus 131. Sinfonie Nr.7. Opus 131. *Peters: Hinrichsen. Unpriced* MME (B72-50963)
Prologue for an unwritten play: for SATB chorus with B flat clarinet, orchestra chimes (or hand bells) and piano. (Boyd, Jack). *Warner: Blossom. Unpriced* ENYFVDW (B72-50839)
Prologue, Night piece and Blues for two: for clarinet (B flat) and piano. (Banks, Don). *Schott. Unpriced* VVPJ (B72-51189)
Promised land. (Arch, Gwyn). *Feldman. £0.40* FDE (B72-50069)
Psalm singer's amusement. - *Excerpts.* The angel's carol: SATBB a capella. (Billings, William). *Peters: Hinrichsen. £0.50* EZDP/LF (B72-50404)
Psalm singer's amusement. - *Excerpts.* The bird: SATBB. (Billings, William). *Peters: Hinrichsen. £0.40* DM (B72-50363)
Psalm-singer's amusement. - *Excerpts.* Modern music: SATB a cappella. (Billings, William). *Peters: Hinrichsen. £0.75* EZDW (B72-50410)
Psylex (1968): für Mezzosopran, Flöte und Tonband. (Karkoschka, Erhard). *Bosse: Bärenreiter. £2.25* KFNE/VRDX (B72-50479)
Puer natus: SSAATTBB (or SSAA or TTBB). (Hoddinott, Alun). *Oxford University Press. Unpriced* DP/LF (B72-50374) ISBN 0 19 343030 4
Purcell, Harold. Good-night Vienna: an operetta in three acts. (Posford, George). *Keith Prowse. £1.25* CF (B72-50797)
Purcell, Henry.
Come, let us drink: compleat, pleasant and divertive. *Galliard. £0.93* GEZDW/XD/AZ (B72-50893)
King Arthur. The music in King Arthur: a dramatic opera (1691),. *Novello. £1.50* CC (B72-50342)
Ode for Queen Mary's birthday, 1694. Come ye sons of art. *Schott. £0.75* DX (B72-50048)
Thou knowest, Lord, the secrets of our hearts. Z.580. *Oxford University Press. Unpriced* FLDK (B72-50890) ISBN 0 19 351113 4
Purple heather. (Ewing, Montague). *Norman Richardson Band Arrangements. Unpriced* UMMHW (B72-50718)
Purple heather. (Ewing, Montague). *Norman Richardson Band Arrangements. Unpriced* WMHW (B72-50766)
Purslow, Frank. The constant lovers: more English folk songs from the Hammond & Gardiner Mss. *English Folk Dance Society Publications. £0.50* KEZDW/G/AYD (B72-50127)
Put thou thy trust in the Lord: introit for double choir (unaccompanied). (Bliss, *Sir* Arthur). *Novello. £0.07* EZDK (B72-50846)
Put your hand in the hand: for mixed chorus SATB. (MacLellan, Gene). *Ardmore and Beechwood. Unpriced* ENYGNTDH (B72-50387)
Queen's fanfare: for trumpets and trombones. (Walton, *Sir* William). *Oxford University Press. £0.40* WNGN (B72-50781) ISBN 0 19 368186 2
Quine, Hector. Introduction to the guitar. *Oxford University Press. £0.80* TS/AC (B72-50245) ISBN 0 19 322325 2
Räby. (Allan, Geoffrey). *Peter Maurice. Unpriced* WMGM (B72-50301)
Radio Corporation of America. *Record Division.* Complete catalogue of RCA Red Seal, RCA Victor, RCA Victrola, RCA International, RCA Neon, Vanguard, Barclay records and tapes
1971: ... all records listed up to October 31st, 1971. *50 Curzon St., W1Y 8EU: RCA Ltd, Record Division. £3.50* A/FD(WM) (B72-30326) ISBN 0 9500382 1 0
Ragtime blues guitarists. (Grossman, Stefan). *Oak Publications; 78 Newman St., W.1: Music Sales Ltd. £1.60* ATS/HHW/E(M) (B72-50003) ISBN 0 8256 0118 5
Raguenet, François. Paralèle des Italiens et des François, en ce qui regard la musique et les opéras. A comparison between the French and Italian musick and operas. 1st English ed., reprinted. *Gregg. £11.40* AC(YJ/XF/ZB) (B72-09123) ISBN 0 576 28446 7
Rail. Op.57: symphonic picture for orchestra. (Josephs, Wilfred). *Galaxy: Galliard. Unpriced* MM/JR (B72-50140)
Rainbow, Bernarr. Music in the classroom. 2nd ed. *Heinemann Educational. £1.25* A(VC) (B72-26088) ISBN 0 435 81746 9
Ralph Vaughan Williams, 1872-1958: a guide to the centenary exhibition at the British Museum, 29 September to 15 December 1972. (Willetts, Pamela Joan). *British Museum. £0.10* BVD(WJ) (B72-28008) ISBN 0 7141 0337 3
Ralston, Alfred. Young Winston. - *Excerpts.* Jennie's theme: from the film. *Chappell. £0.25* QPK/JR (B72-51047)
Rameau, Jean Philippe. Treatise on harmony. *Dover Publications: Constable. £8.75* A/R (B72-01562) ISBN 0 486 22461 9
Ramsbotham, A. Give almes of thy goods. (Tye, Christopher). *Oxford University Press. Unpriced* DK (B72-50361) ISBN 0 19 352113 x
Rapaport, Dulce. Arion and the dolphins: for unison choir and instruments. (Marshall, Nicholas). *Chester. Unpriced* CQN (B72-50348)
Raphael, Günther. Die Gesänge zu Georg Christian Schmellis 'Musicalischen Gesang-Buch' S.439-507 sowie sechs Lieder aus dem 'Klavierbüchlein für Anne Magdalena Bach'. S.511-14, 516, 517. (Bach, Johann Sebastian). *Bärenreiter. Unpriced* KFXDH/AY (B72-50490)
Rapley, Felton. Oklahoma!. - *Excerpts.* Four songs. (Rodgers, Richard). *Williamson. Unpriced* LNSK/DW (B72-50137)
Rastall, Richard. Complete keyboard works. (Rogers, Benjamin). *Stainer and Bell. Unpriced* QSQ/AZ (B72-51052)
Raxach, Enrique.
The looking glass: for organ. *Hinrichsen. £1.25* RJ (B72-50213)
The looking-glass: for organ. *Peters. Unpriced* RJ (B72-51057)
Paraphrase: pour voix d'alto et 11 instrumentistes. *Peters, Hinrichsen. £1.80* KFQE/MRDX (B72-50130)
Raynor, Henry.
Haydn. (Landon, Howard Chandler Robbins). *3 Queen Sq., WC1N 3AU: Faber and Faber Ltd. £1.75* BHE(N) (B72-09750) ISBN 0 571 08361 7
A social history of music: from the middle ages to Beethoven. *Barrie and Jenkins. £5.00* A(XA1827) (B72-12717) ISBN 0 214 65783 3
Raynor, John. Eleven Songs. *Galliard. Unpriced* KDW (B72-50466) ISBN 0 85249 040 2
R.C.A. *See* Radio Corporation of America.
Reaks, Brian. Nursery songs from Humberside. *British and Continental. £0.25* JFDW/GJ/AYDJGX (B72-50101)
Rebecca. (Patterson, Paul). *Weinberger. Unpriced* KHYE/MPQ (B72-50946)
Record Bargains. *See* Record Collector.
Record Collector: monthly guide to your kind of music No.1- ; Feb. 1972-. *Hanover Publications; 34 Foubert's Place, W.1: Haymarket Publishing Ltd. £0.10* A/FD(B) (B72-07362)
Recorder: how to play the descant recorder, complete with rudiments of music, fingering and studies. (Slaney, Ivor). *Campbell, Connelly. £0.40* VSR/AC (B72-51173)
Recordmasters. *(Allan)*
Blyth, Alan. Colin Davis. *Allan. £1.50* A/EC(P) (B72-50792) ISBN 0 7110 0319 x
Greenfield, Edward. Joan Sutherland. *Allan. £1.50* AKFL/E(P) (B72-15424) ISBN 0 7110 0318 1
Red Arrows march. (Banks, Eric). *Robbins Music. £0.20* QPK/AGM (B72-50610)
Reda, Siegfried.
Ich weiss ein lieblich Engelspiel: Choralkonzert für Orgel. *Bärenreiter. £1.50* RF (B72-50633)
Neujahrslied 'Der du die Zeit in Handen hast'. *Bärenreiter. £0.05* EZDP/LGM (B72-50407)
Reder, Philip. The great piano virtuosos of our time. (Lenz, Wilhelm von). *Regency Press. £1.20* AQ/E(M/XHH45) (B72-13443) ISBN 0 7212 0138 5
Reed, John. Schubert - the final years. *3 Queen Sq., WC1N 3AU: Faber. £5.00* BSF(N/XHF4) (B72-26089) ISBN 0 571 09842 8
Rees, Gordon. Sleepy shores. (Pearson, Johnny). *Keith Prowse Music. Unpriced* MSJ (B72-50157)
Rees, Wendy U. Babe of Bethlehem: a nativity, for unison voices, piano, recorders, tuned and untuned percussion. (Burtch, Mervyn). *Chappell. £0.50* JFE/NYFSDP/LF (B72-50911)
Reflections: piano solo. (Panufnik, Andrzej). *Boosey and Hawkes. £0.75* QPJ (B72-50192)
Régeny, Rudolf Wagner-. *See* Wagner-Régeny, Rudolf.
Regner, Hermann. Percussion-Duos. *Schott. Unpriced* XNU (B72-50789)
Regney, Noel. Do you hear what I hear?: Stadium dimension for marching bands. *Jewel Music. Unpriced* UMMK/DW (B72-50258)
Reicha, Anton. Variations for two flutes. Op.20. *Peters. £1.60* VRNU/T (B72-50729)
Reimann, Aribert. Zyklus: cycle for baritone and orchestra. *Schott. £3.00* KGNE/MDW (B72-50494)
Reingold, Carmel Berman. Johann Sebastian Bach. *32 Palmer St., S.W.1: F. Watts. £1.50* BBC(N) (B72-22482) ISBN 0 85166 320 6
Reisinger. Frühlingsbotschaft: Konzertwalzer. (Fucik, Julius). *Bosworth. £0.50* MSHW (B72-50982)
Relton, William. Beg, steal or borrow: Britain's Eurovision song 1972. (Cole, Tony). *Valley Music. Unpriced* UMMK/DW/JS (B72-50259)
Renaissance music. (Hendrie, Gerald). *Walton Hall, Bletchley, Bucks.: Open University Press. £1.10* A(XRE201) (B72-50334) ISBN 0 335 00657 4
Renbourn, John. Guitar pieces. *Oak Publications: Pentangle, Music Sales. Unpriced* TSPMK/AAY (B72-51152)
Rendell, Don. Robbins flute tutor: a contemporary method Part 1. *Robbins. £1.50* VR/AC (B72-50725)
Repliche: per flauto e zimbalo ungherese (o clavicembalo) by Miklos Kocsár. (Kocsár, Miklos). *Boosey and Hawkes. £0.85* VRPLTWT (B72-50738)
Report on 'The star-spangled banner', 'Hail Columbia', 'America', 'Yankee Doodle'. (Sonneck, Oscar George). *Dover Publications: Constable. £1.25* ADW(KM/YT) (B72-31292) ISBN 0 486 22237 3
Requiem. Op.39: for solo bass-baritone, chorus, string quintet and orchestra. (Josephs, Wilfred). *Weinberger. Unpriced* EMDE/KDN (B72-50049)
Responses: for SATB chorus, a cappella. (Rhodes, Joseph W). *Warner: Blossom Music. £0.35* EZDH (B72-50843)
Resurrection canticle: for sixteen solo voices. (Mellers, Wilfrid). *Galliard. £0.83* EZDH/LL (B72-50056)
Retrospect. *See* Billings, Williams.
Reynolds, Gordon.
Full swell. *Borough Green, Sevenoaks, Kent: Novello. £0.40* AR/E (B72-22496) ISBN 0 85360 039 2
Spare time for music. (Epps, David). *British Broadcasting Corporation. £1.20* C/AY (B72-50793) ISBN 0 563 10689 1
Reynolds, Vernon. 48 études for French horn. 48 études for trumpet: transcribed from 48 études for French horn. *Schirmer: Chappell. Unpriced* WS/AF (B72-50317)
Rhodes, Joseph W. Responses: for SATB chorus, a cappella. *Warner: Blossom Music. £0.35* EZDH (B72-50843)
Rice, Tim. Jesus Christ superstar. - *Excerpts.* Jesus Christ superstar: a rock opera. (Webber, Andrew Lloyd). *Leeds Music. £1.25* KDW (B72-50119)
Richard Strauss: a critical commentary on his life and works Vol.3. (Del Mar, Norman). *Barrie and Jenkins. £7.00* BSU(N) (B72-20309) ISBN 0 214 65158 4
Richardson, Norman.
Nabucodonosor. - Va pensiero. The chorus of Hebrew slaves. (Verdi, Giuseppe). *Norman Richardson Band Arrangements. Unpriced* WMK/DW (B72-50310)
The white company - overture. *Boosey and Hawkes. £3.30* WMJ (B72-51216)
Richmond, Stanley. Clarinet and saxophone experience. *Darton, Longman and Todd. £3.25* AVV(B) (B72-50004) ISBN 0 232 51148 9
Ricordanza: for piano solo. (Liszt, Franz). *Bärenreiter. £0.65* QPJ (B72-50595)
Riders to the sea: an opera in one act. (Vaughan Williams, Ralph). *Oxford University Press. £5.00* CQC (B72-50805) ISBN 0 19 339335 2
Ridley, George. Blaydon races. *Boosey and Hawkes. £0.30* KGXDW (B72-50944)
Riedel, Friedrich W. (Selected works for keyboard instruments, *by Johann Joseph Fux, edited by Friedrich W. Riedel*). *Nagel. £1.15* PWPJ (B72-50559)
Ries, Ferdinand. Sonata sentimentale for flute & piano in E flat major. Op.169. Sonata in E flat major for flute or clarinet and piano. *Bärenreiter. £2.45* VRPE (B72-50733)
Rigaudon. (Handel, George Frideric). *Bosworth. £1.80* MJ (B72-50958)
Ring ding bells: a song for Christmas. (Verrall, Pamela). *British and Continental. Unpriced* JE/XTPDW/LF (B72-50902)
Ripin, Edwin M. Keyboard instruments: studies in keyboard organology. *Edinburgh University Press. £3.00* APW/B (B72-15427) ISBN 0 85224 202 6
Rise of the Peking Opera, 1770-1870: social aspects of the theatre in Manchu China. (Mackerras, Colin P). *Clarendon Press. £6.00* BZHKAC(XFYK101) (B72-31290) ISBN 0 19 815137 3
Rise up shepherd: a hymn-sequence with readings for voices with optional baritone solo with accompaniments for piano and optional instruments. (Parry, William Howard). *Keith Prowse. £0.50* DPDE/LF (B72-50042)
Ritrovata figlia. Op. 39. - *Excerpts.* Andantino. (Kozeluch, Leopold). *Charnwood Music. Unpriced* RSPMK (B72-51082)
Robbins, Jerome. West Side story: a musical. (Laurents, Arthur). *Heinemann Educational. £0.50* BBMMACM (B72-08533) ISBN 0 435 23529 x
Robbins flute tutor: a contemporary method
Part 1. (Rendell, Don). *Robbins. £1.50* VR/AC (B72-50725)
Robert-Blunn, John. Northern accent: the life story of the Northern School of Music. *Sherratt. £2.00* A(VP/YDJE(X) (B72-18915) ISBN 0 85427 029 9
Robert Brown - instant hero: for voices, glockenspiels or chime-bars and piano. (Arch, Gwyn). *Feldman. Unpriced* JFE/XPQDX (B72-50454)
Roberts, Don.
An album of classical guitar studies. *Francis, Day and Hunter. £0.40* TS/AF (B72-51146)
Preset chords for guitar. *Francis, Day and Hunter. £0.75* TS/AF (B72-50706)
Robertson, Alec. The church cantatas of J.S. Bach. *Cassell. £5.00* BBCADE (B72-26660) ISBN 0 304 93822 x
Robinson, Louie. Nat King Cole: an intimate biography. (Cole, Maria). *W.H. Allen. £2.10* AKG/E(P) (B72-23643) ISBN 0 491 00782 5
Robinson, Michael Finlay. Naples and Neapolitan opera. *Clarendon Press. £8.00* AC(YJN/XF101) (B72-30742) ISBN 0 19 816124 7
Robson, Alan.
Three Parisian chansons: for 4 voices (SATB). (Thomas, Bernard). *North Horton, Lustleigh, Newton Abbot, Devon: Antico. Unpriced* EZDU/AYHP (B72-50860)
Vingt et sept chansons musicales à quatre parties. - *Excerpts.* Fourteen chansons: for four recorders or voices, ATTB,. (Attaingnant, Pierre). *Pro musica. Unpriced* EZDU/AY (B72-50857)
Robson, Max. Seven double canons: for four instruments or voices. (Thomas, Bernard). *Pro musica. Unpriced* EZDU/X/AY (B72-50861)
Rocherolle, Eugénie R.
And so it was (Christmas): for SATB chorus and piano. *Warner: Blossom Music. Unpriced* EZDH/LF (B72-50055)
Christmas day is comin': for unison, two-part or three part chorus. *Warner: Blossom Music. Unpriced* FDW/LF (B72-50423)
Rock, Gordon F.
A Mass for all ages and Offertory hymn. *Gordon F. Rock. Unpriced* JE/TSDG (B72-50094)

Missa de saeculis. *Gordon F. Rock. Unpriced* JE/TSDG (B72-50095)

Rockbooks. *(Studio Vista)*

Laing, Dave. Buddy Holly. *Studio Vista. £1.40* AKGDW/GB/E(D) (B72-07981) ISBN 0 289 70129 5

Morse, David. Motown & the arrival of black music. *Studio Vista. £1.40* A/GB (B72-30069) ISBN 0 289 70131 7

Rockwell, Anne. Savez-vous planter les choux?, and other French songs. *Hamilton. £1.80* JFE/TSDW/GJ/AYH (B72-50914) ISBN 0 241 02256 8

Rococo symphony. (Stamitz, Johann). *Bosworth. £2.25* ME (B72-50957)

Rödding, Gerhard. Choralbuch zum Evangelischen Kirchengesangbuch: mit den Begleitsätzen des Württembergischen Choralbuches bearbeitet von Karl Gerok und Hans-Arnold Metzger und mit Begleitsätzen zu den Liedern des Anhangs zum Rheinisch-Westfälisch-Lippischen Gesangbuch. *Bärenreiter. Unpriced* DM/LSET/AY (B72-50371)

Rodgers, Richard.

Oklahoma!. - *Excerpts.* Four songs. *Williamson. Unpriced* LNSK/DW (B72-50137)

Rodgers & Hammerstein revisited

Vol.1. *Williamson Music. £0.75* KDW (B72-50114)

Vol.2. *Williamson Music. £0.75* KDW (B72-50115)

Symphonic marches for concert band. *Williamson. Unpriced* UMGM (B72-50254)

Rodgers & Hammerstein revisited

Vol.1. (Rodgers, Richard). *Williamson Music. £0.75* KDW (B72-50114)

Vol.2. (Rodgers, Richard). *Williamson Music. £0.75* KDW (B72-50115)

Roe, Betty.

9 songs: for voice and keyboard. *Thames. Unpriced* KDW (B72-50116)

A flourish of fanfares: for 4 flat trumpets. *Thames. Unpriced* WSNSGN (B72-50322)

Jazz songs for soprano & double bass. *Yorke. Unpriced* KFLE/SSDW (B72-50478)

Roe, Leonard McDermott. The John McCormack discography. *Oakwood Press. £1.20* AKGH/FD(P/WT) (B72-27620) ISBN 0 85361 106 8

Rogers, Benjamin. Complete keyboard works. *Stainer and Bell. Unpriced* QSQ/AZ (B72-51052)

Rohwer, Jens. Die Seligpreisungen: ein Lobgesang für Chor und Gemeinde. *Bärenreiter. £0.10* EZDH (B72-50396)

Rokos, K W.

Symphony in D major. Op.5, no.5. Rococo symphony. (Stamitz, Johann). *Bosworth. £2.25* ME (B72-50957)

Sympony no.40 in G minor. K.550. - Allegro molto. Exposition of Mozart's Symphony no.40 (1st movement). (Mozart, Wolfgang Amadeus). *Bosworth. £2.30* MJ (B72-50959)

Rolland, Paul.

New tunes for strings

Book 1. (Fletcher, Stanley). *Boosey and Hawkes. £4.90* RXM/AF (B72-51085)

Book 2. (Fletcher, Stanley). *Boosey and Hawkes. £4.90* RXM/AF (B72-51086)

Rolling Stones. (Dalton, David). *Amsco Music Publishing; 78 Newman St., W1E 4JZ: Music Sales Ltd. Unpriced* AB/GB/E(P) (B72-24870) ISBN 0 8256 2653 6

Romano Drum song book

Vol.1. (Hurley, Bernard). *Romanestan Publications. £0.25* JFEZDW/GJ/AYCG (B72-50105)

Rome, Harold. Gone with the wind: souvenir music album. *Chappell. £0.75* KDW (B72-50467)

'Ronde: experiment in collective work by an indefinite number of performers. (Globokar, Vinko). *Litolff: Peters. Unpriced* CB (B72-50795)

Rooke, Pat.

A golden legend. (Arch, Gwyn). *British and Continental. Unpriced* CQN/L (B72-50808)

The promised land. (Arch, Gwyn). *Feldman. £0.40* FDE (B72-50069)

Robert Brown - instant hero: for voices, glockenspiels or chime-bars and piano. (Arch, Gwyn). *Feldman. Unpriced* JFE/XPQDX (B72-50454)

Roper, Alan. Clochemerle. *Francis, Day and Hunter. £0.20* QPK/JS (B72-50619)

Rorem, Ned.

Gloria: for two solo voices and piano. *Boosey and Hawkes. £1.25* JNEDGC (B72-50919)

Praises for the nativity: for four solo voices (SATB) mixed chorus and organ. *Boosey and Hawkes. £0.75* DE/LF (B72-50017)

Sonata for piano, no.1. Sonata 1: piano. *Peters. £1.80* QPE (B72-50573)

Sonata for piano, no.3. Sonata 3: piano. *Peters. £2.20* QPE (B72-50574)

Rose, Bernard. Cathedral music. - *Excerpts.* Lord, how long wilt thou be angry?: anthem for SAATB (unaccompanied). (Hayes, William). *£0.10* EZDK (B72-50847)

Rose, Gregory. Everlasting Mary: carol. *Boosey and Hawkes. £0.05* EZDP/LF (B72-50854)

Rose, John Luke. The pleasures of youth. Op.11: cantata for mixed chorus and orchestra. *Boosey and Hawkes. Unpriced* DX (B72-50835)

Rose of Bethlehem: S.S.A. (Verrall, Pamela). *British and Continental. Unpriced* FDP/LF (B72-50872)

Rossetti, Christina. Love came down at Christmas: SATB. (Rutter, John). *Oxford University Press. Unpriced* DP/LF (B72-50040) ISBN 0 19 343025 8

Rossini, Gioacchino Antonio. Il Barbiere di Siviglia. - *Excerpts.* Largo al factotum. *Charnwood Music. Unpriced* RSPMK/DW (B72-51083)

Rostand, Claude. Liszt. *Calder and Boyars. £2.50* BLJ(N) (B72-27438) ISBN 0 7145 0342 8

Rota, Nina.

The godfather. - Love theme. Speak softly, love. *Chappell. £0.25* KDW (B72-50468)

The godfather: selection of themes from the film. *Chappell. Unpriced* WMK/JR (B72-51219)

Rota, Nino.

The godfather. - *Excerpts.* The godfather waltz. *Famous Chappell. £0.20* QPK/AHW/JR (B72-50611)

The godfather - love theme. *Famous Chappell. £0.20* QPK/JR (B72-50615)

The godfather. - Waltz. Come live your life with me. *Famous Chappell. £0.20* QPK/DW/JR (B72-50613)

The godfather: souvenir song album. *Chappell. £1.25* KDW/JR (B72-50932)

Roth, Ernst. The nymph and the farmer. La Fée et le cultivateur = The nymph and the farmer, Op.72: a lyric legend. (Cherepnin, Alexander). *Boosey and Hawkes. £4.50* CC (B72-50337)

Rothenberg, Peter.

The electronic organ: a course for beginners. *Schott. Unpriced* RPV/AC (B72-50646)

Folksongs: for 2 manuals and pedal. *Schott. £1.20* RPVK/DW/G/AY (B72-51063)

Routh, Francis.

Contemporary British music: the twenty-five years from 1945 to 1970. *Macdonald and Co. £6.95* A(YC/XPE26) (B72-26091) ISBN 0 356 03773 8

Dialogue. Op. 16: for violin and orchestra. *Lengnick. £1.00* SPK (B72-51119)

Lumen Christi. Op. 15: a meditation on the festival of Easter: organ solo. *Boosey and Hawkes. £1.30* R/LL (B72-50631)

Rowley, Alec. Monsieur de la plume: fragments from the life of Robert Louis Stevenson: music for children's voices and piano. *Ashdown. Unpriced* CN (B72-50800)

Royal School of Church Music. Festival service books 6. *Royal School of Church Music. Unpriced* DGM (B72-50022) ISBN 0 85402 047 0

Royal School of Church Music. English church music: a collection of essays 1972. *Addington Palace, Croydon, CR9 5AD: Royal School of Church Music. £0.76* A/LD(YC/D) (B72-18918) ISBN 0 85402 048 9

Rubbra, Edmund.

Discourse. Op.27: for harp & cello. *Lengnick. £0.25* SRPLTS (B72-50243)

Sinfonia sacra: 'The resurrection'. Op.140: for soprano, contralto, baritone, chorus and orchestra. *Lengnick. £1.00* DE/LL (B72-50812)

To Him we sing, Op. 34: unison carol for children's voices and piano. *Lengnick. £0.05* JFDP/LF (B72-50905)

Ruf, Hugo.

Concerto for keyboard & string orchestra in A major. Op 26, no.2. Concerto 2, A-Dur: für Cembalo oder Orgel und Streicher. (Corrette, Michel). *Schott. £1.20* RXMPPWF (B72-51090)

Sonatas by old English masters: for treble recorder and basso continuo

Vol.1. *Bärenreiter. £1.50* VSSPE/AYD (B72-50752)

Vol.2. *Bärenreiter. £1.50* VSSPE/AYD (B72-50753)

Ruffo, Vincenzo. Capricci in musica a tre voci. - *Excerpts.* Four pieces, nos. 9,15,23,5: for threee instruments, ATB. *Pro musica. Unpriced* LNT (B72-50955)

Ruft es aus in alle Welt. (In Festo Nativatatis): Weihnachts Kantate, für Sopran, Alt, Tenor, Bass, Vierstimmigen gemischten Chor, drei Trompeten, Pauken, Streicher und Basso continuo. (Telemann, Georg Philipp). *Bärenreiter. £1.25* EMDE/LF (B72-50382)

Rüggeberg, Wilhelm Brückner-. *See* Brückner-Rüggeberg, Wilhelm.

Ruppel, Paul Ernst. Ernte des Lebens/ by Paul Ernst Ruppel; Worte from 2. Korinther and Gerhard Valentin with Osterlied/ by Paul Ernst Ruppel; Worte: Alter Osterruf and Gerhard Valentin. *Bärenreiter. Unpriced* EZDH (B72-50397)

Russell, Ross. Jazz style in Kansas City and the Southwest. *2 Brook St., W1Y 1AA: University of California Press. £5.95* AMT/E(M/YTSWK/XNF15) (B72-02169) ISBN 0 520 01853 2

Russell-Smith, Geoffry.

The arms of Hungary: SATB unaccompanied. (Kodály, Zoltán). *Boosey and Hawkes. £0.05* EZDW (B72-50412)

Chorus music. 18 part songs: for unaccompanied choir Vol.1. (Bartók, Béla). *Boosey and Hawkes. £0.40* FEZDW (B72-50885)

Chorus music. 18 part songs: for unaccompanied choir Vol.2. (Bartók, Béla). *Boosey and Hawkes. £0.40* FEZDW (B72-50886)

Chorus music. 18 part songs: for unaccompanied choir Vol.3. (Bartók, Béla). *Boosey and Hawkes. £0.40* FEZDW (B72-50887)

Eve, my sweet: S.fl unaccompanied. (Kodály, Zoltán). *Boosey and Hawkes. £0.05* FEZDW (B72-50428)

False spring: SSA unaccompanied. (Kodály, Zoltán). *Boosey and Hawkes. £0.05* FEZDW (B72-50429)

God's mercy: T. Bar. B. unaccompanied. (Kodály, Zoltán). *Boosey and Hawkes. £0.09* GEZDH (B72-50435)

The good housewife: folk-song, S.S. unaccompanied. (Kodály, Zoltán). *Boosey and Hawkes. £0.05* FLEZDW (B72-50434)

Greeting on St John's day: SAB unaccompanied. (Kodály, Zoltán). *Boosey and Hawkes. £0.05* EZDW (B72-50413)

Grow, tresses = Hajinśvesztö: SSA unaccompanied. (Kodály, Zoltán). *Boosey and Hawkes. £0.05* FEZDW (B72-50888)

Mid the oak trees: folk song SSA unaccompanied. (Kodály, Zoltán). *Boosey and Hawkes. y0.05* FEZDW (B72-50427)

Pentatonic music

Vol.3: 100 Cheremissian melodies. (Kodály, Zoltán). *Boosey and Hawkes. £0.30* JFEZDW/PP (B72-50917)

Wine, sweet wine = Méz, méz: SSSAAA unaccompanied. (Kodály, Zoltán). *Boosey and Hawkes. Unpriced* FEZDW (B72-50889)

Rust, Brian Arthur Lovell. The dance bands. *Allan. £3.75* ALH(QB/XMP35) (B72-27440) ISBN 0 7110 0341 6

Rutland, Harold. Trinity College of Music, the first hundred years. *Mandeville Place, W.1: Trinity College of Music. £0.70* A(VP/YDB/X) (B72-13439) ISBN 0 9502340 0 1

Rutter, John.

Communion service: for congregational use with optional SATB choir. *Oxford University Press. Unpriced* JDGS (B72-50085) ISBN 0 19 351638 1

From east to west: SATB unacc. *Oxford University Press. Unpriced* EZDM (B72-50061) ISBN 0 19 343026 6

Love came down at Christmas: SATB. *Oxford University Press. Unpriced* DP/LF (B72-50040) ISBN 0 19 343025 8

Sacrae concentus ac symphoniae. - *Excerpts.* Canzona quarta: for 4 trumpets and 4 trombones (4 trumpets, 2 horns and 2 trombones). (Grillo, Giovanni Battista). *Musica rara. £1.50* WNN (B72-51220)

Sacrae symphoniae. Bk. 1. Symphoniae sacrae

Vol.1: Canzon primi toni à 8: for 4 trumpets and 4 trombones. (Gabrieli, Giovanni). *Musica rara. Unpriced* WMJ (B72-51198)

Sacrae symphoniae. Bk. 1. Symphoniae sacrae

Vol.2: Canzon septimi toni à 8 (no.1): for 4 trumpets and 4 trombones. (Gabrieli, Giovanni). *Musica rara. Unpriced* WMJ (B72-51199)

Sacrae symphoniae. Bk. 1. Symphoniae sacrae

Vol.3: Canzon septimi toni à 8 (no.2): for 4 trumpets and 4 trombones. (Gabrieli, Giovanni). *Musica rara. Unpriced* WMJ (B72-51200)

Sacrae symphoniae. Bk. 1. Symphoniae sacrae

Vol.4: Canzon noni toni à 8: for 4 trumpets and 4 trombones. (Gabrieli, Giovanni). *Musica rara. Unpriced* WMJ (B72-51201)

Sacrae symphoniae. Bk. 1. Symphoniae sacrae

Vol.5: Canzon duo decimi toni à 8: for 4 trumpets and 4 trombones. (Gabrieli, Giovanni). *Musica rara. £2.00* WMJ (B72-51202)

Sacrae symphoniae. Bk. 1. Symphoniae sacrae

Vol.6: Sonata pian e forte à 8: for 2 trumpets and 6 trombones. (Gabrieli, Giovanni). *Musica rara. £1.80* WMJ (B72-51203)

Sacrae symphoniae. Bk. 1. Symphoniae sacrae

Vol.7: Canzon primi toni à 10: for 7 trumpets and 3 trombones, (5 trumpets and 5 trombones). (Gabrieli, Giovanni). *Musica rara. £2.50* WMJ (B72-51204)

Sacrae symphoniae. Bk. 1. Symphoniae sacrae

Vol.8: Canzon duo decimi toni à 10 (no.1): for 6 trumpets and 4 trombones. (Gabrieli, Giovanni). *Musica rara. £2.85* WMJ (B72-51205)

Sacrae symphoniae. Bk. 1. Symphoniae sacrae

Vol.9: Canzon duo decimi toni à 10 (no.2): for 6 trumpets and 4 trombones. (Gabrieli, Giovanni). *Musica rara. £3.00* WMJ (B72-51206)

Sacrae symphoniae. Bk. 1. Symphoniae sacrae

Vol.10: Canzon duo decimi toni à 10 (no.3): for 5 trumpets and 5 trombones. (Gabrieli, Giovanni). *Musica rara. £2.50* WMJ (B72-51207)

Sacrae symphoniae. Bk. 1. Symphoniae sacrae

Vol.11: Canzon duo decimi toni à 10 (no.4): for 6 trumpets and 4 trombones. (Gabrieli, Giovanni). *Musica rara. £3.50* WMJ (B72-51208)

Sacrae symphoniae. Bk. 1. Symphoniae sacrae

Vol.12: Canzon in echo duo decima toni à 10: for 6 trumpets, 4 trombones and 2 organs (4 trumpets, 2 horns, 4 trombones and 2 organs). (Gabrieli, Giovanni). *Musica rara. £3.00* WMJ (B72-51209)

Sacrae symphoniae. Bk. 1. Symphoniae sacrae

Vol.13: Canzon septimi octavi toni à 12: for 6 trumpets and 6 trombones. (Gabrieli, Giovanni). *Musica rara. Unpriced* WMJ (B72-51210)

Sacrae symphoniae. Bk. 1. Symphoniae sacrae

Vol.14: Canzon noni toni à 12: for 6 trumpets and 6 trombones. (Gabrieli, Giovanni). *Musica rara. Unpriced* WMJ (B72-51211)

Sacrae symphoniae. Bk. 1. Symphoniae sacrae

Vol.15: Sonata octavi toni à 12: for 2 trumpets and 10 trombones (2 trumpets, 2 horns and 8 trombones). (Gabrieli, Giovanni). *Musica rara. Unpriced* WMJ (B72-51212)

Sacrae symphoniae. Bk. 1. Symphoniae sacrae

Vol.16: Canzon quarti toni à 15: for 3 trumpets and 12 trombones. (Gabrieli, Giovanni). *Musica rara. Unpriced* WMJ (B72-51213)

Sadie, Stanley. Handel concertos. *British Broadcasting Corporation. £0.45* BHCAMF (B72-28683) ISBN 0 563 10349 3

Sadleir, Richard. A book of ballet: arranged and compiled for recorder by Richard Sadleir. *British & Continental. Unpriced* VSPMK/AHM/AY (B72-50747)

Sailing in: a Christmas carol, SATB. (Tate, Phyllis). *Oxford University Press. Unpriced* DP/LF (B72-50041) ISBN 0 19 343021 5

St Francis and the wolf of Gubbio; or, Brother Francis' lamb chops: an opera in 2 acts. (Themerson, Stefan). *De Harmonie: Gaberbocchus. Unpriced* CC (B72-50796)

St Paul's suite: for string orchestra. (Holst, Gustav). *Curwen Edition. Unpriced* RXMG (B72-50649)

Saint-Saens, Camille. The music of Saint-Saëns. *Francis, Day and Hunter. £0.35* QPK (B72-50607)

St Thomas Wake: foxtrot for orchestra on a pavan by John Bull. (Davies, Peter Maxwell). *Boosey and Hawkes. Unpriced* MMHKEF (B72-50511)
St Thomas Wake: foxtrot for orchestra on a pavan by John Bull. (Davies, Peter Maxwell). *Boosey and Hawkes. £2.50* MMHKEF (B72-50512)
Salkeld, Robert. Play the recorder. *Chappell. £1.40* VSR/AC (B72-50275)
Salter, Lionel. Chaconne: for violin and harpsichord. (Vitali, Tomaso). *Oxford University Press. £0.70* SPHJN (B72-50680) ISBN 0 19 359210 x
Salto de agna: accordion solo. (Bishop, Chiz). *Charnwood Music. Unpriced* RSPMHW (B72-51074)
Salute to spring: SSA. (Tomlins, Greta). *Lengnick. £0.13* FDW (B72-50078)
Salvation Army. Salvation Army Brass Band Journal (General series)
Nos.1625-1628: Gospel bells: song arrangement, by Ray Steadman-Allen; and, Calling to-day: flugel horn solo, by Ken James; Songs of the faith: selection, by Dean Goffin; Contemplation: meditation, by Philip Catelinet; The fight of faith: march, by Charles Skinner. *Salvationist Publishing and Supplies. Unpriced* WM/AY (B72-50298)
Salvation Army Brass Band Journal (Festival series)
Nos.341-344: Lift up your heads '(Gopsal): variations, by Dean Goffin. The present age: tone poem/ by Leslie Condon. My Christ (is all in all): euphonium solo/ by William Himes. Pledge for service: festival march/ by Eric Ball. *Salvationist Publishing & Supplies. Unpriced* WM/AY (B72-50760)
Salvation Army Brass Band Journal (Triumph series)
Nos 741-744: Never alone; selection, by Eiliv Herikstad. Variations on 'Nativity new', by Michael Kenyon. O return unto God; cornet solo, by Paul Marti. Mancunian; march, by Norman Hall. *Salvationist Publishing and Supplies. Unpriced* WM/AY (B72-50299)
Salvation Army Brass Band Journal (Triumph series).
Nos.745-748. God is love: cornet solo/ by Ray Steadman-Allen. Songs of friendship; selection/ by Kenneth Ketteringham. With gladsome mind:/ song arrangement by Derek Jordan. The harvest home. *Salvationist Publishing & Supplies. Unpriced* WM/AY (B72-50761)
Salve regina, A-moll: für Sopran, Alt und Basso continuo. (Scarlatti, Domenico). *Bärenreiter. £1.00* JNFEDJ (B72-50456)
Sammartini, Giuseppe.
Concerto for descant recorder & string orchestra in F major. Concerto in F: for descant recorder, strings and harpischord (piano). *Schott. Unpriced* RXMPVSRF (B72-50224)
Concerto for organ in A Major. Op.9 No.1. Concerto 1, A major: for harpsichord (organ), two violins and basso continuo. *Bärenreiter. £2.15* RXMPRF (B72-50657)
Sams, Eric. Brahms songs. *British Broadcasting Corporation. £0.45* BBTAKDW (B72-15425) ISBN 0 563 10431 7
Sancho Panza: orchestral overture. (Kelly, Brian). *Chappell. £4.25* MMJ (B72-50147)
Sancta Maria, Thomas de. *See* Thomas de Sancta Maria.
Sanctify, O Lord: a chorister's prayer. (Middleton, James Roland). *Royal School of Church Music. Unpriced* FDH (B72-50417)
Sandy, Stephen. Home from the range: for full chorus of mixed voices a cappella. (Wilson, Richard). *Schirmer Chappell. Unpriced* EZDW (B72-50067)
Sansom, Clive A. Favourites for recorder
No.1. *Feldman. £0.25* VSPMK/DW/G/AY (B72-50274)
Sar-Orain le Catriona Dhughlas. (Douglas, Katherine). *Domhnall Budge. £0.30* KEZDW (B72-50126)
Sargent, A W. Voices, pipes and pedals: the story of a life in music. *Mitre Press. £1.75* AD/EC(P) (B72-03928) ISBN 0 7051 0108 8
Sári, József. Contemplazione: per flauto e pianoforte. *Boosey and Hawkes. £1.00* VRPJ (B72-50736)
Sauer, Emil von. Two episodes from Lenau's Faust, no.2. - First Mephisto waltz. Mephisto waltz no.1. (Liszt, Franz). *Peters. £0.50* QPHW (B72-50182)
Savez-vous planter les choux?, and other French songs. (Rockwell, Anne). *Hamilton. £1.80* JFE/TSDW/GJ/AYH (B72-50914) ISBN 0 241 02256 8
Scaduto, Anthony.
Bob Dylan. *30 Gray's Inn Rd, WC1X 8JL: Abacus. £0.60* AKG/E(P) (B72-23642) ISBN 0 349 13127 9
Bob Dylan. *W.H. Allen. £2.50* AKG/E(P) (B72-12015) ISBN 0 491 00662 4
Scarlatti, Alessandro. Arianna: Kantate für Sopran, zwei Violinen und Basso continuo. *Peters. £2.00* KFLE/SNTPWDX (B72-50477)
Scarlatti, Domenico. Salve regina, A-moll: für Sopran, Alt und Basso continuo. *Bärenreiter. £1.00* JNFEDJ (B72-50456)
Scenes and arias: for soprano, mezzo-soprano, contralto and orchestra. (Maw, Nicholas). *Boosey and Hawkes. £7.50* JNFDE/MDW (B72-50107)
Schaeffer, Burghard. Annotated fingering tables for the Boehm flute. *Rahter. Unpriced* VR/ELM (B72-50726)
Schäfer, Gerhart. Akuomenon: drei Sätze für Alt-Blockflöte und Klavier. *Bosse: Bärenreiter. £1.50* VSSPJ (B72-50754)
Schedrin, Rodion. Anna Karenina: ballet in three acts. *Anglo-Soviet Music: Distributed by Boosey and Hawkes. £10.00* MM/HM (B72-50961)
Scheffau, Rolf.
Tanzrhythmen für electronische Orgel
Band 1. *Schott. £1.20* RPVH/AY (B72-51061)
Band 2. *Schott. £1.20* RPVH/AY (B72-51062)
Scheidemann, Heinrich.
Orgelwerke
Band 1: Magnificat - Bearbeitungen. *Bärenreiter. £2.75* R/AZ (B72-50628)
Band 3: Praeambulen, Fugen, Fantasien, Canzonen und Toccaten. *Bärenreiter. £2.25* R/AZ (B72-50629)
Schein, Johann Hermann. Diletti pastorali, nos.1, 5, 6, 13, 15. Hirten last: fünf weltliche Madrigale, für fünf stimmen und Basso Continuo. *Bärenreiter. £0.95* DU (B72-50377)
Schelle, Johann. Sechs Kantaten
für Bass, zwei Violinen und Basso continuo. *Bärenreiter. £3.65* KGXE/SNTPWDE (B72-50496)
Schingerlin, Rudolf. Percussion-Duos. (Regner, Hermann). *Schott. Unpriced* XNU (B72-50789)
Schlenning, Peter. Fantasias for keyboard. Klavier fantasien. (Bach, Wilhelm Friedemann). *Schott. £2.00* PWPJ (B72-50556)
Schmelli, Georg Christian. Die Gesänge zu Georg Christian Schmellis 'Musicalischen Gesang-Buch' S.439-507 sowie sechs Lieder aus dem 'Klavierbüchlein für Anne Magdalena Bach'. S.511-14, 516, 517. (Bach, Johann Sebastian). *Bärenreiter. Unpriced* KFXDH/AY (B72-50490)
Schmitt, Aloys. Exercises préparatoires aux 60 études. Op. 16. - *Excerpts.* Preparatory exercises, Op. 16: for piano. *Chappell. £0.45* Q/AF (B72-51005)
Schmitz, Hans Peter.
Introduction and variations on a theme from Carl Maria von Weber's 'Euryanthe' Op.63. (Kuhlau, Friedrich). *Bärenreiter. £1.50* VRP/T (B72-50730)
Sonata sentimentale for flute & piano in E flat major. Op.169. Sonata in E flat major for flute or clarinet and piano. (Ries, Ferdinand). *Bärenreiter. £2.45* VRPE (B72-50733)
Schneider, Max. Sonatas for two violins & basso continuo. Op.5 nos.7,1. Two triosonatas for two violins and basso continuo. (Handel, Georg Frideric). *Nagel. £1.25* NXNT (B72-50547)
Schneider, Walther. Einsingen in Chor: methodische Anleitung und Übungen zur chorischen Stimmbildung. *Litolff: Peters. Unpriced* D/AC (B72-50809)
Schneider, Willy. Chorische Bläserchule. Method for brass. *Schott. £0.50* WM/AC (B72-51194)
Schoenberg chamber music. (Whittall, Arnold). *British Broadcasting Corporation. £0.45* BSETAN (B72-22494) ISBN 0 563 10489 9
School of English Church Music. *See* Royal School of Church Music.
Schools Council. Music. (Horton, John). *Macmillan for the Anglo-American Primary Education Project. £0.60* A(VG) (B72-13853) ISBN 0 333 13332 3
Schostakowitsch, Dmitri. *See* Shostakovich, Dmitri.
Schrade, Leo. Monteverdi: creator of modern music. *Gollancz. £2.50* BMN(N) (B72-17504) ISBN 0 575 01472 5
Schubert - the final years. (Reed, John). *3 Queen Sq., WC1N 3AU: Faber. £5.00* BSF(N/XHF4) (B72-26089) ISBN 0 571 09842 8
Schubert, Franz.
6 divertimenti da camera: for harpsichord (piano) and violin
Vol.2: Nos.4 - 6. *Nagel. SPJ* SPJ (B72-50682)
Ausgewählte Lieder: für Gesang und Klavier. *Peters. £1.40* KFTDW (B72-50482)
Ave Maria. Op.52, no.6. *Gould & Bolttler. £0.89* FDW (B72-50422)
Das Dreimäderlhaus. Lilac time: operetta in three acts. *Chappell: Weinberger. Unpriced* CF (B72-50012)
Goethe songs: original pitch (high). *Bärenreiter. £1.15* KFTDW (B72-50483)
Intende voci orationis mea: offertory for tenor solo and four-part chorus of mixed voices with organ or piano accompaniment. *Schirmer: Chappell. Unpriced* DGKAF (B72-50021)
Six minuets for wind instruments
Vol.1: Nos.1 - 3. *Bärenreiter. £1.20* WMHR (B72-50764)
Sonata for piano in E flat. D.568. Sonata, E flat. Opus. 122: piano solo. *Peters. Unpriced* QPE (B72-51029)
Two songs: original pitch (high). First edition. *Bärenreiter. £0.50* KFTDW (B72-50484)
Schults-Hauser, Karlheinz. Trio sonata for violin, viola da gamba & harpsichord in G major. Sonate, G-dur: für Violine, Viola da gamba (Viola) und Cembalo. (Telemann, Georg Philipp). *Peters: Hinrichsen. £1.60* NXNTE (B72-50550)
Schultze-Biesantz, Clemens. One hand alone: album of 17 well-known pieces arranged for either left hand or right hand solo. *Peters. Unpriced* QPPR (B72-51049)
Schulz, Johann Abraham Peter. Six diverses pièces. Op.1, nos.2-3, 5-6. Vier Stücke: fur Klavier oder Cembalo. *Peters: Hinrichsen. £1.75* PWPJ (B72-50558)
Schumann, Robert. Album für die Jugend, Op.68. Part 1.8: Wilder Reiter. *Adaptations.* The wild horseman: arranged for two-part singing, with piano accompaniment. (Dexter, Harry). *Ashdown. £0.09* FDW (B72-50074)
Schumann, Robert.
Ausgewählte Lieder: für Gesang und Klavier. *Peters. £1.40* KFTDW (B72-50485)
Concerto for cello in A minor. Op.129. Cello concerto, A minor. Op.129. *Eulenburg. £0.80* MPSRF (B72-50149)
Dichterliebe. *Chappell. Unpriced* KDW (B72-50469) ISBN 0 900277 04 1
Schumann piano music. (Chissell, Joan). *British Broadcasting Corporation. £0.45* BSGAQ (B72-22495) ISBN 0 563 12241 2
Schumann songs. (Desmond, Astra). *British Broadcasting Corporation. £0.45* BSGAKDW (B72-14737) ISBN 0 563 12140 8
Schunemann, Georg. Così fan tutte: komische Oper in zwei Akten. (Mozart, Wolfgang Amadeus). *Peters: Hinrichsen. Unpriced* CQC (B72-50804)
Schurmann, Gerard. Variants for small orchestra. *Novello. £3.50* MR/T (B72-50977)
Schuster, Joseph. 6 divertimenti da camera: for harpsichord (piano) and violin
Volume 1: Divertimenti 1 & 2. *Nagel. £1.75* SPJ (B72-50683)
Schütz, Heinrich. Ausgewählte geistliche Chorsätze, zum Schutz-Jahr 1972. *Bärenreiter. £0.50* EZDM (B72-50403)
Schwaen, Kurt. Sonatina for violin & piano. Sonatine für Violine und Klavier. *Peters: Hinrichsen. £0.80* SPE (B72-50675)
Schwartz, Stephen. Mass: a theatre piece for singers, players and dancers. (Bernstein, Leonard). *Amberson: Chappell. Unpriced* CM (B72-50013)
Schwarz, Boris. Music and musical life in Soviet Russia, 1917-1970. *Barrie and Jenkins. £6.00* A(YM/XMS58) (B72-04570) ISBN 0 214 65264 5
Scott, David, *b.1943.* The music of St Paul's Cathedral. *Stainer and Bell; 82 High Rd, East Finchley, N2 9PW Distributed by Publishing Services Partnership. £0.60* AD/LE(YDBB) (B72-30071) ISBN 0 903000 08 3
Scott, *Sir* Walter. Ave Maria. Op.52, no.6. (Schubert, Franz). *Gould & Bolttler. £0.89* FDW (B72-50422)
Scott-Archer, G. Life's olympics: a demonstration service of song and praise for young people. (Larbalestier, Philip George). *John Blackburn. Unpriced* JFDM (B72-50097)
Scottish National Orchestra Society. SNO 1971: an anniversary study of the Scottish National Orchestra (1950-1971), the Scottish Orchestra (1891-1950) and their antecedents. *150 Hope St., Glasgow, C2: Scottish National Orchestra Society Ltd. £0.45* AMM/E(QB/X) (B72-26096) ISBN 0 9502512 0 8
Scottish Opera - the first ten years. (Wilson, Conrad). *Collins. £5.00* AC(YDL/XQB11) (B72-21778) ISBN 0 00 410584 2
Scottish street dance: descant recorders and/or melody instruments and piano. (Dexter, Harry). *Ashdown. Unpriced* NWSRH (B72-50543)
Scottish street dance for string orchestra with ad lib. melody instruments. (Dexter, Harry). *Ashdown. £1.05* MH (B72-50504)
Scratch anthology of compositions. *The Scratch Orchestra. Unpriced* C/AY (B72-50006)
Scratch music. (Cardew, Cornelius). *4 Alwyne Villas, N1 2HQ: Latimer New Dimensions Ltd. £3.00* AY (B72-24248) ISBN 0 901539 18 x
Scruggs, Earl. Earl Scruggs and the five-string banjo. *Music Sales. £1.75* TT/AC (B72-51154)
Sea tang: 3 pieces for clarinet and piano. (Fly, Leslie). *Forsyth. Unpriced* VVPJ (B72-50292)
Search for the Nile. (Horovitz, Joseph). *Francis, Day and Hunter. £0.20* QPK/JS (B72-50617)
Searle, Humphrey. Twentieth century composers
Vol.3: Britain, Scandinavia and the Netherlands. *Weidenfeld and Nicolson. £3.50* A(XM71) (B72-28679) ISBN 0 297 99377 1
Second set of madrigals, 1609. (Wilbye, John). *Scolar Press. £7.75* BWNRBADU (B72-10330) ISBN 0 85417 572 5
Secondary school music: philosophy, theory and practice. (Glenn, Neal Edwin). *Prentice-Hall. £4.00* A(VK) (B72-50333) ISBN 0 13 797522 8
Selected works for keyboard instruments, *by Johann Joseph Fux, edited by Friedrich W. Riedel. Nagel. £1.15* PWPJ (B72-50559)
Seligpreisungen: ein Lobgesang für Chor und Gemeinde. (Rohwer, Jens). *Bärenreiter. £0.10* EZDH (B72-50396)
Senaillé, Jean Baptiste. Sonata for violin & basso continuo, no.4, in D minor. Liv. 4. - Allegro spirituoso. Allegro. *Associated Board of the Royal Schools of Music. £0.25* SRPK (B72-51139)
Senior-Ellis, Olive. At the piano with Debussy. (Long, Marguerite). *Dent. £2.75* BDJAQ (B72-03316) ISBN 0 460 03821 4
Sentimental sarabande. (Britten, Benjamin). *Oxford University Press. £0.50* QNVK/AHVL (B72-50175) ISBN 0 19 372374 3
Sept sequences pour orchestre. (Gelalian, Boghos). *Peters Hinrichsen. £3.00* MMJ (B72-50515)
'Septalie': Studie für 7 Spieler - 6 beliebige Instrumente und Klavier. (Hashagen, Klaus). *Bosse: Bärenreiter. £0.95* LNPQ (B72-50501)
Sequenza 7: per oboe solo. (Berio, Luciano). *Universal. Unpriced* VTPMJ (B72-50284)
Sequenza 7: per oboe solo. (Berio, Luciano). *Universal. Unpriced* VTPMJ (B72-50285)
Serenate auf die erste hundertjährige Jubelfeyer der Hamburgische Löbliche Handlungs-Deputation - Excerpts. Symphonie: für Kammerorchester und Basso continuo. (Telemann, Georg Philipp). *Simrock. Unpriced* MRE (B72-50153)
Service music for the organ: preludes, interludes and postludes grouped according to keys
Vol.3. (Funk, Heinrich). *Hinrichsen. £2.70* R/AY (B72-50623)
Sette gogli: una collezione occulta. (Bussotti, Sylvano). *Universal. Unpriced* LJ (B72-50947)
Seven double canons: for four instruments or voices. (Thomas, Bernard). *Pro musica. Unpriced* EZDU/X/AY (B72-50861)
Shakespeare, William. Three Shakespeare songs: for unaccompanied mixed voices. (Swayne, Giles). *Oxford University Press. £0.50* EZDW (B72-50865) ISBN 0 19 343729 5
Sharp, Geoffrey B. Lassus & Palestrina. *Novello. £0.15* BLC(N) (B72-18916) ISBN 0 85360 038 4
Sharpe, Trevor L. Selections. The music of Eric Coates.

(Coates, Eric). *Chappell. Unpriced* UMK (B72-50256)

Shaw, Eric.

Coppélia. My daughter Coppelia: a musical play adapted from the ballet. (Delibes, Léo). *Oxford University Press. £1.20* CN (B72-50014) ISBN 0 19 338227 x

My daughter Coppelia: a musical play (adapted from Delibes' ballet 'Coppelia'). (Griffiths, Philip). *Oxford University Press. £0.40* BDKACN (B72-03927) ISBN 0 19 338228 8

Shaw, Martin. The Oxford book of carols. Revised ed.. *Oxford University Press. £0.90* DP/LF/AY (B72-50827) ISBN 0 19 313120 x

Shaw, Watkins.

Awake, awake my lyre: for soprano (or tenor), solo optional baritone, chorus, strings and continuo. (Blow, John). *Hinrichsen. Unpriced* DX (B72-50047)

Awake awake my lyre: for soprano (or tenor) solo, optional baritone, chorus, strings and continuo. (Blow, John). *Hinrichsen. Unpriced* ERXMDX (B72-50053)

Service in F major. - Excerpts. Magnificat and Nunc dimittis: for SATB. (Blow, John). *Novello. £0.17* DGPP (B72-50023)

Shayne, Gloria. Do you hear what I hear?: Stadium dimension for marching bands. (Regney, Noel). *Jewel Music. Unpriced* UMMK/DW (B72-50258)

Shepherd, Audrey. Three simple solos: for accordion. *Charnwood Music. Unpriced* RSPMJ (B72-51081)

Shepherds in fields: SATB. (Nops, Marjory). *British and Continental. Unpriced* EZDP/LF (B72-50851)

Shiloah, Amnon. Yuval: studies of the Jewish Music Research Centre

Vol.2. *Magnes Press: Distributed by Oxford University Press. £6.15* A(YBU) (B72-12719) ISBN 0 19 647627 5

Ship ahoy: for piano. (Longmire, John). *Bosworth. Unpriced* QPGM (B72-51031)

Shoemakers' holiday: a ballad-opera based on the play by Thomas Dekker. (Argento, Dominick). *Boosey and Hawkes. £6.00* CLM (B72-50343)

Short Communion service: for unison voices and organ. (Nourse, John). *Novello. £0.14* JDGS (B72-50896)

Short history of Spanish music. (Livermore, Ann). *43 Gloucester Cres., N.W.1: Duckworth. £4.45* A(YK/X) (B72-24251) ISBN 0 7156 0634 4

Short history of Western music. (Jacobs, Arthur). *Penguin. £0.60* A(X) (B72-21774) ISBN 0 14 021421 6

Short history of Western music: a listener's guide. (Jacobs, Arthur). *David and Charles. £3.75* A(X) (B72-30740) ISBN 0 7153 5743 3

Shostakovich, Dmitri.

Sonata for violin & piano. Op.134. Sonate für Violine und Klavier. Opus 134. *Peters. Unpriced* SPE (B72-51118)

Symphony no.7. Opus 60. *Peters: Hinrichsen. Unpriced* MME (B72-50964)

Siao Yu. The nymph and the farmer. La Fée et le cultivateur = The nymph and the farmer, Op.72: a lyric legend. (Cherepnin, Alexander). *Boosey and Hawkes. £4.50* CC (B72-50337)

Sibelius, a personal portrait. (Levas, Santeri). *Dent. £2.95* BSH(N) (B72-11000) ISBN 0 460 03978 4

Siebert, Edrich.

Ballycastle Bay: for brass band. (Barratt, Bob). *Ambleside: Keith Prowse. Unpriced* WMK/DW (B72-50311)

The Delaware waltz. *Studio Music. Unpriced* WMHW (B72-50767)

Latin American album: for B flat trumpet(s) and piano. *Boosey and Hawkes. £0.95* WSPK/AAY (B72-50324)

The Louisiana polka. *Studio Music. Unpriced* WMHVH (B72-50765)

Mexican shuffle. (Stone, Pol). *Peter Maurice. Unpriced* WMK (B72-50772)

Sleepy shores: theme from the BBC TV series Owen M.D. (Pearson, Johnny). *Keith Prowse Music. Unpriced* UMMK/JS (B72-50260)

Sleepy shores: theme from the BBC TV series Owen M.D. (Pearson, Johnny). *Keith Prowse Music. Unpriced* WMK/JS (B72-50313)

Spartak-Adagio. The Adagio from Spartacus. (For my love). (Khachaturian, Aram). *Feldman. Unpriced* WMK (B72-50309)

Two vesper hymns. *Studio Music. Unpriced* WMK/DM (B72-50775)

We shall not be moved: traditional. *Studio Music. Unpriced* WMK/DW (B72-50778)

Sigmund, Oskar. La Folia: neue Variationen nach Farinelli - Corelli, für 4 Soloviolinen. *Bosse: Bärenreiter. £1.20* RXNS/T (B72-50669)

Silverman, Jerry.

Blues: an anthology, complete words and music of 53 great songs. (Handy, William Christopher). *Macmillan: Collier-Macmillan. Unpriced* KDW/HHW/AY (B72-50471)

The liberated woman's songbook: seventy-seven singable folk songs about women and their battles with husbands, lovers, the devil, the system ... and themselves with lyrics, guitar arrangements, and entertaining photographs. *Collier Books: Collier-Macmillan. £1.25* KFE/TSDW/G/AY (B72-50128) ISBN 0 02 082040 2

Simon, George Thomas. The big bands. Revised enlarged ed. *Macmillan (N.Y.): Collier-Macmillan. £2.75* AMT/E(QB/XNQ12) (B72-12017) ISBN 0 02 610970 0

Simple symphony. Op.4. *Excerpts.* Playful pizzicato. (Britten, Benjamin). *Oxford University Press. £0.50* QNVK (B72-50173) ISBN 0 19 372375 1

Simple symphony. Op.4. *Excerpts.* Sentimental sarabande. (Britten, Benjamin). *Oxford University Press. £0.50* QNVK/AHVL (B72-50175) ISBN 0 19 372374 3

Simplicity of playing the violin. (Whone, Herbert). *Gollancz. £2.20* AS/E (B72-11001) ISBN 0 575 01343 5

Simpson, Gordon. Sing life, sing love. (Lewis, Peter). *Holmes McDougall. Unpriced* DM/AY (B72-50370) ISBN 0 7157 1005 2

Simpson, John. A little suite: for two descant recorders & treble recorders. *Feldman. Unpriced* VSNTG (B72-50272)

Simpson, Robert.

The symphony

Vol.1: Haydn to Dvořák. *David and Charles. £3.25* AMME (B72-12018) ISBN 0 7153 5523 6

Vol.2: Mahler to the present day. *David and Charles. £2.75* AMME (B72-12019) ISBN 0 7153 5524 4

Sinfonia sacra: 'The resurrection'. Op.140: for soprano, contralto, baritone, chorus and orchestra. (Rubbra, Edmund). *Lengnick. £1.00* DE/LL (B72-50812)

Sinfonie da chiesa. Op. 5. - *Excerpts.* Sinfonia 1 und 9, for strings and basso continuo. (Bononcini, Giovanni Battista). *Schott. £1.40* RXME (B72-51087)

Sing a son, play a song: a recorder book for sixes and sevens. (Dinn, Freda). *Schott. £0.95* VSK/DW/AY (B72-50740)

Sing life, sing love. (Lewis, Peter). *Holmes McDougall. Unpriced* DM/AY (B72-50370) ISBN 0 7157 1005 2

Sing, say and play: a book of junior music making and poetry for primary and junior schools. (Adams-Jeremiah, Dorothy). *Lengnick. £0.45* JFE/LDW (B72-50104)

Sing unto the Lord a new song: motet for SATB with divisions, unaccompanied. (Horovitz, Joseph). *Novello. £0.35* EZDH (B72-50842)

Singers: a directory of freelance amateur singers in London and the Home Counties

'72. *14 Barlby Rd, W10 6AR: Autolycus Publications. £0.30* AB/E(YDC/BC) (B72-14106) ISBN 0 903413 00 0

Singers of an empty day: last sacraments for the superstars. (Dallas, Karl). *25 Thurloe St., S.W.7: Kahn and Averill. £2.00* A/GB(XPQ17) (B72-02167) ISBN 0 900707 12 7

Singet dem herrn ein neues Lied. S.225: motet for two four-part mixed choirs. (Bach, Johann Sebastian). *Bärenreiter. £0.50* EZDH (B72-50394)

Singing heart: from Venice to the alps of L'Abri. (Carlson, Betty). *Hodder and Stoughton. £0.45* AKF/E(P) (B72-23640) ISBN 0 340 15866 2

Singing master's assistant. - *Excerpts.* Bethlehem: SAATB a cappella. (Billings, William). *Peters: Hinrichsen. £0.40* EZDP/LF (B72-50405)

Singing master's assistant. - *Excerpts.* David's lamentation: SATBB a cappella. (Billings, William). *Peter Hinrichsen. £0.40* EZDM (B72-50401)

Singing master's assistant. - *Excerpts.* Lamentation over Boston; and, Jargon: SATB (or male chorus or mixed quartet). (Billings, William). *Peters: Hinrichsen. £0.75* EZDW (B72-50411)

Singing master's assistant. - *Excerpts.* Peace be on earth = Retrospect: an anthem from sundry Scriptures, for SATB (or male chorus or mixed chorus). (Billings, William). *Peters: Hinrichsen. Unpriced* DK (B72-50360)

Sister Mary had - a but one child: negro spiritual, SSA and piano. (Nelson, Havelock). *Boosey and Hawkes. Unpriced* FDW/LC (B72-50878)

Sitsky, Larry. Concerto for two solo pianos. *Boosey and Hawkes. £2.50* QNUF (B72-50171)

Sitwell, *Dame* Edith. Façade: an entertainment. (Walton, *Sir* William). *Oxford University Press. £12.00* HYE/NYENQ (B72-50084) ISBN 0 19 359402 1

Six Afro-American carols for Christmas. (Clark, Rogie). *Piedmont: Distributed by Weinberger. £0.15* DP/LF/AYTLD (B72-50828)

Six German songs. Op.103: for voices, clarinet and piano. (Spohr, Louis). *Bärenreiter. £0.90* KE/VVPDW (B72-50474)

Six part suite: for solo guitar. (Mairants, Ivor). *Fenette Music, Breitkopf and Härtel. Unpriced* TSPMG (B72-51147)

Sixième livre de danceries: for four instruments, SATB. (Gervaise, Claude). *Pro musica. Unpriced* LNSH (B72-50953)

Skriabin, Alexander. 2 poèmes. Op.63. - *Excerpts.* Etrangété. Op.63, no.2: piano solo. *Peters. £0.25* QPJ (B72-50604)

Skye boat song: air (founded on an old 'chanty'). (MacLeod, Anne Campbell). *Cramer. £0.18* RK/DW (B72-50220)

Slaney, Ivor. The recorder: how to play the descant recorder, complete with rudiments of music, fingering and studies. *Campbell, Connelly. £0.40* VSR/AC (B72-51173)

Slater, Christopher. Concerto for organ, strings and timpani. (Wills, Arthur). *Boosey and Hawkes. £1.50* RK (B72-50218)

Slatford, Rodney. Yorke studies for double bass

Vol.1: Half and first positions. *Yorke. Unpriced* SS/AF (B72-51140)

Slavonic dances. Op.72, no.2. Moon rainbow. (Dvořák, Antonín). *Ashdown. £0.05* JDW (B72-50443)

Sleep soft, my babe. (Brahms, Johannes). *Ashdown. £0.09* FDW (B72-50421)

Sleepy shores. (Pearson, Johnny). *Keith Prowse Music. Unpriced* MSJ (B72-50157)

Sleepy shores: theme from the BBC TV series Owen M.D. (Pearson, Johnny). *Keith Prowse Music. Unpriced* UMMK/JS (B72-50260)

Sleepy shores: theme from the BBC TV series Owen M.D. (Pearson, Johnny). *Keith Prowse Music. Unpriced* WMK/JS (B72-50313)

Slim, H Colin.

A gift of madrigals and motets

Vol. 1: Description and analysis. *Chicago University Press. Unpriced* EZDU/AY (B72-50858) ISBN 0 226 76271 8

Vol.2: Transcriptions. Description and analysis. *Chicago University Press. Unpriced* EZDU/AY (B72-50859) ISBN 0 226 76272 6

Slonimsky, Nicolas. Music since 1900. 4th ed. *Cassell. £21.00* A(XM73) (B72-17502) ISBN 0 304 29069 6

Smet, Robin de. *See* De Smet, Robin.

Smetana. (Clapham, John, *b.1908*). *Dent. £2.10* BSIM (B72-15423) ISBN 0 460 03133 3

Smith, Dick. Do you hear what I hear?: Stadium dimension for marching bands. (Regney, Noel). *Jewel Music. Unpriced* UMMK/DW (B72-50258)

Smith, Geoffry Russell-. *See* Russell-Smith, Geoffry.

Smith, Hettie. Diamond jubilee songbook. *Girl Guides Association. £0.10* JFEZDW/AY (B72-50916)

Smith, Peter. New orbit: songs and hymns for under elevens. *Galliard. Unpriced* JFE/LPDM/AY (B72-50908) ISBN 0 85249 134 4

Smith, Robert, *b.Dec. 1922.* A complete catalogue of contemporary Welsh music

No.5. (Guild for the Promotion of Welsh Music). *c/o G. Williams, 10 Llanerch Path, Fairwater, Cwmbran, Mon. NP4 4QN: Guild for the Promotion of Welsh Music. Unpriced* A(YDK/TC) (B72-19872) ISBN 0 901248 01 0

Smith-Masters, Stanley. Cum Baija: African folk song. *Studio Music. Unpriced* WMK/DW (B72-50779)

Snakes: song for unison voices and piano. (Jenkyns, Peter). *Elkin. £0.07* JFDW (B72-50906)

SNO 1971: an anniversary study of the Scottish National Orchestra (1950-1971), the Scottish Orchestra (1891-1950) and their antecedents. (Scottish National Orchestra Society). *150 Hope St., Glasgow, C2: Scottish National Orchestra Society Ltd. £0.45* AMM/E(QB/X) (B72-26096) ISBN 0 9502512 0 8

So much to sing: over 50 songs for young people. (Maynard, John). *Vanguard Music. Unpriced* JFDM/AY (B72-50098)

Social history of music: from the middle ages to Beethoven. (Raynor, Henry). *Barrie and Jenkins. £5.00* A(XA1827) (B72-12717) ISBN 0 214 65783 3

Soirées de l'orchestre. (Berlioz, Hector). *Gregg. £9.60* A(E) (B72-06098) ISBN 0 576 28420 3

Soldan, Kurt. Così fan tutte: komische Oper in zwei Akten. (Mozart, Wolfgang Amadeus). *Peters: Hinrichsen. Unpriced* CQC (B72-50804)

Soliloquy. (Wilson, Thomas). *Stainer & Bell. £0.66* TSPMJ (B72-50710)

Solitudine: cantata for alto solo and basso continuo. (Handel, George Frideric). *Bärenreiter. £1.00* KFQDX (B72-50480)

Son of Assisi: a musical based on incidents from the life of St Francis of Assisi. (Verrall, Pamela). *British and Continental. Unpriced* CN/L (B72-50801)

Sonata accademiche. Op.2: für Violine und bezifferten Bass, Violine und Klavier (Cembalo, Orgel) mit Violoncello ad libitum

Sonata 10, F-Dur. (Veracini, Francesco Maria). *Peters Hinrichsen. £0.90* SPE (B72-50676)

Sonata 11, E-Dur. (Veracini, Francesco Maria). *Peters Hinrichsen. £0.90* SPE (B72-50677)

Sonata da camera: for flute, oboe and harpsichord. (Jones, Kelsey). *Peters. Unpriced* NWPNTE (B72-50992)

Sonata for clarinet, cello & piano (1969). (McCabe, John). *Novello. £1.50* NUVNTE (B72-50161)

Sonatine for piano. (Hopkins, Antony). *Oxford University Press. £0.45* QPEM (B72-50178) ISBN 0 19 372902 4

Sonatine for piano solo. (Lee, Noël). *Oxford University Press. £0.50* QPEM (B72-50179) ISBN 0 19 373205 x

Sondheim, Stephen.

Company: song book. *Valando Music. £0.60* KDW (B72-50117)

West Side story: a musical. (Laurents, Arthur). *Heinemann Educational. £0.50* BBMMACM (B72-08533) ISBN 0 435 23529 x

Song & dance man: the art of Bob Dylan. (Gray, Michael) *3 Upper James St., W1R 4BP: Hart-Davis, MacGibbon. £2.50* AKG/E(P) (B72-30744) ISBN 0 261 10000 9

Song of freedom. Op.109: for chorus of sopranos and altos, and piano. (Arnold, Malcolm). *Henrees Music. Unpriced* FDX (B72-50879)

Song of little Jesus = Cân y baban Jesu: unison. (Thomas, Mansel). *Oxford University Press. Unpriced* JDP/LF (B72-50898) ISBN 0 19 342049 x

Song of rest: accordion solo. (Pitfield, Thomas Baron). *Charnwood Music. Unpriced* RSPMJ (B72-51080)

Song of Scotland. *Wise, Music Sales. £1.25* KDW/AYDL (B72-50926)

Song of the brigands. (Friml, Rudolf). *Feldman. £0.20* KDW (B72-50460)

Songs for Dov: for tenor and orchestra. (Tippett, *Sir* Michael). *Schott. £1.50* KGHE/MDW (B72-50943)

Songs for living and words of worship: a hymn and worship book for the young. (Knight, Sydney H). *The Lindsey Press. £1.25* JFDM/LSL/AY (B72-50100)

Songs for one step forward. (Gilbert, Bryan). *Marshall, Morgan and Sc tt. £0.30* JE/TSDM/AY (B72-50096)

Songs for the seventies: a collection of contemporary hymns. *Galliard. £0.83* DM/AY (B72-50035)

Sonneck, Oscar George. Report on 'The star-spangled banner', 'Hail Columbia', 'America', 'Yankee Doodle'. *Dover Publications: Constable. £1.25* ADW(KM/YT) (B72-31292) ISBN 0 486 22237 3

Sophocles. The death of Antigone: opera. (Brindle, Reginald Smith). *Peters. £2.20* CQC (B72-50347)

Sor, Fernando. Die Zauberflöte. - *Excerpts.* Six airs. (Mozart, Wolfgang Amadeus). *Regina Music. Unpriced* TSPMK/DW (B72-50712)

Sospan fach = The little saucepan: march: a prelude to a

Welsh football match, for brass band. (Jacob, Gordon). *Novello. £1.75* WMGM (B72-51196)
Sostenuto: study no.2 (1969), for piano. (McCabe, John). *Novello. £0.50* QPJ (B72-50601)
Sound approaches for slow learners: a report on experimental work in schools being part of the Music for Slow Learners Project at Dartington College of Arts. (Ward, David). *Bedford Square Press for the Standing Conference for Amateur Music. £0.35* A(VMWR) (B72-16605) ISBN 0 7199 0829 9
Sound of the city. (Gillett, Charlie). *Sphere. £0.60* A/GB(YT/XPE25) (B72-07349) ISBN 0 7221 3860 1
Sounds like folk
No.1: Songs for and about drinking. *EFDS Publications. £0.30* JE/TSDW/G/AY (B72-50446)
Sources of English church music, 1549-1660. (Daniel, Ralph T). *82 High Rd, N2 9BZ: Stainer and Bell for the British Academy. £8.00* AD/LD(TE/XDXJ112) (B72-22016) ISBN 0 903000 10 5
Sous, Alfred. Neue Oboenschule. *Litolff: Peters. £3.80* VT/AC (B72-50282)
Soutar, William. Who are these children? Op. 84: lyrics, rhymes and riddles, for tenor and piano. (Britten, Benjamin). *Faber Music. Unpriced* KGHDW (B72-50942)
Space between the bars: a book of reflections. (Swann, Donald). *Hodder and Stoughton. £0.45* BSWN(N) (B72-16877) ISBN 0 340 16001 2
Space-dragon of Galatar. (Paynter, John). *Universal. Unpriced* CQN (B72-50807)
Spacious firmament: SSATTBB. (Drayton, Paul). *Oxford University Press. Unpriced* DH (B72-50024)
Spare time for music. (Epps, David). *British Broadcasting Corporation. £1.20* C/AY (B72-50793) ISBN 0 563 10689 1
Spartak. - Adagio. For my love. (Khachaturian, Aram). *Plantagenet music. £0.20* KDW (B72-50112)
Spartak - Excerpts. The 'Onedin Line'. (Khachaturian, Aram). *Palace Music. £0.20* QPK (B72-50194)
Spartak - Excerpts. The 'Onedin Line' theme. (Khachaturian, Aram). *Essex Music International. £0.20* QPK (B72-50195)
Spartak-Adagio. The Adagio from Spartacus. (For my love). (Khachaturian, Aram). *Feldman. Unpriced* WMK (B72-50309)
Speak softly, love. (Rota, Nina). *Chappell. £0.25* KDW (B72-50468)
Spearing, Robert. H.H.: a tribute to Herbert Howells on his eightieth birthday. *10e Prior Bolton St., Canonbury, N.1: Triad Press. £0.90* BHS(N) (B72-30070) ISBN 0 902070 05 3
Specimen sight reading tests: guitar, grades 3,4,5,6 & 8. (Associated Board of the Royal Schools of Music). *Associated Board of the Royal School of Music. £0.10* TS/EG (B72-50246)
Speckner, Anna Barbara. Aus alten Spielbüchern: 32 Tänze und Stücke aus dem 16, und 17. Jahrhundert, für Tasteninstrumente. *Schott. £1.20* PWP/AY(XD126) (B72-51002)
Spells and incantations: for horn and piano. (Bishop, Jeffrey). *Novello. £0.90* VWPJ (B72-50295)
Spencer, Sheila R. Margetts; (hymn). *Flying Dragon Publications. £0.04* DM (B72-50366)
Spiel im Duett: leichte Stücke für zwei Sopran-Blockflöten. (Böhn, Liselotte). *Schott. £0.60* VSRNU (B72-51174)
Spink, Reginald. Music: for chorus (SATB). (Gow, David). *Chester. Unpriced* EZDW (B72-50863)
Spohr, Louis. Six German songs. Op.103: for voices, clarinet and piano. *Bärenreiter. £0.90* KE/VVPDW (B72-50474)
Spratley, Philip. Trent march: accordion solo. *Charnwood Music. £0.22* RSPMGM (B72-51068)
Spring and the fall: for voice and piano. (Lekberg, Sven). *Schirmer: Chappell. Unpriced* KDW (B72-50113)
Srebotnjak, Alojz. Sonatina for violin and piano. *Schirmer Chappell. Unpriced* SPE (B72-50234)
'St Nicholas' suite for flute, viola & harp. (Papastavrou, Krinió). *Stackwood Cottage, Monks Eleigh, Ipswich: Krinió Papastavrou. Unpriced* NVRNTG (B72-50540)
Stadler, Werner. Percussion-Duos. (Regner, Hermann). *Schott. Unpriced* XNU (B72-50789)
Stadlmair, Hans. Concerto for trumpet & string orchestra. Konzert für Trompete in D und Streicher. *Litolff Hinrichsen. Unpriced* RXMPWSF (B72-51105)
Stamitz, Carl.
Concerto for cello, no.1, in G major. Concerto 1, G major, violoncello - small orchestra. *Bärenreiter. £1.00* SRPK/LF (B72-50699)
Concerto for cello, no.3, in C major. Concerto 3, C major, violoncello - small orchestra. *Bärenreiter. £1.05* SRPK/LF (B72-50700)
Concerto for clarinet & string orchestra, no.1, in F major. Konzert No.1, F - Dur: für Klarinette (C oder B). *Schott. £3.00* RXMPVVF (B72-51094)
Stamitz, Johann. Symphony in D major. Op.5, no.5. Rococo symphony. *Bosworth. £2.25* ME (B72-50957)
Standford, Patric.
Metamorphosis. *Novello. £0.33* RJ (B72-51058)
Nocturne: for small orchestra. *Novello. £0.60* MRJ (B72-50155)
Notte: for chamber orchestra. *Novello. £1.25* MRJ (B72-50981)
Variations for piano. Opus 23. *Novello. £0.50* QP/T (B72-51027)
Standing Conference for Amateur Music. Sound approaches for slow learners: a report on experimental work in schools being part of the Music for Slow Learners Project at Dartington College of Arts. (Ward, David). *Bedford Square Press for the Standing Conference for Amateur Music. £0.35* A(VMWR) (B72-16605) ISBN 0 7199 0829 9
Stanley, John.
English solos for flute (violin) and harpsichord, (v'c/va. da gamba ad lib.). Opus 1. *Peters. Unpriced* VRPE (B72-51165)
Vier Sonaten: für Querflöte und Basso continuo, Cembalo (Pianoforte, Violoncello, Viola da gamba), ad lib.
Band 1: Sonate 1, G-Dur. Op.4, no.3; Sonate 2, G-Moll Op.1, no.2. *Schott. £1.20* VRPE (B72-51163)
Band 2: Sonate 3, D-Dur. Op.1, no.4; Sonate 4, D-Moll Op.1, no.7. *Schott. £1.20* VRPE (B72-51164)
Stapleton, Eric. In praise of Essex. *Feldman. Unpriced* FDW (B72-50076)
Staquet, Willy. Bluette: continental accordion solo. *Charnwood Music. £0.19* RSPMHW (B72-51075)
Star carol: SSA. (Verrall, Pamela Motley). *British and Continental. Unpriced* FEZDP/LF (B72-50884)
Star clusters, Nebulae and Places in Devon. (Bedford, David). *Universal. Unpriced* DX (B72-50046)
Star for Maria: a carol in two parts with optional descant for voices or instruments. (Verrall, Pamela Motley). *British and Continental. Unpriced* FDP/LF (B72-50873)
Stayt, Michael J. Margetts; (hymn). (Spencer, Sheila R). *Flying Dragon Publications. £0.04* DM (B72-50366)
Steal away - Were you there?: a quodlibet based on two negro spirituals, (for either trebles 1 and 2, or basses 1 and 2, or treble 1 and bass 2). (Hudson, Hazel). *Ashdown. £0.10* FLDW/LC (B72-50430)
Stein, Charlotte von. Goethe-Briefe: Kantate für Bariton, gemischten Chor und Orchester nach Texten von Johann Wolfgang von Goethe und Charlotte von Stein in einer Auswahl des Komponisten. (Baird, Tadensz). *Peters. £2.20* DX (B72-50379)
Stein, Gertrude. Portrait of F.B. (Frances Blood): for voice and piano. (Thomson, Virgil). *Schirmer: Chappell. Unpriced* KDW (B72-50118)
Stendhal. Lives of Haydn, Mozart and Metastasio. *Calder and Boyars. £5.50* BHE(N) (B72-14734) ISBN 0 7145 0349 5
Stent, Keith. Two carols in modern vein. *Novello. £0.20* DP/LF (B72-50376)
Stephens, Denzil. Lindum suite. *Novello. £3.50* WMG (B72-50762)
Stephenson, B C. The zoo: a musical folly. (Sullivan, *Sir* Arthur). *William Reeves. Unpriced* CF (B72-50798)
Stereo record guide
Vol.7: Composer index A-Ma. *Squires Gate, Station Approach, Blackpool, Lancs. FY82 SP: Long Playing Record Library Ltd. £1.95* A/FF(WT) (B72-08760) ISBN 0 901143 02 2
Stevenson, Robert Louis. Monsieur de la plume: fragments from the life of Robert Louis Stevenson: music for children's voices and piano. (Rowley, Alec). *Ashdown Unpriced* CN (B72-50800)
Stevenson, Ronald.
Peter Grimes fantasy on themes from Britten's opera: piano solo. *Boosey and Hawkes. Unpriced* QPJ (B72-51042)
Prelude and fugue on a theme by Liszt. *Oxford University Press. £0.50* R/Y (B72-50209) ISBN 0 19 375780 x
Western music: an introduction. *25 Thurloe St., S.W.7: Kahn and Averil. £2.50* A(X) (B72-00906) ISBN 0 900707 10 0
Stingl, Anton. Improvisation über ein mittelalterliches Lied 'Es sass ein edly maget schön'. Op 46: fur Gitarre. *Schott. Unpriced* TSPMJ (B72-50709)
Stockmeier, Wolfgang. Gleich wie der Regen und Schnee von Himmel fällt = Like as the raindrops and snow from heaven fall, S.18: cantata for Sunday, sexagesimae. (Bach, Johann Sebastian). *Bärenreiter. £0.65* DE/LG (B72-50352)
Stoddard, Tom. The autobiography of a New Orleans Jazzman. (Foster, Pops). *2 Brook St., W1Y 1AA: University of California Press. £4.25* AMT/E(P) (B72-02170) ISBN 0 520 01826 5
Stoker, Richard.
The noble nature: two part songs for SATB a cappella,. *Leeds Music. Unpriced* EZDW (B72-50065)
Sonatina: for clarinet and piano. *Leeds Music. Unpriced* VVPE (B72-50290)
Three epigrams: for cor anglais and piano (or horn in F and piano). *Leeds Music. Unprinced* VTTPJ (B72-50287)
Trio for flute, oboe, clarinet. *Leeds Music. Unpriced* VNT (B72-50264)
Stolzenbach, Lorenz.
Il Parataio. - Overture. Sinfonia D-Dur: für Streichorchester und zwei Horner ad lib. (Jomelli, Nicolò). *Peters: Hinrichsen. £1.20* RXMJ (B72-50653)
Symphony for string orchestra in D major. Sinfonia, D-Dur: für Streichorchester und zwei Hörner ad lib. (Angelo, Bacchi). *Peters: Hinrichsen. £1.20* RXME (B72-50647)
Stone, David.
Danzas españolas. - *Excerpts.* Villanesca. Vol.2, no.4. (Granados, Enrique). *Boosey and Hawkes. £3.65* MK/AH (B72-50960)
The Old Hundredth psalm tune: All people that on earth do dwell, for mixed or unison voices and orchestra. (Vaughan Williams, Ralph). *Oxford University Press. Unpriced* EMDM (B72-50836) ISBN 0 19 369530 8
Stone, Pol. Mexican shuffle. *Peter Maurice. Unpriced* WMK (B72-50772)
Stork carol. (Surplice, Alwyn). *Royal School of Church Music. Unpriced* EZDP/LF (B72-50855)
Story of Christmas: a cantata. (Peterson, John W). *Marshall, Morgan and Scott. Unpriced* DE/LF (B72-50016) ISBN 0 551 05128 0
Stover, Harold. Te decet hymnus Deus in Sion: organ solo. *Boosey and Hawkes. £0.40* RJ (B72-50642)
Stradella, Alessandro.
Il Barcheggio. - Sinfonia to part 2. Sinfonia: for trumpet, 2 violins and continuo. *Musica rara. £3.00* RXMPWS (B72-51097)
Il Barcheggio. - Sinfonia to part 2. Sinfonia: for trumpet, 2 violins and continuo. *Musica rara. £1.00* WSPK (B72-51236)
Stramm, August. Kriegslieder = Tears of battle: for solo tenor, mixed chorus, trumpet and percussion. (Victory, Gerard). *Fairfield Music. £1.00* KGHE/NYHXSDX (B72-50133)
Strauss, Johann, *b.1825.* Explosions - Polka. Op.43. *Studio Music. Unpriced* WMK/AHVH (B72-50773)
Strauss, Richard.
Songs. Lieder
Vol. 1. *Boosey and Hawkes. £7.50* KDW/AZ (B72-50927)
Songs. Lieder
Vol. 2. *Boosey and Hawkes. £7.50* KDW/AZ (B72-50928)
Songs. Lieder
Vol. 3. *Boosey and Hawkes. £7.50* KDW/AZ (B72-50929)
Songs. Lieder
Vol. 4. *Boosey and Hawkes. £10.00* KDW/AZ (B72-50930)
Strauss family: the era of the Great Waltz. (Bailey, George). *Pan Books. £0.50* BSQB(N) (B72-29417) ISBN 0 330 23437 4
Stravinsky - chronicle of a friendship, 1948-1971. (Craft, Robert). *Gollancz. £4.00* BSV(N/XPH24) (B72-28680) ISBN 0 575 01503 9
Stravinsky, Igor. Themes and conclusions. *Faber. £6.00* A(D) (B72-28007) ISBN 0 571 08308 0
Stravinsky. (McCaldin, Denis). *Novello. £0.15* BSV(N) (B72-12718) ISBN 0 85360 009 0
Strawinsky, Igor. *See* Stravinsky, Igor.
Street, Allan.
Doon valley: a suite for brass. *Boosey and Hawkes. £3.30* WMG (B72-51195)
The godfather: selection of themes from the film. (Rota, Nina). *Chappell. Unpriced* WMK/JR (B72-51219)
Nott'num town: suite for symphonic band. *Boosey and Hawkes. £5.25* UMG (B72-50253)
Till. (Danvers, Charles). *Chappell. Unpriced* WMK/DW (B72-50776)
Yellow bird. (Luboff, Norman). *Frank Music. Unpriced* WMK/DW (B72-50777)
Street boys' song = Choeur des gamins. (Bizet, Georges). *Schott. £0.60* JFE/NYFSRDW (B72-50913)
Strehlow, Adalbert.
Il Parataio. - Overture. Sinfonia D-Dur: für Streichorchester und zwei Horner ad lib. (Jomelli, Nicolò). *Peters: Hinrichsen. £1.20* RXMJ (B72-50653)
Symphony for string orchestra in D major. Sinfonia, D-Dur: für Streichorchester und zwei Hörner ad lib. (Angelo, Bacchi). *Peters: Hinrichsen. £1.20* RXME (B72-50647)
Structures: 2 pianos à 4 mains
Livre 2: Chapitre 1 - Première pièce - Deuxième pièce - Textes 1,2,3 - Textes 4, 5, 6- Encart 1-4. (Boulez, Pierre). *Universal. Unpriced* QNU (B72-51018)
Stuart, Forbes. A medley of folk-songs. *Longman. Unpriced* JDW/G/AY (B72-50444) ISBN 0 582 15331 x
Stubbs, John Heath-. *See* Heath-Stubbs, John.
Studies for snare drum
Vol.6: Studies for 2-3-4 snare drums. (Fink, Siegfried). *Simrock. Unpriced* XQ/AF (B72-50790)
Sturman, Paul. A collection of seven two-part songs. *Feldman. £0.35* FDW/AY (B72-50079)
Sullivan, *Sir* Arthur.
Gilbert and Sullivan song book: for all-organs. *Francis, Day & Hunter. £0.75* RK/DW (B72-50644)
The zoo: a musical folly. *William Reeves. Unpriced* CF (B72-50798)
Sullivan, *Sir* Arthur Seymour. Saint Gertrude. *Adaptations.* Processional prelude. (Butterworth, Arthur). *Novello. £1.00* WMJ (B72-51197)
Supreme command: for fanfare trumpets and brass band. (Dunn, F Vivian). *Boosey and Hawkes. £0.45* WMPWSVN (B72-50780)
Surplice, Alwyn. The stork carol. *Royal School of Church Music. Unpriced* EZDP/LF (B72-50855)
Swann, Donald. The space between the bars: a book of reflections. *Hodder and Stoughton. £0.45* BSWN(N) (B72-16877) ISBN 0 340 16001 2
Swarsenski, H. L'Isle joyeuse: piano solo. (Debussy, Claude). *Peters. Unpriced* QPJ (B72-51034)
Swayne, Giles.
Four lyrical pieces: for cello & piano. *Oxford University Press. £1.20* SRPJ (B72-51138) ISBN 0 19 358935 4
Three Shakespeare songs: for unaccompanied mixed voices. *Oxford University Press. £0.50* EZDW (B72-50865) ISBN 0 19 343729 5
Swedish rhapsody: for brass band. (Jacob, Gordon). *Novello. £3.40* WMJ (B72-51215)
Sweet: for alto (treble) recorder. (Andriessen, Louis). *Schott. Unpriced* VSSPMJ (B72-51179)
Swinburne, A C. Thou whose birth on earth: carol for Christmas. (Pasfield, William Reginald). *Ashdown. £0.05* FDP/LF (B72-50419)
Swyddfa Gymreig. *See* Great Britain. *Welsh Office.*
Symphoniae sacrae
Vol.1: Canzon primi toni à 8: for 4 trumpets and 4 trombones. (Gabrieli, Giovanni). *Musica rara. Unpriced* WMJ (B72-51198)

Vol.2: Canzon septimi toni à 8 (no.1): for 4 trumpets and 4 trombones. (Gabrieli, Giovanni). *Musica rara. Unpriced* WMJ (B72-51199)
Vol.3: Canzon septimi toni à 8 (no.2): for 4 trumpets and 4 trombones. (Gabrieli, Giovanni). *Musica rara. Unpriced* WMJ (B72-51200)
Vol.4: Canzon noni toni à 8: for 4 trumpets and 4 trombones. (Gabrieli, Giovanni). *Musica rara. Unpriced* WMJ (B72-51201)
Vol.5: Canzon duo decimi toni à 8: for 4 trumpets and 4 trombones. (Gabrieli, Giovanni). *Musica rara. £2.00* WMJ (B72-51202)
Vol.6: Sonata pian e forte à 8: for 2 trumpets and 6 trombones. (Gabrieli, Giovanni). *Musica rara. £1.80* WMJ (B72-51203)
Vol.7: Canzon primi toni à 10: for 7 trumpets and 3 trombones, (5 trumpets and 5 trombones). (Gabrieli, Giovanni). *Musica rara. £2.50* WMJ (B72-51204)
Vol.8: Canzon duo decimi toni à 10 (no.1): for 6 trumpets and 4 trombones. (Gabrieli, Giovanni). *Musica rara. £2.85* WMJ (B72-51205)
Vol.9: Canzon duo decimi toni à 10 (no.2): for 6 trumpets and 4 trombones. (Gabrieli, Giovanni). *Musica rara. £3.00* WMJ (B72-51206)
Vol.10: Canzon duo decimi toni à 10 (no.3): for 5 trumpets and 5 trombones. (Gabrieli, Giovanni). *Musica rara. £2.50* WMJ (B72-51207)
Vol.11: Canzon duo decimi toni à 10 (no.4): for 6 trumpets and 4 trombones. (Gabrieli, Giovanni). *Musica rara. £3.50* WMJ (B72-51208)
Vol.12: Canzon in echo duo decima toni à 10: for 6 trumpets, 4 trombones and 2 organs (4 trumpets, 2 horns, 4 trombones and 2 organs). (Gabrieli, Giovanni). *Musica rara. £3.00* WMJ (B72-51209)
Vol.13: Canzon septimi octavi toni à 12: for 6 trumpets and 6 trombones. (Gabrieli, Giovanni). *Musica rara. Unpriced* WMJ (B72-51210)
Vol.14: Canzon noni toni à 12: for 6 trumpets and 6 trombones. (Gabrieli, Giovanni). *Musica rara. Unpriced* WMJ (B72-51211)
Vol.15: Sonata octavi toni à 12: for 2 trumpets and 10 trombones (2 trumpets, 2 horns and 8 trombones). (Gabrieli, Giovanni). *Musica rara. Unpriced* WMJ (B72-51212)
Vol.16: Canzon quarti toni à 15: for 3 trumpets and 12 trombones. (Gabrieli, Giovanni). *Musica rara. Unpriced* WMJ (B72-51213)

Symphonic dance. Op.64, no.2. (Grieg, Edvard). *Oxford University Press. Unpriced* MH (B72-50505) ISBN 0 19 363819 3

Symphonic marches for concert band. (Rodgers, Richard). *Williamson. Unpriced* UMGM (B72-50254)

Symphony, (Les Echanges): for percussion-ensemble (7 players). (Liebermann, Rolf). *Simrock. Unpriced* XNPK (B72-50330)

Symphony no.2. Op.132. - Andante con moto. Mysterious mountain. (Hovhaness, Alan). *Associated Music. Unpriced* UMK (B72-50257)

Symphony
Vol.1: Haydn to Dvořák. (Simpson, Robert). *David and Charles. £3.25* AMME (B72-12018) ISBN 0 7153 5523 6
Vol.2: Mahler to the present day. (Simpson, Robert). *David and Charles. £2.75* AMME (B72-12019) ISBN 0 7153 5524 4

Synesius. Lord Jesus, think on me: for mixed chorus and organ. (Talmadge, Charles L). *Galaxy: Galliard. Unpriced* DM (B72-50820)

Synge, John M. Riders to the sea: an opera in one act. (Vaughan Williams, Ralph). *Oxford University Press. £5.00* CQC (B72-50805) ISBN 0 19 339335 2

Szelenyi, Istvan.
Ab irato; and, Two concert studies for piano solo. (Liszt, Franz). *Bärenreiter. £0.90* QPJ (B72-50590)
Etudes d'execation transcendante, no.4. Mazeppa for piano solo. (Liszt, Franz). *Bärenreiter. £0.65* QPJ (B72-50591)

Szelenyi, István. Etudes d'exécution transcendante, no.5. Feux follets: for piano solo. (Liszt, Franz). *Bärenreiter. £0.65* QPJ (B72-50592)

Szelényi, István.
Etudes d'exécution transcendante, no.7. Eroica: for piano solo. (Liszt, Franz). *Bärenreiter. £0.50* QPJ (B72-50593)
Etudes d'exécution transcendante, no.8. Wilde Jagd: for piano solo. (Liszt,, Franz). *Bärenreiter. £0.65* QPJ (B72-50594)
Etudes d'exécution transcendante, no.9. Ricordanza: for piano solo. (Liszt, Franz). *Bärenreiter. £0.65* QPJ (B72-50595)
Etudes d'exécution transcendante, no.10. Study in F minor for piano solo. (Liszt, Franz). *Bärenreiter. £0.65* QPJ (B72-50596)
Etudes d'exécution transcendante, no.11. Harmonies du Soir: for piano solo. (Liszt, Franz). *Bärenreiter. £0.50* QPJ (B72-50597)

Szelenyi, Istvan.
Grandes études de Paganini: for piano solo. (Liszt, Franz). *Bärenreiter. £1.25* QPJ (B72-50598)
Piano works
Vol.1: Studies 1. (Liszt, Franz). *Bärenreiter. £2.00* QP/AZ (B72-50566)
Vol.2: Studies 2. (Liszt, Franz). *Bärenreiter. £2.00* QP/AZ (B72-50567)
Trois études de concert: trois caprices poetiques, for piano solo. (Liszt, Franz). *Bárenreiter. £0.90* QPJ (B72-50599)

Szenen: für Flöte, Oboe und Klavier. (Kiesewetter, Peter). *Bosse: Bärenreiter. £4.75* NWPNT (B72-50542)

Talbot, Michael.
Concerto for trumpet, oboe, bassoon & string orchestra in D Major. Concerto for trumpet, oboe, bassoon, violins and continuo. (Biscogli, Francesco). *Musica rara. Unpriced* RXMPWNTE (B72-51095)
Concerto for trumpet, strings & basso continuo, no.1 in D major. MWV IV/12. Concerto no.1: for solo trumpet, strings and continuo (bassoon ad lib.). (Molter, Johann Melchior). *Musica rara. Unpriced* WSPK/LF (B72-50327)
Concerto for trumpet, strings & basso continuo no.1 in D major. MWV IV/14. Concerto no.1 in D major: for solo trumpet, strings and continuo (bassoon ad lib.). (Molter, Johann Melchior). *Musica rara. Unpriced* RXMPWSF (B72-50225)
Concerto for trumpet, strings & basso continuo, no.2 in D major. MWV IV/13. Concerto no.2: for solo trumpet, strings and continuo (bassoon ad lib) (Molter, Johann Melchior). *Musica rara. Unpriced* RXMPWSF (B72-50226)
Concerto for trumpet, strings & basso continuo, no.2 in D major. MWV IV/13. Concerto no.2: for solo trumpet, strings and continuo (bassoon ad lib.). (Molter, Johann Melchior). *Musica rara. Unpriced* WSPK/LF (B72-50328)
Concerto for trumpet, strings & basso continuo, no.3 in D major. MWV IV/14. Concerto no.3: for solo trumpet, strings and continuo (bassoon ad lib.). (Molter, Johann Melchior). *Musica rara. Unpriced* RXMPWSF (B72-50227)
Concerto for trumpet, strings & basso continuo, no.3 in D major. MWV IV/14. Concerto no.3: for solo trumpet, strings and continuo (bassoon ad lib.). (Molter, Johann Melchior). *Musica rara. Unpriced* WSPK/LF (B72-50329)

Tales of Beatrix Potter - Excerpts. Peter Rabbit and the tales of Beatrix Potter: music from the film. (Lanchbery, John). *EMI Film Music. Unpriced* QPK/JR (B72-50197)

'Talking Machine Review'.
Catalogue. Bell 'popular' phonograph records, new catalogue no.9. (Edison-Bell Consolidated Phonograph Company). *19 Glendale Rd, Bournemouth, Hants. BH6 4JA: 'Talking Machine Review'. Unpriced* A/FE(WM) (B72-05227) ISBN 0 902338 13 7
Catalogue. List of records (no.3) possessing great volume, perfect reproduction and superb quality of tone. (Edison-Bell Consolidated Phonograph Company). *19 Glendale Rd, Bournemouth, Hants. BH6 4JA: 'Talking Machine Review'. £0.45* A/FE(WM) (B72-04764) ISBN 0 902338 12 9

Tallis, Thomas.
Hear the voice and prayer: anthem for S (or A) ATB. *Novello. £0.10* EZDK (B72-50849)
If ye love me: SATB. *Oxford University Press. Unpriced* EZDK (B72-50060) ISBN 0 19 352138 5
O sacrum convivium. I call and cry to thee: anthem for SAATB. *Novello. £0.17* EZDJ (B72-50845)

Talmadge, Charles L. Lord Jesus, think on me: for mixed chorus and organ. *Galaxy: Galliard. Unpriced* DM (B72-50820)

Tanzbüchlein für zwei Bratschen: Tanzlieder und Volkstänze. (Hoffmann, Adolf). *Schott. £0.80* SQNUH (B72-50688)

Tanzrhythmen für electronische Orgel
Band 1. (Scheffau, Rolf). *Schott. £1.20* RPVH/AY (B72-51061)
Band 2. (Scheffau, Rolf). *Schott. £1.20* RPVH/AY (B72-51062)

Tarr, Edward H.
Concerto for trumpet & string orchestra in E flat. Concerto no.2 in E flat: for trumpet, strings and major continuo. (Hertel, Johann Wilhelm). *Musica rara. Unpriced* RXMPWSF (B72-51104)
Concerto for trumpet & string orchestra in E flat major. Concerto no.2 in E flat: for trumpet, strings and continuo. (Hertel, Johann Wilhelm). *Musica rara. Unpriced* WSPK/LF (B72-51243)
Concerto for trumpet, no.2, in C major. Trumpet concerto no.2 in C major: for trumpet, 2 flutes, strings and continuo. (Haydn, Michael). *Musica rara. Unpriced* WSPK/LF (B72-50326)
Concerto for trumpet, oboe & string orchestra in E flat major. Doppel Konzert, Es-dur: für Trompete, Oboe, Streicher und Basso continuo. (Hertel, Johann Wilhelm). *Schott. £2.00* RXMPVTPLWSF (B72-51093)
Concerto for trumpet, oboe, bassoon & string orchestra. Concerto for trumpet, oboe, bassoon, violins and continuo. (Biscogli, Francesco). *Musica rara. Unpriced* NWXPNSK/LF (B72-50995)
Concerto for trumpet, strings & basso continuo no.1 in C major. Concerto no.1 in C major: for solo trumpet, strings and continuo (bassoon ad lib.). (Haydn, Michael). *Musica rara. Unpriced* MPWSF (B72-50151)
Eight sonatas: for trumpet and organ. (Fantini, Girolamo). *Musica rara. Unpriced* WSPLRE (B72-51245)
Sonata for trumpet & string orchestra. Op. 35, no.10, 'La Cappara'. Sonata à 5, 'La Cappara': for trumpet and strings. (Cazzati, Mauritio). *Musica rara. £1.00* WSPK/LE (B72-51239)
Sonata for trumpet & string orchestra. Op.35, no.11, 'La Bianchina'. Sonata à 5, 'La Bianchina': for trumpet and strings. (Cazzati, Mauritio). *Musica rara.* RXMPWSE (B72-51101)
Sonata for trumpet & string orchestra. Op.35, no.12, 'La Zambecari. Sonata à 5, 'La Zambecari': for trumpet and strings. (Cazzati, Mauritio). *Musica rara. £2.50* RXMPWSE (B72-51102)
Sonata for trumpet, cello & string orchestra in D major. Sonata no.4 in D: for trumpet, strings and basso continuo. (Gabrielli, Domenico). *Musica rara. £1.00* NUXSNTK/LE (B72-50985)
Sonata for trumpet, cello & string orchestra in D major. Sonata no.4 in D: for trumpet, strings and basso continuo. (Gabrielli, Domenico). *Musica rara. y2.50* RXMPWSPLSRE (B72-51106)
Sonata for trumpets & string orchestra. Op.35, no.11, 'La Bianchina'. Sonata à 5, 'La Bianchina': for trumpet and strings. (Cazzati, Mauritio). *Musica rara. £1.00* WSPK/LE (B72-51241)

Tarr, E.H. Modo per imparare a sonare di tromba. - *Excerpts.* Eight sonatas: for trumpet & organ. (Fantini, Girolamo). *Musica rara. Unpriced* WSLRE (B72-50318)

Tarr, Edward H. Sonata for trumpet & string orchestra. Op.35, no.12, 'La Zambecari'. Sonata à 5, 'La Zambecari': for trumpet and strings. (Cazzati, Mauritio). *Musica rara. £1.00* WSPK/LE (B72-51240)

Tate, Nahum. The psalm singer's amusement. - *Excerpts.* The bird: SATBB. (Billings, William). *Peters: Hinrichsen. £0.40* DM (B72-50363)

Tate, Phyllis.
Apparitions: a ballad sequence for tenor, harmonica, string quartet and piano. *Oxford University Press. £2.50* KGHE/NUPNQDX (B72-50132) ISBN 0 19 345822 5
Sailing in: a Christmas carol, SATB. *Oxford University Press. Unpriced* DP/LF (B72-50041) ISBN 0 19 343021 5
Variegations: for solo viola. *Oxford University Press. £0.75* SQPMJ (B72-50239) ISBN 0 19 359027 1
A Victorian garland: three poems by Matthew Arnold set for soprano and contralto solo voices, horn, and piano by Phyllis Tate. *Oxford University Press. £1.80* JNFEE/WTPDW (B72-50921) ISBN 0 19 345824 1

Tavener, John. Celtic requiem: for soprano, children's choir, chorus and orchestra. *Chester. Unpriced* EMDGKAV (B72-50383)

Taverner: an opera in two acts. (Davies, Peter Maxwell). *Boosey and Hawkes. £0.50* BDEAC (B72-18917) ISBN 0 85162 005 1

Taverner: an opera in two acts. (Davies, Peter Maxwell). *Boosey and Hawkes. Unpriced* CC (B72-50338)

Taylor, Ian. How to produce concert versions of Gilbert & Sullivan. *Hale. £3.50* BSWACF/E (B72-31878) ISBN 0 7091 2973 4

Taylor, Jeremy.
Jeremy Taylor - songs Vol. 2. *Galliard. Unpriced* KE/TSDW/AY (B72-50936) ISBN 0 85249 102 6
Jeremy Taylor: songs Vol.1. *Galliard. Unpriced* JE/TSDW (B72-50900) ISBN 0 85249 099 2

Taylor, John.
Charlie girl. (Heneker, David). *Chappell. £1.75* CM (B72-50799)
Charlie girl: a comedy musical in two acts. (Williams, Hugh). *Chappell. £0.75* BHJJACM (B72-23641) ISBN 0 85360 040 6

Taylor, Ross. Charlie girl: a comedy musical in two acts. (Williams, Hugh). *Chappell. £0.75* BHJJACM (B72-23641) ISBN 0 85360 040 6

Tchaikovsky, Peter. Symphony no.5 in E minor. Op.64. - Andante cantabile. Andante da 5a sinfonia. *MCA: Leeds Music. Unpriced* QPK (B72-50608)

Te decet hymnus Deus in Sion: organ solo. (Stover, Harold). *Boosey and Hawkes. £0.40* RJ (B72-50642)

Te Deum: for mixed voices (with soprano and tenor solo) and orchestra. (Bizet, Georges). First edition. *Simrock. Unpriced* DH (B72-50356)

Telemann, Georg Philipp.
Harmonischer Gottes-Dienst - Excerpts. Ew'ge Quelle, milder Strom: Kantate auf den Sonntag Cantate, für mittlere Stimme, Querflöte (Violine) und Basso continuo. *Bärenreiter. £1.00* KFTE/SPLRDE (B72-50486)
Harmonischer Gottes-Dienst. - *Excerpts.* Gott will Mensch und sterblich werden: Kantate zum Fest der Verkündigung Mariä, für hohe Stimme, Violine und Basso continuo. *Bärenreiter. £1.00* KFTE/SPLRDE (B72-50487)
Harmonischer Gottes-Dienst - Excerpts. Jauchzt, ihr Christen, seid vergnügt: Kantate am dritten Osterfreitag, für hohe Stimme, Violine and Basso Continuo. *Bärenreiter. £1.00* KFTE/SPLRDE (B72-50488)
Harmonischer Gottes-Dienst. *Excerpts.* Ihr Völker, hört: Kantate am Fest der Heiligen drei Könige, für mittlere Stimme, Querflöte und Basso continuo. *Bärenreiter. £1.00* KFVE/VRPLRDE/LFP (B72-50489)
Ruft es aus in alle Welt. (In Festo Nativatatis): Weihnachts Kantate, für Sopran, Alt, Tenor, Bass, Vierstimmigen gemischten Chor, drei Trompeten, Pauken, Streicher und Basso continuo. *Bärenreiter. £1.25* EMDE/LF (B72-50382)
Serenate auf die erste hundertjährige Jubelfeyer der Hamburgische Löbliche Handlungs-Deputation - Excerpts. Symphonie: für Kammerorchester und Basso continuo. *Simrock. Unpriced* MRE (B72-50153)
Sonata for two violins, two violas, cello & harpsichord in F minor. Sonata in F minor for two violins, two violas, violoncello and harpsichord (double bass ad lib). *Bärenreiter. £1.50* NXNQE (B72-50544)
Suite for string orchestra in F major. Overture F-dur. (Suite): für Streichorchester und Cembalo (zwei Oboen und Fagott ad libitum). *Peters: Hinrichsen. £2.10* RXMG (B72-50650)
Suite for tenor oboe, two violins & basso continuo, with Chaconne for two flutes, tenor oboe, two violins & basso continuo in F minor. *Excerpts.* Chaconne. *Schott. £1.60* NUPNQHJN (B72-50158)
Suite for treble recorder & string orchestra in A minor. Suite in A minor: for treble recorder and string orchestra. *Schott. £1.25* VSSPK/LG (B72-50279)

Trio sonata for violin, viola da gamba & harpsichord in G major. Sonate, G-dur: für Violine, Viola da gamba (Viola) und Cembalo. *Peters: Hinrichsen. £1.60* NXNTE (B72-50550)
Tellstrom, A Theodore. Music in American education: past and present. *Holt, Rinehart and Winston. £4.40* A(VF/YT/X) (B72-07977) ISBN 0 03 083579 8
Temperance songbook: a peerless collection of temperance songs and hymns for the Women's Christian Temperance Union, Loyal Temperance Union, Prohibitionists, Temperance Praise Meetings, Medal contests, etc. (Coleman, Emmet G). *Wolfe. £1.25* DM/LRT/AY (B72-50037) ISBN 0 7234 0486 0
Tempest, Ronald. Folk music of Hungary. (Kodály, Zoltán). 2nd ed. *Barrie and Jenkins. £2.25* A/G(YG/XA1914 (B72-13442) ISBN 0 214 65327 7
Ten trios for developing clarinet technique: for 3 clarinets. (Brooks, Keith). *Boosey and Hawkes. £0.60* VVNT (B72-51188)
Tennyson, Alfred, *Baron Tennyson.* Love, the sentinel: for chorus a capella sic. (Williamson, Malcolm). *Weinberger. £0.15* EZDW (B72-50066)
Terpsichore. (Tull, Fisher). *Boosey and Hawkes. £33.95* UMMJ (B72-51159)
Tertre, Etienne du. *See* Du Tertre, Etienne.
Tessmer, Manfred. Clavierübung. Tl.3. - *Excerpts.* Duets. S.802-805. (Bach, Johann Sebastian). *Bärenreiter. £0.50* RJ (B72-50634)
Textur: fur Streicher. (Veerhoff, Carlos). *Litolff: Hinrichsen. Unpriced* RXMJ (B72-51089)
Thackray, Roy. Pleasure it is: unison. *Oxford University Press. Unpriced* JDP/LF (B72-50897) ISBN 0 19 351115 0
Theatre organ world, 'the organist entertained'
  Specifications - four major examples of the art of unification in organ building by four famous firms. *23 Portland Cres., Leeds LS1 3DR: Turntable Enterprises. £0.80* ARPV/B(YC) (B72-30747) ISBN 0 902844 06 7
Thee we adore. (Holman, Derek). *Royal School of Church Music. Unpriced* FLDH (B72-50081)
Thematic catalogue of the works of Matthew Locke: with a calendar of the main events of his life. (Harding, Rosamond Evelyn Mary). *R.E.M. Harding: Distributed by Blackwell. £7.00* BLOC(TD) (B72-02957) ISBN 0 9502117 0 2
Themerson, Stefan. St Francis and the wolf of Gubbio; or, Brother Francis' lamb chops: an opera in 2 acts. *De Harmonie: Gaberbocchus. Unpriced* CC (B72-50796)
Themes and conclusions. (Stravinsky, Igor). *Faber. £6.00* A(D) (B72-28007) ISBN 0 571 08308 0
Themes from T.V. and film classics. (Bolton, Cecil). *Francis, Hunter and Day. £0.75* QPK/JR/AY (B72-50616)
There was a Maid: a carol for SATB, organ, piano or unaccompanied. (Nops, Marjory). *British and Continental. Unpriced* EZDP/LF (B72-50852)
Thiele, Siegfried.
  Concerto for flute, no.2, in D major. K.314. Konzert Nr.2, D dur, für Flöte und Orchester. K.314. (Mozart, Wolfgang Amadeus). *Peters. Unpriced* VRPK/LF (B72-51168)
  Sonatina for young people's string orchestra. Sonatine: für Jugendstreichorchester. *Peters: Hinrichsen. £1.20* RXMEM (B72-50648)
Thiman, Eric Harding.
  Christ is the world's light: anthem for SATB and organ. *Novello. £0.10* DH (B72-50026)
  Love will find out the way: for S.A. and piano. *Novello. £0.10* FDW (B72-50077)
Third Penguin guide to bargain records. (Greenfield, Edward). *Penguin. £0.60* A/FD(WT) (B72-21267) ISBN 0 14 003454 4
Thirty-five songs from thirty-five counties. *See* Brace, Geoffrey.
This endris night: a Christmas cantata for tenor solo, women's or boy's voices and brass. (Burgon, Geoffrey). *Stainer and Bell. £0.75* DE/LF (B72-50811)
This way Mary: love theme from the film 'Mary, Queen of Scots'. (Barry, John). *Leeds Music. £0.20* KDW/JR (B72-50121)
Thomas, Bernard.
  A la bataglia: for four instruments, ATTB, by Heinrich Isaac. (Isaac, Heinrich). *Pro musica. Unpriced* LNS (B72-50950)
  Andernaken: anon., for five instruments, ATTBB. *Pro musica. Unpriced* LNR (B72-50948)
  'Browning' fantasy: for five instruments, SATTB. (Woodcock, Clement). *Pro musica. Unpriced* LNR (B72-50949)
  Canzoni alla francese a quatro voci, nos.10, 11. Two canzonas: for 2 trumpets and 2 trombones, (2 trumpets, horn and trombone). (Banchieri, Adriano). *Musica rara. £0.90* WNS (B72-51226)
  Canzoni alla francese a quattro voci, nos.6, 8. Two canzonas: for 2 trumpets and 2 trombones, (2 trumpets, horn and trombone). (Banchieri, Adriano). *Musica rara. £0.90* WNS (B72-51227)
  Capricci in musica a tre voci. - *Excerpts.* Four pieces, nos. 9,15,23,5: for threee instruments, ATB. (Ruffo, Vincenzo). *Pro musica. Unpriced* LNT (B72-50955)
  Crumhorn consort anthology
  Vol.1. *Musica rara. Unpriced* VTWNSK/AAY (B72-51187)
  Four double canons: for 4 voices or instruments; (ATTB). *Antico. Unpriced* EZDU/X/AYH (B72-50862)
  La Guamina: for 2 trumpets and 2 trombones, (2 trumpets, horn and trombone). (Guami, Gioseffo). *Musica rara. £0.70* WNS (B72-51231)
  Libro primo de canzoni da sonare, nos.5, 7. Two canzonas: for 2 trumpets and 2 trombones (2 trumpets, horn and trombone). (Maschera, Florentino). *Musica rara. £0.70* WNS (B72-51232)
  Libro primo de canzoni da sonare, nos.13, 12. Two canzonas: for 2 trumpets and 2 trombones (2 trumpets, horn and trombone). (Maschera, Florentio). *Musica rara. £0.80* WNS (B72-51233)
  Musica a quattro voci. - *Excerpts.* Two canzonas: for 2 trumpets and 2 trombones (2 trumpets, horn and trombone). (Cavaccio, Giovanni). *Musica rara. £0.80* WNS (B72-51230)
  Sacrae concentus ac symphoniae. - *Excerpts.* Canzona quarta: for 4 trumpets and 4 trombones (4 trumpets, 2 horns and 2 trombones). (Grillo, Giovanni Battista). *Musica rara. £1.50* WNN (B72-51220)
  Secondo libro delle canzoni da suonare. - *Excerpts.* Canzona 'La Monteverde': for 2 trumpets and 2 trombones (2 trumpets, horn and trombone). (Bargagni, Ottavio). *Musica rara. £0.70* WNS (B72-51228)
  Septème livre de danceries: for four instruments, SATB. (Du Tertre, Etienne). *Pro musica. Unpriced* LNSH (B72-50952)
  Seven double canons: for four instruments or voices. *Pro musica. Unpriced* EZDU/X/AY (B72-50861)
  Seven double canons: for four instruments or voices. (Thomas, Bernard). *Pro musica. Unpriced* EZDU/X/AY (B72-50861)
  Sinfonia musicale. - *Excerpts.* Sinfonia, 'La Bergamasca': for 4 trumpets and 4 trombones, (4 trumpets, 2 horns and 2 trombones). (Viadana, Lodovico). *Music rara. £2.00* WNN (B72-51221)
  Sinfonia musicale. - *Excerpts.* Sinfonia, 'La Padovana': for 4 trumpets and 4 trombones (4 trumpets, 2 horns and 2 trombones). (Viadana, Lodovico). *Musica rara. £1.50* WNN (B72-51222)
  Sixième livre de danceries: for four instruments, SATB. (Gervaise, Claude). *Pro musica. Unpriced* LNSH (B72-50953)
  Sonate & canzone. Lib. 6. - *Excerpts.* Canzon à 5: for 2 cornetti and 3 trombones (2 trumpets/oboes and 3 trombones). (Buonamente, Giovanni Battista). *Musica rara. Unpriced* WNR (B72-51223)
  Three late 15th century instrumental pieces: for 3 instruments (ATB). *North Horton, Lustleigh, Newton Abbot, Devon: Antico. Unpriced* LNT (B72-50956)
  Three Parisian chansons: for 4 voices (SATB). *North Horton, Lustleigh, Newton Abbot, Devon: Antico. Unpriced* EZDU/AYHP (B72-50860)
  Troisième livre de danceries: for four instruments, SATB. (Gervaise, Claude). *Pro Musica. Unpriced* LNSH (B72-50954)
  Vingt et sept chansons musicales à quatre parties. - *Excerpts.* Fourteen chansons: for four recorders or voices, ATTB,. (Attaingnant, Pierre). *Pro musica. Unpriced* EZDU/AY (B72-50857)
Thomas, Mansel.
  Four prayers from the Gaelic. *University of Wales Press. Unpriced* KDH (B72-50108)
  Sing, say and play: a book of junior music making and poetry for primary and junior schools. (Adams-Jeremiah, Dorothy). *Lengnick. £0.45* JFE/LDW (B72-50104)
  The song of little Jesus = Cân y baban Jesu: unison. *Oxford University Press. Unpriced* JDP/LF (B72-50898) ISBN 0 19 342049 x
  Two Welsh love songs: SATB unacc. *Oxford University Press. Unpriced* EZDW (B72-50866) ISBN 0 19 343032 0
Thomas, Susanna.
  Pieces for three, four and five cellos. *Schott. Unpriced* SRNRK/DW/AY (B72-51131)
  Pieces for two and three cellos. *Schott. Unpriced* SRNTK/AAY (B72-51132)
Thomas de Sancta Maria. Libro llamado arte de tañer fantasia. *Gregg. £14.40* AQT/E (B72-30746) ISBN 0 576 28229 4
Thomson, Virgil. Portrait of F.B. (Frances Blood): for voice and piano. *Schirmer: Chappell. Unpriced* KDW (B72-50118)
Thou knowest, Lord, the secrets of our hearts. Z.580. (Purcell, Henry). *Oxford University Press. Unpriced* FLDK (B72-50890) ISBN 0 19 351113 4
Thou whose birth on earth: carol for Christmas. (Pasfield, William Reginald). *Ashdown. £0.05* FDP/LF (B72-50419)
Three Greek pastorals: flute and piano. (Veal, Arthur). *Peters. Unpriced* VRPJ (B72-51167)
Three limericks: for voices, instruments and piano. (Pehkonen, Elis). *Lengnick. £0.25* HYE/LDW (B72-50437)
Three Westmorland sketches: oboe and piano. (Wilson, John). *Forsyth. Unpriced* VTPJ (B72-50283)
Thy Kingdom come= Adveniat regnum tuum: for mixed chorus a capella. (Wood, James). *Galaxy: Galliard. Unpriced* EZDH (B72-50844)
Till. (Danvers, Charles). *Chappell. Unpriced* WMK/DW (B72-50776)
Tilmouth, Michael.
  Musica Britannica: a national collection of music
  Vol.31: Matthew Locke: Chamber music 1. *Published for the Royal Music Association by Stainer and Bell. £10.00* C/AYD (B72-50007)
  Vol.32: Matthew Locke: Chamber music 2. *Published for the Royal Music Association by Stainer and Bell. £10.00* C/AYD (B72-50008)
Times five: for flute, trombone, harp, violin, cello and 4 channels of tape sound. (Brown, Earle). *Universal. Unpriced* NVXPNR (B72-50990)
Timme, Traugott. Choralvorspiele in tiefer Lage zum Auswahlchoralbuch. *Bärenreiter. £3.15* R/AY (B72-50625)
Tindle, Anna. My land. *Ashdown. £0.09* GEZDW (B72-50436)
Tindle, Peter. My land. (Tindle, Anna). *Ashdown. £0.09* GEZDW (B72-50436)
Tippett, Michael. Ode for Queen Mary's birthday, 1694. Come ye sons of art. (Purcell, Henry). *Schott. £0.75* DX (B72-50048)
Tippett, *Sir* Michael. Songs for Dov: for tenor and orchestra. *Schott. £1.50* KGHE/MDW (B72-50943)
Tissington variations: for four trombones. (Premru, Raymond). *Musica rara. Unpriced* WUNS/T (B72-51247)
To Him we sing, Op. 34: unison carol for children's voices and piano. (Rubbra, Edmund). *Lengnick. £0.05* JFDP/LF (B72-50905)
Toccata: for trumpet and piano. (Burgon, Geoffrey). *Stainer and Bell. £0.40* WSPJ (B72-51235)
Toccatina for two pianos. (Konietzny, Heinrich). *London: Simrock. Unpriced* QNU (B72-50562)
Todo o mundo passo. (Villa-Lobos, Heitor). *Arthur Napoleão: Essex Music. Unpriced* QPJ (B72-50605)
Tom Sawyer suite: for B flat clarinet and piano. (Collis, James). *Boosey and Hawkes. £1.25* VVPG (B72-50757)
Tom Tiddler's tunes: little piano pieces
  Book 1. (Last, Joan). *Bosworth. Unpriced* QPJ (B72-50188)
  Book 2. (Last, Joan). *Bosworth. Unpriced* QPJ (B72-50189)
Tomlins, Greta. Salute to spring: SSA. *Lengnick. £0.13* FDW (B72-50078)
Top pop scene. *Purnell. £0.60* A/GB(M) (B72-21771) ISBN 0 361 02016 3
Toplis, Margot. The Faber book of French folk songs. *Faber Music. £3.00* JDW/G/AYH (B72-50899) ISBN 0 571 09944 0
Torches: for treble voices and organ. (Pehkonen, Elis). *Chappell. Unpriced* FLDP/LF (B72-50892)
Tovey, *Sir* Donald Francis.
  Essays in musical analysis
  Supplementary volume: Chamber music. *Oxford University Press. £0.80* A/CB (B72-26081) ISBN 0 19 315136 7
  Vol.1: Symphonies. *Oxford University Press. £0.80* A/CB (B72-26082) ISBN 0 19 315137 5
  Vol.2: Symphonies (2), variations and orchestral polyphony. *Oxford University Press. £0.80* A/CB (B72-26083) ISBN 0 19 315138 3
  Vol.3: Concertos. *Oxford University Press. £0.80* A/CB (B72-26084) ISBN 0 19 315139 1
  Vol.3: Concertos. *Oxford University Press. £0.80* 780.15 (B72-26084) ISBN 0 19 315139 1
  Vol.4: Illustrative music. *Oxford University Press. £0.80* A/CB (B72-26085) ISBN 0 19 315140 5
  Vol.5: Vocal music. *Oxford University Press. £0.80* A/CB (B72-26086) ISBN 0 19 315141 3
  Vol.6: Supplementary essays, glossary and index. *Oxford University Press. £0.80* A/CB (B72-26087) ISBN 0 19 315142 1
Townsend, Paul. The space-dragon of Galatar. (Paynter, John). *Universal. Unpriced* CQN (B72-50807)
Traditional tunes of the Child ballads: with their texts, according to the extant records of Great Britain and America
  Vol.2: Ballads 54 to 113. (Bronson, Bertrand Harris). *Princeton University Press: Oxford University Press. Unpriced* KEZDW/K/G/AY (B72-50940)
  Vol.3: Ballads 114 to 243. (Bronson, Bertrand Harris). *Princeton University Press: Oxford University Press. £10.00* KEZDW/K/G/AY (B72-50941)
  Vol. 4 Ballads 245 to 299, with addenda to volumes 1-4. (Bronson, Bertrand Harris). *Princeton University Press Oxford University Press. Unpriced* KEZDW/K/G/AY (B72-50939)
Traherne, Thomas. How like an Angel came I down: anthem for SATB and organ. (Drayton, Paul). *Novello. £0.14* DH (B72-50357)
Traité d'instrumentation et d'orchestration: suivie de 'L'Art du chef d'orchestre'. (Berlioz, Hector). Nouvelle éd. reprinted. *Gregg. £21.00* AM/DF (B72-06769) ISBN 0 576 28418 1
Trakl, Georg. Fünf Orchestergesänge nach Georg Trakl. Op.27: für Bariton und Orchester. (Erbse, Heimo). *Peters. £3.20* KGNE/MDW (B72-50492)
Traver, James Ferris. Praise the Lord our King: for mixed chorus and organ with optional brass accompaniment. *Galaxy: Galliard. Unpriced* DH (B72-50359)
Treatise on harmony. (Rameau, Jean Philippe). *Dover Publications: Constable. £8.75* A/R (B72-01562) ISBN 0 486 22461 9
Trees revisited: for piano. (Chapple, Brian). *Chester. Unpriced* QPJ (B72-50581)
Treibmann, Karl Ottomar. Sonata for cello & piano. Sonate für Violoncello und Klavier. *Peters: Hinrichsen. £1.80* SRPE (B72-50695)
Trend, J B. Torches: for treble voices and organ. (Pehkonen, Elis). *Chappell. Unpriced* FLDP/LF (B72-50892)
Trenner, Franz.
  Songs. Lieder
  Vol. 1. (Strauss, Richard). *Boosey and Hawkes. £7.50* KDW/AZ (B72-50927)
  Songs. Lieder
  Vol. 2. (Strauss, Richard). *Boosey and Hawkes. £7.50* KDW/AZ (B72-50928)
  Songs. Lieder
  Vol. 3. (Strauss, Richard). *Boosey and Hawkes. £7.50* KDW/AZ (B72-50929)

Songs. Lieder
Vol. 4. (Strauss, Richard). *Boosey and Hawkes. £10.00* KDW/AZ (B72-50930)
Trent march: accordion solo. (Spratley, Philip). *Charnwood Music. £0.22* RSPMGM (B72-51068)
Tres apuntes = Three sketches. (Brouwer, Leo). *Schott. £0.90* TSPMJ (B72-51151)
Trevor, C H.
Old English organ music for manuals
Book 6. *Oxford University Press. £0.50* R/AYD (B72-50626) ISBN 0 19 375829 6
The progressive organist: all grades Associated Board standard
Book 8. *Elkin. £0.55* R/AY (B72-50205)
Trevor, Caleb Henry.
Old English organ music for manuals
Book 5. *Oxford University Press. £0.50* R/AYD (B72-50208) ISBN 0 19 375828 8
Organ music for manuals
Book 1. *Oxford University Press. £0.65* R/AY (B72-50206) ISBN 0 19 375833 4
Book 2. *Oxford University Press. £0.65* R/AY (B72-50207) ISBN 0 19 375834 2
Trinité: musica sacramenti, für drei Vibraphone. (Blarr, Oskar Gottlieb). *Bosse: Bärenreiter. £1.85* XTRNT (B72-50791)
Trinity College of Music, the first hundred years. (Rutland, Harold). *Mandeville Place, W.1: Trinity College of Music. £0.70* A(VP/YDB/X) (B72-13439) ISBN 0 9502340 0 1
Triplo concerto a tre. (Menotti, Gian Carlo). *Schirmer. Unpriced* MMF (B72-50141)
Triptych for piano. (Bliss, *Sir* Arthur). *Novello. £0.60* QPJ (B72-51033)
Trois études de concert: trois caprices poetiques, for piano solo. (Liszt, Franz). *Bárenreiter. £0.90* QPJ (B72-50599)

Troisième livre de danceries: for four instruments, SATB. (Gervaise, Claude). *Pro Musica. Unpriced* LNSH (B72-50954)
Trona. (Bedford, David). *Universal. Unpriced* MRJ (B72-50154)
Troutbeck, J. Come, let us all this day/ melody and bass by J.S. Bach, words by J. Troutbeck interludes and inner parts by Gerald H. Knight; and, Prepare thyself, Zion, from the Christmas Oratorio. (Bach, Johann Sebastian). *Royal School of Church Music. Unpriced* JDH (B72-50439)
Truth of the Lord endureth forever: for four-part chorus of mixed voices a cappella. (Lekberg, Sven). *Schirmer Chappell. Unpriced* EZDK (B72-50059)
Tschaikowsky, Peter. *See* Tchaikowsky, Peter.
Tucker, Norman.
Der Besuch der alten Dame = The visit of the old lady. Op.35: Oper in drei Akten. (Einem, Gottfried von). *Boosey and Hawkes. £8.00* CC (B72-50339)
Der Besuch der alten Dame= The visit of the old lady. Op.35: opera in three acts after Friedrich Dürrenmatt's tragi-comedy. (Einem, Gottfried von). *Boosey and Hawkes. £10.00* CQC (B72-50803)
The visit of the old lady. (Dürrenmatt, Friedrich). *Boosey and Hawkes. £0.55* BELAC (B72-19611) ISBN 0 85162 006 x
Tull, Fisher.
Antiphon. *Boosey and Hawkes. £30.00* UMMJ (B72-51158)
Lieutenant Kije. Op.60. - Wedding of Kije, Troika. Two pieces. (Prokofiev, Sergei). *Boosey and Hawkes. £3.00* WMK/JR (B72-50312)
Sonatina for percussion ensemble. *Boosey and Hawkes. £1.75* XNSEM (B72-50331)
Terpsichore. *Boosey and Hawkes. £33.95* UMMJ (B72-51159)
Tunes for my viola: fourteen pieces for viola and piano. (Murray, Eleanor). *Boosey and Hawkes. £0.75* SQPJ (B72-50236)
Turner, Michael R. The parlour song book: a casquet of vocal gems. *Joseph. £5.00* KDW/GB/AY(XHS64) (B72-30931) ISBN 0 7181 0381 5
Turok, Paul.
Concerto for horn and orchestra. (Amram, David). *Peters. £1.60* WTPK/LF (B72-50788)
Elegy in memory of Karol Rathaus. Op. 23: for 3 trumpets, 2 horns, 3 trombones and baritone and tuba. *Musica rara. Unpriced* WMJ (B72-51217)
Tutankhamun. (Odam, George). *Chester. Unpriced* CQN (B72-50806)
Twentieth century composers
Vol.3: Britain, Scandinavia and the Netherlands. *Weidenfeld and Nicolson. £3.50* A(XM71) (B72-28679) ISBN 0 297 99377 1
Two fanfares: for four equal instruments with optional percussion. (Chagrin, Francis). *Novello. £1.30* LNSGN (B72-50951)
Two London sketches. (Newsome, R). *Feldman. Unpriced* WNR (B72-50314)
Two sentences: for SATB with divisions and organ. (Hurford, Peter). *Novello. £0.10* DGSKAD (B72-50816)

Two wedding hymns: set to chorale melodies. *Royal School of Church Music. Unpriced* DM/KDD (B72-50821)
Tye, Christopher. Give almes of thy goods. *Oxford University Press. Unpriced* DK (B72-50361) ISBN 0 19 352113 x
Tynan, Katherine. Thy Kingdom come= Adveniat regnum tuum: for mixed chorus a capella. (Wood, James). *Galaxy: Galliard. Unpriced* EZDH (B72-50844)
Tyree, Ronald. Concerto for bassoon in F major. Grand concerto: for bassoon and orchestra. (Hummel, Johann Nepomuck). *Musica rara. £2.50* VWPK/LF (B72-51193)

Understanding pop. (Jasper, Tony). *S.C.M. Press. £1.95* A/GB(XPQ17) (B72-10327) ISBN 0 334 01728 9
University of Oxford. *Bodleian Library. See* Bodleian Library.
Urdd er Hyrwyddo Cerddoriaeth Cymru. *See* Guild for the Promotion of Welsh Music.
Uwertura bohaterska. Heroic overture. (Panufnik, Andrzej). *Boosey and Hawkes. UNpriced* MMJ (B72-50518)
Uwertura bohaterska. Heroic overture. (Panufnik, Andrzej). *Boosey and Hawkes. Unpriced* MMJ (B72-50519)
Vagabond king. - Come all you beggars. Song of the brigands. (Friml, Rudolf). *Feldman. £0.20* KDW (B72-50460)
Valentia extramaterial: flute, piano, 2 or 4 percussion. (Lawson, Peter). *Peters. £1.50* NYFR (B72-50551)
Valentin, Gerhard. Ernte des Lebens/ by Paul Ernst Ruppel; Worte from 2. Korinther and Gerhard Valentin, with Osterlied/ by Paul Ernst Ruppel; Worte: Alter Osterru and Gerhard Valentin. (Ruppel, Paul Ernst). *Bärenreiter. Unpriced* EZDH (B72-50397)
Valses poéticas. (Granados, Enrique). *British and Continental. Unpriced* TSPMK/AHW (B72-51153)
Van Beethoven, Ludwig. *See* Beethoven, Ludwig van.
Van Eyk, Jacob. *See* Eyk, Jacob van.
Vanhal, Jan. Quartet for clarinet, viola & cello in F major. Quartet in F: for clarinet, violin and cello. *Musica rara. Unpriced* NVVNS (B72-50163)
Varak. Opus 47: violin and piano. (Hovhaness, Alan). *Peters. £1.00* SPJ (B72-50681)
Vargyas, Lajos. Folk music of Hungary. (Kodály, Zoltán). 2nd ed. *Barrie and Jenkins. £2.25* A/G(YG/XA1914 (B72-13442) ISBN 0 214 65327 7
Variants for small orchestra. (Schurmann, Gerard). *Novello. £3.50* MR/T (B72-50977)
Variationen über ein Menuett von Joseph Haydn. Op.29: für Klavier. (Burkhard, Willy). *Bärenreiter. £1.00* QPHR/T (B72-50576)
Variationen über ein Volkslied. Op.8: für Klavier. (Burkhard, Willy). *Bärenreiter. £1.00* QP/T (B72-50568)

Variations for piano in C major, 'Ah vous dirai - je maman'. K.265. Twelve variations in C major, 'Ah, vous dirai - je maman', K.265: for piano. (Mozart, Wolfgang Amadeus). *Nagel. £0.35* QP/T (B72-50570)
Variations for piano. Opus 23. (Standford, Patric). *Novello. £0.50* QP/T (B72-51027)
Variegations: for solo viola. (Tate, Phyllis). *Oxford University Press. £0.75* SQPMJ (B72-50239) ISBN 0 19 359027 1
Vaughan, Henry. Celtic requiem: for soprano, children's choir, chorus and orchestra. (Tavener, John). *Chester. Unpriced* EMDGKAV (B72-50383)
Vaughan Williams, Ralph.
National music, and other essays. *Oxford University Press. £2.50* A(D) (B72-15421) ISBN 0 19 311207 8
The Old Hundredth psalm tune: All people that on earth do dwell, for mixed or unison voices and orchestra. *Oxford University Press. Unpriced* EMDM (B72-50836) ISBN 0 19 369530 8
The Oxford book of carols. Revised ed.. *Oxford University Press. £0.90* DP/LF/AY (B72-50827) ISBN 0 19 313120 x
Riders to the sea: an opera in one act. *Oxford University Press. £5.00* CQC (B72-50805) ISBN 0 19 339335 2
Symphony no.2. A London Symphony. Centenary ed. *Stainer & Bell. £2.50* MME (B72-50510)
Vaughan Williams symphonies. (Ottaway, Hugh). *British Broadcasting Corporation. £0.45* BVDAMME (B72-28682) ISBN 0 563 12242 0
Veal, Arthur. Three Greek pastorals: flute and piano. *Peters. Unpriced* VRPJ (B72-51167)
Veerhoff, Carlos. Textur: fur Streicher. *Litolff: Hinrichsen. Unpriced* RXMJ (B72-51089)
Venezianische Musik um 1600: Stücke von Frescobaldi, Castello und Fontana, für Sopran - oder Tenorblockflöte oder andere Melodieinstrumente und Basso continuo. (Linde, Hans Martin). *Schott. £1.10* VSRP/AYJV(XE) (B72-51175)
Veracini, Francesco Maria.
Sonatas for violin & harpsichord. Op.2. Sonata accademiche. Op.2: für Violine und bezifferten Bass, Violine und Klavier (Cembalo, Orgel) mit Violoncello ad libitum
Sonata 10, F-Dur. *Peters: Hinrichsen. £0.90* SPE (B72-50676)
Sonatas for violin & harpsichord. Op.2. Sonata accademiche. Op.2: für Violine und bezifferten Bass, Violine und Klavier (Cembalo, Orgel) mit Violoncello ad libitum
Sonata 11, E-Dur. *Peters: Hinrichsen. £0.90* SPE (B72-50677)
Verdi, Giuseppe. Nabucodonosor. - Va pensiero. The chorus of Hebrew slaves. *Norman Richardson Band Arrangements. Unpriced* WMK/DW (B72-50310)
Veris gratia. Opus 9: suite for oboe, cello & strings. (Leighton, Kenneth). *Novello. £1.60* MRG (B72-50529)
Verrall, Pamela.
Cameos for clarinets. *Feldman. £0.40* VVNT (B72-50289)
The little king's carol: calypso. *British and Continental. Unpriced* FE/XDP/LF (B72-50883)
Ring ding bells: a song for Christmas. *British and Continental. Unpriced* JE/XTPDW/LF (B72-50902)
The rose of Bethlehem: S.S.A. *British and Continental. Unpriced* FDP/LF (B72-50872)
Son of Assisi: a musical based on incidents from the life of St Francis of Assisi. *British and Continental. Unpriced* CN/L (B72-50801)
Verrall, Pamela Motley.
The Christmas journey: S.A. *British and Continental. Unpriced* FE/NYFSDP/LF (B72-50881)
The dove. *Bosworth. Unpriced* FDW (B72-50876)
The lollipop tree: two-part song (with optional recorders, glockenspiel, xylophone and timps). *Bosworth. £0.175* FDW (B72-50877)
The star carol: SSA. *British and Continental. Unpriced* FEZDP/LF (B72-50884)
A star for Maria: a carol in two parts with optional descant for voices or instruments. *British and Continental. Unpriced* FDP/LF (B72-50873)
Verses for ensembles: for 13 woodwind, brass and percussion instruments. (Birtwistle, Harrison). *Universal. Unpriced* MRJ (B72-50979)
Vesperae solemnes de confessore. K.339. - *Excerpts.* Laudate Dominum. K.339, no.5. (Mozart, Wolfgang Amadeus). *Novello. £0.10* FDGKJ (B72-50867)
Viadana, Lodovico.
Sinfonia musicale. - *Excerpts.* Sinfonia, 'La Bergamasca': for 4 trumpets and 4 trombones, (4 trumpets, 2 horns and 2 trombones). *Music rara. £2.00* WNN (B72-51221)

Sinfonia musicale. - *Excerpts.* Sinfonia, 'La Padovana': for 4 trumpets and 4 trombones (4 trumpets, 2 horns and 2 trombones). *Musica rara. £1.50* WNN (B72-51222)
Sinfonie musicali. Op.18. - *Excerpts.* Canzona - La Padovana: 8 recorders. *Universal. Unpriced* VSNN (B72-51169)
Vicar of Bray: piano duet. (Johnson, Thomss Arnold). *Bosworth. Unpriced* QNV (B72-51021)
Victor, John. Liszt. (Rostand, Claude). *Calder and Boyars. £2.50* BLJ(N) (B72-27438) ISBN 0 7145 0342 8
Victorian garland: three poems by Matthew Arnold set for soprano and contralto solo voices, horn, and piano by Phyllis Tate. (Tate, Phyllis). *Oxford University Press. £1.80* JNFEE/WTPDW (B72-50921) ISBN 0 19 345824 1
Victorian sheet music covers. (Pearsall, Ronald). *David and Charles. £3.25* A(RC/XHS64) (B72-28659) ISBN 0 7153 5561 9
Victory, Gerard. Kriegslieder = Tears of battle: for solo tenor, mixed chorus, trumpet and percussion. *Fairfield Music. £1.00* KGHE/NYHXSDX (B72-50133)
Vier Gesänge auf den Heiligen Geist. Op.45: für gemischten Chor und Orgel. (Krol, Bernhard). *Simrock. Unpriced* DH (B72-50818)
Vies de Haydn, de Mozart et de Métastase. Lives of Haydn, Mozart and Metastasio. (Stendhal). *Calder and Boyars. £5.50* BHE(N) (B72-14734) ISBN 0 7145 0349 5
Villa-Lobos, Heitor. Cirandinhas, no.7. Todo o mundo passo. *Arthur Napoleão: Essex Music. Unpriced* QPJ (B72-50605)
Villanesca. Vol.2, no.4. (Granados, Enrique). *Boosey and Hawkes. £3.65* MK/AH (B72-50960)
Vincenzo Bellini: his life and operas. (Weinstock, Herbert). *Weidenfeld and Nicolson. £6.00* BBJH(N) (B72-12014) ISBN 0 297 00457 3
Viola in my life
1: Flute, violin, viola (solo), cello, piano, percussion. (Feldman, Morton). *Universal. Unpriced* NYDRNQ (B72-51000)
2: Flute, clarinet, violin, viola (solo), cello, piano, percussion. (Feldman, Morton). *Universal. Unpriced* NYDPNP (B72-50998)
3: Viola and piano. (Feldman, Morton). *Universal. Unpriced* SQPJ (B72-51128)
Violin and viola. (Nelson, Sheila M). *Benn. £3.00* AS/B(X) (B72-15430) ISBN 0 510 36651 1
Violin: six lessons with Yehudi Menuhin. (Menuhin, Yehudi). *38 Russell Sq., W.C.1: Faber Music Ltd. £2.50* AS/CY (B72-11002) ISBN 0 571 10000 7
Vision: full chorus and seven soloists. (Jergenson, Dale). *Schirmer: Chappell. Unpriced* HY (B72-50083)
Visit of the old lady. *See* Einem, Gottfried von.
Visit of the old lady. (Dürrenmatt, Friedrich). *Boosey and Hawkes. £0.55* BELAC (B72-19611) ISBN 0 85162 006 x
Vitali, Tomaso. Chaconne: for violin and harpsichord. *Oxford University Press. £0.70* SPHJN (B72-50680) ISBN 0 19 359210 x
Vivaldi, Antonio.
Concerto for treble recorder in G minor. P.402. Concerto in G minor: for flute, (clarinet), oboe and bassoon or treble recorder, oboe and basso continuo ad lib. *Musica rara. Unpriced* NWNSF (B72-50165)
Sinfonia 'Al santo sepulcro'. Rinaldi Op.50. *c/o Stanley Glasser, Goldsmiths' College, S.E.14: Piers Press. Unpriced* VSNSK/AE (B72-50744)
Vogt, Paul G. Fiesta: ein Anti-Lehrstück mit Musik. *Schott. £3.20* DX (B72-50381)
Voices, pipes and pedals: the story of a life in music. (Sargent, A W). *Mitre Press. £1.75* AD/EC(P) (B72-03928) ISBN 0 7051 0108 8
Von Bülow, Hans. *See* Bülow, Hans von.
Von Einem, Gottfried. *See* Einem, Gottfried von.
Von Fischer, Kurt. *See* Fischer, Kurt von.
Von Goethe, Johann Wolfgang. *See* Goethe, Johann Wolfgang von.
Von Herzogenberg, Heinrich. *See* Herzogenberg, Heinrich von.
Von Lenz, Wilhelm. *See* Lenz, Wilhelm von.
Von Sauer, Emil. *See* Sauer, Emil von.
Von Stein, Charlotte. *See* Stein, Charlotte von.
Von Weber, Carl Maria, *Freiherr. See* Weber, Carl Maria von, *Freiherr.*
Von Webern, Anton. *See* Webern, Anton von.
Vorisek, Jan Hugo. Grand overture in C minor: for two pianos. Op. 16. *Bärenreiter. £1.50* QNU (B72-50563)

Vörösmarty, Mihaly. The arms of Hungary: SATB unaccompanied. (Kodály, Zoltán). *Boosey and Hawkes. £0.05* EZDW (B72-50412)
Voxpop: profiles of the pop process. (Wale, Michael). *Harrap. £2.10* A/GB (B72-28678) ISBN 0 245 50904 6
Voyage musical en Allemagne et en Italie: études sur Beethoven, Gluck et Weber, mélanges et nouvelles. (Berlioz, Hector). *Gregg. £18.60* A(D) (B72-06763) ISBN 0 576 28419 x
Voyage. Op.27: seven pieces for brass trio (B flat trumpet, F horn, trombone). (Muczynski, Robert). *Schirmer Chappell. Unpriced* WNT (B72-50316)
Wachet auf ruft uns die Stimme = Wake ye maids! hark, strikes the hour. S.140: cantata for 27. Sunday after Trinity. (Bach, Johann Sebastian). *Bärenreiter. £1.00* DE (B72-50350)
Wade, Steuart. Wayside sketches: six characteristic pieces for piano. *Keith Prowse Music. £0.25* QPJ (B72-50193)
Wagner-Régeny, Rudolf. Hermann-Hesse-Gesänge, 'Gesänge des Abschieds': für Bariton und Orchester. *Peters Hinrichsen. £2.80* KGNE/MDW (B72-50493)
Waldteufel, Emile. Two waltzes. *Oxford University Press. £0.90* MHW (B72-50139) ISBN 0 19 368017 3
Wale, Michael. Voxpop: profiles of the pop process. *Harrap. £2.10* A/GB (B72-28678) ISBN 0 245 50904 6
Wales, Tony. Folk directory
1972. *English Folk Dance and Song Society. £1.00 (£0.75 to members of the EFDSS)* A/G(BC) (B72-06764) ISBN 0 85418 034 6
Wales education surveys. *(Welsh Education Office)* Great Britain. *Welsh Office.* Music. *31 Cathedral Rd, Cardiff CF1 9UJ: Welsh Education Office. £0.20* A(V/YDK) (B72-31877) ISBN 0 903702 00 2
Walker, Arthur D. Overture in G minor. (Bruckner, Anton). *Eulenburg. £0.75* MMJ (B72-50513)
Walker, Richard, *b.1925.* H.H.: a tribute to Herbert Howells on his eightieth birthday. (Spearing, Robert). *10e Prior Bolton St., Canonbury, N.1: Triad Press. £0.90* BHS(N) (B72-30070) ISBN 0 902070 05 3
Walker, Wilfred.
Playa las canteras: Spanish dance: accordion solo. *Charnwood Music. £0.19* RSPMH (B72-51069)
Sonatina for accordion, no.1, in C major. Sonatina no.1 in C: accordion solo. *Charnwood Music. £0.25* RSPMEM (B72-51065)
Sonatina for accordion, no.2 in G major. Sonatina no.2 in G: accordion solo. *Charnwood Music. £0.26* RSPMEM (B72-51066)
Walsh, Stephen. The lieder of Schumann. *Cassell. £1.75* BSGAKDW (B72-01563) ISBN 0 304 93736 3
Walton, *Sir* William.
Façade: an entertainment. *Oxford University Press. £12.00* HYE/NYENQ (B72-50084) ISBN 0 19 359402 1
A Queen's fanfare: for trumpets and trombones. *Oxford University Press. £0.40* WNGN (B72-50781) ISBN 0 19 368186 2
Wangenheim, Volker. Klangspiel 1: für Streicher. *Peters. £2.20* RXMJ (B72-50655)
Wanhall, Johann Baptist. *See* Vanhal, Jan.
Ward, David. Sound approaches for slow learners: a report on experimental work in schools being part of the Music for Slow Learners Project at Dartington College of Arts. *Bedford Square Press for the Standing Conference for Amateur Music. £0.35* A(VMWR) (B72-16605) ISBN 0 7199 0829 9
Wark, Graham. SNO 1971: an anniversary study of the Scottish National Orchestra (1950-1971), the Scottish Orchestra (1891-1950) and their antecedents. (Scottish National Orchestra Society). *150 Hope St., Glasgow, C2: Scottish National Orchestra Society Ltd. £0.45* AMM/E(QB/X) (B72-26096) ISBN 0 9502512 0 8
Warlock, Peter. Cod-pieces. Liber 1. - *Excerpts.* Two cod-pieces. Nos.3.4. *Thames. Unpriced* QNVK (B72-50174)
Waters, Frank. Nursery songs and carols. *Franklin Watts. £0.25* JFDW/GK/AY (B72-50103) ISBN 0 85166 258 7
Watkins, David.
Anthology of English music for the harp
Vol.1. *Stainer and Bell. £1.00* TQPMK/AYD (B72-51144)
Vol.4. *Stainer and Bell. £1.00* TQPMK/AYD (B72-51145)
Complete method for the harp. *Boosey and Hawkes. Unpriced* TQ/AC (B72-50704)
Watts, Isaac.
Come, dearest Lord: anthem for SATB and organ. (Naylor, Peter). *Novello. £0.10* DH (B72-50358)
The singing master's assistant. - *Excerpts.* Bethlehem: SAATB a cappella. (Billings, William). *Peters Hinrichsen. £0.40* EZDP/LF (B72-50405)
Wayside sketches: six characteristic pieces for piano. (Wade, Steuart). *Keith Prowse Music. £0.25* QPJ (B72-50193)
We shall not be moved: traditional. (Siebert, Edrich). *Studio Music. Unpriced* WMK/DW (B72-50778)
Weary travellers: negro spiritual, SATB and piano. (Nelson, Havelock). *Boosey and Hawkes. Unpriced* DW/LC (B72-50829)
Webber, Andrew Lloyd. Jesus Christ superstar. - *Excerpts.* Jesus Christ superstar: a rock opera. *Leeds Music. £1.25* KDW (B72-50119)
Weber, Carl Maria von, *Freiherr.* Twelve easy pieces for piano duet. Op.3 and Op.10. *Barenreiter. £1.25* QNV (B72-50564)
Webern, Anton von. Orchestra pieces, (1913). *Boosey and Hawkes. £2.40* MMJ (B72-50520)
Wechsberg, Joseph. The opera. *Weidenfeld and Nicolson. £4.95* AC (B72-24252) ISBN 0 297 99508 1
Wedding march. (Mendelssohn, Felix). *Ashdown. Unpriced* RK/KDD (B72-50221)
Weep no more, my lady: an intimate biography of Judy Garland. (Deans, Mickey). *W.H. Allen. £2.50* AKF/E(P) (B72-08534) ISBN 0 491 00941 0
Weigart, Bernhard.
Vier Sonaten: für Querflöte und Basso continuo, Cembalo (Pianoforte, Violoncello, Viola da gamba), ad lib.
Band 1: Sonate 1, G-Dur. Op.4, no.3; Sonate 2, G-Moll Op.1, no.2. (Stanley, John). *Schott. £1.20* VRPE (B72-51163)
Band 2: Sonate 3, D-Dur. Op.1, no.4; Sonate 4, D-Moll Op.1, no.7. (Stanley, John). *Schott. £1.20* VRPE (B72-51164)
Weihnachtslieder Op.8. - Die Könige. The kings: SSATB (acc. or unacc.). (Cornelius, Peter). *Oxford University Press. Unpriced* DP/LF (B72-50373) ISBN 0 19 343029 0
Weinstock, Herbert. Vincenzo Bellini: his life and operas. *Weidenfeld and Nicolson. £6.00* BBJH(N) (B72-12014) ISBN 0 297 00457 3
Weismann, Wilhelm. Concerto for violin in D major. K.218. Konzert, D-dur: für Violine und Orchester. (Mozart, Wolfgang Amadeus). *Peters. Unpriced* SPK/LF (B72-51120)
Welcome Yule: carol for voices, violins or flutes, descant recorders, guitars, percussion and piano. (Hunt, Reginald). *Ashdown. £0.09* FE/NYDSRDP/LF (B72-50424)
Wellesz, Egon. Arnold Schoenberg. 1st ed. reprinted. *Queen Anne's Rd, Great Yarmouth, Norfolk: Galliard Ltd. Unpriced* BSET (B72-01561) ISBN 0 85249 104 2
Welsh Education Office. *See* Great Britain. *Welsh Education Office.*
Welsh Office. *See* Great Britain. *Welsh Office.*
Wembley way: quick march. (Elms, Albert). *Boosey and Hawkes. £0.55* UMMGM (B72-50717)
Wembley way: quick march. (Elms, Albert). *Boosey and Hawkes. £0.45* WMJ (B72-50770)
Wendt, Wolfgang. Studies for the piano
Book 1: Basic kinds of touch: portato-legato-staccato. *Peters. Unpriced* Q/AF (B72-51006)
Wenz, Josef. Die goldene Brücke: Volkskinderlieder für Hans und Kindergarten, Spielplatz und Schule. *Bärenreiter. £1.00* JFDW/GJ/AYE (B72-50453)
Wesley, Samuel Sebastian. Blessed be the God and Father. - *Excerpts.* Love one another/ by S.S. Wesley; words from I St Peter; and, O worship the Lord/ by John Travers; words from Psalm 96. *Royal School of Church Music. Unpriced* JDK (B72-50441)
West Side story: a musical. (Laurents, Arthur). *Heinemann Educational. £0.50* BBMMACM (B72-08533) ISBN 0 435 23529 x
Western music: an introduction. (Stevenson, Ronald). *25 Thurloe St., S.W.7: Kahn and Averil. £2.50* A(X) (B72-00906) ISBN 0 900707 10 0
Wette, Adelheid.
Hänsel and Gretel. - *Excerpts.* Hänsel and Gretel song book
by Engelbert Humperdinck. (Humperdinck, Engelbert). *Francis, Day and Hunter. £0.35* KDW (B72-50461)
Hansel and Gretel: a fairy opera in three acts. (Humperdinck, Engelbert). *Schott. £1.05* CC (B72-50340)
What is the meaning of it all?: two-part song with piano accompaniment. (Dexter, Harry). *Novello. £0.10* FDW (B72-50875)
Whitcomb, Ian. After the ball. *Allen Lane. £3.00* A/GB(X) (B72-28006) ISBN 0 7139 0308 2
White company - overture. (Richardson, Norman). *Boosey and Hawkes. £3.30* WMJ (B72-51216)
Whittall, Arnold. Schoenberg chamber music. *British Broadcasting Corporation. £0.45* BSETAN (B72-22494) ISBN 0 563 10489 9
Whittier, John Greenleaf. O brother man, fold to thy heart thy brother: SATB. (Hopson, Hal H). *Warner: Blossom Music. Unpriced* EZDH (B72-50054)
Who are these children? Op. 84: lyrics, rhymes and riddles, for tenor and piano. (Britten, Benjamin). *Faber Music. Unpriced* KGHDW (B72-50942)
Whone, Herbert. The simplicity of playing the violin. *Gollancz. £2.20* AS/E (B72-11001) ISBN 0 575 01343 5
Who's who in music, and musicians' international directory. 6th ed. *Burke's Peerage. £8.00* A(N/BC) (B72-12013) ISBN 0 85011 013 0
Wickham, E H . Golden classics: a selection of the world's best loved classics for piano. *Keith Prowse. Unpriced* QP/AY (B72-50565)
Wiesenfeldt, Eva. Tanzbüchlein für zwei Bratschen: Tanzlieder und Volkstänze. (Hoffmann, Adolf). *Schott. £0.80* SQNUH (B72-50688)
Wilbye, John. The second set of madrigals, 1609. *Scolar Press. £7.75* BWNRBADU (B72-10330) ISBN 0 85417 572 5
Wild horseman: arranged for two-part singing, with piano accompaniment. (Dexter, Harry). *Ashdown. £0.09* FDW (B72-50074)
Wilde Jagd: for piano solo. (Liszt,, Franz). *Bärenreiter. £0.65* QPJ (B72-50594)
Willan, Healey. I beheld her, beautiful as a dove: SATB unacc. *Oxford University Press. Unpriced* EZDW (B72-50415) ISBN 0 19 343027 4
Willetts, Pamela Joan. Ralph Vaughan Williams, 1872-1958: a guide to the centenary exhibition at the British Museum, 29 September to 15 December 1972. *British Museum. £0.10* BVD(WJ) (B72-28008) ISBN 0 7141 0337 3
Williams, Charles. The dream of Olwen: piano solo. *Lawrence Wright Music. £0.25* QPK/JR (B72-51048)
Williams, Hugh.
Charlie girl. (Heneker, David). *Chappell. £1.75* CM (B72-50799)
Charlie girl: a comedy musical in two acts. *Chappell! £0.75* BHJJACM (B72-23641) ISBN 0 85360 040 6
Williams, Margaret.
Charlie girl. (Heneker, David). *Chappell. £1.75* CM (B72-50799)
Charlie girl: a comedy musical in two acts. (Williams, Hugh). *Chappell. £0.75* BHJJACM (B72-23641) ISBN 0 85360 040 6
Williams, Patrick.
Choice lessons for the harpsichord or spinnet. - Allmand in D major. Prelude in D. (Greene, Maurice). *Leonard, Gould & Bolttler. £0.18* RK/AHJ (B72-51059)
Easy album for the organ
3rd. *Bosworth. £0.60* KE/TSDW/AY (B72-50937)
Williams, Peter, *b.1937.* Bach organ music. *British Broadcasting Corporation. £0.45* BBCAR (B72-15429) ISBN 0 563 10348 5
Williams, Ralph Vaughan. *See* Vaughan Williams, Ralph.
Williamson, Malcolm.
Carols of King David: for unison choir, congregation and organ
No.2: O Jerusalem: Psalm 122. *Weinberger. £0.05* JDR (B72-50090)
No.4: Who is the king of glory?: Psalm 24. *Weinberger. £0.05* JDR (B72-50091)
No.5: The King of love: Psalm 23. *Weinberger. £0.05* JDR (B72-50092)
Concerto for piano, no.3. Concerto no.3: for piano and orchestra. *Weinberger. Unpriced* QNUK/LF (B72-51020)
Love, the sentinel: for chorus a capella sic. *Weinberger. £0.15* EZDW (B72-50066)
Partita for viola on themes of Walton. *Weinberger. Unpriced* SQPMG (B72-51130)
Peace pieces: for organ, by Malcolm Williamson
Book 1. *Weinberger. Unpriced* RJ (B72-50214)
Book 2. *Weinberger. Unpriced* RJ (B72-50215)
Sonata for piano, no.2. Piano sonata no.2. *Weinberger. Unpriced* QPE (B72-50575)
Wills, Arthur. Concerto for organ, strings and timpani. *Boosey and Hawkes. £1.50* RK (B72-50218)
Willy Wonka and the chocolate factory: vocal selections. (Bricusse, Leslie). *Taradam Music. £0.75* KDW/JR (B72-50122)
Wilmer, Valerie. The jazz scene. (Fox, Charles). *Hamlyn. £1.75* AMT(X) (B72-24869) ISBN 0 600 02119 x
Wilson, Conrad. Scottish Opera - the first ten years. *Collins. £5.00* AC(YDL/XQB11) (B72-21778) ISBN 0 00 410584 2
Wilson, George H. Secondary school music: philosophy, theory and practice. (Glenn, Neal Edwin). *Prentice-Hall. £4.00* A(VK) (B72-50333) ISBN 0 13 797522 8
Wilson, John. Three Westmorland sketches: oboe and piano. *Forsyth. Unpriced* VTPJ (B72-50283)
Wilson, Richard. Home from the range: for full chorus of mixed voices a cappella. *Schirmer: Chappell. Unpriced* EZDW (B72-50067)
Wilson, Sandy.
The boy friend: a play in three acts. *Penguin. £0.25* BWNTMACM (B72-06766) ISBN 0 14 001350 4
The boy friend: song album. *Chappell. £0.60* KDW (B72-50120)
Wilson, Thomas.
Ave Maria and Pater noster. *Galliard. £0.10* EZDJ (B72-50057)
Soliloquy. *Stainer & Bell. £0.66* TSPMJ (B72-50710)
Winckler, C. Lives of Haydn, Mozart and Metastasio. (Stendhal). *Calder and Boyars. £5.50* BHE(N) (B72-14734) ISBN 0 7145 0349 5
Wind sings on the mountain. (Bennett, F Roy). *Ashdown. £0.05* JDW (B72-50442)
Windhover: SATB unacc. (Paynter, John). *Oxford University Press. Unpriced* EZDW (B72-50414) ISBN 0 19 343006 1
Windsor variations: for chamber orchestra. (Berkeley, Lennox). *Chester. Unpriced* MR/T (B72-50976)
Wine, sweet wine = Méz, méz: SSSAAA unaccompanied. (Kodály, Zoltán). *Boosey and Hawkes. Unpriced* FEZDW (B72-50889)
Winkworth, Katherine.
Praise to the Lord, the Almighty: SATB. (Gilbert, Norman). *Oxford University Press. Unpriced* DH (B72-50817) ISBN 0 19 351112 6
Praise to the Lord, the Almighty: two-part. (Gilbert, Norman). *Oxford University Press. Unpriced* FDH (B72-50869) ISBN 0 19 341506 2
Winters, Geoffrey. A medley of folk-songs. (Stuart, Forbes). *Longman. Unpriced* JDW/G/AY (B72-50444) ISBN 0 582 15331 x
Wish now was then: from the film, 'Mary, Queen of Scots'. (Barry, John). *Leeds Music. £0.20* KDW/JR (B72-50109)
Wohl, Waldemar. Le Journal de printemps. - Suites 5, 6. Suites for four strings or wind instruments and basso continuo, nos.5 in G major, 6 in F major. (Fischer, Johann Caspar Ferdinand). *Bärenreiter. £1.50* NXNRG (B72-50545)
Wohlgemuth, Gerhard. Classisches Spielbuch: für Sopran-Blockflöte, Alt-Blockflöte und Klavier. *Peters Hinrichsen. Unpriced* VSNTPWK/AAY (B72-51172)
Wohltemperierte Klavier. S.846-893
Band 1. (Bach, Johann Sebastian). *Peters: Hinrichsen. Unpriced* PWP/Y (B72-51003)
Band 2. (Bach, Johann Sebastian). *Peters: Hinrichsen. Unpriced* PWP/Y (B72-51004)

Wojciechowski, Johannes. Te Deum: for mixed voices (with soprano and tenor solo) and orchestra. (Bizet, Georges). First edition. *Simrock. Unpriced* DH (B72-50356)

Wolfe, Steve. Beg, steal or borrow: Britain's Eurovision song 1972. (Cole, Tony). *Valley Music. Unpriced* UMMK/DW/JS (B72-50259)

Wolfe old time stars' books. *(Wolfe)* Gammond, Peter. Best music hall and variety songs. *Wolfe. £5.00* ADW/GM(YD) (B72-30743) ISBN 0 7234 0451 8

Wolff, Christian. Lines: for string quartet, or quartet of stringed instruments. *Peters. Unpriced* RXNS (B72-51109)

Wölki, Konrad. Alte Lautenmusik: für drei Gitarren;. *Schott. £0.80* TSNTK/AAY (B72-50707)

Wood, Helen. The apple: unison song. (Cope, Cecil). *Boosey and Hawkes. £0.09* JFDP (B72-50904)

Wood, Hugh.
  Capriccio. Op.8. *Novello. £0.45* RJ (B72-50216)
  Concerto for violoncello and orchestra. Op.12. *Universal. Unpriced* SRPK/LF (B72-50242)

Wood, James. Thy Kingdom come= Adveniat regnum tuum: for mixed chorus a capella. *Galaxy: Galliard. Unpriced* EZDH (B72-50844)

Woodcock, Clement. 'Browning' fantasy: for five instruments, SATTB. *Pro musica. Unpriced* LNR (B72-50949)

Woodford, James Russell. Thee we adore. (Holman, Derek). *Royal School of Church Music. Unpriced* FLDH (B72-50081)

Working with R.V.W. (Douglas, Roy). *Oxford University Press. £0.80* BVD(N/XPDI5) (B72-21776) ISBN 0 19 315427 7

World of art library: music. *(Thames and Hudson)* Orrey, Leslie. A concise history of opera. *Thames and Hudson. £2.50* AC(X) (B72-28009) ISBN 0 500 18130 6

World of musical instruments. (Kendall, Alan). *Hamlyn. £1.75* AL/B (B72-08532) ISBN 0 600 35957 3

World of Stanley Holloway: songs and musical monologues by various composers and writers. (Holloway, Stanley). *Francis, Day and Hunter. £0.75* KHY (B72-50497)

World that sings: an account of the 26 years of the International Musical Eisteddfod. (Humphries, Mary). *21 Duffryn Close, Cardiff CF2 6HT: John Jones Cardiff Ltd. £0.50* AD(YDKRL/WB/XPG26) (B72-22481) ISBN 0 902375 24 5

Wright, Rosemary. Music-box polka: accordion solo. *Charnwood Music. Unpriced* RSPMHVH (B72-51072)

Wuorinen, Charles. Trio: violin, viola, violoncello. *Peters. £3.40* RXNT (B72-50670)

Yellow bird. (Luboff, Norman). *Frank Music. Unpriced* WMK/DW (B72-50777)

Yonge, Nicolas. Musica Transalpina
  Vol.1. 1st ed. reprinted. *Gregg. £12.00* AEZDU (B72-26095) ISBN 0 576 28178 6

York: per flauto, oboe (ossia tromba), fagotto, mandolina, pianoforte, triangolo e contrabasso. (Komorous, Rudolf). *Universal. Unpriced* NYDPNP (B72-50999)

Yorke studies for double bass
  Vol.1: Half and first positions. (Slatford, Rodney). *Yorke. Unpriced* SS/AF (B72-51140)

Young, Freda Elton. London sparrow: unison song for children. (Ager, Laurence). *Cramer. £0.06* JFDW/GJ (B72-50451)

Young, Percy Marshall. Sibelius, a personal portrait. (Levas, Santeri). *Dent. £2.95* BSH(N) (B72-11000) ISBN 0 460 03978 4

Young pianist: a new approach for teachers and students. (Last, Joan). 2nd ed. *Oxford University Press. £1.40* AQ/E(VC) (B72-10331) ISBN 0 19 318420 6

Young Winston. - *Excerpts*. Jennie's theme: from the film. (Ralston, Alfred). *Chappell. £0.25* QPK/JR (B72-51047)

Yuval: studies of the Jewish Music Research Centre
  Vol.2. *Magnes Press: Distributed by Oxford University Press. £6.15* A(YBU) (B72-12719) ISBN 0 19 647627 5

Zacharias, Helmut. Munich melody: original theme of BBC TV Olympic Grandstand. *Ardmore and Beechwood. Unpriced* QPK/AGM/JS (B72-51045)

Zauberflöte. - *Excerpts*. Six airs. (Mozart, Wolfgang Amadeus). *Regina Music. Unpriced* TSPMK/DW (B72-50712)

Zehm, Friedrich.
  Neue Bläserstücke. Partitur in C: für 4 Blechbläser (Trompeten Posaunen). *Schott. £0.80* WNSG (B72-50783)
  Neue Duettstudien: für Querflöten. *Schott. Unpriced* VRNU (B72-51161)

Zimmer, Ulrich. Musae Sioniae. - *Excerpts*. 'Allein Gott in der Hör sei Ehr'. T.3, no.11, T1.9, no.54, T1.5, no.21: chorale arrangements for three, four and eight voices. (Praetorius, Michael). *Bärenreiter. £0.60* EZDM (B72-50402)

Zimmerman, Bernd Alois. 'I turned and saw all the injustices that are committed under the sun': ecclesiastical action for two speakers, bass soloist and orchestra. *Schott. £3.20* KGXE/MDE (B72-50945)

Zimmermann, Bernd Alois. Concerto for cello in the form of a 'pas de trois'. Concerto pour violoncelle et orchestra en forme de 'pas de trios' sic. *Schott. Unpriced* MPSRF (B72-50524)

Zimmermann, Reiner. Quartet for strings. Op. 10. Streichquartett. Op. 10. (Debussy, Claude). *Peters Hinrichsen. Unpriced* RXNS (B72-51108)

Zink, Anton. Fiesta: ein Anti-Lehrstück mit Musik. (Vogt, Paul G). *Schott. £3.20* DX (B72-50381)

Zipp, Friedrich. Lobe den Herren, den mächtigen König der Ehren: Choralkantate für vierstimmigen gemischten Chor, Gemeindegesang (ad lib.), sechstimmigen

Bläserchor und Orgel. *Bärenreiter. y1.75* EWNPRDE (B72-50391)

Zoephel, Klaus. Trio for violin, cello & piano. Trio für Violine, Violoncello und Klavier. *Peters: Hinrichsen. £2.00* NXNT (B72-50548)

Zoo: a musical folly. (Sullivan, *Sir* Arthur). *William Reeves. Unpriced* CF (B72-50798)

Zuckerova, Olga. Grand overture in C minor: for two pianos. Op. 16. (Vorisek, Jan Hugo). *Bärenreiter. £1.50* QNU (B72-50563)

Zyklus: cycle for baritone and orchestra. (Reimann, Aribert). *Schott. £3.00* KGNE/MDW (B72-50494)

# SUBJECT INDEX

Accompaniment: Instrumental ensemble
LN/ED
Accordion RS
Advent: Carols: Female voices, Children's voices
FDP/LEZ
Aesthetics: Books A/CC
Afro-American: Christmas carols: Collections
DP/LF/AYTLD
Allemandes: Arrangements for organ
RK/AHJ
Alto voice KFQ
Analytical guides A/CB
Anglican liturgy: Choral works DGM
Anglican liturgy: Unaccompanied works
EZDGM
Anglican liturgy: Unison JDGM
Anthems DK
Anthems: Female voices, Children's voices
FDK
Anthems: Male voices GDK
Anthems: Soprano voices FLDK
Anthems: Unaccompanied works EZDK
Anthems: Unison JDK
Appalachian dulcimer TWT
Arrangements: Accordion solos RSPMK
Arrangements: Brass & keyboard quartet
NWXPNSK
Arrangements: Bassoon & piano VWPK
Arrangements: Brass band WMK
Arrangements: Cello & piano SRPK
Arrangements: Cello quintet SRNRK
Arrangements: Cello trio SRNTK
Arrangements: Clarinet & piano VVPK
Arrangements: Clarinets (3) & piano
VVNSQK
Arrangements: Cornet & piano WRPK
Arrangements: Crumhorn quartet
VTWNSK
Arrangements: Descant recorder solo
VSRPMK
Arrangements: Descant recorder trio
VSRNTK
Arrangements: Descant recorders (2) & piano
VSRNTQK
Arrangements: Double bass & piano SSPK
Arrangements: Electric organs RPVK
Arrangements: Flute & piano VRPK
Arrangements: Guitar solo TSPMK
Arrangements: Guitar trio TSNTK
Arrangements: Harp solo TQPMK
Arrangements: Horn & piano WTPK
Arrangements: Instrumental quartets LNSK
Arrangements: Military band UMMK
Arrangements: Oboe & piano VTPK
Arrangements: Oboe d'amore & string orchestra
RXMPVTQK
Arrangements: Orchestra MK
Arrangements: Organ RK
Arrangements: Piano duet, 4 hands QNVK
Arrangements: Piano solos QPK
Arrangements: Pianos (2), four hands
QNUK
Arrangements: Recorder VSK
Arrangements: Recorder duet VSNUK
Arrangements: Recorder quartet VSNSK
Arrangements: Recorder quintet VSNRK
Arrangements: Recorder solo VSPMK
Arrangements: Recorders (2) & keyboard
VSNTPWK
Arrangements: Septets: Percussion instruments
XNPK
Arrangements: String orchestra RXMK
Arrangements: Treble recorder & piano
VSSPK
Arrangements: Trumpet & piano WSPK
Arrangements: Trumpet, strings & keyboard trio
NUXSNTK
Arrangements: Viola & piano SQPK
Arrangements: Violin & piano SPK
Arrangements: Violin & string orchestra
RXMPSK
Arrangements: Violins (3) & string orchestra
RXMPSNTK
Arrangements: Violin trio SNTK
Arrangements: Wind band UMK
Arrangements: Wind instruments (2) & piano
UNTQK
Arrangements: Wind quartet UNSK
Arrangements: Wind quintet UNRK

Asia: Books BZB
Australia: Folk songs: Books
ADW/G(YX)
Austria: Books A(YEM)
Authors: Aesthetics & criticism: Books
A/CC(M)

Bach, Johann Sebastian: Books BBC
Backward children: Education: Books
A(VMWR)
Bagpipes VY
Ballad opera: Vocal scores CLM
Ballads: Folk songs: Unaccompanied solo voice
KEZDW/K/G
Ballads: Solo voice: Accompanied by guitar
KE/TSDW/K
Ballet: Arrangements for unaccompanied recorder
VSPMK/AHM
Ballet music: Arrangements for piano solo
QPK/HM
Ballet music: Symphony orchestra MM/HM
Bands: Brass instruments WM
Bands: Jazz: Books AMT/E(QB)
Bands: Melodic percussion instruments
XPQM
Bands: Wind instruments UM
Banjo TT
Bantock, Sir Granville: Books BBE
Banyard, Edmund: Books BBDN
Banyard, Stephen: Books BBDNB
Baritone voice KGN
Bass SS
Bass, Double: Accompanying soprano voice
KFLE/SS
Bass, Double: Books ASS
Bass viol STU
Bass viols (2) & keyboard STUNTPW
Bass voice KGX
Bassoon VW
Bawdy: Ballads: Folk songs: Solo voice: Accompanied by guitar KE/TSDW/K/G/KDX
Bax, Sir Arnold: Books BBH
Beethoven, Ludwig van: Books BBJ
Bellini, Vincenzo: Books BBJH
Berlioz, Hector: Books BBM
Bernstein, Leonard: Books BBMM
Bibliographies: Brass band AWM(T)
Bibliographies: Choral works AD(T)
Bibliographies: Church choral music
AD/LD(T)
Bibliographies: Folk music: Books A/G(T)
Bibliographies: Handel, G. F. BHC(T)
Bibliographies: Locke, M. BLOC(T)
Bibliographies: Music A(T)
Bibliographies: Orchestral music: Books
AM(T)
Bibliographies: Wales A(YDK/TC)
Biographies, Collected: Musicians A(N)
Biographies: Bach, J. S. BBC(N)
Biographies: Bantock, Sir G BBE(N)
Biographies: Bellini, V BBJH(N)
Biographies: Berlioz, H BBM(N)
Biographies: Bing, Sir R. AC(WB/P)
Biographies: Byrd, W. BBX(N)
Biographies: Caruso, E. AKGH/E(P)
Biographies: Cole, N. K. AKG/E(P)
Biographies: Debussy, C. BDJ(N)
Biographies: Delius, F. BDL(N)
Biographies: Dylan, B. AKG/E(P)
Biographies: Elgar, Sir E. BEP(N)
Biographies: Frazier, K. AQ/E(P)
Biographies: Garland, J. AKF/E(P)
Biographies: Hallé, Sir C. A(P)
Biographies: Handel, G. F. BHC(N)
Biographies: Haydn, J. BHE(N)
Biographies: Holst, G. BHP(N)
Biographies: Howells, H. BHS(N)
Biographies: Jolson, Al AKG/E(P)
Biographies: Joplin, J. AKDW/HHW/E(P)
Biographies: Lasso, O. di BLC(N)
Biographies: Liszt, F. BLJ(N)
Biographies: Mendelssohn family BMJB(N)
Biographies: Monteverdi, C. BMN(N)
Biographies: Osmonds, The AB/GB/E(P)
Biographies: Palestrina, G. P. da BPC(N)
Biographies: Presley, E.
AKGDW/HK/E(P)
Biographies: Schubert, F. BSF(N)
Biographies: Sibelius, J. BSH(N)
Biographies: Smith, J. S.: Books AKF/E(P)
Biographies: Strauss, R. BSU(N)
Biographies: Strauss family BSQB(N)
Biographies: Stravinsky, I. BSV(N)
Biographies: Sutherland, J. AKFL/E(P)
Biographies: Swan, D. BSWN(N)
Biographies: Vaughan Williams, R.
BVD(N)
Blues: Songs: Solo voice KDW/HHW
Blues: Songs: Solo voice: Books
AKDW/HHW
Blues guitarists: Books ATS/HHW/E(M)
Bowed string instruments RX
Bowed string instruments: Accompanying baritone
voice KGNE/RX
Bowed string instruments: Books ARX
Bowed string instruments & string orchestra
RXMPRX

Bowed string solo instrument & orchestra
MPRX
Brahms, Johannes: Books BBT
Brass & keyboard: Chamber music NWXP
Brass & percussion: Ensembles: Accompanying
tenor voice KGHE/NYHX
Brass & strings: Chamber music NVXP
Brass band: Books AWM
Brass bands WM
Brass instrument & orchestra MPW
Brass instrument & string orchestra
RXMPW
Brass instruments W
Brass instruments: Accompanying choral music
EW
Brass instruments: Books AW
Brass, strings & keyboard: Ensembles: Chamber
music NUXP
Brass, strings & percussion: Ensembles: Accompanying choral works ENYEXP
Brian, Havergal: Books BBTN
Byrd, William: Books BBX

Canons: Madrigals: Unaccompanied works
EZDU/X
Canons: Trumpet trios WSNT/X
Canons: Quartets: Instrumental ensembles
LNS/X
Cantatas, Religious DE
Cantatas, Religious: Accompanied by brass & organ
septet ENWNPRDE
Cantatas, Religious: Accompanied by keyboard &
percussion ENYLDE
Cantatas, Religious: Accompanied by orchestra
EMDE
Cantatas, Religious: Accompanied by violins (2) &
organ JNFLEE/SNTRDE
Cantatas, Religious: Bach, J. S.: Books
BBCADE
Cantatas, Religious: Bass voice: Accompanied by
orchestra KGXE/MDE
Cantatas, Religious: Bass voice: Accompanied by
violins (2) & keyboard
KGXE/SNTPWDE
Cantatas, Religious: Carols DPDE
Cantatas, Religious: High voice: Accompanied by
violin & organ KFTE/SPLRDE
Cantatas, Religious: Middle voice: Accompanied by
flute & organ KFVE/VRPLRDE
Cantatas, Religious: Unison JDE
Cantatas, Religious: Vocal duets JNEDE
Cantatas, Secular DX
Cantatas, Secular: Accompanied by cello
ESRDX
Cantatas, Secular: Accompanied by orchestra
EMDX
Cantatas, Secular: Accompanied by string orchestra
ERXMDX
Cantatas, Secular: Accompanied by woodwind,
keyboard & percussion ENYFPDX
Cantatas, Secular: Baritone voice: Accompanied by
french horn & string orchestra
KGNE/RXMPWTDX
Cantatas, Secular: Contralto voice KFQDX
Cantatas, Secular: Contralto voice: Accompanied by
chamber orchestra KFQE/MRDX
Cantatas, Secular: Female voices, Children's voices
FDX
Cantatas, Secular: Female voices, Children's
voices: Accompanied by descant recorder, keyboard & percussion FE/NYFSRDX
Cantatas, Secular: Female voices, Children's
voices: Accompanied by keyboard & percussion
FE/NYLDX
Cantatas, Secular: Mezzo-soprano voice: Accompanied by flute KFNE/VRDX
Cantatas, Secular: Soprano voice: Accompanied by
violins (2) & keyboard
KFLE/SNTPWDX
Cantatas, Secular: Tenor voice: Accompanied by
brass & percussion
KGHE/NYHXSDX
Cantatas, Secular: Tenor voice: Accompanied by
woodwind, strings & keyboard sextet
KGHE/NUPNQDX
Cantatas, Secular: Treble voices: Accompanied by
keyboard & percussion quartet
FLE/NYLNSDX
Cantatas, Secular: Unaccompanied works
EZDX
Cantatas, Secular: Unison: Accompanied by keyboard & percussion JE/NYLDX
Canticles: Evening Prayer: Anglican liturgy
DGPP
Canticles: Evening Prayer: Anglican liturgy: Unaccompanied works EZDGPP
Careers: Music: Books A(MN)
Carols DP
Carols: Accompanied by descant recorder, strings,
keyboard & percussion FE/NYDSRDP
Carols: Female voices, Children's voices
FDP
Carols: Female voices, Children's voices: Accompanied by percussion FE/XDP
Carols: Female voices, Children's voices: Accompanied by recorders, keyboard & percussion
FE/NYFSDP

Carols: Female voices, Children's voices: Unison
   JFDP
Carols: Female voices, Children's voices: Unison:
   Accompanied by recorder, keyboard & per-
   cussion ensemble   JFE/NYFSDP
Carols: Male voices   GDP
Carols: Soprano voices   FLDP
Carols: Unaccompanied female voices, children's
   voices   FEZDP
Carols: Unaccompanied works   EZDP
Carols: Unison   JDP
Caruso, Enrico: Books   AKGH/E(P)
Casey, Peter: Books   BCBW
Catalogues, Trade: Recorded music
   A/FD(WM)
Catalogues: Bax, *Sir* A.   BBH(WJ)
Catches: Unaccompanied male voices
   GEZDW/XD
Cathedral music: Choral works: Books
   AD/LE
Cello   SR
Cello: Accompanying choral works   ESR
Cello & guitar   SRPLTS
Cello & percussion   SRPLX
Cello & viola   SQPLSR
Cello & violin   SPLSR
Cello & wind band   UMPSR
Cello, trumpet & string orchestra
   RXMPWSPLSR
Chaconnes: Sextets: Woodwind, strings, & key-
   board   NUPNQHJN
Chaconnes: Violin & piano   SPHJN
Chamber music   N
Chamber music: Brass   WN
Chamber music: Clarinets   VVN
Chamber music: Crumhorn   VTWN
Chamber music: Descant recorders   VSRN
Chamber music: Flutes   VRN
Chamber music: Guitars   TSN
Chamber music: Oboes   VTN
Chamber music: Percussion   XN
Chamber music: Pianos   QN
Chamber music: Recorders   VSN
Chamber music: Schoenberg, A.: Books
   BSETAN
Chamber music: Strings   RXN
Chamber music: Trumpets   WSN
Chamber music: Vibrophone   XTQTN
Chamber music: Wind   UN
Chamber music: Woodwind   VN
Chamber orchestra   MR
Chamber orchestra: Accompanying contralto voice
   KFQE/MR
Chansons: Unaccompanied works   EZDU
Children's hymns: Female voices, Children's
   voices: Unison   JFDM/GJ
Children's musical plays: Delibes, L.: Books
   BDKACN
Children's musical plays: Full scores   CQN
Children's musical plays: Vocal scores   CN
Children's songs: Female voices, Children's voices:
   Unison   JFDW/GJ
Children's songs: Female voices, Children's voices:
   Unison: Accompanied by guitar
   JFE/TSDW/GJ
Children's songs: Unaccompanied female voices,
   children's voices: Unison
   JFEZDW/GJ
Children's voices: Choral works   F
Children's voices: Unison   JF
Children's voices: Vocal ensembles   JNF
Child's voice   KF
Chime bars: Accompanying high voices: Unison
   JFTE/XTPR
China: Books   BZH
Choirmasters: Books   AD/EC(M)
Choirs: Music   D
Choirs: Music: Books   AD
Chopin, Frédéric: Books   BCE
Choral music   D
Choral music: Books   AD
Choral speaking   HY
Christmas: Anthems, Hymns, Carols, etc.: Un-
   accompanied works   EZDH/LF
Christmas: Carol cantatas   DPDE/LF
Christmas: Carols   DP/LF
Christmas: Carols: Accompanied by descant
   recorder, strings, keyboard & percussion
   FE/NYDSRDP/LF
Christmas: Carols: Female voices, Children's
   voices   FDP/LF
Christmas: Carols: Female voices, Children's
   voices: Accompanied by percussion
   FE/XDP/LF
Christmas: Carols: Female voices, Children's
   voices: Accompanied by recorders, keyboard &
   percussion   FE/NYFSDP/LF
Christmas: Carols: Female voices, Children's
   voices: Unison   JFDP/LF
Christmas: Carols: Female voices, Children's
   voices: Unison: Accompanied by recorder,
   keyboard & percussion ensemble
   JFE/NYFSDP/LF
Christmas: Carols: Male voices   GDP/LF
Christmas: Carols: Soprano voices
   FLDP/LF
Christmas: Carols: Unaccompanied female voices,
   children's voices   FEZDP/LF

Christmas: Carols: Unaccompanied works
   EZDP/LF
Christmas: Carols: Unison   JDP/LF
Christmas: Motets, Anthems, Hymns, Carols, etc.
   DH/LF
Christmas: Religious cantatas   DE/LF
Christmas: Religious cantatas: Accompanied by
   orchestra   EMDE/LF
Christmas: Songs: Choral music   DW/LF
Christmas: Songs: Female voices, Children's
   voices   FDW/LF
Christmas: Songs: Unison: Accompanied by
   glockenspiel & piano   JE/XTPDW/LF
Church bells: Books   AXSR
Church choral music: Books   AD/LD
Church music: Books   A/LD
Church music: Vocal music   CB/LD
Cinema: Arrangements for brass band
   WMK/JR
Cinema: Arrangements for military band
   UMMK/JR
Cinema: Arrangements for piano solo
   QPK/JR
Cinema: Jazz: Books   AMT/JR
Cinema: Songs: Arrangements for piano solo
   QPK/DW/JR
Cinema: Songs: Solo voice   KDW/JR
Cinema: Symphony orchestra   MM/JR
Cinema: Waltzes: Arrangements for piano solo
   QPK/AHW/JR
Clarinet: Accompanying solo voice   KE/VV
Clarinet: Books   AVV
Clarinet & string orchestra   RXMPVV
Clarinet & strings: Chamber music   NVV
Clarinet (B flat)   VV
Clarinet, keyboard & percussion: Accompanying
   choral works   ENYFV
Clarinet, strings & keyboard: Chamber music
   NUV
Clarinets (3) & piano   VVNSQ
Clavichord: Books   AQT
Cole, Nat King: Books   AKG/E(P)
Collected works of individual composers
   C/AZ
Collected works of individual composers: Catches:
   Unaccompanied male voices
   GEZDW/XD/AZ
Collected works of individual composers: Church
   music: Vocal music   CB/LD/AZ
Collected works of individual composers:
   Ensembles: Trumpets   WSN/AZ
Collected works of individual composers: Harpsi-
   chord solos   QRP/AZ
Collected works of individual composers: Organ
   R/AZ
Collected works of individual composers: Piano
   solo   Q/AZ
Collected works of individual composers: Solo
   voice   KDW/AZ
Collected works of individual composers: Viol
   ensembles   STN/AZ
Collected works of individual composers: Virginals
   QSQ/AZ
Communion: Anglican liturgy   DGS
Communion: Anglican liturgy: Unison
   JDGS
Composers, Individual: Books   B
Composition: Books   A/D
Composition: Electronic music: Books
   APV/D
Compositino: Keyboard   APW/ED
Concertinos: Piano & orchestra   MPSFL
Concertinos: Violin & piano   SPFL
Concertos: Arrangements: Brass & keyboard
   quartet   NWXPNSK/LF
Concertos: Arrangements for oboe d'amore &
   string orchestra   RXMPVTQK/LF
Concertos: Arrangements for violin & string
   orchestra   RXMPSK/LF
Concertos: Arrangements for violins (3) & string
   orchestra   RXMPSNTK/LF
Concertos: Bassoon & orchestra: Arrangements for
   bassoon & piano   VWPK/LF
Concertos: Brass trio & string orchestra
   RXMPWNTF
Concertos: Cello & orchestra   MPSRF
Concertos: Cello & orchestra: Arrangements for
   cello & piano   SRPK/LF
Concertos: Cello & wind band   UMPSRF
Concertos: Clarinet & orchestra: Arrangements for
   clarinet & piano   VVPK/LF
Concertos: Clarinet & string orchestra
   RXMPVF
Concertos: Descant recorder & string orchestra
   RXMPVSRF
Concertos: Flute & orchestra: Arrangements for
   flute & piano   VRPK/LF
Concertos: Guitar & orchestra   MPTSF
Concertos: Handel, G. F.: Books
   BHCAMF
Concertos: Horn & orchestra: Arrangements for
   horn & piano   WTPK/LF
Concertos: Keyboard & string orchestra
   RXMPPWF
Concertos: Oboe & orchestra: Arrangements for
   oboe & piano   VTPK/LF
Concertos: Oboe & string orchestra
   RXMPVTF
Concertos: Orchestra   MF

Concertos: Organ   RF
Concertos: Organ & orchestra   MPRF
Concertos: Organ & string orchestra
   RXMPRF
Concertos: Piano & orchestra   MPQF
Concertos: Piano & orchestra: Arrangements for
   pianos (2), 4 hands   QNUK/LF
Concertos: Piano & orchestra: Pianos (2) four
   hands   QNUK/LF
Concertos: Pianos (2), four hands   QNUF
Concertos: Quartets: Woodwind & keyboard
   NWNSF
Concertos: Symphony orchestra   MMF
Concertos: Treble recorder & orchestra: Arrange-
   ments for treble recorder & piano
   VSSPK/LF
Concertos: Treble recorder & string orchestra
   RXMPVSSF
Concertos: Trumpet & orchestra   MPWSF
Concertos: Trumpet & orchestra: Arrangements
   for trumpet & piano   WSPK/LF
Concertos: Trumpet & string orchestra
   RXMPWSF
Concertos: Viola & orchestra   MPSQF
Concertos: Violin & orchestra: Arrangements for
   violin & piano   SPK/LF
Concertos: Wind instruments (2) & orchestra:
   Arrangements for wind instruments (2) & piano
   UNTQK/LF
Concerts: Books   A(W)
Contralto voice   KFQ
Cor anglais   VTT
Cornet   WR
Cornwall: Folk songs: Collections: Solo voice
   KDW/G/AYDFR
Country 'n' western: Songs: Books
   ADW/GCW
Critics: Aesthetics & criticism: Books
   A/CC(M)
Crumhorn   VTW
Cylinder records: Books   A/FE

Dances: Accordion solos   RSPMH
Dances: Arrangements for bassoon & piano
   VWPK/AH
Dances: Arrangements for brass band
   WMK/AH
Dances: Arrangements for guitar solo
   TSPMK/AH
Dances: Arrangements for orchestra
   MK/AH
Dances: Arrangements for recorder duet
   VSNUK/AH
Dances: Brass band   WMH
Dances: Brass quintet   WNRH
Dances: Chamber orchestra   MRH
Dances: Descant recorder & keyboard
   NWSRH
Dances: Descant recorder, unaccompanied
   VSRPMH
Dances: Electronic organ   RPVH
Dances: Guitar solo   TSPMH
Dances: Instrumental music   LH
Dances: Instrumental music: Books   ALH
Dances: Keyboard solos   QPH
Dances: Light orchestra   MSH
Dances: Military band   UMMH
Dances: Orchestra   MH
Dances: Piano solos   QPH
Dances: Quartets: Instrumental ensemble
   LNSH
Dances: Sextets: Woodwind, strings & keyboard
   NUPNQH
Dances: Suites: Brass quintet   WNRHG
Dances: Symphony orchestra   MMH
Dances: Trios: Horn, strings & keyboard
   NUXTNTH
Dances: Viola duet   SQNUH
Davies, Peter Maxwell: Books   BDE
Debussy, Claude: Books   BDJ
Delibes, Leo: Books   BDK
Delius, Frederick: Books   BDL
Denbighshire: Choral music: Books
   AD(YDKR)
Descant recorder   VSR
Descant recorder & keyboard: Chamber music
   NWSR
Descant recorder & string orchestra
   RXMPVSR
Descant recorder, keyboard & percussion:
   Ensembles: Accompanying female voices,
   children's voices   FE/NYFSR
Descant recorder, keyboard & percussion:
   Ensembles: Accompanying female voices,
   children's voices: Unison
   JFE/NYFSR
Descant recorder, percussion & keyboard: Chamber
   music   NYFSR
Descant recorder, strings & keyboard: Chamber
   music   NUSR
Descant recorder, strings, keyboard & percussion:
   Ensembles: Accompanying female voices,
   children's voices   FE/NYDSR
Descant recorder, strings, keyboard & percussion:
   Ensembles: Accompanying female voices,
   children's voices: Unison
   JFE/NYDSR

Directories: Great Britain: Libraries: Books
    A(U/YC/BC)
Divine Office    DGKB
Divine Office: Female voices, Children's voices
    FDGKB
Divine Office: Soprano voice: Accompanied by
    saxophone, strings & keyboard trio
    KFLE/NUUNTDGKB
Donizetti, Gaetano: Books    BDR
Dorset: Folk songs: Collections: Unaccompanied
    works: Unison    JEZDW/G/AYDFK
Dorset: Organs: Books    AR/B(YDFK)
Double bass    SS
Double bass: Accompanying soprano voice
    KFLE/SS
Double bass: Books    ASS
Dowland, John: Books    BDT
Drum    XQ
Duets: Cello    SRNU
Duets: Descant recorder    VSRNU
Duets: Female voices: Vocal ensembles
    JNFE
Duets: Flute    VRNU
Duets: Harpsichords (2), four hands
    QRNU
Duets: Percussion    XNU
Duets: Piano, 4 hands    QNV
Duets: Pianos (2), 4 hands    QNU
Duets: Recorder    VSNU
Duets: Soprano voices    JNFLE
Duets: Treble recorder    VSSNU
Duets: Treble recorder: Accompanying solo voice
    KE/VSSNU
Duets: Viola    SQNU
Duets: Vocal works    JNE
Dulcimer, Appalachian    TWT

Easter: Anthems, Hymns, Carols, etc.: Un-
    accompanied works    EZDH/LL
Easter: Organ    R/LL
Easter: Religious cantatas    DE/LL
Education: Books    A(V)
Education: Instrumental music: Books
    AL/E(V)
Education: Piano: Books    AQ/E(V)
Einem, Gottfried von: Books    BEL
Electric organ    RPV
Electric organ: Books    ARPV
Electrical music: Books    APV
Electronic music: Books    APV
Electronic organ    RPV
Electronic organ: Books    ARPV
Elgar, Sir Edward, bart.: Books    BEP
England: Collections: Harp solo
    TSPMK/AYD
Encyclopaedias: Music    A(C)
England: Cathedral music: Choral works: Books
    AD/LE(YD)
England: Church choral music: Books
    AD/LD(YD)
England: Folk songs: Collections: Accompanied by
    treble recorder duet
    KE/VSSNUDW/G/AYD
England: Folk songs: Collections: Unaccompanied
    solo voice    KEZDW/G/AYD
England: Folk songs: Collections: Unaccompanied
    works: Unison    JEZDW/G/AYD
England: Music: Collections    C/AYD
England: Organ: Books    AR/B(YD)
England: Organ: Collections    R/AYD
England: Recorder ensembles: Collections
    VSN/AYD
England: Sonatas: Collections: Treble recorder &
    piano    VSSPE/AYD
England: Songs: Books    ADW(YD)
England: Viol ensemble: Collections
    STN/AYD
English horn    VTT
Ensembles: Brass    WN
Ensembles: Brass: Accompanying choral music
    EWN
Ensembles: Chamber music    N
Ensembles: Clarinets    VVN
Ensembles: Crumhorn    VTWN
Ensembles: Descant recorders    VSRN
Ensembles: Flutes    VRN
Ensembles: Guitars    TSN
Ensembles: Instrumental music    LN
Ensembles: Oboes    VTN
Ensembles: Percussion    XN
Ensembles: Pianos    QN
Ensembles: Recorders    VSN
Ensembles: Strings    RXN
Ensembles: Trumpets    WSN
Ensembles: Vibraphone    XTQTN
Ensembles: Viols    STN
Ensembles: Voices    JN
Ensembles: Wind    UN
Ensembles: Woodwind    VN
Epiphany: Carols    DP/LFP
Epiphany: Carols: Unison    JDP/LFP
Epiphany: Religious cantatas: Middle voice:
    Accompanied by flute & organ
    KFVE/VRPLRDE/LFP
Europe: Books    A(YB)
Europe: Folk songs: Accompanied by trumpet,
    strings & percussion
    ENYEXSDW/G/AYB

Evening Prayer: Anglican liturgy    DGP
Evening Prayer: Anglican liturgy: Unaccompanied
    works    EZDGP
Examinations: Piano    Q/AL
Examinations: Sight reading: Piano
    Q/EG/AL
Examinations: Sight reading: Solo voice
    K/EG/AL
Examinations: Violin    S/AL

Fanfare trumpet ensemble & brass band
    WMPWSVN
Fanfares: Brass ensemble    WNGN
Fanfares: Instrumental trios    LNTGN
Fanfares: Quartets: Instrumental ensemble
    LNSGN
Fanfares: Trumpet quartet    WSNGN
Female voice    KF
Female voice: Books    AKF
Female voices: Choral works    F
Female voices: Unison    JF
Female voices: Vocal ensembles    JNF
Field, John—influencing Chopin, F.: Books
    BCE(ZF)
Film music: Arrangements for brass band
    WMK/JR
Film music: Arrangements for military band
    UMMK/JR
Film music: Arrangements for piano solo
    QPK/JR
Film music: Songs: Arrangements for piano solo
    QPK/DW/JR
Film music: Songs: Solo voice    KDW/JR
Film music: Symphony orchestra    MM/JR
Film music: Waltzes: Arrangements for piano solo
    QPK/AHW/JR
Films: Jazz: Books    AMT/JR
Fingering: Flute    VR/ELM
Flute    VR
Flute: Accompanying mezzo-soprano voice
    KFNE/VR
Flute & organ: Accompanying middle voice
    KFVE/VRPLR
Flute & psaltery    VRPLTWT
Flute & strings: Chamber music    NVR
Flute, keyboard & percussion    NYFR
Flute, strings & keyboard: Ensembles: Chamber
    music    NUR
Flute, strings & percussion: Ensembles: Accom-
    panying solo voice    KE/NYER
Flute, strings, keyboard & percussion: Chamber
    music    NYDR
Flutes (2) & keyboard    VRNTPW
Folk dances: Instrumental music    LH/G
Folk music: Books    A/G
Folk music—expounding the American Left
    A/G(ZC)
Folk songs: Accompanied by treble recorder duet
    KE/VSSNUDW/G
Folk songs: Accompanied by trumpet, strings &
    percussion    ENYEXSDW/G
Folk songs: Arrangements for descant recorder solo
    VSRPMK/DW/G
Folk songs: Arrangements for electronic organ
    RPVK/DW/G
Folk songs: Arrangements for recorder solo
    VSPMK/DW/G
Folk songs: Arrangements for string orchestra
    RXMK/DW/G
Folk songs: Arrangements for violin trio
    SNTK/DW/G
Folk songs: Ballads: Solo voice: Accompanied by
    guitar    KE/TSDW/K/G
Folk songs: Books    ADW/G
Folk songs: Female voices, Children's voices
    FDW/G
Folk songs: Female voices, Children's voices:
    Unison    JFDW/G
Folk songs: Female voices, Children's voices:
    Unison: Accompanied by descant recorder,
    strings, keyboard & percussion
    JFE/NYDSRDW/G
Folk songs: Female voice, Child's voice: Solos:
    Accompanied by guitar    KFE/TSDW/G
Folk songs: Solo voice    KDW/G
Folk songs: Unaccompanied solo voice
    KEZDW/G
Folk songs: Unison    JDW/G
Folk songs: Unaccompanied works: Unison
    JEZDW/G
Folk songs: Unison: Accompanied by guitar
    JE/TSDW/G
Foster, P.: Books    AMT/E(P)
Fox-trots: Symphony orchestra    MMHKEF
France: Ballet music: Collections: Arrangements
    for piano solo    QPK/AHM/AYH
France: Canons: Madrigals: Collections: Un-
    accompanied works    EXDU/X/AYH
France: Canons: Quartets: Collections: Instru-
    mental ensemble    LNS/X/AYH
France: Children's songs: Collections: Female
    voices, Children's voices: Unison: Accom-
    panied by guitar    JFE/TSDW/GJ/AYH
France: Composition: Books    A/D(YH)
France: Folk songs: Collections: Unison
    JDW/G/AYH
Frazier, Kathleen: Books    AQ/E(P)
French horn    WT

French horn & string orchestra: Accompanying
    baritone voice    KGNE/RXMPWT
French opera—compared with Italian opera, 1700
    AC(YJ/XF/ZB)
Fugues: Keyboard solos    PWP/Y
Fugues: Organ    R/Y
Fugues: Piano solos    QP/Y
Funerals: Religious cantatas: Accompanied by
    orchestra    EMDE/KDN

Garland, J.: Books    AKF/E(P)
Gavottes: Accordion solos    RSPMHM
Gavottes: Piano solos    QPHM
Germany: Children's songs: Collections: Female
    voices, Children's voices: Unison
    JFDW/GJ/AYE
Germany: Fugues: Collections: Keyboard solos
    PWP/Y/AYE
Germany: Motets, Anthems, Hymns, etc.: Collec-
    tions: Unaccompanied works
    EZDH/AYE
Germany: Organ: Collections    R/AYE
Glockenspiel: Accompanying unison works
    JE/XT
Gloria: Ordinary of the Mass: Vocal duets
    JNEDGC
Good Friday: Musical plays: Banyard, E.: Books
    BBDNBACM/LK
Good Friday: Musical plays: Banyard, S.: Books
    BBDNBACM/LK
Good Friday: Musical plays: Casey, P.: Books
    BCBWACM/LK
Graduate & professional education: Books
    A(VP)
Gramophone records: Books    A/FD
Great Britain: Bawdy: Ballads: Folk songs: Collec-
    tions: Solo voice: Accompanied by guitar
    KE/TSDW/K/G/KDX/AYC
Great Britain: Books    A(YC)
Great Britain: Children's songs: Collections:
    Female voices, Children's voices: Unison
    JFEZDW/GJ/AYC
Great Britain: Church music: Books
    A/LD(YC)
Great Britain: Electric organs: Books
    ARPV/B(YC)
Great Britain: Folk dances: Collections: Instru-
    mental music    LH/G/AYC
Great Britain: Folk songs: Books
    ADW/G(YC)
Great Britain: Folk songs: Collections: Arrange-
    ments for string orchestra
    RXMK/DW/G/AYC
Great Britain: Folk songs: Collections: Female
    voices, Children's voices    FDW/G/AYC
Great Britain: Folk songs: Unaccompanied works:
    Unison    JEZDW/G/AYC
Great Britain: Libraries: Books    A(U/YC)
Great Britain: Songs: Collections: Arrangements
    for accordion solo    RSPMK/DW/AYC
Guitar    TS
Guitar: Accompanying female voice, child's voice:
    Solos    KFE/TS
Guitar: Accompanying female voices, children's
    voices: Unison    JFE/TS
Guitar: Accompanying solo voice    KE/TS
Guitar: Accompanying unison choral works
    JE/TS
Guitar: Books    ATS
Guitar & cello    SRPLTS
Guitar & orchestra    MPTS
Gypsies: Great Britain: Children's songs: Collec-
    tions: Female voices, Children's voices: Unison
    JFEZDW/GJ/AYCG

Handel, George Frideric: Books    BHC
Hanslick, Eduard: Aesthetics & criticism: Books
    A/CC(P)
Harmony: Books    A/R
Harp    TQ
Harpsichord    QR
Harvest: Motets, Anthems, Hymns, etc
    DH/LP
Haydn, Joseph: Books    BHE
Heneker, David: Books    BHJJ
Hertfordshire: Church bells: Books
    AXSR/E(YDED)
High voice    KFT
High voices: Unison    JFT
History: Books    A(X)
History: United States: Education: Schools: Books
    A(VF/YT/X)
Holly, B.: Popular songs: Books
    AKGDW/GB/E(P)
Holst, Gustav: Books    BHP
Holy Communion: Anglican liturgy    DGS
Holy Communion: Anglican liturgy: Unison
    JDGS
Home Counties: Singers    AB/E(YDC)
Horn, English    VTT
Horn    WT
Horn: Accompanying female voice, child's voice
    duets    JNFEE/WT
Horn, strings & keyboard: Chamber music
    NUXT
Howells, Herbert: Books    BHS

Humberside: Children's songs: Collections: Female voices, Children's voices: Unison JFDW/GJ/AYDJGX
Hungary: Folk music: Books A/G(YG)
Hymns DM
Hymns: Accompanied by brass ensemble EWNDM
Hymns: Accompanied by orchestra EMDM
Hymns: Arrangements for brass band WMK/DM
Hymns: Arrangements for clarinets (3) & piano VVNSQK/DM
Hymns: Arrangements for organ RK/DM
Hymns: Female voices, Children's voices: Unison JFDM
Hymns: Female voices, Children's voices: Unison: Accompanied by instrument & piano JFE/LPMDM
Hymns: Unaccompanied works EZDM
Hymns: Unison JDM
Hymns: Unison: Accompanied by guitar JE/TSDM

Impresarios: Opera AC(WB/M)
Incidental music: Arrangements for piano solo QPK/JM
India: Books BZF
Instrument makers: Woodwind: Books AV/BC(M)
Instrumental music L
Instrumental music: Accompanying speaker HYE/L
Instrumental music: Books AL
Instruments: Books AL/B
Instruments: Clarinet: Books AVV/B
Instruments: Double bass ASS/B
Instruments: Electric organs: Books ARPV/B
Instruments: Guitar: Books ATS/B
Instruments: Keyboard instruments APW/B
Instruments: Lyre guitar: Books ATJR/B
Instruments: Orchestra: Books AM/B
Instruments: Organ: Books AR/B
Instruments: Saxophone: Books AVU/B
Instruments: Viola: Books ASQ/B
Instruments: Violin: Books AS/B
Instruments, Woodwind: Books AV/B
Ireland: Folk music: Books A/G(YDM)
Italy: Descant recorder & piano: Collections VSRP/AYJ

Jazz: Books AMT
Jews: Musicians: Books A(YBU)
Jolson, Al: Books AKG/E(P)
Joplin, Janis: Books AKDW/HHW/E(P)
Jotas: Accordion solos RSPMHPD

Kansas City: Jazz musicians: Books AMT/E(M/YTSWK)
Keyboard & descant recorders (2) VSRNTPW
Keyboard & orchestra MPPW
Keyboard & percussion: Ensembles: Accompanying choral works ENYL
Keyboard & percussion: Ensembles: Accompanying female voices, children's voices FE/NYL
Keyboard & percussion: Ensembles: Accompanying soprano voices FLE/NYL
Keyboard & percussion: Ensembles: Accompanying unison vocal works JE/NYL
Keyboard & recorders (2) VSNTPW
Keyboard & string orchestra RXMPPW
Keyboard & strings: Accompanying baritone voice KGNE/NX
Keyboard & strings: Chamber music NX
Keyboard & wind: Chamber music NW
Keyboard instruments PW
Keyboard instruments: Books APW
Keyboard, recorders & percussion: Ensembles: Accompanying female voices, children's voices FE/NYFS
Keyboard, strings & wind: Ensembles: Accompanying tenor voice KGHE/NU
Keyboard, strings & woodwind: Ensembles: Accompanying soprano voice KFLE/NUP
Keyboard, trumpet & strings: Chamber music NUXS
Keyboard, wind & percussion: Chamber music NYF
Keyboard, wind & percussion: Ensembles: Accompanying choral music ENYF
Keyboard, wind & percussion: Ensembles: Accompanying female voices, children's voices FE/NYF
Keyboard, wind & strings: Ensembles: Accompanying soprano voice solos KFLE/NU
Keyboard, wind & strings: Ensembles: Chamber music NU
Keyboard, wind, strings & percussion: Accompanying soprano duets JNFLEE/NYD
Keyboard, wind, strings & percussion: Ensembles: Chamber music NYD
Kyrie: Ordinary of the Mass DGB

Lasso, Orlando di: Books BLC
Lent: Religious Cantatas DE/LG
Libraries: Books A(U)
Librettos: Banyard, E. One Friday in eternity BBDNACM/LK
Librettos: Banyard, S. One Friday in eternity BBDNBACM/LK
Librettos: Bernstein, L. West Side story BBMMACM
Librettos: Casey, P. One Friday in eternity BCBWACM/LK
Librettos: Davies, P. M. Taverner BDEAC
Librettos: Donizetti, G. Lucia di Lammermoor BDRAC
Librettos: Einem, Gottfried von. The visit of the old lady BELAC
Librettos: Henecker, D. Charlie girl. BHJJ
Librettos: Maddox, H. Alive! BMDACM/LGZ
Librettos: Wilson, S. The boy friend BWNTMACM
Light orchestra MS
Liszt, Franz: Books BLJ
Liturgical music DF
Liturgical music: Accompanied by orchestra EMDF
Liturgical music: Female voices, Children's voices FDF
Liturgical music: Soprano voice: Accompanied by saxophone, strings & keyboard trio KFLE/NUUNTDF
Liturgical music: Unaccompanied works EZDF
Liturgical music: Unison JDF
Liturgical music: Unison: Accompanied by guitar JE/TSDF
Liturgical music: Vocal duets JNEDF
Lives, Collected: Musicians A(N)
Lives: Bach, J. S. BBC(N)
Lives: Bantock, Sir G. BBE(N)
Lives: Bellini, V. BBJH(N)
Lives: Berlioz, H. BBM(N)
Lives: Bing, Sir R. AC(WB/P)
Lives: Byrd, W. BBX(N)
Lives: Caruso, E. AKGH/E(P)
Lives: Cole, N. K. AKG/E(P)
Lives: Debussy, C. BDJ(N)
Lives: Delius, F. BDL(N)
Lives: Dylan, B. AKG/E(P)
Lives: Elgar, Sir E. BEP(N)
Lives: Frazier, K. AQ/E(P)
Lives: Garland, J. AKF/E(P)
Lives: Hallé, Sir C. A(P)
Lives: Handel, G. F. BHC(N)
Lives: Haydn, J. RHE(N)
Lives: Holst, G. BHP(N)
Lives: Howells, H. BHS(N)
Lives: Jolson, Al AKG/E(P)
Lives: Joplin, J. AKDW/HHW/E(P)
Lives: Lasso, O. di BLC(N)
Lives: Liszt, F. BLJ(N)
Lives: Mendelssohn family BMJB(N)
Lives: Monteverdi, C. BMN(N)
Lives: Osmonds, The AB/GB/E(P)
Lives: Palestrina, G. P. da BPC(N)
Lives: Presley, E. AKGDW/HK/E(P)
Lives: Schubert, F. BSF(N)
Lives: Sibelius, J. BSH(N)
Lives: Smith, J. S.: Books AKF/E(P)
Lives: Strauss, R. BSU(N)
Lives: Strauss family BSQB(N)
Lives: Stravinsky, I. BSV(N)
Lives: Sutherland, J. AKFL/E(P)
Lives: Swan, D. BSWN(N)
Lives: Vaughan Williams, R. BVD(N)
Llangollen: Choral music: Books AD(YDKRL)
Locke, Matthew: Books BLOC
London: Cathedral music AD/LE(YDB)
London: Graduate & professional education: Books A(VP/YDB)
London Philharmonic Orchestra: Books AMM/E(QB)
Lord's Prayer: Unaccompanied works EZDTF
Low voice KFX
Lowlands: Scotland: Books A(YDLG)
Lutheran Church: Hymns DM/LSET
Lyre guitar: Books ATJR

McCormack, John: Recorded music: Tenor voice AKGH/FD(P)
Maddox, Hugh: Books BMD
Madrigals DU
Madrigals: Books AEZDU
Madrigals: Unaccompanied works EZDU
Madrigals: Wilbye, J.: Books BWNRBADU
Magnificat: Vespers: Divine Office: Soprano voice: Accompanied by saxophone strings & keyboard trio KFLE/NUUNTDGKK
Maintenance: Guitar: Books ATS/BT
Male voice KG
Male voice: Books AKG
Male voices: Choral works G
Man's voice KG
Man's voice: Books AKG
Marches: Accordion solos RSPMGM

Marches: Arrangements for piano solo QPK/AGM
Marches: Brass band WMGM
Marches: Military band UMMGM
Marches: Piano solos QPGM
Marriage: Arrangements for organ RK/KDD
Marriage: Hymns DM/KDD
Mass, Ordinary of the: Accompanied by orchestra EMDG
Mass, Ordinary of the: Unaccompanied works EZDG
Mass, Ordinary of the: Unison: Accompanied by guitar JE/TSDG
Mass, Ordinary of the: Vocal duets JNEDG
Mass, Ordinary of the: Vocal scores DG
Mass, Proper of the DGK
Mass, Proper of the: Female voices, Children's voices FDGK
Matins: Divine office DGKH
Melodic percussion: Accompanying female voices, children's voices: Unison JFE/XPQ
Mendelssohn, Felix: Books BMJ
Mendelssohn family: Books BMJB
Men's voices: Choral works G
Menuets: Brass band WMHR
Menuets: Piano solos QPHR
Mezzo-soprano voice KFN
Middle voice KFV
Military band UMM
Minuets: Brass band WMHR
Minuets: Piano solos QPHR
Monteverdi, Claudio: Books BMN
Moravia, South: Folk songs: Unaccompanied works: Unison JEZDW/G/AYFSM
Motets DJ
Motets: Female voice duets JNFEDJ
Motets: Unaccompanied works EZDJ
Motion pictures: Arrangements for brass band WMK/JR
Motion pictures: Arrangements for military band UMMK/JR
Motion pictures: Arrangements for piano solo QPK/JR
Motion pictures: Jazz: Books AMT/JR
Motion pictures: Songs: Arrangements for piano solo QPK/DW/JR
Motion pictures: Songs: Solo voice KDW/JR
Motion pictures: Symphony orchestra MM/JR
Motion pictures: Waltzes: Arrangements for piano solo QPK/AHW/JR
Mozart, Wolfgang Amadeus: Books BMS
Music covers: Printing: Books A(RC)
Music hall: Songs: Books ADW/GM(YD)
Musical literature A
Musical plays: Banyard, E. BBDNACM
Musical plays: Banyard, S. BBDNBACM
Musical plays: Bernstein, L.: Books BBMMACM
Musical plays: Casey, P.: Books BCBWACM
Musical plays: Delibes, L.: Books BDKACM
Musical plays: Full scores CQM
Musical plays: Heneker, D.: Books BHJJACM
Musical plays: Maddox, H.: Books BMDACM
Musical plays: Vocal scores CM
Musical plays: Wilson, S.: Books BWNTMACM
Musicians: Jazz: Books AMT(M)
Musicians: Popular music A/GB(M)
Musicology: Books A(VX)

Naples: Opera AC(YJN)
National songs: Books ADW/KM
New Year: Carols: Female voices, Children's voices FDP/LFM
New Year: Carols: Unaccompanied works EZDP/LFM
Non-European music: Books BZ
Nonets: Descant recorder, strings, keyboard & percussion NYDSRNM
Northern School of Music: Graduate & professional education: Books A(VP/YDJE)
Northumberland: Folk songs: Collections: Unaccompanied works: Unison JEZDW/G/AYDJJ
Nursery rhymes: Female voices, Children's voices: Unison JFDW/GK

Oboe VT
Oboe & string orchestra RXMPVT
Oboe d'amore & string orchestra RXMPVTQ
Oboe, strings, keyboard & percussion: Accompanying soprano duets JNFLEE/NYDT
Oboe, trumpet & string orchestra RXMPVTPLWSF
Octets: Brass ensemble WNN
Octets: Recorder VSNN
Octets: Wind ensemble UNN

Octets: Wind, strings & percussion   NYENN
Offertory: Proper of the Mass: Roman liturgy DGKAF
Office   DGKB
Office: Female voices, Children's voices FDGKB
Office: Soprano voice: Accompanied by saxophone, strings & keyboard trio KFLE/NUUNTDGKB
Opera: Arrangements for brass band WMK/CC
Opera: Books   AC
Opera: Davies, P. M.: Books   BDEAC
Opera: Donizetti, G.: Books   BDRAC
Opera: Einem, G. von: Books   BELAC
Opera: Full scores   CQC
Opera: Mozart, W. A.: Books   BMSAC
Opera: Peking: Books   BZHKAC
Opera: Vocal scores   CC
Operetta: Sullivan, *Sir* A. S.: Books BSWACF
Operetta: Vocal scores   CF
Oratorios: Vocal scores   DD
Orchestral music   M
Orchestral music: Accompanying baritone voice KGNE/M
Orchestral music: Accompanying bass voice KGXE/M
Orchestral music: Accompanying choral works EM
Orchestral music: Accompanying tenor voice KGHE/M
Orchestral music: Accompanying soprano voice KFLE/M
Orchestral music: Accompanying vocal trios JNFDE/M
Orchestral music: Books   AM
Orchestral music: Brass instruments   WM
Orchestral music: String instruments   RXM
Orchestral music: String instruments: Accompanying choral works ERXM
Orchestral music: Vaughan Williams, R.: Books BVDAM
Orchestral music: Wind instruments   UM
Orchestras: Jazz: Books   AMT/E(QB)
Orchestration: Books   AM/DF
Ordinary of the Mass: Accompanied by orchestra EMDG
Ordinary of the Mass: Unaccompanied works EZDG
Ordinary of the Mass: Unison: Accompanied by guitar JE/TSDG
Ordinary of the Mass: Vocal duets   JNEDG
Ordinary of the Mass: Vocal scores   DG
Organ   R
Organ: Bach, J. S.: Books   BBCAR
Organ: Books   AR
Organ & orchestra   MPR
Organ & string orchestra   RXMPR
Organ & trumpet   WSPLR
Organ & violin   SPLR
Oriental music: Books   BZB
Other instruments   AY

Palestrina, Giovanni Pierluigi da: Books BPC
Paris: Chansons: Collections   EZDU/AYHP
Part songs   DW
Part songs: Bass voices   GXDW
Part songs: Choral music: Unaccompanied works EZDW
Part songs: Female voices, Children's voices FDW
Part songs: Soprano voices   FLDW
Part songs: Unaccompanied female voices, children's voices FEZDW
Part songs: Unaccompanied male voices GEZDW
Part songs: Unaccompanied soprano voices FLEZDW
Passiontide: Musical plays: Maddox, H.: Books BMDACM/LGZ
Pavanes: Descant recorder unaccompanied VSRPMHVG
Peking: Books   BZHK
Pentatonic music: Songs: Unaccompanied female voices, children's voices: Unison JFEZDW/PP
Percussion & brass: Ensembles: Accompanying tenor voice KGHE/NYHX
Percussion & cello   SRPLX
Percussion & keyboard: Ensembles: Accompanying choral works ENYL
Percussion & keyboard: Ensembles: Accompanying female voices, children's voices FE/NYL
Percussion & keyboard: Ensembles: Accompanying soprano voices FLE/NYL
Percussion & keyboard: Ensembles: Accompanying unison vocal works JE/NYL
Percussion & wind: Ensembles: Accompanying tenor voice KGHE/NYH
Percussion, brass & strings: Ensembles: Accompanying choral works ENYEXP
Percussion instruments   X
Percussion instruments: Accompanying female voices, children's voices FE/X

Percussion instruments: Accompanying female voices, children's voices: Unison JFE/X
Percussion instruments: Accompanying unison choral works JE/X
Percussion instruments: Books   AX
Percussion, recorders & keyboard: Ensembles: Accompanying female voices, children's voices FE/NYFS
Percussion, strings & wind: Ensembles: Accompanying solo voice KE/NYE
Percussion, strings & wind: Ensembles: Accompanying speaker(s) HYE/NYE
Percussion, trumpet & strings: Accompanying choral works ENYEXS
Percussion, wind & keyboard: Chamber music NYF
Percussion, wind & keyboard: Ensembles: Accompanying choral music ENYF
Percussion, wind & keyboard: Ensembles: Accompanying female voices, children's voices FE/NYF
Percussion, wind & strings: Chamber music NYE
Percussion, wind, strings & keyboard: Accompanying soprano duets JNFLEE/NYD
Percussion, wind, strings & keyboard: Chamber music NYD
Periodicals: Recorded music   A/FD(B)
Physics: Music: Books   A/B
Pianists: Books   AQ/E(M)
Piano   Q
Piano: Beethoven, L. van: Books   BBJAQ
Piano: Books   AQ
Piano: Debussy, C.: Books   BDJAQ
Piano: Schumann, R.: Books   BSGAQ
Piano & orchestra   MPQ
Piano & orchestra: Accompanying speaker KHYE/MPQ
Plays, Musical: Banyard, E.: Books BBDNACM
Plays, Musical: Banyard, S.: Books BBDNBACM
Plays, Musical: Bernstein, L.: Books BBMMACM
Plays, Musical: Casey, P.: Books BCBWACM
Plays, Musical: Delibes, L.: Books BDKACM
Plays, Musical: Full scores   CQM
Plays, Musical: Heneker, D.: Books BHJJACM
Plays, Musical: Maddox, H.: Books BMDACM
Plays, Musical: Vocal scores   CM
Plays, Musical: Wilson, S.: Books BWNTMACM
Plucked string instruments   T
Plucked string instruments: Accompanying female voice, child's voice KFE/T
Plucked string instruments: Accompanying unison choral works JE/T
Plucked string instruments: Books   AT
Poland: String orchestra: Collections RXM/AYLC
Polkas: Accordion solos   RSPMHVH
Polkas: Arrangements for brass band WMK/AHVH
Polkas: Brass band   WMHVH
Polkas: Piano solos   QPHVH
Popular music: Books   A/GB
Popular music: Vocal music   AB/GB
Popular songs: Solo voice   KDW/GB
Porter, Cole: Books   BPNN
Postage stamps—expounded by music: Books A(ZE)
Presley, Elvis: Books   AKGDW/HK/E(P)
Primary schools: Education: Books   A(VG)
Printing: Music: Books   A(R)
Proper of the Mass   DGK
Proper of the Mass: Female voices, Children's voices FDGK
Psalms: Unison   JDR
Psaltery   TWT
Psaltery & flute   VRPLTWT
Psychology: Books   A/CS

Quartets: Brass & keyboard   NWXPNS
Quartets: Brass ensemble   WNS
Quartets: Clarinet & strings   NVVNS
Quartets: Crumhorn   VTWNS
Quartets: Descant recorder, strings & keyboard NUSRNS
Quartets: Flute   VRNS
Quartets: Flute & strings   NVRNS
Quartets: Flute, strings & percussion: Accompanying solo voice KE/NYERNS
Quartets: Instrumental ensemble   LNS
Quartets: Instrumental ensembles   LNS
Quartets: Keyboard & percussion: Accompanying treble voices FLE/NYLNS
Quartets: Percussion instruments   XNS
Quartets: Pianos, 8 hands   QNS
Quartets: Recorder   VSNS
Quartets: String ensembles   RXNS
Quartets: Strings & keyboard   NXNS
Quartets: Strings & keyboard: Accompanying baritone voice KGNE/NXNS

Quartets: Trombone, strings and keyboard NUXUNS
Quartets: Trumpet   WSNS
Quartets: Wind & keyboard   NWNS
Quintets: Brass & keyboard   NWXPNR
Quintets: Brass & strings   NVXPNR
Quintets: Brass instruments   WNR
Quintets: Cello   SRNR
Quintets: Clarinet & strings   NVVNR
Quintets: Instrumental ensemble   LNR
Quintets: Recorder   VSNR
Quintets: Strings & keyboard   NXNR
Quintets: Wind & keyboard   NWNR
Quintets: Wind instruments   UNR
Quintets: Woodwind instruments   VNR

Recorded music: Books   A/FD
Recorded music: Tenor voice   AKGH/FD
Recorder, Unaccompanied: Solos   VSPM
Recorder   VS
Recorder: Accompanying solo voice   KE/VS
Recorder: Books   AVS
Recorder (descant)   VSR
Recorder (descant) & keyboard: Chamber music NWSR
Recorder (descant) & string orchestra RXMPVSR
Recorder (descant), keyboard & percussion: Ensembles: Accompanying female voices, children's voices: Unison JFE/NYFSR
Recorder (descant), percussion & keyboard: Chamber music NYFSR
Recorder (descant), strings & keyboard: Chamber music NUSR
Recorder (descant), strings, keyboard & percussion: Ensembles: Accompanying female voices, children's voices FE/NYDSR
Recorder (descant), strings, keyboard, percussion: Chamber music NYDSR
Recorder, keyboard & percussion: Chamber music NYFS
Recorder, keyboard & percussion: Ensembles: Accompanying female voices, children's voices: Unison JFE/NYFS
Recorder, strings & keyboard: Chamber music NUS
Recorder, strings, keyboard & percussion: Chamber music NYDS
Recorder, strings, keyboard & percussion: Ensembles: Accompanying female voices, children's voices FE/NYDS
Recorder, strings, keyboard & percussion: Ensembles: Accompanying female voices, children's voices: Unison JFE/NYDS
Recorder (treble)   VSS
Recorder (treble): Accompanying solo voice KE/VSS
Recorder (treble) & string orchestra RXMPVSS
Recorder (treble), strings & keyboard: Chamber music NUSS
Recorders & keyboard: Chamber music NWS
Recorders (descant), strings, keyboard & percussion: Ensembles: Accompanying female voices, children's voices: Unison JFE/NYDSR
Recorders, keyboard & percussion: Ensembles: Accompanying female voices, children's voices FE/NYFS
Recording: Books   A/F
Religious cantatas   DE
Religious cantatas: Accompanied by brass & organ septet ENWNPRDE
Religious cantatas: Accompanied by keyboard & percussion ENYLDE
Religious cantatas: Accompanied by violins (2) & organ JNFLEE/SNTRDE
Religious cantatas: Bach, J. S.: Books BBCADE
Religious cantatas: Bass voice: Accompanied by orchestra KGXE/MDE
Religious cantatas: Carols   DPDE
Religious cantatas: High voice: Accompanied by violin & organ KFTE/SPLRDE
Religious cantatas: Middle voice: Accompanied by flute & organ KFVE/VRPLRDE
Religious cantatas: Unison   JDE
Religious cantatas: Vocal duets   JNEDE
Religious choral music   DC
   Accompanied by brass & organ septet EWNPRDC
   Accompanied by keyboard & percussion ENYLDC
   Accompanied by orchestra   EMDC
   Accompanied by violins (2) & organ JNFLEE/SNTRDC
   Bass voice: Accompanied by orchestra KGXE/MDC
   Bass voice: Accompanied by violins (2) & keyboard KGXE/SNTPWDC
   Books   AD/L
   Female voices, Children's voices   FDC
   High voice: Accompanied by violin & organ KFTE/SPLRDC
   Middle voice: Accompanied by flute & organ KFVE/VRPLRDC
   Unison   JDC

6

Religious music: Books   A/L
Religious music: Motets, Anthems, Hymns, etc.
  DH
  Accompanied by brass ensemble
    EWNDH
  Accompanied by descant recorder, strings, keyboard & percussion
    FE/NYDSRDH
  Accompanied by orchestra   EMDH
  Accompanied by string, keyboard & percussion trio   ENYGNTDH
  Arrangements for brass band
    WMK/DH
  Arrangements for clarinets (3) & piano
    VVNSQK/DH
  Arrangements for organ   RK/DH
  Baritone voice: Accompanied by strings & keyboard quartets
    KGNE/NXNSDH
  Female voice duets   JNFEDH
  Female voices, Children's voices   FDH
  Female voices, Children's voices: Accompanied by percussion   FE/XDH
  Female voices, Children's voices: Accompanied by recorders, keyboard & percussion
    FE/NYFSDH
  Female voices, Children's voices: Unison
    JFDH
  Female voices, Children's voices: Unison: Accompanied by instrument & piano
    JFE/LPMDH
  Female voices, Children's voices: Unison: Accompanied by recorder, keyboard & percussion   JFE/NYFSDH
  Low voice   KFXDH
  Male voices   GDH
  Solo voice   KDH
  Soprano voice   KFLDH
  Soprano voices   FLDH
  Unaccompanied female voices, children's voices   FEZDH
  Unaccompanied male voices   GEZDH
  Unaccompanied works   EZDH
  Unison   JDH
  Unison: Accompanied by guitar
    JE/TSDH
Religious musical plays: Maddox, H.: Books
  BMDACM/L
Religious musical plays: Vocal scores   CM/L
Religious musical plays for children: Full scores
  CQN/L
Religious musical plays for children: Vocal scores
  CN/L
Religious songs: Solo voice   KDW/L
Requiem Masses: Accompanied by orchestra
  EMDGKAV
Right hand: Keyboard solos   PWPPR
Right hand: Piano solos   QPPR
Rock 'n' roll: Songs: Male voice: Books
  AKGDW/HK
Roman Catholic Church: Hymns   DM/LSB
Roman liturgy: Accompanied by orchestra
  EMDFF
Roman liturgy: Choral works   DFF
Roman liturgy: Female voices, Children's voices
  FDFF
Roman liturgy: Soprano voice: Accompanied by saxophone, strings & keyboard trio
  KFLE/NUUNTDFF
Roman liturgy: Unaccompanied works
  EZDFF
Roman liturgy: Unison: Accompanied by guitar
  JE/TSDFF
Roman liturgy: Vocal duets   JNEDFF
Rumbas: Light orchestra   MSHVKK
Russia: Books   A(YM)

St. Paul's Cathedral: Cathedral music
  AD/LE(YDBB)
Sarabandes: Arrangements for piano duets, 4 hands
  QNVK/AHVL
Sargent, A. W.: Books   AD/EC(P)
Savoy operas: Sullivan, Sir A. S.: Books
  BSWACF
Saxophone: Books   AVU
Schoenberg, Arnold: Books   BSET
Schools: Education: Books   A(VF)
Schubert, Franz: Books   BSF
Schumann, Robert: Books   BSG
Scotland: Books   A(YDL)
Scotland: Opera: Books   AC(YDL)
Scotland: Songs: Collections: Solo voice
  KDW/AYDL
Scottish National Orchestra: Books
  AMM/E(QB)
Secondary schools: Education: Books
  A(VK)
Secular cantatas   DX
Secular cantatas: Accompanied by cello
  ESRDX
Secular cantatas: Accompanied by orchestra
  EMDX
Secular cantatas: Accompanied by string orchestra
  ERXMDX
Secular cantatas: Accompanied by woodwind, keyboard & percussion   ENYFPDX
Secular cantatas: Contralto voice: Accompanied by chamber orchestra   KFQE/MRDX

Secular cantatas: Female voices, Children's voices
  FDX
Secular cantatas: Female voices, Children's voices: Accompanied by descant recorder, keyboard & percussion   FE/NYFSRDX
Secular cantatas: Female voices, Children's voices: Accompanied by keyboard & percussion
  FE/NYLDX
Secular cantatas: Female voices, Children's voices: Unison: Accompanied by melodic percussion
  JFE/XPQDX
Secular cantatas: Mezzo-soprano voice: Accompanied by flute   KFNE/VRDX
Secular cantatas: Tenor voice: Accompanied by brass & percussion
  KGHE/NYHXSDX
Secular cantatas: Tenor voice: Accompanied by woodwind, strings & keyboard
  KGHE/NUPNQDX
Secular cantatas: Treble voices: Accompanied by keyboard & percussion quartet
  FLE/NYLNSDX
Secular cantatas: Unaccompanied works
  EZDX
Secular cantatas: Unison: Accompanied by keyboard & percussion   JE/NYLDX
Secular choral music   DTZ
  Accompanied by cello   ESRDTZ
  Accompanied by clarinet, keyboard & percussion   ENYFVDTZ
  Accompanied by orchestra   EMDTZ
  Accompanied by string orchestra
    ERXMDTZ
  Accompanied by trumpet, strings & percussion
    ENYEXSDTZ
  Accompanied by various instruments: Female voices, Children's voices   FE/LDTZ
  Accompanied by violin   ESDTZ
  Accompanied by woodwind, keyboard & percussion   ENYFPDTZ
  Arrangements for accordion solo
    RSPMK/DTZ
  Arrangements for brass band
    WMK/DTZ
  Arrangements for cello quintet
    SRNRK/DTZ
  Arrangements for descant recorder solo
    VSRPMK/DTZ
  Arrangements for descant recorder trio
    VSRNTK/DTZ
  Arrangements for double bass & piano
    SSPK/DTZ
  Arrangements for electronic organ
    RPVK/DTZ
  Arrangements for guitar solo
    TSPMK/DTZ
  Arrangements for instrumental quartet
    LNSK/DTZ
  Arrangements for military band
    UMMK/DTZ
  Arrangements for organ   RK/DTZ
  Arrangements for piano solo
    QPK/DTZ
  Arrangements for recorder   VSK/DTZ
  Arrangements for recorder solo
    VSPMK/DTZ
  Arrangements for string orchestra
    RXMK/DTZ
  Arrangements for violin trio
    SNTK/DTZ
  Arrangements for wind quintet
    UNRK/DTZ
  Bass voices   GXDTZ
  Books   ADTZ
  Female voices, Children's voices   FDTZ
  Female voices, Children's voices: Accompanied by descant recorder, keyboard & percussion   FE/NYFSRDTZ
  Female voices, Children's voices: Accompanied by keyboard & percussion
    FE/NYLDTZ
  Female voices, Children's voices: Accompanied by percussion   FE/XDTZ
  Female voices, Children's voices: Duets: Accompanied by horn & piano
    JNFEE/WTPDTZ
  Female voices, Children's voices: Trios: Accompanied by orchestra
    JNFDE/MDTZ
  Female voices, Children's voices: Unison
    JFDTZ
  Female voices, Children's voices: Unison: Accompanied by descant recorder, keyboard & percussion
    JFE/NYFSRDTZ
  Female voices, Children's voices: Unison: Accompanied by descant recorder, strings, keyboard & percussion
    JFE/NYDSRDTZ
  Female voices, Children's voices: Unison: Accompanied by guitar
    JFE/TSDTZ
  Female voices, Children's voices: Unison: Accompanied by melodic percussion
    JFE/XPQDTZ
  Female voices, Children's voices: Unison: Accompanied by various instruments
    JFE/LDTZ

High voices: Accompanied by chime bars
  JFTE/XTPRDTZ
Soprano duets: Accompanied by oboe, strings, keyboard & percussion septets
  JFLEE/NYDTNPDTZ
Soprano voices   FLDTZ
Speaker: Accompanied by instruments
  HYE/LDTZ
Treble voices: Accompanied by keyboard & percussion quartet
  FLE/NYLNSDTZ
Unaccompanied female voices, children's voices
  FEZDTZ
Unaccompanied female voices, children's voices: Unison   JFEZDTZ
Unaccompanied male voices   GEZDTZ
Unaccompanied soprano voices
  FLEZDTZ
Unaccompanied works   EZDTZ
Unaccompanied works: Unison
  JEZDTZ
Unison   JDTZ
Unison: Accompanied by glockenspiel & piano
  JE/XTPDTZ
Unison: Accompanied by guitar
  JE/TSDTZ
Unison: Accompanied by keyboard & percussion   JE/NYLDTZ
Vocal duets   JNEDTZ
Vocal duets: Accompanied by woodwind & string septet   JNEE/NVPNPDTZ
Wilbye, J.: Books   BWNRBADTZ
Secular vocal music   KDTZ
  Accompanied by clarinet & piano
    KE/VVPDTZ
  Accompanied by flute, strings & percussion quartet   KE/NYERNSDTZ
  Accompanied by treble recorder duet
    KE/VSSNUDTZ
  Baritone voice   KGNDTZ
  Baritone voice: Accompanied by french horn & string orchestra
    KGNE/RXMPWTDTZ
  Baritone voice: Accompanied by orchestra
    KGNE/MDTZ
  Bass voice   KGXDTZ
  Books   AKDTZ
  Brahms, J.: Books   BBTAKDTZ
  Contralto voice   KFQDTZ
  Contralto voice: Accompanied by chamber orchestra   KFQE/MRDTZ
  Female voice, Child's voice: Solos: Accompanied by guitar   KFE/TSDTZ
  High voice   KFTDTZ
  Low voice   KFXDTZ
  Mezzo-soprano voice: Accompanied by flute
    KFNE/VRDTZ
  Schumann, R.: Books   BSGAKDTZ
  Solo voice: Accompanied by flute, string & percussion trio   KE/NYERNTDTZ
  Solo voice: Accompanied by guitar
    KE/TSDTZ
  Solos   KDTZ
  Soprano voice: Accompanied by double bass
    KFLE/SSDTZ
  Soprano voice: Accompanied by orchestra
    KFLE/MDTZ
  Soprano voice: Accompanied by violins (2) & keyboard   KFLE/SNTPWDTZ
  Strauss, R.: Books   BSUAKDTZ
  Tenor voice   KGHDTZ
  Tenor voice: Accompanied by brass & percussion   KGHE/NYHXSDTZ
  Tenor voice: Accompanied by orchestra
    KGHE/MDTZ
  Tenor voice: Accompanied by woodwind, strings & keyboard
    KGHE/NUPNQDTZ
  Unaccompanied solo voice   KEZDTZ
Sentences: Communion: Anglican liturgy
  DGSKAD
Septets: Brass & organ: Accompanying choral works   EWNPR
Septets: Instruments & piano   LNPQ
Septets: Oboe, strings, keyboard & percussion: Accompanying soprano duets
  JNFLEE/NYDTNP
Septets: Percussion ensemble   XNP
Septets: Woodwind & strings: Accompanying vocal duets   JNEE/NVPNP
Septets: Woodwind, strings, keyboard & percussion
  NYDFNP
Sextets: Descant recorder, keyboard & percussion
  NYFSRNQ
Sextets: Flute, strings, keyboard & percussion
  NYDRNQ
Sextets: Strings & keyboard   NXNQ
Sextets: Wind, strings & keyboard   NUNQ
Sextets: Wind, strings & percussion: Accompanying speaker(s)   HYE/NYENQ
Sextets: Woodwind, strings & keyboard: Accompanying tenor voice
  KGHE/NUPNQ
Sibelius, Jean: Books   BSH
Sight reading: Guitar playing   TS/EG
Sight reading: Piano playing   Q/EG
Sight reading: Solo voice   K/EG
Sinfoniettas: String orchestra   RXMEM
Sinfoniettas: Symphony orchestra   MMEM

Singers: Blues: Solo voice: Books AKDW/HHW/E(M)

Singers: Female voices: Books AKF/E(M)

Singers: Popular music: Books AKDW/GB/E(M)

Singers: Recorded music: Tenor voice AKGH/FD(M)

Singers: Rock 'n' Roll: Songs: Male voice: Books AKGDW/HK/E(M)

Singers: Soprano voice: Books AKFL/E(M)

Singers: Tenor voice: Books AKGH/E(M)

Singing: Books AB/E

Singing: Tenor voice: Books AKGH/E

Six, *Les*: France, 1917–1929: Books A/D(YH/XMSB/P)

Smith, Jane Stuart: Books AKF/E(P)

Solos, Unaccompanied: Accordion RSPM

Solos, Unaccompanied: Bassoon VWPM

Solos, Unaccompanied: Cello SRPM

Solos, Unaccompanied: Descant recorder VSRPM

Solos, Unaccompanied: Flute VRPM

Solos, Unaccompanied: Guitar TSPM

Solos, Unaccompanied: Harp TQPM

Solos, Unaccompanied: Oboe VTPM

Solos: Unaccompanied: Psaltery TWTPM

Solos, Unaccompanied: Treble recorder VSSPM

Solos, Unaccompanied: Voice KEZ

Solos: Organ R

Solos: Vocal music K

Solos: Vocal music: Books AK

Sonatas: Arrangements: Trumpet, strings & keyboard trio NUXSNTK/AE

Sonatas: Arrangements for clarinet & piano VVPK/AE

Sonatas: Arrangements for treble recorder & piano VSSPE

Sonatas: Bassoon & piano VWPE

Sonatas: Brass & keyboard quartet NWXPNSE

Sonatas: Brass & keyboard quintet NWXPNRE

Sonatas: Brass trio & string orchestra RXMPWNTE

Sonatas: Cello & piano SRPE

Sonatas: Clarinet & piano VVPE

Sonatas: Flute & piano VRPE

Sonatas: Flute & strings trio NVRNTE

Sonatas: Flutes (2) & keyboard VRNTPWE

Sonatas: Harpsichords (2), four hands QRNUE

Sonatas: Organ RE

Sonatas: Piano solos QPE

Sonatas: Piano solo: Beethoven, L. van: Books BBJAQPE

Sonatas: Strings & keyboard sextet NXNQE

Sonatas: Strings & keyboard trio NXNTE

Sonatas: Treble recorder & piano VSSPE

Sonatas: Treble recorder duets VSSNUE

Sonatas: Treble recorder, strings & keyboard trios NUSSNTE

Sonatas: Trios: Clarinet, strings & keyboard NUVNTE

Sonatas: Trombone, strings & keyboard quartet NUXUNSE

Sonatas: Trumpet & organ WSPLRE

Sonatas: Trumpet & string orchestra RXMPWSE

Sonatas: Trumpet, cello & string orchestra RXMPWSPLSRE

Sonatas: Viola & piano SQPE

Sonatas: Violin & piano SPE

Sonatas: Woodwind & keyboard trio NWPNTE

Sonatas: Woodwind, strings & keyboard quartet NUPNSE

Sonatinas: Accordion solos RSPMEM

Sonatinas: Arrangements for cello SRPK/AEM

Sonatinas: Arrangements for viola SQPK/AEM

Sonatinas: Descant recorder & piano VSRPEM

Sonatinas: Harpsichord solos QRPEM

Sonatinas: Oboe & piano VTPEM

Sonatinas: Piano solo QPEM

Sonatinas: Quartets: Percussion instruments XNSEM

Songs: Accompanied by clarinet & piano KE/VVPDW

Songs: Accompanied by clarinet, keyboard & percussion ENYFVDW

Songs: Accompanied by flute, strings & percussion quartet KE/NYERNSDW

Songs: Accompanied by treble recorder duet KE/VSSNUDW

Songs: Accompanied by trumpet, strings & percussion ENYEXSDW

Songs: Accompanied by various instruments: Female voices, Children's voices FE/LDW

Songs: Accompanied by violin ESDW

Songs: Arrangements for accordion solo RSPMK/DW

Songs: Arrangements for brass band WMK/DW

Songs: Arrangements for cello quintet SRNRK/DW

Songs: Arrangements for descant recorder solo VSRPMK/DW

Songs: Arrangements for descant recorder trio VSRNTK/DW

Songs: Arrangements for double bass & piano SSPK/DW

Songs: Arrangements for electronic organ RPVK/DW

Songs: Arrangements for guitar solo TSPMK/DW

Songs: Arrangements for instrumental quartet LNSK/DW

Songs: Arrangements for military band UMMK/DW

Songs: Arrangements for organ RK/DW

Songs: Arrangements for piano solo QPK/DW

Songs: Arrangements for recorder VSK/DW

Songs: Arrangements for recorder solo VSPMK/DW

Songs: Arrangements for string orchestra RXMK/DW

Songs: Arrangements for violin trio SNTK/DW

Songs: Arrangements for wind quintet UNRK/DW

Songs: Baritone voice KGNDW

Songs: Baritone voice: Accompanied by orchestra KGNE/MDW

Songs: Bass voice KGXDW

Songs: Bass voices GXDW

Songs: Choral music DW

Songs: Choral music: Unaccompanied works EZDW

Songs: Female voice, Child's voice solos: Accompanied by guitar KFE/TSDW

Songs: Female voices, Children's voices FDW

Songs: Female voices, Children's voices: Accompanied by percussion FE/XDW

Songs: Female voices, Children's voices: Duets: Accompanied by horn & piano JNFEE/WTPDW

Songs: Female voices, Children's voices: Unison JFDW

Songs: Female voices, Children's voices: Unison: Accompanied by descant recorder, keyboard & percussion JFE/NYFSRDW

Songs: Female voices, Children's voices: Unison: Accompanied by descant recorder, strings, keyboard & percussion JFE/NYDSRDW

Songs: Female voices, Children's voices: Unison: Accompanied by guitar JFE/TSDW

Songs: Female voices, Children's voices: Unison: Accompanied by various instruments JFE/LDW

Songs: Female voices, Children's voices: Trios: Accompanied by orchestra JNFDE/MDW

Songs: Female voices, Children's voices: Unison: Accompanied by melodic percussion JFE/XPQDW

Songs: High voice KFTDW

Songs: High voices: Accompanied by chime bars JFTE/XTPRDW

Songs: Low voice KFXDW

Songs: Male voice: Books AKGDW

Songs: Musical literature ADW

Songs: Schumann, R.: Books BSGAKDW

Songs: Solo voice KDW

Songs: Solo voice: Accompanied by flute, string & percussion trio KF/NYERNTDW

Songs: Solo voice: Accompanied by guitar KE/TSDW

Songs: Solo voice: Books AKDW

Songs: Solo voice: Schumann, R.: Books BSGAKDW

Songs: Soprano duets: Accompanied by oboe, strings, keyboard & percussion septets JFLEE/NYDTNPDW

Songs: Soprano voice: Accompanied by double bass KFLE/SSDW

Songs: Soprano voice: Accompanied by orchestra KFLE/MDW

Songs: Soprano voices FLDW

Songs: Speaker: Accompanied by instruments HYE/LDW

Songs: Tenor voice KGHDW

Songs: Tenor voice: Accompanied by orchestra KGHE/MDW

Songs: Unaccompanied female voices, children's voices FEZDW

Songs: Unaccompanied female voices, children's voices: Unison JFEZDW

Songs: Unaccompanied male voices GEZDW

Songs: Unaccompanied solo voice KEZDW

Songs: Unaccompanied soprano voices FLEZDW

Songs: Unaccompanied works: Unison JEZDW

Songs: Unison JDW

Songs: Unison: Accompanied by glockenspiel & piano JE/XTPDW

Songs: Unison: Accompanied by guitar JE/TSDW

Songs: Vocal duets JNEDW

Songs: Vocal duets: Accompanied by woodwind & string septet JNEE/NVPNPDW

Songs: Vocal solos: Brahms, J.: Books BBTAKDW

Songs, etc.: Strauss, R.: Books BSUAKDW

Soprano voice KFL

Soprano voice: Books AKFL

Soprano voices: Choral works FL

Soprano voices: Vocal ensembles JNFL

South Moravia: Folk songs: Unaccompanied works: Unison JEZDW/G/AYFSM

Spain: Books A(YK)

Speaker KHY

Speaking chorus HY

Spirituals: Bass voices GXDW/LC

Spirituals: Female voices, Children's voices FDW/LC

Spirituals: Songs: Choral music DW/LC

Spirituals: Treble voices FLDW/LC

Spirituals: Unaccompanied male voices GEZDW/LC

Stereophonic records: Books A/FF

Strauss, Richard: Books BSU

Strauss family: Books BSQR

Stravinsky, Igor: Books SS

String bass SS

String instrument & orchestra MPRW

String instruments RW

String instruments: Accompanying baritone voice KGNE/RW

String instruments: Accompanying choral works ERW

String instruments: Accompanying unison choral works JE/RW

String instruments: Books ARW

Strings & keyboard: Accompanying baritone voice KGNE/NX

Strings & keyboard: Chamber music NX

Strings & wind: Accompanying vocal duets JNEE/NV

Strings & wind: Ensembles: Chamber music NV

Strings, brass & percussion: Accompanying choral works ENYEXP

Strings, keyboard & percussion: Ensembles: Accompanying choral music ENYG

Strings, saxophone & keyboard: Accompanying soprano voice KFLE/NUU

Strings, trumpet & keyboard: Chamber music NUXS

Strings, trumpet & percussion: Accompanying choral works ENYEXS

Strings, wind & keyboard: Ensembles: Accompanying soprano voice KFLE/NU

Strings, wind & keyboard: Ensembles: Accompanying tenor voice KGHE/NU

Strings, wind & keyboard: Ensembles: Chamber music NU

Strings, wind & percussion: Accompanying speaker(s) HYE/NYE

Strings, wind & percussion: Ensembles: Accompanying solo voice KE/NYE

Strings, wind & percussion: Ensembles: Chamber music NYE

Strings, wind, keyboard & percussion: Accompanying soprano duets JNFLEE/NYD

Strings, wind, keyboard & percussion: Ensembles: Chamber music NYD

Strings, woodwind & keyboard: Ensembles: Accompanying soprano voice KFLE/NUP

Suites: Arrangements for treble recorder VSSPK/LG

Suites: Arrangements for trumpet & piano WSPK/AG

Suites: Bassoon solo VWPMG

Suites: Brass band WMG

Suites: Brass quartet WNSG

Suites: Chamber orchestra MRG

Suites: Clarinet & piano VVPG

Suites: Dances: Piano solos QPHG

Suites: Flute & piano VRPG

Suites: Flute & string trio NVRNTG

Suites: Guitar solo TSPMG

Suites: Orchestra MG

Suites: Organ RG

Suites: Piano solos QPG

Suites: Recorder trio VSNTG

Suites: String orchestra RXMG

Suites: Strings & keyboard quintet NXNRG

Suites: Trumpet & orchestra MPWSG

Suites: Trumpets (2) & piano WSNTQG

Suites: Viola solo SQPMG

Suites: Violin & piano SPG

Suites: Wind & keyboard quintet NWNRG

Suites: Woodwind quintet VNRG

Sullivan, Sir Arthur Seymour: Books BSW

Sutherland, Joan: Books AKFL/E(P)

Swann, Donald: Books BSWN

Symphonies MME

Symphonies: Arrangements for recorder quartet VSNSK/AE

Symphonies: Arrangements for wind quartet UNSK/AE

Symphonies: Books  AMME
Symphonies: Chamber orchestra  MRE
Symphonies: Orchestra  ME
Symphonies: String orchestra  RXME
Symphonies: Trumpet & orchestra: Arrangements for trumpet & piano  WSPK/LE
Symphonies: Vaughan Williams, R.: Books  BVDAMME
Symphony orchestra  MM
Symphony orchestras: Books  AMM/E(QB)

Tangos: Keyboard solos  QPHVR
Tangos: Piano solos  QPHVR
Te Deum: Matins: Divine Office  DGKHB
Teaching: Instrumental music: Books  AL/E(VC)
Teaching: Piano: Books  AQ/E(VC)
Teaching: Psychology: Books  A/CS(VC)
Teaching methods: Education: Books  A(VC)
Technique: Violin playing: Books  AS/CY
Television music: Arrangements for brass band  WMK/JS
Television music: Arrangements for military band  UMMK/JS
Television music: Arrangements for piano solo  QPK/JS
Television music: Hymns: Arrangements for organ  RK/DM/JS
Television music: Marches: Arrangements for piano solo  QPK/AGM/JS
Television music: Songs: Arrangements for military band  UMMK/DW/JS
Temperance: Hymns  DM/LRT
Tenor voice  KGH
Tenor voice: Books  AKGH
Theatre: Music: Arrangements for piano solo  QPK/J
Trade catalogues: Recorded music  A/FD(WM)
Treble recorder  VSS
Treble recorder: Accompanying solo voice  KE/VSS
Treble recorder & string orchestra  RXMPVSS
Treble recorder, strings & keyboard: Chamber music  NUSS
Treble voice  KFL
Treble voice: Books  AKFL
Treble voices: Choral works  FL
Treble voices: Vocal ensembles  JNFL
Trinity College: Graduate & professional education: Books  A(VP/YDB)
Trios: Brass instruments  WNT
Trios: Brass instruments & string orchestra  RXMPWNT
Trios: Cello  SRNT
Trios: Clarinet  VVNT
Trios: Clarinet, strings & keyboard  NUVNT
Trios: Descant recorder  VSRNT
Trios: Female voices, Children's voices  JNFD
Trios: Flute & strings  NVRNT
Trios: Flute, strings & keyboard  NURNT
Trios: Flute, strings & percussion: Ensembles: Accompanying solo voice  KE/NYERNT
Trios: Guitar  TSNT
Trios: Horn, strings & keyboard  NUXTNT
Trios: Instrumental ensembles  LNT
Trios: Recorder  VSNT
Trios: Saxophone, strings & keyboard: Accompanying soprano voice  KFLE/NUUNT
Trios: Strings & keyboard  NXNT
Trios: String ensembles  RXNT
Trios: Strings, keyboard & percussion ensemble: Accompanying choral music  ENYGNT
Trios: Treble recorder, strings & keyboard  NUSSNT
Trios: Trumpet  WSNT
Trios: Trumpet, strings & keyboard  NUXSNT
Trios: Vibrophone ensemble  XTQTNT
Trios: Violin  SNT
Trios: Woodwind & keyboard  NWPNT
Trios: Woodwind instruments  VNT
Trombone & trumpet  WSPLWU
Trombone, strings & keyboard: Chamber music  NUXU
Trumpet  WS
Trumpet & orchestra  MPWS
Trumpet & organ  WSPLR
Trumpet & percussion: Ensembles: Accompanying tenor voice  KGHE/NYHXS
Trumpet & string orchestra  RXMPWS
Trumpet, cello & string orchestra  RXMPWSPLSR
Trumpet, oboe & string orchestra  RXMPVTPLWSF
Trumpet, strings & keyboard: Chamber music  NUXS
Trumpet, strings & percussion: Accompanying choral works  ENYEXS
Trumpets (2) & keyboard  WSNTPW
Tutors: Banjo  TT/AC
Tutors: Brass band  WM/AC
Tutors: Choirs: Music  D/AC
Tutors: Descant recorder  VSR/AC

Tutors: Electronic organ  RPV/AC
Tutors: Flute  VR/AC
Tutors: Guitar  TS/AC
Tutors: Harp  TQ/AC
Tutors: Horn  WT/AC
Tutors: Oboe  VT/AC
Tutors: Recorder  VS/AC
Tyneside: Folk songs: Books  ADW/G(YDJHT)

Unaccompanied accordion solos  RSPM
Unaccompanied bassoon solos  VWPM
Unaccompanied cello solos  SRPM
Unaccompanied choral works  EZ
Unaccompanied descant recorder solos  VSRPM
Unaccompanied female voices, children's voices: Choral works  FEZ
Unaccompanied female voices, children's voices: Unison  JFEZ
Unaccompanied flute solos  VRPM
Unaccompanied guitar  TSPM
Unaccompanied harp solos  TQPM
Unaccompanied male voices: Choral music  GEZ
Unaccompanied oboe solos  VTPM
Unaccompanied recorder: Solos  VSPM
Unaccompanied solos: Psaltery  TWTPM
Unaccompanied soprano voices  FLEZ
Unaccompanied treble recorder  VSSPM
Unaccompanied unison choral works  JEZ
Unaccompanied vocal solos  KEZ
Unaccompanied works: Choral music: Books  AEZ
Unison choral works  J
Unison songs  JDW
Unitarian church: Hymns: Female voices, Children's voices: Unison  JFDM/LSL
United States: Blues: Songs: Solo voice  KDW/HHW
United States: Education: Schools: Books  A(VF/YT)
United States: Folk songs: Collections: Unison: Accompanied by guitar  JE/TSDW/G/AYT
United States: National songs: Books  ADW/KM(YT)
United States: Popular music: Books  A/GB(YT)

Variations: Chamber orchestra  MR/T
Variations: Flute & piano  VRP/T
Variations: Flute duet  VRNU/T
Variations: Keyboard solos  PWP/T
Variations: Minuets: Piano solos  QPHR/T
Variations: Pavanes: Descant recorder, unaccompanied  VSRPMHVG/T
Variations: Piano solos  QP/T
Variations: String quartet  RXNS/T
Variations: Violin & piano  SP/T
Vaughan Williams, Ralph: Books  BVD
Venice: Descant recorder & piano collections  VSRP/AYJV
Vespers: Divine Office: Female voices, Children's voices  FDGKJ
Vespers: Divine Office: Soprano voice: Accompanied by saxophone, strings & keyboard trio  KFLE/NUUNTDGKJ
Vibraphone  XTQT
Vienna: Books  A(YEMB)
Vienna: Concerts: Books  A(W/YEMB)
Viol  ST
Viola  SQ
Viola: Books  ASQ
Viola & cello  SQPLSR
Viola & orchestra  MPSQ
Viola & violin  SPLSQ
Viola da gamba  STU
Violin  S
Violin: Accompanying choral music  ES
Violin: Books  AS
Violin & cello  SPLSR
Violin & orchestra  MPS
Violin & organ  SPLR
Violin & organ: Accompanying high voice  KFTE/SPLR
Violin & string orchestra  RXMPS
Violin & viola  SPLSQ
Violins (2) & keyboard: Accompanying bass voice  KGXE/SNTPW
Violins (2) & keyboard: Accompanying soprano voice  KFLE/SNTPW
Violins (2) & organ: Accompanying treble duets  JNFLEE/SNTR
Violins (3) & string orchestra  RXMPSNT
Violoncello  SR
Violoncello & orchestra  MPSR
Violoncello & viola  SQPLSR
Virginals  QSQ
Vocal music  CB
Vocal music: Books  AB
Voice: Books  AB

Wales: Books  A(YDK)
Wales: Choral music  AD(YDK)
Wales: Education: Books  A(V/YDK)
Waltzes: Accordion solos  RSPMHW

Waltzes: Arrangements: Guitar solo  TSPMK/AHW
Waltzes: Arrangements for piano solo  QPK/AHW
Waltzes: Brass band  WMHW
Waltzes: Light orchestra  MSHW
Waltzes: Military band  UMMHW
Waltzes: Orchestra  MHW
Waltzes: Piano solos  QPHW
Weddings: Arrangements for organ  RK/KDD
Weddings: Hymns  DM/KDD
Whitsuntide: Religious cantatas  DE/LN
Wilbye, John: Books  BWNRB
Wilson, Sandy: Books  BWNTM
Wimborne: Organs: Books  AR/B(YDFKW)
Wimborne Minster: Organs: Books  AR/B(YDFKWB)
Wind & keyboard: Chamber music  NW
Wind & percussion: Ensembles: Accompanying tenor voice  KGHE/NYH
Wind & strings: Ensembles: Accompanying vocal duets  JNEE/NV
Wind & strings: Ensembles: Chamber music  NV
Wind instruments  U
Wind instruments: Accompanying choral music  EU
Wind instruments: Books  AU
Wind instruments & string orchestra  RXMPU
Wind instruments (2) & keyboard  UNTPW
Wind, keyboard & percussion: Chamber music  NYF
Wind, keyboard & percussion: Ensembles: Accompanying choral music  ENYF
Wind, keyboard & percussion: Ensembles: Accompanying female voices, children's voices: Unison  JFE/NYF
Wind, strings & keyboard: Ensembles: Accompanying tenor voice  KGHE/NU
Wind, strings & keyboard: Ensembles: Chamber music  NU
Wind, strings & percussion: Accompanying speaker(s)  HYE/NYE
Wind, strings & percussion: Ensembles: Accompanying choral music  ENYE
Wind, strings & percussion: Ensembles: Accompanying solo voice  KE/NYE
Wind, strings & percussion: Ensembles: Chamber music  NYE
Wind, strings, keyboard & percussion: Accompanying soprano duets  JNFLEE/NYD
Wind, strings, keyboard & percussion: Ensembles: Accompanying female voices, children's voices  FE/NYD
Wind, strings, keyboard & percussion: Ensembles: Accompanying female voices, children's voices: Unison  JFE/NYD
Wind, strings, keyboard & percussion: Ensembles: Chamber music  NYD
Woman's voice  KF
Woman's voice: Books  AKF
Women's voices: Choral works  F
Women's voices: Unison  JF
Women's voices: Vocal ensembles  JNF
Woodwind & keyboard: Chamber music  NWP
Woodwind & strings: Ensembles: Accompanying vocal duets  JNEE/NVP
Woodwind instruments: Books  AV
Woodwind instrument & string orchestra  RXMPV
Woodwind instruments  V
Woodwind, keyboard & percussion: Chamber music  NYFP
Woodwind, keyboard & percussion: Ensembles: Accompanying choral works  ENYFP
Wind, keyboard & percussion: Ensembles: Accompanying female voices, children's voices  FE/NYF
Woodwind, keyboard & percussion: Ensembles: Accompanying female voices, children's voices: Unison  JFE/NYFP
Woodwind, strings & keyboard: Ensembles: Accompanying tenor voice  KGHE/NUP
Woodwind, strings & percussion: Ensembles: Accompanying solo voice  KE/NYEP
Woodwind, strings, keyboard & percussion: Accompanying soprano duets  JNFLEE/NYDP
Woodwind, strings, keyboard & percussion: Ensembles: Accompanying female voices, children's voices  FE/NYDP
Woodwind, strings, keyboard & percussion: Ensembles: Accompanying female voices, children's voices: Unison  JFE/NYDP
Woodwind, strings, keyboard & percussion: Ensembles: Chamber music  NYDP
Writers: Aesthetics & criticism: Books  A/CC(M)

York: Cathedral music: Books  AD/LE(YDJGY)
York Minster: Cathedral music: Books  AD/LE(YDJGYB)
Yorkshire: Cathedral music: Books  AD/LE(YDJG)

# LIST OF MUSIC PUBLISHERS

While every effort has been made to check the information given in this list with the publishers concerned, the Council of the British National Bibliography cannot hold itself responsible for any errors or omissions.

ALLAN & Co. (Pty.), Ltd., Australia.
*British Agent:* Freeman, H., & Co.

ALLEN, George, & Unwin, Ltd. 40 Museum St., London, W.C.2: *Tel:* 01-405 8577. *Grams:* Deucalion.
*Trade:* Park Lane, Hemel Hempstead, Herts.
*Tel:* 0442 3244

AMERICAN Institute of Musicology, U.S.A.
*British Agent:* Hinrichsen Edition, Ltd.

AMICI della Musica da Camera, Rome.
*British Agent:* Hinrichsen Edition, Ltd.

ARNOLD, Edward, (Publishers), Ltd. (Music Scores). *See* Novello & Co., Ltd.

ARTIA, Prague.
*British Agent:* Boosey & Hawkes Music Publishers, Ltd.

ASCHERBURG, Hopwood & Crewe, 50 New Bond St., W.1.

ASHDOWN, Edwin, Ltd. 275-281 Cricklewood Broadway, London, NW2 6QR. *Tel:* 01-450 5237.

ASSOCIATED Board of the Royal Schools of Music (Publications Dept.). 14 Bedford Sq., London, WC1B 3JG.
*Tel:* 01-636 6919. *Grams:* Musexam London WC1.

AVENUE Music Publishing Co., Ltd. 50 New Bond St., London, W.1. *Tel:* 01-629 7600. *Grams:* Symphony Wesdo London.

BANK, Annie, Editions, Amsterdam.
*British Agent:* J. & W. Chester, Ltd.

BARENREITER, Ltd. 32 Gt. Titchfield St., London, W.1.
*Tel:* 01-580 9008

BARON, H. 136 Chatsworth Rd., London, NW2 5QU.
*Tel:* 01-459 2035. *Grams:* Musicbaron, London.

BARRY & Co., Buenos Aires.
*British Agent:* Boosey & Hawkes Music Publishers, Ltd.

BAYLEY & Ferguson, Ltd. 65 Berkeley St., Glasgow C3.
*Tel:* CENtral 7240. *Grams:* Bayley Glasgow.

BELWIN-MILLS Music, Ltd. 230 Purley Way, Croydon, CR9 4QD. *Tel:* 01-681 0855. *Grams:* Belmil Croydon.

BERLIN, Irving, Ltd. 14 St. George St., London, W.1.
*Tel:* 01-629 7600.

BESSEL, W. & Co. Paris.
*British Agent:* Boosey & Hawkes Music Publishers, Ltd.

BIELER, Edmund, Musikverlag, Cologne.
*British Agent:* J. & W. Chester, Ltd.

BLOSSOM Music, Ltd. 139 Piccadilly, London, W.1.
*Tel:* 01-629 7211. *Grams:* Leedsmusik London, W.1.

BOOSEY & Hawkes Music Publishers, Ltd. 295 Regent St., London, W1A 1BR. *Tel:* 01-580 2060.
*Grams:* Sonorous London W.1.

BOSTON Music Co., Boston (Mass.).
*British Agent:* Chappell & Co., Ltd.

BOSWORTH & Co., Ltd. 14-18 Heddon St., London, W.1. *Tel:* 01-734 4961/2. *Grams:* Bosedition Piccy London.

BOURNE MUSIC Ltd. 34/36 Maddox St., London, W1R 9PD.
*Tel:* 01-493 6412/6583. *Grams:* Bournemusic London, W.1.

BRADBURY Wood, Ltd. 16 St. George St., London, W.1.

BREGMAN, Vocco & Conn, Ltd. 50 New Bond St., London, W.1. *Tel:* 01-629 7600.

BREITKOPF & Härtel, Leipzig.
*British Agent:* Breitkopf & Härtel (London), Ltd.

BREITKOPF & Härtel (London), Ltd. 8 Horse and Dolphin Yard, London, W1V 7LG.

BREITKOPF & Härtel, Wiesbaden, W. Germany.
*British Agent:* Breitkopf & Härtel (London), Ltd.

BRITISH & Continental Music Agencies, Ltd. 64 Dean St., London, W.1. *Tel:* GERrard 9336. *Grams:* Humfriv Wesdo London.

BROCKHAUS, Max, Germany.
*British Agent* (Orchestral music only): Novello & Co., Ltd.

BRUZZICHELLI, Aldo, Florence.
*British Agent:* Hinrichsen Edition, Ltd.

CAMPBELL, Connelly, & Co., Ltd. *See* CONNELLY, Campbell, & Co., Ltd.

CARY, L.J., & Co. Ltd. 50 New Bond St., London, W1A 2BR.
*Tel:* 01-629 7600. *Grams:* Symphony London W1.

CEBEDEM Foundation, Brussels.
*British Agent:* Lengnick & Co., Ltd.

CHAPPELL & Co., Ltd. 50 New Bond St., London, W.1. *Tel:* 01-629 7600. *Grams:* Symphony Wesdo London.

CHESTER, J. & W., Ltd. Eagle Court, London, E.C.1.
*Tel:* 01-253-6947. *Grams:* Guarnerius, London E.C.1.

CHURCH, John, Co., Pennsylvania.
*British Agent:* Alfred A. Kalmus, Ltd.

CLIFFORD Essex Music Co., Ltd. *See* ESSEX, Clifford, Music Co., Ltd.

COLLIER/DEXTER Music, Ltd. 50 New Bond St., London, W1A 2BR. *Tel:* 01-629 7600.

COLUMBIA Music Co., Washington, D.C.
*British Agent:* Breitkopf & Härtel (London) Ltd.

COMPASS Music Ltd. 50 New Bond St., London, W.1.
*Tel:* 01-629 7600

CONNELLY, Campbell & Co., Ltd. 10 Denmark St., London, W.C.2. *Tel:* TEMple Bar 1653. *Grams:* Dansmelodi Westcent London.

CONSTABLE & Co., Ltd. 10 Orange St., London, WC2H 7EG.
*Tel:* 01-930 0801. *Grams:* Dhagoba London WC2.
*Trade:* Tiptree Book Services Ltd., Tiptree, Colchester, Essex. *Tel:* Tiptree 6362/7

CRAMER, J. B., & Co., Ltd. 99 St. Martin's Lane, London, WC2N 4AZ. *Tel:* 01-240 1612.

CURWEN, J., & Sons, Ltd.
*Agents:* Faber Music, & Roberton Publications.

DELHI Publications, Inc., Cincinnati.
*British Agent:* Chappell & Co., Ltd.

DELRIEU, Georges, & Cie, Nice.
*British Agent:* Galliard, Ltd.

DE SANTIS, Rome.
*British Agent:* Hinrichsen Edition, Ltd.

DEUTSCH, André, Ltd. 105 Gt. Russell St., London, W.C.1.
*Tel:* 01-580 2746. *Grams:* Adlib London.
*Trade:* Amabel House, 14-24 Baches St., London, N.1.
*Tel:* 01-253 8589.

DE WOLFE, Ltd. 80-82 Wardour St., London, W1V 3LF.
*Tel:* 01-437 4933. *Grams:* Musicall London.

DISNEY, Walt, Music Co., Ltd. 52 Maddox St., London, W.1.
*Tel:* 01-629 7600.

DITSON, Oliver, Co., Pennsylvania.
*British Agent:* Alfred A. Kalmus, Ltd.

DOBLINGER Edition, Vienna.
*British Agent:* Alfred A. Kalmus, Ltd.

DONEMUS Foundation, Amsterdam.
*British Agent:* Alfred Lengnick, & Co., Ltd.

EDITIO Musica, Budapest.
*British Agent:* Boosey & Hawkes Music Publishers, Ltd.

EDITION Tonos, Darmstadt.
*British Agent:* Breitkopf & Härtel (London), Ltd.

EDIZIONI Berben, Ancona, Italy.
*British Agent:* Breitkopf & Härtel (London) Ltd.

EDIZIONI Suvini Zerboni, Milan.
*British Agent:* Schott & Co., Ltd.

EDWARD B. Marks Music Corporation, New York.
*British Agent:* Boosey & Hawkes Music Publishers, Ltd.

ELKIN & Co., Ltd. Borough Green, Sevenoaks, Kent. *Tel:* Borough Green 3261. *Grams:* Novellos Sevenoaks

ENGLISH Folk Dance and Song Society. Cecil Sharp House, 2 Regent's Park Road, London, NW1 7AY.
*Tel:* 01 485 2206.

ESCHIG, Max, Paris.
*British Agent:* Schott & Co., Ltd.

ESSEX, Clifford, Music Co., Ltd. 20 Earlham St., London, W.C.2. *Tel:* 01-836 2810. *Grams:* Triomphe London, W.C.2.

ESSEX Music Group. Essex House, 19/20 Poland St., London, W1V 3DD. *Tel:* 01-434 1621. *Grams:* Sexmus London.
*Trade:* Music Sales Ltd. 78 Newman St., London, W.1.

EULENBURG, Ernst, Ltd. 48 Great Marlborough St., London, W1V 2BN. *Tel:* 01-437 1246/8.

FABER Music, Ltd. 38 Russell Sq., London, WC1B 5DA.
*Tel:* 01-636 1344. *Grams:* Fabbaf London WC1.

FAITH Press, Ltd. Wing Rd, Leighton Buzzard, Beds.
LU7 7NQ. *Tel:* 052-53 3365.

FAMOUS Chappell, Ltd. 50 New Bond St., London, W.1.
*Tel:* 01-629 7600. *Grams:* Symphony Wesdo London.

FELDMAN, B., & Co., Ltd. 64 Dean St., London, W.1.
*Tel:* GERrard 9336. *Grams:* Humfriv Wesdo London.

FISCHER, Carl, New York.
*British Agent:* Hinrichsen Edition, Ltd.

FOETISCH Freres, Editions, Lausanne.
*British Agent:* J. & W. Chester, Ltd.

FORBERG, Robert, Bad Godesberg.
*British Agent:* Hinrichsen Edition, Ltd.

FORSYTH Brothers, Ltd. 190 Grays Inn Rd., London,
WC1X 8EW. *Tel:* 01-837 4768.

FORTISSIMO-Verlag, Vienna.
*British Agent:* Clifford Essex Music Co., Ltd.

FOX, Sam, Publishing Co. *See* SAM Fox Publishing Co.

FRANCIS, Day & Hunter, Ltd. 138 Charing Cross Rd., London, W.C.2. *Tel:* 01-836 9351. *Grams:* Arpeggio
Westcent London.

FRANK Music Co., Ltd. 50 New Bond St., London W.1.
*Tel:* 01-629 7600.

FREEMAN, H., Ltd. 64 Dean St., London, W.1.
*Tel:* 01-437 9336/9.

FRENCH, Samuel, Ltd. 26 Southampton St., Strand, London,
W.C.2. *Tel:* 01-836 7513. *Grams:* Dramalogue
London W.C.2.

G. & C. Music Corporation, New York.
*British Agent:* Chappell & Co., Ltd.

GALAXY Music Corporation, New York.
*British Agent:* Stainer & Bell, Ltd.

GALLIARD, Ltd. 82 High Rd, London N.2.

GLOCKEN Verlag, Ltd. 10-16 Rathbone St., London,
W1P 2BJ. *Tel:* 01-580 2827. *Grams:* Operetta
London W1.

GRAPHIC, Graz, Austria.
*British Agent:* Alfred A. Kalmus, Ltd.

GREGG International Publishers, Ltd. Westmead,
Farnborough, Hants.

GWASG Prifysgol Cymru, Merthyr House, James St., Cardiff,
CF1 6EU. *Tel:* Cardiff 31919.

HANSEN, Wilhelm, Edition, Copenhagen.
*British Agent:* J. & W. Chester, Ltd.

HÄNSSLER, Verlag, Germany.
*British Agent:* Novello & Co., Ltd.

HARGAIL Music Press, New York.
*British Agent:* Alfred A. Kalmus, Ltd.

HARMONIA Uitgave, Hilversum.
*British Agent:* Alfred A. Kalmus, Ltd.

HARRIS, Frederick, Music Co., Ltd.
*British Agent:* Alfred Lengnick & Co., Ltd.

HART, F. Pitman, & Co., Ltd. 99 St. Martin's Lane, London,
WC2N 4AZ. *Tel:* 01-240 1612.

HEINRICHSHOFEN, Wilhelmshaven.
*British Agent:* Clifford Essex Music Co., Ltd.

HENLE, G., Verlag, Germany.
*British Agent:* Novello & Co., Ltd.

HENMAR Press, New York.
*British Agent:* Hinrichsen Edition, Ltd.

HEUWEKEMEIJER, Holland.
*British Agent:* Hinrichsen Edition, Ltd.

HINRICHSEN Edition, Ltd. Bach House, 10-12 Baches St.,
London, N1 6DN. *Tel:* 01-253 1638. *Grams:* Musipeters
London.

HOFMEISTER, Friedrich, Hofheim, W. Germany.
*British Agent:* Breitkopf & Härtel (London) Ltd.

HOFMEISTER Figaro Verlag, Vienna.
*British Agent:* Alfred A. Kalmus, Ltd.

HUG & Co., Zurich.
*British Agent:* Hinrichsen Edition, Ltd.

HUGHES a'i Fab (Hughes & Son) Publishers, Ltd. 29 Rivulet
Rd., Wrexham, Denbighshire, North Wales. *Tel:* Wrexham
4340.

HUNTZINGER, R. L., Inc., Cincinnati.
*British Agent:* Chappell & Co., Ltd.

IMPERIAL Society of Teachers of Dancing. 70 Gloucester
Place, London, W1H 4AJ. *Tel:* 01-935 0825/6.
*Grams:* Istod, London W1.

INTER-ART Music Publishers. 10-16 Rathbone St., London,
W1P 2BJ. *Tel:* 01-580 2827. *Grams:* Operetta
London W1.

INTERNATIONAL Music Co., New York.
*British Agent:* Alfred A. Kalmus, Ltd.

INTERNATIONALEN Musikbisliothek, Berlin.
*British Agent:* Breitkopf & Härtel (London), Ltd.

ISTITUTO Italiano per la Storia della Musica.
*British Agent:* Alfred A. Kalmus, Ltd.

JUSKO, Ralph, Publications, Inc., Cincinnati.
*British Agent:* Chappell & Co., Ltd.

KAHNT, C. F., Germany.
*British Agent:* Novello & Co., Ltd.

KALMUS, Alfred A., Ltd. 2-3 Fareham St., London, W1V 4DU.
*Tel:* 01-437 5203. *Grams:* Alkamus London W.1.

KALMUS, Edwin, New York.
*British Agent:* Alfred A. Kalmus, Ltd.

KEITH Prowse Music Publishing Co., Ltd. 21 Denmark St.,
London, WC2H 8NE. *Tel:* 01-836 5501.

KISTNER & Siegel & Co., Germany.
*British Agent:* Novello & Co., Ltd.

KNEUSSLIN, Switzerland.
*British Agent:* Hinrichsen Edition, Ltd.

LAUDY & Co. c/o Bosworth & Co., Ltd. 14-18 Heddon St.,
London, W.1. *Tel:* 01-734 4961/2. *Grams:* Bosedition
Piccy London.

LEA Pocket Scores, New York.
*British Agent:* Alfred A. Kalmus, Ltd.

LEEDS Music, Ltd. 139 Piccadilly, London, W.1. *Tel:*
MAYfair 7211. *Grams:* Leedsmusik London.

LENGNICK, Alfred, & Co., Ltd. Purley Oaks Studios,
421a Brighton Rd., South Croydon, Sy. *Tel:* 01-660-7646.

LEONARD, Gould & Bolttler. 99 St. Martin's Lane, London,
WC2N 4AZ. *Tel:* 01-240 1612.

LEUCKART, F. E. C., Germany.
*British Agent:* Novello & Co., Ltd.

LIENAU, Robert (Schlesinger), Germany.
*British Agent:* Hinrichsen Edition, Ltd.

LITOLFF Verlag. Bach House, 10-12 Baches St., London,
N1 6DN. *Tel:* 01-253 1638.

LUVERNE Inc., New York.
*British Agent:* Boosey & Hawkes Music Publishers, Ltd.

LYCHE, Oslo.
*British Agent:* Hinrichsen Edition, Ltd.

McGINNIS & Marx, New York.
*British Agent:* Hinrichsen Edition, Ltd.

MADDOX Music Co., Ltd. 52 Maddox St., London, W.1.
*Tel:* MAYfair 7600.

MAURICE, Peter. *See* PETER Maurice.

MERION Music Co., Pennsylvania.
*British Agent:* Alfred A. Kalmus, Ltd.

MERSEBURGER Verlag, Berlin.
*British Agent:* Hinrichsen Edition, Ltd. ; Musica Rara.

METROPOLIS, Antwerp.
*British Agent:* Hinrichsen Edition, Ltd.

MEZHDUNARODNAJA Kniga, Moscow.
*British Agent:* Boosey & Hawkes Music Publishers, Ltd.

MIDLAND Music Ltd. 50 Ladbroke Grove, London, W.11.
*Tel:* 01-229 1129

MOORIS, Edwin H., & CO., Ltd. 50 New Bond St., London,
W1A 2BR. *Tel:* 01-629 0576.

MÖSELER Verlag, Germany.
*British Agent:* Novello & Co., Ltd.

MÜLLER, Willy, Germany.
*British Agent:* Novello & Co., Ltd.

MUSIA International (Export and Import), Frankfurt.
*British Agent:* Hinrichsen Edition, Ltd.

MUSICA Islandica, Reykjavik.
*British Agent:* Alfred Lengnick & Co., Ltd.

MUSICA Rara. 2 Great Marlborough St., London, W.1. *Tel:*
01-437 1576.

NEW American Music Awards Series (Sigma Alpha Iota),
New York.
*British Agent:* Hinrichsen Edition, Ltd.

NEW Music Edition, Pennsylvania.
*British Agent:* Alfred A. Kalmus, Ltd.

NEW Wind Music Co. 23 Ivor Pl., London, N.W.1.
*Tel:* 01-262 3797.

NEW World Publishers, Ltd. 50 New Bond St., London, W.1.
*Tel:* 01-629 7600. *Grams:* Symphony Wesdo London.

NOETZEL, Wilhelmshaven, Germany.
*British Agent:* Hinrichsen Edition, Ltd.

NORDISKA Musikforlaget, Stockholm.
*British Agent:* J. & W. Chester, Ltd.

NORMAN Richardson Band Arrangements. 27 A'Becket's
Avenue, Bognor Regis, Sussex, PO21 4LX.

NORSK Musikforlag, Oslo.
*British Agent:* J. & W. Chester, Ltd.

NORTHERN Songs, Ltd. 12 Bruton St., London, W.1.
*Tel:* 01-499 0673. *Grams:* Atumusic London.
*Telex:* 28526.

NOVELLO & Co., Ltd. Borough Green, Sevenoaks, Kent.
*Tel:* Borough Green 3261. *Grams:* Novello Sevenoaks

OCTAVA Music Co., Ltd.
*British Agent:* Josef Weinberger, Ltd.

OXFORD University Press (Music Department). 44 Conduit
St., London, W1R ODE. *Tel:* 01-734 5364. *Grams and
Cables:* Fulscore London W1.

PARAGON, New York.
*British Agent:* Hinrichsen Edition, Ltd.

PATERSON'S Publications, Ltd. 38 Wigmore St., London,
W1H 0EX. *Tel:* 01-935 3551. *Grams:* Paterwia
London W1.

PENNSYLVANIA State University Press. 70 Great Russell
St., London, WC1B 3BY. *Tel:* 01-405 0182.
*Grams:* Amunpress London.

PETER Maurice Music Co., Ltd. 21 Denmark St., London,
WC2H 8NE. *Tel:* 01-836 5501. *Grams:* Mauritunes
London WC2.

PETERS Edition, Bach House, 10-12 Baches St., London,
N1 6DN. *Tel:* 01-253 1638. *Grams:* Musipeters London.

PITMAN, Hart, & Co., Ltd. *See* HART, F. Pitman, & Co., Ltd.

POLISH Music Publications, Poland.
*British Agent:* Alfred A. Kalmus, Ltd.

POLYPHONIC Reproductions Ltd. 89-91 Vicarage Rd,
London, NW10 2VA. *Tel:* 01-459 6194.

PRESSER, Theodore, Co., Pennsylvania.
*British Agent:* Alfred A. Kalmus, Ltd.

PRO ART Publications, Inc. New York.
*British Agent:* Alfred A. Kalmus, Ltd.

PRO MUSICA Verlag, Leipzig.
*British Agent:* Breitkopf & Härtel (London) Ltd.

PROWSE, Keith, Music Publishing Co., Ltd. *See* KEITH
Prowse Music Publishing Co., Ltd.

RAHTER, D. Lyra House, 67 Belsize La., London, NW3 5AX
*Tel:* 01-794 8038.

REGINA Music Publishing Co., Ltd. Old Run Rd., Leeds,
LS10 2AA. *Tel:* Leeds 700527.

RICHARDSON, Norman, Ltd. *See* Norman Richardson Band
Arrangements.

RIES & Erler, Berlin.
*British Agent:* Hinrichsen Edition, Ltd.

ROBBINS Music Corporation, Ltd. 1-6 Denmark Place,
London, WC2H 8NL. *Tel:* 01-240 2156.

ROBERTON Publications. The Windmill, Wendover,
Aylesbury, Bucks. *Tel:* Wendover 3107.

ROYAL Academy of Dancing. 48 Vicarage Cres., London,
SW11 3LT. *Tel:* 01-223 0091. *Grams:* Radancing
London SW11 3LT.

ROYAL School of Church Music. Addington Palace, Croydon,
CR9 5AD. *Tel:* 01-654 7676. *Grams:* Cantoris,
Croydon.

ROYAL Scottish Country Dance Society. 12 Coates Crescent,
Edinburgh EH3 7AF. *Tel:* 031-225 3854.

RUBANK Inc. U.S.A.
*British agent:* Novello & Co., Ltd.

ST. MARTINS Publications, Ltd. Addington Palace, Croydon
CR9 5AD. *Tel:* 01-654 7676

SAM Fox Publishing Co., New York.
*British Agent:* Keith Prowse Music Publishing Co., Ltd.

SCHIRMER, G., Inc., New York.
*British Agents:* Chappell & Co., Ltd.
   Curwen, J.C. & Sons. Ltd.

SCHMIDT, C. F., Heilbronn, Germany.
*British Agent:* Hinrichsen Edition, Ltd.

SCHOFIELD & Sims, Ltd. 35 St. John's Rd., Huddersfield,
Yorkshire HD1 5DT. *Tel:* Huddersfield 30684. *Grams:*
Schosims, Huddersfield.

SCHOTT & Co. Ltd. 48 Great Marlborough St., London,
W1V 2BN. *Tel:* 01-437 1246. *Grams:* Shotanco London.

SCRIPTURE Union. 5 Wigmore St., London, W.1.
*Tel:* 01-486 2561.
*Trade:* 79 Hackney Rd., London, E.2. *Tel:* 01-739 2941.

SIMROCK, N. Lyra House, 67 Belsize Lane, London,
NW3 5AX. *Tel:* 01-794 8038.

SOCIETAS Universalis Santae Ceciliae.
*British Agent:* Alfred A. Kalmus, Ltd.

SOUTHERN Music Company, San Antonio, Texas.
*British Agent:* Boosey & Hawkes Music Publishers, Ltd.

STAINER & Bell, Ltd. 82 High Road, London, N2 9PW.
*Tel:* 01-444 9135.

STEINGRABER Verlag, Germany.
*British Agent:* Bosworth & Co., Ltd.

STUDIO Music Co. 89-91 Vicarage Rd, London, NW10 2VA.
*Tel:* 01-459 6194/5

SUPRAPHON Czechoslovakia.
*British Agent:* Alfred A. Kalmus, Ltd.

TALZEHN Music Corporation, New York.
*British Agent:* Hinrichsen Edition, Ltd.

TAUNUS Verlag, Frankfurt.
*British Agent:* Hinrichsen Edition, Ltd.

TURRET Books. 1B, 1C, 1D, Kensington Church Walk,
London, W8 4NB.
*Tel:* 01-937 7583.

UNIVERSAL Edition (London), Ltd. 2-3 Fareham St., London,
W1V 4DU.

UNIVERSAL Edition Vienna-London-Zurich
*British Agent:* Alfred A. Kalmus, Ltd.

UNIVERSITY of Wales Press. Merthyr House, James St.,
Cardiff, CF1 6EU. *Tel:* Cardiff 31919.

V.E.B. Deutscher Verlag für Musik, Leipzig.
*British Agent:* Breitkopf & Härtel (London), Ltd.

V.E.B. Friedrich Hofmeister, Leipzig.
*British Agent:* Breitkopf & Härtel (London), Ltd.

VALANDO Music Co., Ltd. 50 New Bond St., London, W.1.
*Tel:* 01-629 7600. *Grams:* Symphony Wesdo London.

VERLAG Neue Musik, Berlin.
*British Agent:* Breitkopf & Härtel (London), Ltd.

VICTORIA Music Publishing Co., Ltd. 52 Maddox St., London, W.1. *Tel:* MAYfair 7600.

WALTON Music Corporation, California.
*British Agent:* Walton Music, Ltd.

WALTON Music, Ltd. 50 New Bond St., London, W.1. *Tel:*
01-629 7600. *Grams:* Symphony Wesdo London.

WARNE, Frederick, & Co., Ltd. 40 Bedford Sq., London,
WC1B 3HE. *Tel:* 01-580 9622. *Grams:* Warne
London WC1

WEINBERGER, Josef, Ltd. 10-16 Rathbone St., London,
W1P 2BJ. *Tel;* 01-580 2827. *Grams;* Operetta London
W.1.

WILHELMIANA Musikverlag, Frankfurt am Main.
*British Agent:* J. & W. Chester, Ltd.

WILLIAMSON Music, Ltd. 14 St. George St., London, W.1.
*Tel:* 01-629 7600.

WILLIS Music Co., Cincinnati (Ohio).
*British Agent:* Chappell & Co., Ltd.

WOOD, B.F., Music Co., Ltd. See BELWIN-Mills Music Ltd.

WOOD, Bradbury, Ltd. See BRADBURY Wood Ltd.

ZANIBON Edition, Padua.
*British Agent:* Hinrichsen Edition, Ltd.

ZIMMERMANN, Musikverlag, Germany.
*British Agent:* Novello & Co., Ltd.